RADIOISOTOPES IN BIOLOGY AND AGRICULTURE

Principles and Practice

RADIOISOTOPES IN
BIOLOGY AND AGRICULTURE

Principles and Practice

C. L. COMAR

Oak Ridge Institute of Nuclear Studies
Formerly Laboratory Director and Research Coordinator
University of Tennessee–Atomic Energy Commission
Agricultural Research Program

McGRAW-HILL BOOK COMPANY, INC.

New York   Toronto   London

1955

574.1
C 728

RADIOISOTOPES IN BIOLOGY AND AGRICULTURE

Library of Congress Catalog Card Number 54-11261

THE MAPLE PRESS COMPANY, YORK, PA.

To my wife

PREFACE

Radioisotope techniques, to the naïve, may represent the panacea for investigational difficulties—the royal road to successful experimentation; to the cynic they may appear as gadgetry, a fad that creates more problems than it solves. As always, the truth lies somewhere between the extremes. The really important contributions of these procedures in the biological field will be realized only insofar as they are utilized by investigators who are well grounded and have been working in the field of application. This is not to belittle the physical scientist, whose tremendous contribution is acclaimed by all. Nevertheless it is the biologist who recognizes the important problems in his own field, is familiar with the experimental material, and must be counted upon to make the interpretations.

A primary purpose of this volume is to bring home to the student and investigator an appreciation and understanding of how radioisotopes can fit into his program, and then to show how the experimental work can be undertaken. Chapter 1 presents certain basic principles unobscured by considerations of nuclear physics and experimental details. These principles are illustrated by examples drawn from such diverse fields as physiology, nutrition, entomology, and soils and fertilizers. The section on kinetics may be difficult for the reader with no background in mathematics, but an understanding of logarithms will enable him to use the methods. To follow the derivations will require some little knowledge of calculus.

Chapter 2 deals with certain difficulties inherent in tracer studies, describes the pitfalls, and attempts to show how they may be recognized, avoided, or taken into account in the interpretations. Chapter 3 is concerned with the practical problems of health physics and introduces the various units and physical concepts that are necessary for work with radioactive materials. Chapters 4 and 5 describe the facilities required and procedures suitable for studies with plants, laboratory animals, and domestic animals. Although it is recognized that methods and instrumentation have been improving rapidly, it seems that the approach is now fairly standard and that it is of value to know which methods have proved to be adequate in use. Rather than attempt to describe all the procedures and modifications which may confuse the uninitiated faced with choosing among them—some degree of arbitrary selection has been employed.

Chapter 6 presents in summary form a description of the characteristics of each radioisotope sufficient to allow decisions as to suitable counting methods, facilities required, and amounts of radioactivity to be employed. Typical studies are presented, and where possible, details are given in regard to those perversities which are so simple when explained but so exasperating and time-consuming when unrecognized in the laboratory. Chapters 7 to 10 describe the principles and application of corollary techniques that have been found of particular value in radioisotope methodology. To avoid the inclusion of an overwhelming amount of experimental detail, an attempt has been made first to present enough information so that the investigator can determine whether or not a given study is within his scope of facilities and experience. Frequently, sufficient details have been given so that the procedures can be undertaken without need for further reference. However, it is expected that most often the reader will wish to consult the original literature for additional information on specific methods.

Obviously it was possible to refer to only a small proportion of the literature, and the choice of material to be included was primarily based on its suitability for the illustration of certain points. No attempt has been made to discuss the status of knowledge in any scientific field as correlated with radioisotope research; this falls more properly within the purview of the *Annual Review* type of article. It is hoped that the illustrative examples will suggest the potentialities possible in the various fields of research. Emphasis has been placed on the biological and practical aspects of the subject, with no discussion of electronic circuits and with the inclusion of only such mathematics and physics as are essential to the methods. The interested investigator will want to develop his background in nuclear physics and instrumentation from standard texts. But let no biologist with training in quantitative chemistry be discouraged from undertaking tracer studies, at least on a small scale.

It is hoped that this book will provide stimulation for the biologist and the agriculturalist who have not yet considered the use of radioisotopes, as well as some degree of useful methodology for the investigator who is already engaged in this field. If the physical scientist can gain from this material an appreciation of the peculiar problems of his biologist colleague as well as an urge to collaborate, this will be an added dividend.

This opportunity is taken to acknowledge gratefully the enthusiastic cooperation of the following individuals, who supplied unpublished data, criticized parts of the manuscript, and made valuable suggestions: L. F. Belanger, C. J. Collins, S. L. Hansard, S. L. Hood, P. M. Johnston,

U. S. G. Kuhn III, G. W. Leddicotte, W. E. Lotz, R. A. Monroe, G. W. Morgan, R. T. Overman, J. H. Rust, C. W. Sheppard, N. E. Tolbert, B. F. Trum, W. J. Visek, H. Wiebe, L. P. Zill, and D. B. Zilversmit. Especial thanks are due to I. B. Whitney for permission to use unpublished data and for assistance with Chap. 6. Numerous individuals and organizations, whose names may be noted in the references, have been most gracious in granting permission to quote published material. I am deeply indebted to Mary Alice Carneal for secretarial help.

C. L. COMAR

CONTENTS

CHAPTER 1

PRINCIPLES OF TRACER METHODOLOGY

DIRECT MOVEMENT OF ORGANISMS, ELEMENTS, AND COMPOUNDS. GROSS RATES OF MOVEMENT. SOME QUANTITATIVE ASPECTS—Concept of Specific Activity; Determination of Ion Movement under Conditions of No Net Mass Transfer; A Substitute for Difficult Chemical Analysis; Isotope Dilution: *Volume determinations; Contribution of two sources to a product; Application to analytical chemistry; Modifications of isotope dilution;* The Kinetic Approach: *Simple removal from one phase; Radioactive decay—composite curves; Simple accumulation in one phase; Simple turnover—no return of labeled substance; Turnover or exchange—return of labeled substance; Reversible exchange into more than one compartment; Transfer between phases—precursor relationships; General considerations.* METABOLIC PATHWAYS—Biosynthesis. ADVANTAGES OF DOUBLE LABELING. MISCELLANEOUS APPLICATIONS—Bioassays; Steric Relations and Enzyme Action; Radiocarbon Dating; Criteria for Blood Preservation; Study of Rooting Patterns.

The atom consists of a nucleus or central core, about which revolve particles called *electrons*. The mass of the atom resides primarily in the nucleus, which for present purposes may be pictured as comprised of particles called *protons*, having a positive charge, and *neutrons*, having no charge. In the neutral atom, then, the charge on the nucleus, called the *atomic number*, will equal that of the extranuclear electrons. The chemical and biological properties of an element are determined by the number of extranuclear electrons and therefore by the atomic number, so that an element may be defined as *a form of matter all atoms of which have the same nuclear charge*. The atomic number is usually designated by means of a subscript at the lower left-hand corner of the chemical symbol: carbon, $_6$C. The subscript is frequently omitted, since the designation of the chemical element suffices to identify the atomic number. The *mass number* of the atom, which corresponds to the total number of neutrons and protons, is designated by means of a superscript: C^{12}. The atoms of a given element may have different numbers of neutrons in the nucleus, so that the masses may be different, but the nuclear charge, the atomic number, and therefore the chemical identity are unchanged. These atoms of the same element but of different atomic weights or mass numbers are called *isotopes* and are designated symbolically as above, for example, C^{12} and C^{13}. Some naturally occurring elements contain atoms of only one mass,

1

such as P^{31} and Na^{23}.   However, in many cases the elements are comprised of several isotopes, such as Cu^{63}-Cu^{65} or O^{16}-O^{17}-O^{18}.

The atoms of certain elements are known to undergo spontaneous disintegration with the emission of atomic particles (radiation) and to leave behind a system lighter than before and possessing physical and chemical properties different from those of the parent element.   Such unstable atoms are described as *radioactive*, and the prefix *radio-* is used to designate this behavior.   In other words, radioisotopes differ from stable isotopes in that the protons and neutrons of the nuclei of the former are in an unstable arrangement and therefore undergo spontaneous disintegration, a process that cannot be altered in any way known to man.   The adjective *labeled* is used to describe an element, compound, or organism that contains an altered isotopic content.   The asterisk is also employed to designate an element labeled with the radioisotope (e.g., labeled phosphorus, radiophosphorus, P^{32}, and P* are used here interchangeably unless otherwise noted).

In addition to the natural radioisotopes of the heavy elements of atomic number greater than 81, the following lighter radioelements are known to occur naturally: K^{40}, Rb^{87}, In^{115}, La^{138}, Sm^{147}, Lu^{176}, Re^{187}.   Of these, only K^{40} may be of importance in biological radioisotope studies because of its presence in tissues.   The major contribution to biological research, of course, has resulted from the availability of the artificially produced radioisotopes.

The above discussion has been primarily to establish terminology, and the general references (1 to 14) may be consulted for background information on the subjects of atomic theory, structure of the atom, and production of radioisotopes.   Such information is of collateral interest but not essential for the biological use of radioisotopes.

In consideration of the principles of application, it is necessary only to recognize that (*a*) before decay the radioisotope will behave in the system similarly to its stable counterpart, and (*b*) the radiation that it emits upon decay can be conveniently measured, thus providing an estimate of the amount of radioisotope present.   There are situations, as outlined in Chap. 2, where these assumptions do not hold, but they are of sufficient general validity to serve as a basis for the present discussion.   An arbitrary classification of principles in increasing order of complexity has been employed for purposes of clarity.   It will be apparent that data derived from more complex experiments would automatically provide information of a qualitative or locational nature as discussed in the first two sections below.   The inclusion of experimental details has been purposely minimized at this time so that there will be no distraction from the fundamentals involved.   Although the subject matter has been primarily limited to radioisotopes, it will be recognized that the principles will also apply to studies involving an altered stable-isotope content, restricted only by experimental limitations.

DIRECT MOVEMENT OF ORGANISMS, ELEMENTS, AND COMPOUNDS

Obviously, radioisotopes may be used simply to follow movement or transport. If it is physically possible, a radioisotope can be attached to or implanted in the organism. Cobalt 60 and tantalum 182 are especially suited for this purpose, since they are relatively inert chemically and biologically and emit gamma rays that can be conveniently detected even though considerable mass may be interposed between the source and the detecting device. The depth, location, and lateral movement underground of wireworm larvae have been followed by the insertion of Co^{60} wire in the body cavity, and wireworm beetles have been labeled by placing Ra^{226} under the wings. An alternative procedure with small organisms is to use a radioisotope that becomes incorporated metabolically in the body. Malaria, house, and rock-pool mosquitoes; houseflies, fruit flies, root maggot flies, black flies, and screwworm flies have been labeled usually by mixing P^{32} or Sr^{89} with the food of the larvae, resulting in the production of adults that could be distinguished by Geiger counting. Cockroaches and flesh flies have been injected with Zr^{95} so that they could be detected at a distance. In this manner entomological studies are practical on distribution from breeding sites, flight habits, dispersion, food relationships, food contamination, infestation patterns, longevity in the field, disease transmission, predation, and similar points of interest (15 to 24). Bacteria labeled with P^{32} have been used to determine the retention and initial distribution of air-borne microorganisms in studies of respiratory infection (25, 26).

In the above type of application the radioisotope is not primarily used as a label for a specific chemical element, and the choice of isotope is chiefly dependent on physical characteristics. For general metabolic studies, however, it is necessary that a specific element or compound be labeled and traced. From a nutritional and physiological point of view, the mere knowledge of the movement of an element or compound in a system may not be particularly fruitful. Nevertheless these observations may serve as a good starting point for additional investigation, especially with substances that have been little studied. The fact that most of the important biochemicals are now available in labeled form has greatly broadened this approach. Just a few areas of interest are cited for illustrative purposes (the reader will undoubtedly recognize similar applications in his specific field): (*a*) absorption from the gastrointestinal tract of nutrients or medicinals as a function of chemical state and physiological conditions, with subsequent tissue distribution and excretion (27, 28);

(b) permeability and transport through physiologic boundaries, including placental transfer (29); (c) labeling and tracing protein antigens and antibodies in immunological studies (30 to 32); (d) evaluation of movement characteristics of new drugs for compliance with food and drug laws (33); (e) movement of substances applied to soil and uptake by roots for translocation in plants (34 to 35a); (f) absorption and translocation in plants of substances applied to foliage, including both nutrients and plant-growth regulators (36, 37); and (g) distribution and action of pesticides (38 to 40).   General discussions of many of these topics can be found in references (9 to 13).

A primary advantage of the radioisotope technique in studies of this type is the great sensitivity of measurement usually obtainable.   Many of the elements and compounds of interest are normally present in the organism in such small amounts that chemical studies are impossible under physiological conditions.   As an example, it is known that a dietary intake of about 1 mg cobalt per day will satisfy the requirements of a 1000-lb cow for this element.   The chemical measurement of this amount of cobalt distributed through the tissues and excreted by such an animal was impractical.   By the use of radiocobalt it was a relatively simple matter to study in detail the distribution of less than 0.1 mg cobalt in the bovine (27).   This tremendous sensitivity also allows information to be obtained when the net mass movement of the substance is small.

The fact that radioisotopes emit radiation that can traverse the tissues and be measured outside the organism has led to a most useful type of measurement called *in vivo* or *surface measurement* (see Chap. 5 for more details).   The main advantage is that a continuous measurement on the intact organism is available during the course of the experiment, and the same organism may be used repeatedly for observation.   This is in contrast to orthodox procedures, which require samples to be taken and evaluated.   Though possible, in vivo methods are difficult to perform quantitatively, and in any case only the radioactivity is measured, so that metabolic information on turnover is not usually available.   However, there are many types of studies where this procedure is invaluable.   A major application has been in the study of transfer dynamics, which is treated in the next section.   The following is a survey listing of metabolic research that has been undertaken by the in vivo method [compiled primarily from (41)]:

Radioisotope	*In vivo study*
Na²⁴	Circulation times in normal and diseased humans; arm to arm, arm to heart, heart to arm, arm to foot, arm to brain, hand to axilla, foot to groin
	Retention of aerosols
	Accumulation in hands after ingestion

Radioisotope   *In vivo study*

    Testing of pulmonary resuscitative procedures
    Rate of disappearance from muscle
    Function of lymphatic system
    Effect of tourniquets
    Rates of mixing
    Blood flow through chambers of the heart
    Absorption from ointments
    Dissolving of coated capsules

I^{131} Thyroid function in normal and disease conditions
    Localization of metastases
    Localization of diiodofluorescein in brain tumors
    Effects of antithyroid compounds
    Absorption of insulin
    Breakdown of fat molecules in humans
    Diagnosis of metastatic cancer

P^{32} Accumulation in foot after intravenous injection
    Liver accumulation of chromic phosphate
    Effect of inhibitors on uptake by mussels
    Uptake by tissue culture
    Selective uptake in pathological skin areas
    Selective uptake in breast, brain, and testis tumors
    Rate of movement in plants

K^{42} Accumulation in hands after ingestion
    Uptake by tissue culture
    Pattern of uptake by plants

Br^{82} Accumulation in hands after ingestion
    Uptake by abscesses

Sr^{89} Bone accumulation

Au^{198} In connection with therapeutic use

Kr^{80} Hand, leg, thigh, and knee measurements after inhalation; effects of temperature and various drugs

C^{11} CO distribution

Zn^{65} Distribution pattern in humans

GROSS RATES OF MOVEMENT

The next logical extension of the studies mentioned above would involve measurement of the rate of movement to provide information on the dynamics of transfer of biological material. In animals considerable attention has been given to estimation of the velocity of blood flow through various tissues and organs. The circulation time, or rate of circulation, is usually determined by measurement of the time elapsing from injection of a substance into the blood at one point to its detection at another point. Obviously, the in vivo type of measurement is ideal for studies of this nature, many of which have been reviewed by Strajman and Pace (41). Earlier workers used radium C (Bi^{214}). However, Na^{24} is now usually preferred. In general, faster circulation times were found for children, and slower circulation times were found for patients suffering from cardiac diseases and peripheral vascular diseases. A reduction in circulation time was also found during the digestive period and during exercise and low environmental temperatures. Another useful procedure for the evaluation of pathologic and therapeutic variables on blood circulation has been the measurement of the rate of accumulation of radioisotopes in the extremities, hands or feet. For measurement of peripheral flow, the clearance of Na^{24} or I^{131} from tissues is often employed. Radiophosphorus has been used for the investigation of fetal circulation (42) and body-fluid circulation in insects (43).

In plant studies the rate of translocation of various elements and the effect of such treatments as temperature variations, use of respiratory poisons, and killing of the stems by steam have yielded pertinent information as to theories and mode of nutrient transport. Chen (44), for example, described the simultaneous movement in the phloem tissue in opposite directions of C^{14}-labeled organic solutes and P^{32}-labeled minerals, which is contrary to theories based on a unidirectional mass flow. Studies on the influence of petiole temperature on the rate of distribution of foliar-applied P^{32}, K^{42}, Ca^{45}, and Cs^{137} have been described by Swanson and Whitney (36). When the isotopes were studied simultaneously in pairs, the results indicated independent rates of export. Translocation from the leaf was markedly inhibited by both low and high petiole temperatures, and killing a 5-mm zone on the petiole by steaming completely stopped the outward movement of P^{32}, K^{42}, and Cs^{137} from the leaf.

Care must be taken in the interpretation of any study in which the radioactivity is administered at some location in a system and the time measured for it to appear at another site. The appearance of the first trace of the injected substance cannot be observed since generally the concentration will be lower than the detectable limit of measurement. Thus the measured time of arrival will be a function of the amount of radioactivity used, the sensitivity of the measurement, and the volume of circulating fluid with which the isotope becomes diluted.

SOME QUANTITATIVE ASPECTS

Many of the procedures discussed so far do not require more than the qualitative detection of radioactivity. Since the amount of radioactivity from a sample is directly proportional to the radioisotope content, the measurements may readily be made quantitative. Therefore, in many of the applications already described, comparisons can be made of the degree of movement as a function of experimental variables.

Concept of Specific Activity. If measurements can be made both of the radioisotope content and of the total amount of the element in the sample, then a most powerful approach is available for metabolic investigations. The relationship between the radioisotope and the total element content can be expressed as the *specific activity*, a term that has been given various meanings. To avoid ambiguity, it will be used here to designate the amount of radioactive element per unit weight of the element present, this weight to include both active and stable isotopes. As will be discussed in a later section, it makes no difference what units are used so long as they are consistent between the values which are to be compared. This usage of the term seems most practical, since the actual value is directly derived from the measurements usually made. For example, if a biological sample is measured to contain A mg phosphorus by chemical analysis and B counts/min of P^{32} under some specific counting conditions, the specific activity may be expressed as B/A counts/min/-mg (for purposes of discussion *counts per minute* is used as a measure of radioactivity).

In any comparison of this value with others it would be necessary that identical counting conditions be used. In practice, this procedure would be feasible since the same counting arrangements are usually employed for all samples. Otherwise it would be necessary to convert all counts to a standard base by the use of a single standard or sample on all the counting instruments used. It may seem unnecessary to caution that the radioassay and chemical assay of the sample must represent the same functional state of the element or compound. For instance, there would be no meaning to a specific activity for P^{32} in plasma based on a chemical determination of the plasma inorganic phosphorus and a radioassay of the total P^{32} content of the plasma, since the plasma inorganic phosphorus is only a part of the total plasma phosphorus.

Determination of Ion Movement under Conditions of No Net Mass Transfer. Before the advent of radioisotopes it was virtually impossible to measure the transport of ions between a tissue and a surrounding medium under conditions in which there was little or no net transfer of mass. This led to many theories and concepts of selective accumulation and physiologic transport which were based on the selective permeability of membranes. Radioisotope studies have in many cases provided unequivocal evidence for the transport of ions in both directions through membranes that were previously considered impermeable.

Let us consider a simple system of a tissue suspended in a medium in which all the ions of a given element are moving randomly from the tissue to the medium and likewise, at the same rate, from the medium to the tissue. Such ions are said to be *exchangeable*. If the appropriate radioisotope is introduced into the medium, then the specific activity of the tissue will increase with a concomitant decrease in that of the medium until an equal value is reached at equilibrium. The relative specific activities of the tissue and medium then give information as to the rate of transport and, in cases where all the ions are not involved, also as to what proportions are taking part in the process (see page 28 for kinetic aspects).

An example of this behavior has been reviewed by Sheppard (45) in a discussion of potassium and cell physiology. Earlier, potassium was regarded as a more or less passive cation, with its selective accumulation in cells controlled by the permeability of the membranes. Radiopotassium studies, however, have shown definitely that concentration gradients in cells are not the result of membrane impermeability. Experiments with such tissues and organisms as *Escherichia coli*, squid nerve, chicken embryo muscle, and mammalian erythrocytes have indicated the continual movement of potassium ions between the tissue and the suspension media. Cultures of *E. coli* showed a labile potassium fraction that exchanged completely with the potassium of the suspension medium in less than 5 min, and a tightly bound fraction that increased as metabolism progressed. The entire cellular potassium of human erythrocytes was found to exchange at a uniform rate under normal conditions of about 1.7 per cent of the cellular potassium per hour. Another example is the behavior of calcium ions in the blood. Chemical calcium determinations indicate that the plasma concentration of this element remains relatively constant. However, measurement of the rate of removal of labeled calcium introduced into the blood indicates that roughly 70 per cent of the individual calcium ions are being removed and replaced per minute (46). Similarly, in man, about 78 per cent of the plasma sodium and 105 per cent of the plasma water are exchanged per minute with extravascular sodium and water (47). This phenomenon is also important in plant-physiology studies, as demonstrated by Overstreet and Broyer (48), who reported on exchangeable potassium in the tissues of barley roots.

The necessity for recognizing this behavior and taking it into consideration in the design and interpretation of experiments is discussed in Chap. 2 under Exchange Reactions.

A Substitute for Difficult Chemical Analysis. As already implied, if an element is in equilibrium between two or more phases of a system and its radioisotope is introduced into the system, then the specific activity will be equal in each phase after the radioisotope has reached equilibrium conditions. In other words, under such conditions the radioisotope will distribute itself in proportion to the stable form already present in the system. For example, the calcium of blood exists in at least two forms: diffusible calcium, which is considered to be ionized, and nondiffusible, which is bound to a protein. The equilibrium may probably be represented by the following equation:

$$Ca^{++} + Prot^= \rightleftharpoons Ca\ Prot \qquad (1\text{-}1)$$

Visek et al. (49) have shown that, if Ca^{45} is added to plasma, the specific activities of the ionized calcium and the protein-bound calcium become equal within a matter of minutes. This supports the idea that the Ca ions are in equilibrium in the two phases or at least are interchangeable.

This situation leads to a very important application by means of which a simple radioisotope measurement may yield the same information as a difficult or often impracticable chemical analysis. It is clear that in the above simple blood calcium system the relative proportions of ionizable and bound calcium may be estimated by the addition of Ca^{45}, the separation of the two fractions, and the measurement of Ca^{45} in each fraction. To illustrate, assume that Ca^{45} is added to a serum sample which then measures 1000 counts/min/0.1 ml and that this sample is forced through a cellophane or collodion membrane to give a solution containing only ionizable calcium which measures 400 counts/min/0.1 ml. It is clear that 40 per cent of the original calcium was ionizable and 60 per cent was bound. To estimate the absolute amounts of calcium in each fraction, it would be necessary only to determine the total serum calcium in the usual way: If the serum calcium were 10 mg/100 ml, then the "ionizable" and "bound" calcium values in the serum would be 4 and 6 mg/100 ml, respectively. Small corrections would have to be made, in the usual way, for the volume of protein, etc., but these would not invalidate the general principles. This advantage is accentuated in dealing with more complex systems. For example, Visek et al. (49) separated labeled blood calcium into four fractions and demonstrated that the specific activities were equal in all cases. In this separation it was difficult at times to get enough sample for chemical analysis, but the counting of the Ca^{45} added to the system was always a simple matter and served to measure the proportions of the original blood calcium in each fraction.

A further example of how this principle might be applied is as follows: The estimation of the natural cobalt content in animal tissues is difficult because, except for the liver, the tissue content is very low and the methods are generally tedious. If it could be shown that radiocobalt administered to an animal reached an equal specific activity in all tissues, then the natural cobalt content could be easily determined by a simple radiocobalt assay on all tissues of interest plus a chemical cobalt determination on one tissue, presumably the liver. Obviously this method cannot be used until the investigator is certain by experiment that constant specific activities do obtain in the system.

In certain cases the equilibrium may be attained by repeated administration of the isotope over long periods of time. Van Middlesworth (50) has used this technique in a study of thyroid function in rats on an extremely low iodine intake. Because of the low iodine levels in the diet and in the body, it was not practical to analyze for the various iodine fractions in the blood. By incorporation of radioiodine in the diet to be used over the experimental period, it was considered that after a few days all the iodine fractions in the animal's body would reach an equal specific activity. It must be remembered that the specific activities of the diet and body iodine were all decreasing at the same rate owing to radioactive decay. Thus the various iodine fractions of the blood could be separated in the usual way and contained enough radioiodine to be counted and to give a measure of the stable iodine variations due to the experimental treatment. This general procedure may become very valuable, especially in radioisotope studies with calcium and phosphorus where the exchange of ions between blood and bone interferes with single-dose studies (see Chap. 2).

Isotope Dilution. Isotope-dilution methods and variations thereof represent most valuable procedures in biochemistry and analytical chemistry, since they provide data that are not at all or only with difficulty available from other procedures. In principle, the method consists in incorporating uniformly a small amount of the labeled test substance in the material to be analyzed, isolating some of the test substance from the mixture, and determining its isotopic content. The amount of dilution that has occurred is a function of the amount of the test substance in the original material.

Volume Determinations. If 1000 counts/min of radioactivity in a negligible volume is mixed into a volume of water that then measures 10 counts/min/ml, it is obvious that the volume of water was 100 ml. The general statement may be derived simply from the fact that the amount of radioisotope in the system is constant regardless of dilution. Thus, if a known amount of radioactivity, let us say A counts/min in B ml solution, is thoroughly mixed with an unknown volume, V ml, and a small sample is taken which measures S counts/min/ml, then the following is true:

$$V = \frac{A}{S} - B \qquad \text{which reduces to} \qquad V = \frac{A}{S} \qquad (1\text{-}2)$$

when B is small compared with V, as is often the case.

The greatest advantage of this technique will be in situations where it is impossible to measure the unknown volume directly or to disturb the system in which it occurs. This is the case in humans and animals for the estimation of such physiological entities as the red-blood-cell volume, plasma volume, lymph volume, and body water. In addition, the volumes occupied by other ions of biological interest can be estimated, so that we see values designated as *chloride space, bromide space, total exchangeable sodium,* and *total exchangeable potassium.* Various dyes and chemicals have been used for some of these determinations, but the radioisotope can generally provide a label with more desirable characteristics in regard to completeness of mixing, minimum of metabolic or physical loss from the space to be estimated, and ease of measurement. The general application to humans has been presented by Edelman et al. (51), blood-volume determinations have been reviewed by Gregersen (52), and red-blood-cell volumes for various species of domestic animals have been reported by Hansard et al. (53).

Blood-volume measurements are usually based on the labeling of red cells or on the direct labeling of the plasma. The former methods consist in putting the tag into the red cells directly by in vivo synthesis or in vitro exchange. Radioisotopes of iron, phosphorus, chromium, and potassium have been successfully used for this purpose. A measured amount of tagged red cells is then injected into the animal, and after time allowed for mixing, a sample of blood is withdrawn for estimation of the dilution taking place. Albumin tagged with I^{131}, which is distributed throughout the plasma, is used for the direct measurement of plasma volume similarly to the Evans blue-dye technique. There may be a tendency for the albumin tracer to equilibrate into areas outside the plasma, specifically into lymph. For valid results the plasma should be sampled before appreciable leakage to the lymph has occurred. Storey et al. (54) have made use of these relationships to estimate lymph space by a procedure with I^{131}-labeled albumin which does not require a sample of lymph. The equation used with dogs was as follows:

$$R^*e^{-kt} = R_p^{(t)}(V_p + 0.6V_L) \qquad (1\text{-}3)$$

where R^* = total injected radioactivity

e = base of natural logarithms

k = disappearance constant as determined from several daily measurements of plasma after injection

$R_p^{(t)}$ = radioactivity per milliliter of plasma measured at time t, where t is greater than 1 day so as to allow equilibration between plasma and lymph

V_p = plasma volume as determined by measurements within a few minutes after injection

V_L = lymph space

This equation was based on the assumptions, experimentally supported, that (a) the tagged albumin disappeared at the same rate from the plasma and lymph after equilibration, and (b) the lymph-to-blood albumin ratio was 0.6, and therefore after equilibration the lymph-to-blood radioactivity ratio was also 0.6 (note the application of pages 8 to 10).

Values for total blood volume are now obtainable from the sum of the red-cell volume and plasma volume as determined simultaneously by direct dilution measurement in the animal. In the past, blood volume was usually estimated from the plasma volume and hematocrit (as determined by centrifugation of venous blood) or from the red-cell volume and hematocrit. It is well known that there are fewer red cells per unit blood volume in the animal as a whole than there are in a sample of blood from a large vein. This introduces a serious systematic error in any quantity calculated from the large-vessel hematocrit. The *whole-body hematocrit* can be calculated from the independently determined red-cell volume and plasma volume.

By estimation of radioactivity in organ tissues after equilibration, it is possible to determine the blood content, red-blood-cell content, and plasma content of the tissue. This may be of value in the elimination of perfusion procedures, by allowing calculations from blood and tissue concentrations to determine what proportion of a substance found in a tissue is there as a result of the blood content of the tissue at the time of analysis.

Contribution of Two Sources to a Product. There are many biological problems in which it would be of particular value to be able to estimate what proportion of an element or compound in a given product came from one source and what proportion came from another. The labeled-element procedure is perhaps unique in that it makes this type of information available. The principle may be illustrated by consideration of a plant growing in a soil to which fertilizer labeled with P^{32} has been added. The specific activities in the plant and fertilizer are determined experimentally. It is clear from the dilution of the fertilizer phosphorus with the soil phosphorus that the following relationship holds:

$$\frac{\text{Specific activity of plant}}{\text{Specific activity of fertilizer}} \times 100 = \begin{array}{l} \% \text{ of phosphorus in} \\ \text{plant that was derived} \\ \text{from fertilizer} \end{array} \qquad (1\text{-}4)$$

The general statement is as follows: The specific activity of the product divided by the specific activity of a labeled contributor substance equals the fraction of the element or compound in the product which was contributed by the labeled source.

An important agronomic problem is concerned with the availability to the plant of fertilizer nutrients added to the soil. Fertilizers labeled with P^{32} and other radioisotopes have been widely used for direct measurements, as indicated in the above example. Another equally important problem is the evaluation of the availability of a nutrient element in the soil.   Actually the plant under the specific growing conditions is the best judge of nutrient availability.   Fried and Dean (55) used the principle of isotope dilution to evaluate experimentally the availability of soil phosphorus to the plant.   The method was based on the assumption that a plant confronted with two sources of phosphorus would utilize them in direct proportion to the availability of the element in each.   The above equation may then be expressed as

$$\frac{S_P}{S_b} = \frac{B}{A+B} \qquad \text{or} \qquad A = \frac{B[1-(S_P/S_b)]}{S_P/S_b} \qquad (1\text{-}5)$$

where A = amount of nutrient available in soil

B = amount of labeled nutrient added as a standard

S_p = specific activity in plant

S_b = specific activity in standard labeled nutrient

It must be remembered that in these studies the soil-nutrient availability is expressed in terms of the added standard nutrient.   In practice, a P^{32}-labeled phosphate source, usually monocalcium phosphate, is thoroughly mixed with the soil at some arbitrary rate, and plants are then grown and harvested after a given period.   The specific activities of the phosphorus in the harvested plants and in the standard source are measured.   Typical A values are shown for three soils in Table 1-1, as quoted by Hendricks (56).   It is noted, as expected theoretically, that the yield and rate of fertilizer phosphate addition did not affect the values of

TABLE 1-1. The Phosphate-supplying Capacity, A Value, of Three Soils.   Test Crop: Millet

Soil	Added monocalcium phosphate, lb P_2O_5/acre	Yield of millet, g/pot	Phosphate in crop derived from fertilizer, %	A value for soil, lb P_2O_5/acre
Davidson	0	0.6		
	40	4.9	39	62
	160	13.4	71	67
Bozeman	0	26.3		
	40	25.5	16	210
	160	28.6	43	220
Caribou	0	28.6		
	40	30.6	4	930
	160	29.9	14	1010

[Results of M. Fried, quoted by Sterling B. Hendricks, Radioisotopes in Fertilizer Usage, Soil Fertility and Plant Nutrition, in "Use of Isotopes in Plant and Animal Research" (Conference Sponsored by Kansas State College, Argonne National Laboratory, and Isotopes Division, U.S. Atomic Energy Commission, June 12–14, 1952), TID-5098, pp. 41–47, April, 1953.]

phosphate-supplying capacity.   The A values have been used to evaluate the phosphorus fertility of more than 100 soils, and good correlation has been obtained with estimations by yield methods in the field (35).   The fertility of other elements in the soil can also be estimated by this procedure.   Obviously this same method can also be used to measure the efficiency of fertilizer sources added to a particular soil.   Some of the factors which must be taken into account and which may require investigation for specific conditions include the character of the standard compound, the method of placement, the degree of mixing, the characteristics of the test plant, and the soil acidity.

As stated by Hendricks (56), almost 100 field experiments were in progress during 1952, employing 18 crops and with the following objectives:

1. Comparative availability of fertilizer materials
2. Effect of granulation of fertilizers on availability
3. Effects of time and placement of fertilizer application
4. Effectiveness of surface applications to sod crops
5. Availability of materials applied as foliar sprays
6. Effect of lime, nitrogen, and potassium supply on phosphorus availability
7. Effect of irrigation on phosphorus availability
8. Comparison of crop species in utilization of phosphatic fertilizers
9. The residual value from phosphates in rotation and permanent fertility experiments
10. Availability of soil phosphates

An important application in the field of animal nutrition involving estimation of endogenous fecal excretion was proposed by Hevesy (11) and extended to cattle by Kleiber et al. (57), who worked with P^{32}, and by Visek et al. (58) and Comar et al. (59), who used Ca^{45}.   It has always been difficult to estimate the true digestibility or utilization of inorganic materials, primarily because they can be recycled and reused in the body processes by secretion into the tract at one level and reabsorption at another.   In this respect they are unlike many organic nutrients which undergo a one-way catabolism and whose utilization may be determined from excreted catabolic end products.

The basis of this application may be described from Fig. 1-1, which for convenience has been based on the ingestion of 100 units of dietary calcium.   If 100 units of calcium is ingested by an animal and A units is absorbed from the tract, then $100 - A$ units will appear in the feces as unabsorbed calcium.   If E represents the endogenous calcium for every 100 units of the element ingested, then

$$\text{Total fecal calcium} = 100 - A + E \qquad (1\text{-}6)$$

which is easily measured by chemical analysis of the feces. If the plasma calcium is labeled by injection with Ca^{45} and has a specific activity of S_p, then from relationships already discussed it follows that

$$\frac{S_f}{S_P} = \frac{E}{100 - A + E} \qquad (1\text{-}7)$$

where S_f is the specific activity of the feces. From these two equations can be calculated the value for A, which is the "true" availability, and the value for E, which is the contribution from the body stores to the fecal calcium excretion. It is clear that any dietary calcium that is absorbed

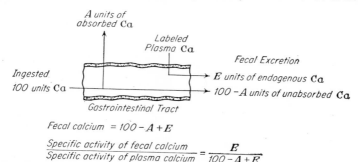

Fecal calcium $= 100 - A + E$

$$\frac{\text{Specific activity of fecal calcium}}{\text{Specific activity of plasma calcium}} = \frac{E}{100 - A + E}$$

FIG. 1-1. Schematic diagram of principle of isotope-dilution method for determination of endogenous fecal calcium. [From C. L. Comar, R. A. Monroe, W. J. Visek, and Sam L. Hansard, Comparison of Two Isotope Methods for Determination of Endogenous Fecal Calcium, J. Nutrition, **50**: 459–467 (1953).]

reaches the plasma pool, becomes labeled, and is measured as endogenous calcium.

In practice, the tagged calcium is injected intravenously daily for 10 to 15 days to produce uniform mixing in the plasma and steady-state conditions in the movement of endogenous calcium into the feces. It is also possible to get valid results after a single intramuscular injection with samples taken at several days postinjection. For example, a 113-kg calf was found to have an average daily calcium intake of 16.7 g and a fecal excretion of 15.9 g. After daily injections of Ca^{45} the ratio of the specific activity of feces to that of plasma averaged 0.227. It was calculated that the animal was excreting 3.6 g of endogenous fecal calcium daily and that the "true" absorption A was 26.6 per cent as compared with the apparent absorption of 5 per cent. This isotope-dilution procedure would be valid for any labeled substance, provided that the specific activity of the substance being secreted into the intestinal tract from the body were the same as that of the plasma.

Application to Analytical Chemistry. The isotope-dilution method has a general application to chemical analysis. In principle, if a labeled form of the element or compound to be determined can be incorporated in the sample to be analyzed, then a quantitative determination can be made without requiring a quantitative separation.   To illustrate this, let us assume that a sample is to be analyzed for sulfate by the usual barium sulfate procedure: 1000 counts/min of labeled sulfate is added before precipitation, and the final precipitate collected nonquantitatively is found by the usual methods to contain 1 mg sulfate and 500 counts/min. Assuming that the labeled sulfate added no significant mass of sulfate to the sample, we know immediately that $500/1000 \times 100$, or 50 per cent, of the sulfate was lost and that the true content of the sample must have been 2 mg sulfate.   When the labeled element or compound adds no significant mass to that being analyzed, the general relationship is obvious from the above.   When this is not the case, it is necessary to employ the specific-activity relationship, a useful form of which follows:

$$M = M^* \left(\frac{SA^*}{SA} - 1 \right) \qquad (1\text{-}8)$$

where M = unknown mass of substance in sample

M^* = known mass of labeled substance added to sample

SA^* = known specific activity of labeled substance added to sample

SA = measured specific activity of mixture of sample and added labeled substance

This equation is easily derived from the fact that the added radioactivity is constant before and after mixing, and therefore the added radioactivity $= (SA^*)(M^*) = (SA)(M^* + M)$.

A practical illustration of the use of this method has been given by Rosenblum (60) in connection with the difficult analysis of vitamin B_{12} in feed supplements.   Cobalt-60-labeled vitamin B_{12} in the amount of 26.6 μg was thoroughly mixed with 100 g of sample, which was then extracted with water, and the extracts were further purified by reextraction and chromatography to give a product showing the typical absorption spectrum of vitamin B_{12}.   The amount of vitamin B_{12} recovered at this point was 43 μg, as estimated from the extinction coefficient.   The amount of radioactivity associated with this 43 μg vitamin B_{12} was found to be 14.6 per cent of that originally present in the added labeled vitamin B_{12}.   Substituting in Eq. (1-8),

$$M = \mu\text{g vitamin } B_{12} \text{ in sample} = 26.6 \left(\frac{1/26.6}{0.146/43} - 1 \right) = 270$$

In this procedure it is necessary only to isolate an amount of the substance to be estimated sufficient to allow chemical and radioactive measurement with the desired precision.   Gravimetric, volumetric, colorimetric, or other usual methods can be used for the chemical determination.

This means that many methods may now be used which in the past showed some advantages but were discarded because of poor or uncertain recoveries. Likewise many procedures may be shortened because it will not be necessary to accomplish complete collection of precipitates and complete electroplating or to attain quantitative transfers from one vessel to another throughout a complex determination. The advantage of the isotope-dilution method used in this way will depend upon the added burden of the isotope incorporation and measurement, as compared with the saving in the elimination of the necessity for quantitative recoveries.

The fact that the isotope-dilution method does not require quantitative isolation of the substance to be measured is of particular interest in systems where purity and recovery are mutually exclusive. The assays for amino acids in a protein hydrolysate or for individual fatty acids fall into this category because there are so many chemically similar substances present in each case. Assays for these materials are performed in the same manner as described above for elements. However, they require the availability of the individual substance with an appropriate label. These methods have been especially effective with stable isotopes, and general equations have been reported (61).

Modifications of Isotope Dilution. The dilution methods so far described involve the addition of the isotopically labeled substance to the analytical sample. If the unknown in the sample can be produced in labeled form, then the procedure can be carried out according to the same principles and methods by adding a known amount of the unlabeled substance. Two advantages of this *inverse method* over the *direct method* are that smaller amounts of the unknown can be determined and that it is not necessary to have available the labeled diluting substance. A convenient form of the equation is

$$M^* = \frac{(M)(SA)}{SA^* - SA} \tag{1-9}$$

where M^* = unknown mass of labeled substance in sample

M = known mass of normal substance added to sample

SA^* = measured specific activity of substance isolated from original sample

SA = measured specific activity of substance isolated from mixture of sample and added normal substance

This procedure may be illustrated as follows: Assume that a plant has been treated with a radioisotope known to become incorporated in an amino acid A, for which an analysis is desired. Many other amino acids besides A could become labeled, but this will not interfere, for presumably A can be isolated and highly purified, since yield can be sacrificed. Let us suppose that 1 mg of the labeled amino acid A is isolated from 10 g of

tion of time.   The fraction of A removed is $(A_0 - A)/A_0$.   Substituting from Eq. (1-15),

$$\text{Fraction removed} = \frac{A_0 - A_0 e^{-kt}}{A_0} = 1 - e^{-kt} \qquad (1\text{-}18)$$

In addition to the illustrations below, these equations are widely applicable and well known for such phenomena as absorption of light (Beer's law), rate of growth of bacterial cultures under specific conditions, radioactive decay (see below), and absorption of gamma rays (see Chap. 3).

Simple Removal from One Phase.   The data in Table 1-2, taken from the graph in reference (47), may be used to illustrate the exponential removal of injected labeled ferric β-globulinate from plasma of man.   The

TABLE 1-2. REMOVAL OF INJECTED LABELED FERRIC β-GLOBULINATE FROM PLASMA OF MAN

Time, min	Iron, $\mu g/ml$ plasma
0	0.26
60	0.14
120	0.11
180	0.09
240	0.043
360	0.02

[From graph in Louis B. Flexner, Dean B. Cowie, and Gilbert J. Vosburgh, Studies on Capillary Permeability with Tracer Substances, in "Biological Applications of Tracer Elements," *Cold Spring Harbor Symposia Quant. Biol.*, **13**: 88–98 (1948).]

semilog plot is illustrated in Fig. 1-2, and it is apparent that the removal was exponential.   From the data and graph it can be calculated that the process was represented by the equation $A = A_0 e^{-0.0072t}$, that $t_{1/2}$ was 96 min, and that 0.7 per cent of the ferric globulinate was lost per minute from the plasma over the time interval during which the observations were made.

Radioactive Decay—Composite Curves.   The spontaneous disintegration, or decay, of radioactive elements has been shown by statistical theory and by experimental observation to be an exponential process.   As such, Eqs. (1-10) to (1-18) apply directly, and radioactive decay can be considered as exponential removal from a single phase.   The symbols are usually given the following terminology when used with decay rates:

$$k = \text{disintegration constant}$$
$$t_{1/2} = \text{half-life}$$

Since all atoms of a given radioisotope have the same decay probability, which is independent of the age of any particular atom, the life of a given

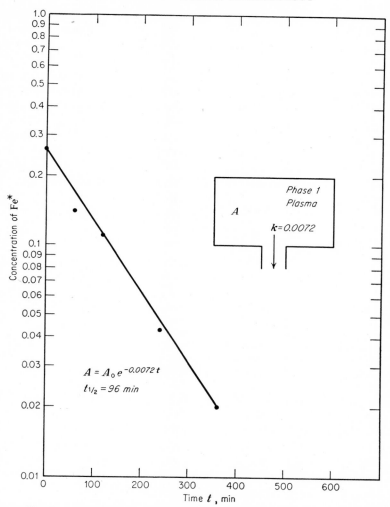

FIG. 1-2. Simple removal from one phase. Exponential removal of injected labeled ferric β-globulinate from plasma of man. [*From Louis B. Flexner, Dean B. Cowie, and Gilbert J. Vosburgh, Studies on Capillary Permeability with Tracer Substances, in "Biological Applications of Tracer Elements," Cold Spring Harbor Symposia Quant. Biol.*, **13**: 88–98 (1948).]

atom may have any value from zero to infinity.   It can be shown that the *average life* $= 1/k$.

If two isotopes of different half-lives are present, the decay curve will be a composite one.   If the half-lives are sufficiently different, it is possible to analyze the composite curve graphically to estimate the half-life of each component and the proportions of each component present.   This procedure, which is valid for other systems of exponential removal besides decay, is illustrated in Table 1-3 and Fig. 1-3. Column 2 gives the observed counts per minute of a mixture as a function of time, and these are plotted on a log scale to give the composite curve in Fig. 1-3. It is noted that at the longer time intervals a straight line is obtained which represents the exponential removal of the long-lived component. The extrapolation of this line intercepts the ordinate at 2000, which represents the counts per minute due to this component at zero time. From this line B are taken the values that are shown in column 3. The values in

TABLE 1-3. ANALYSIS OF COMPOSITE DECAY CURVE (TWO COMPONENTS)

(1) Time, days	(2) Observed cpm	(3) Cpm from extrapolated curve B	(4) (2) − (3) Cpm calculated to give curve A
0	3000	2000	1000
2	2876	1968	908
4	2762	1938	824
6	2654	1906	748
10	2462	1846	616
15	2257	1774	483
20	2085	1706	379
40	1598	1454	144
60	1295	1240	55
100	910	902	8
140	656	656	
200	406	406	

column 3 are subtracted from those in column 2 and are plotted to give the curve for component A. The intercept gives the value of 1000 counts/-min, which represents the relative amount of A present at zero time. The respective slopes give values of 0.0484 and 0.00795 for the disintegration constants, from which the half-lives are calculated as 14.3 and 87 days. This particular curve can be expressed as counts per minute at time $t = 1000e^{-0.0484t} + 2000e^{-0.00795t}$. *It may be helpful in consideration of the following systems to note the physical meaning of the numerical constants in this equation.*

Multicomponent systems may be treated in the same way, but the analysis becomes less precise as the number of components increases, especially if the rate constants k are close together. Frequently the method of least squares must be applied to the raw data for accuracy. Often the existence of several components cannot be detected from the data even by careful statistical analysis. The behavior of several components is thus said to be *lumped* into that of only one component.

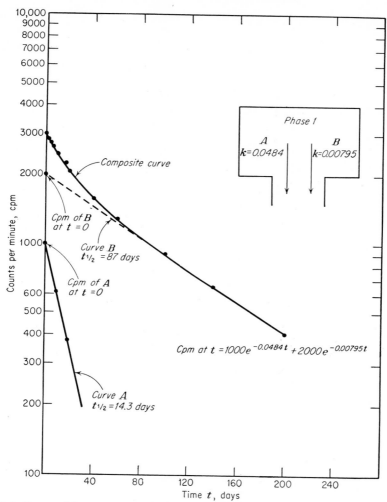

FIG. 1-3. Removal from one phase at two rates, as illustrated by radioactive decay of two isotopes. Resolution of composite curves.

Simple Accumulation in One Phase. If substance A is being removed from one phase and exponentially transferred to another, then the amount in the second phase will be equal to $A_0 - A$, using previous terminology. Since $A = A_0 e^{-kt}$, it follows that

$$A_0 - A = A_0 - A_0 e^{-kt} \quad \text{or} \quad A_0 - A = A_0(1 - e^{-kt}) \quad (1\text{-}19)$$

In the event that only part of substance A that is being removed from phase 1 is transferred to phase 2, then Eq. (1-19) becomes

$$A_2 = A_{eq}(1 - e^{-kt}) \tag{1-20}$$

where A_2 = amount of A in phase 2 at time t

A_{eq} = amount of A in phase 2 at equilibrium

Equation (1-20) can be expressed as follows for purposes of graphical analysis:

$$2.3 \log \left(1 - \frac{A_2}{A_{eq}} \right) = -kt \tag{1-21}$$

In this case a semilog plot of $(1 - A_2/A_{eq})$ vs. t will result in a straight line.

TABLE 1-4. ACCUMULATION OF Ca^{45} IN THE RABBIT FEMUR

Time, min	% of Injected dose in femur	$\dfrac{A_2}{A_{eq}}$	$1 - \dfrac{A_2}{A_{eq}}$
0	0	0	0
30	2.5	0.50	0.50
60	3.7	0.74	0.26
90	4.3	0.86	0.14
120	4.7	0.94	0.06
180	5.0	1	
210	5.0	1	
300			

[From graph in R. O. Thomas, T. A. Litovitz, M. I. Rubin, and C. F. Geschickter, Dynamics of Calcium Metabolism: Time Distribution of Intravenously Administered Radiocalcium, *Am. J. Physiol.*, **169**: 568–575 (1952).]

This treatment may be illustrated by the data in Table 1-4, which were taken from the graphs of Thomas et al. (46) and which represent the accumulation of injected Ca^{45} in the bones of young rabbits. The data are plotted in Fig. 1-4. It is noted that the maximum reaching the bone (A_{eq}) is 5.0 per cent. The value of k is estimated from the curve to be 0.022. The equation for the data then becomes

$$A_2 = 0.05(1 - e^{-0.022t})$$

These workers found the corresponding equation for adult rabbits to be

$$A_2 = 0.023(1 - e^{-0.022t})$$

This was interpreted to mean that the fractional rate of uptake k (and therefore the mechanism) was independent of age. However, the bones

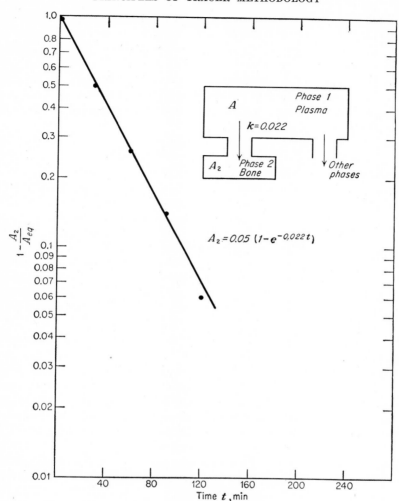

FIG. 1-4. Simple accumulation in one phase. Deposition of Ca^{45} in rabbit bone. [*From R. O. Thomas, T. A. Litovitz, M. I. Rubin, and C. F. Geschickter, Dynamics of Calcium Metabolism: Time Distribution of Intravenously Administered Radiocalcium, Am. J. Physiol.*, **169**: 568–575 (1952).]

of the younger animals were able to accumulate about twice as much Ca^{45} as were those of the older animals.

Simple Turnover—No Return of Labeled Substance. It is generally recognized that many of the body constituents are continually undergoing simultaneous formation and degradation. These are usually independent processes, and the net change in the concentration of the constituent will depend upon the relative rates of synthesis and degradation. Certainly in the adult organism, in which many constituents are characterized by a constancy of composition, these relative reaction rates must be equal for such substances. Likewise in younger animals this situation may be approximated, where the net change in concentration of a substance may be small over some given time period. Theoretically, isotope techniques can be used to estimate the rates of such opposing reactions, and in actuality the validity of kinetic experiments will primarily depend upon the choice of a sufficiently simple system.

The following considerations apply only to steady-state conditions in a uniformly mixed system, in other words, to situations where there is zero net concentration change as a result of equal rates of formation and degradation. It must be remembered that these are constant rates, in contradistinction to the exponential rates discussed previously. The term *turnover* refers to the renewal of a substance, and the term *turnover rate* or *renewal rate* is used to indicate the amount of a substance renewed in a given time. A useful term, *turnover time*, is defined as the time required to renew completely the amount of substance present in the tissue. The turnover rate or turnover time may perhaps be most readily estimated by measurement of the rate of disappearance of the label from the substance of interest. The primary advantage of this procedure is that no information is required in regard to the precursor.

This situation differs in one important respect from those cases already discussed in that the label introduced disappears at an exponential rate, whereas the substance is renewed at a constant rate because its concentration remains constant. *Essentially the problem is to determine this constant rate of renewal from measurements of the label concentration, which is being decreased exponentially.* In this treatment it is assumed that there will be no significant reentry of the label into phase 1. At the risk of repetition, it is emphasized that in cases up to now the radiotracer and the substance it labels have moved at the same rate at all times. We are now considering a very important typical biological system in which the label is removed but the substance it labels remains constant because of replenishment.

This system may be illustrated by the studies of Zilversmit, Chaikoff, and associates (68, 69), who injected labeled plasma phosphatides into the dog and calculated the amount of phosphatides removed from the plasma and replaced by tissue phosphatides per unit time from the rate of disappearance of the label. A schematic representation is given in Fig. 1-5.

If p = rate of disappearance of phospholipids A from plasma
A^* = amount of labeled phospholipids present at time t
A_0^* = amount of labeled phospholipids present at zero time

then

$$\frac{dA^*}{dt} = -p\,\frac{A^*}{A} \tag{1-22}$$

which reduces to the usual form:

$$2.3 \log \frac{A_0^*}{A^*} = \frac{p}{A}\,t \tag{1-23}$$

Equation (1-22) is based on the fact that the removal of A^* will be proportional to p and to the ratio of labeled to total phospholipid. *This is an important concept, an understanding of which will be helpful in handling the more complex systems.* It should be noted that the constant of Eq. (1-23), p/A, which is analogous to the k of previous equations, represents the fraction of the phospholipids which is renewed in unit time. The reciprocal A/p is the *turnover time* t_t. The turnover time may be conveniently calculated by the use of $t_{1/2}$, the time for the labeled phospholipids to reach one-half the zero-time value. By analogy with Eq. (1-16),

$$\frac{p}{A} = \frac{0.693}{t_{1/2}} \tag{1-24}$$

and therefore

$$\frac{A}{p} = t_t = 1.44 t_{1/2} \tag{1-25}$$

These relationships may perhaps be more easily visualized by the use of numerical values. If there is 1000 units of phospholipids in plasma which are being renewed at the rate of 500 units/hr, then it will take $1000/500 = 2$ hr for complete renewal t_t. If 100 units of labeled phospholipids is introduced into the system, then the *initial* rate of removal of the label must be $100 \times 500/1000$, which is another way of stating Eq. (1-22).

In experiments of this type it is advisable to plot log A^* vs. time, since any deviation from a straight line will indicate interferences that should be taken into account. It is also advisable to restrict the observations to a period over which a small fraction of the substance has been renewed, since the calculations will not be valid when considerable numbers of molecules are turned over more than once.

Figure 1-5 presents typical data on the amount of labeled phospholipids found in the blood of a dog at varying times after injection (69). The P^{32}-labeled phospholipids had been produced by administration of P^{32} to a dog, sacrifice of the animal, and isolation of the phospholipids for injection into another dog. It is clear that a straight-line relationship was

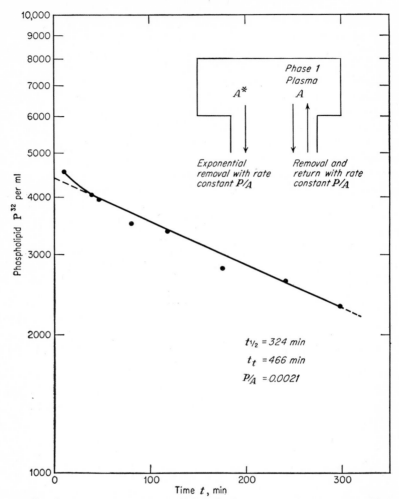

FIG. 1-5. Simple turnover—no return of labeled substance.   Disappearance of injected labeled phospholipids from plasma of dog.   [*From I. L. Chaikoff and D. B. Zilversmit, Radioactive Phosphorus: Its Application to the Study of Phospholipid Metabolism, Advances in Biol. and Med. Phys.*, **1**: 321–352 (1948).]

found.   The half-time value as determined graphically or by Eq. (1-17) was about 324 min, which gave a turnover time of 466 min, as calculated by Eq. (1-25).   Thus it was shown that, in dogs weighing from 6.6 to 8.5 kg, an amount of plasma phospholipid equal to that contained in their plasma was completely renewed in 8 to 9 hr.

Turnover or Exchange—Return of Labeled Substance.   As indicated previously (page 8), there are many biological processes in which ions move from one phase to another under steady-state conditions. This situation is analogous to simple turnover as discussed above. However, it is usually denoted as an *exchange* phenomenon. A relatively simple system, the kinetics of which have been widely studied (70 to 73), is the exchange of potassium between plasma and erythrocytes. Under ideal experimental conditions this may be considered as a closed two-compartment system in that the labeled potassium ions incubated with the blood will leave the plasma for stoichiometric entry into the red cells. The small net movement of potassium into the cells can be disregarded to a first approximation. However, a mathematical correction for this effect has been described (72). The process is represented schematically in Fig. 1-6.

A_1 and A_2 = concentration of potassium in plasma and cells, respectively

A_1^* and A_2^* = concentration of labeled potassium in plasma and cells, respectively, at time t

$A_0^* = A_1^* + A_2^*$ = concentration of labeled potassium in plasma at zero time

$\frac{A_1^*}{A_1} = S_1$ and $\frac{A_2^*}{A_2} = S_2$ are the specific activities in plasma and cells, respectively, at time t

p = rate of movement of K from phase 1 to phase 2 and vice versa

On the basis of the reasoning developed for Eq. (1-22), it can be seen that the rate of movement of labeled K out of phase 1 will be $-pA_1^*/A_1$, and the rate of movement into phase 1 will be pA_2^*/A_2. Therefore the net movement of labeled K may be represented as follows:

$$\frac{dA_1^*}{dt} = -p\frac{A_1^*}{A_1} + p\frac{A_2^*}{A_2} \tag{1-26}$$

This equation can be converted to terms of specific activity and becomes

$$\frac{dS_1}{dt} = -\frac{p}{A_1}(S_2 - S_1) \tag{1-27}$$

Substituting for S_2 in terms of S_1 and integrating,

$$\frac{S_1}{S_0} = \frac{A_1 + A_2 e^{-pt[(1/A_1)+(1/A_2)]}}{A_1 + A_2} \tag{1-28}$$

where $S_0 = A_0^*/A_1$. The relationship between p and $t_{1/2}$ is

$$p = \frac{0.693 A_1 A_2}{t_{1/2}(A_1 + A_2)} \tag{1-29}$$

The handling of data may be illustrated by Table 1-5 and Fig. 1-6. Inspection of Table 1-5 indicates the following: (a) The labeled K that left the plasma entered the cells; (b) the total K in the plasma and cells remained constant at values of about 0.28 and 4.9, respectively; and (c) an equilibrium relative specific activity of about 0.065 was reached. A semi-log plot of specific activity in plasma minus equilibrium specific activity ($S_i - S_{eq}$) vs. time gives the straight line in Fig. 1-6, from which the slope is calculated to be 0.0057. This gives $t_{1/2} = 0.693/0.0057 = 121$ min. The exchange rate is calculated from Eq. (1-29), and $p = 0.0015$ mg

TABLE 1-5. POTASSIUM EXCHANGE IN HUMAN BLOOD

Time, min	Cpm		Total K, mg		Relative specific activity	
	Plasma	Cells	Plasma	Cells	Plasma	Cells
0	798	28	0.284	4.87	1.0	0.002
60	689	282	0.284	4.87	0.73	0.017
124	416	388	0.284	4.87	0.52	0.029
181	316	504	0.275	4.95	0.41	0.036
300	192	628	0.275	4.95	0.25	0.045
420	138	692	0.279	5.13	0.175	0.048
540	100	768	0.275	4.95	0.123	0.052
1270	60	858	0.292	4.95	0.065	0.055

[From C. W. Sheppard and W. R. Martin, Cation Exchange between Cells and Plasma of Mammalian Blood. I. Methods and Application to Potassium Exchange in Human Blood, *J. Gen. Physiol.*, **33**: 703–722 (1950).]

potassium per minute or about 1.8 per cent of the cellular potassium per hour.

It should be noted that the values $t_{1/2}$ and the slope refer only to the change in concentration of labeled K and that conversions must be made to express results in terms of the exchange rate of potassium. The rate of K movement is the same in both directions but has different values when expressed as a percentage of cellular or plasma potassium. If, in a system of this sort, it can be assumed that the specific activities become equal at equilibrium, then the rate of movement in terms of a percentage of the amount in a phase can be obtained by radioactivity measurements without the necessity of chemical analysis. This is illustrated in the next case.

Reversible Exchange into More Than One Compartment. The movement of elements such as sodium, calcium, and chlorine between the plasma and the extravascular compartments has been studied successfully by kinetic methods. The situation is similar to that just discussed in that

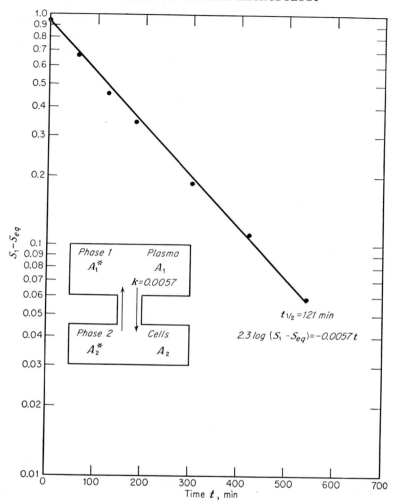

FIG. 1-6. Exchange—return of labeled substance.   Equilibration of labeled potassium between plasma and red cells. [*From C. W. Sheppard and W. R. Martin, Cation Exchange between Cells and Plasma of Mammalian Blood.   I. Methods and Application to Potassium Exchange in Human Blood, J. Gen. Physiol.,* **33** : 703–722 (1950).]

the label disappears exponentially, whereas the element in the plasma remains essentially constant because of replacement from the other compartments, and the backflow is taken into account.   However, it is necessary to consider that there is more than one rate and that nothing is known of the compartments to which movement occurs.   The derivation of the formulas is relatively complex, but it is emphasized that the experimental observations are not difficult and that the application of the equations requires little more than algebraic manipulation.

The procedures may perhaps best be explained by use of the data on sodium and the equations as presented in the classic paper of Gellhorn, Merrell, and Rankin (75). Experimental observations, as indicated later, showed that labeled Na ions injected into man or dog were removed from the plasma at two exponential rates to reach an equilibrium value. The process is represented schematically in Fig. 1-7. By extension of the reasoning used for Eq. (1-22) it can be shown that the change in plasma of labeled sodium per unit time may be expressed (original notation used) as

$$\frac{dN_p^*}{dt} = -r_A \frac{N_p^*}{n_p} + r_A \frac{N_A^*}{n_A} - r_B \frac{N_p^*}{n_p} + r_B \frac{N_B^*}{n_B} \tag{1-30}$$

where N_p^*, N_A^*, N_B^* = number of labeled sodium ions in each area, respectively, at time t

n_p, n_A, n_B = number of sodium ions in each area, respectively

r_A = number of sodium ions passing from plasma to area A and vice versa per unit time

r_B = as above, but from plasma to area B

By expressing Eq. (1-30) in terms of N_p^* and concentration, the following is derived by integration:

$$C_p - C_{eq} = a_1 e^{-b_1 t} + a_2 e^{-b_2 t} \tag{1-31}$$

where C_p = plasma concentration of labeled Na at time t

C_{eq} = plasma concentration of labeled Na at equilibrium

a_1, a_2 = concentration constants

b_1, b_2 = rate constants for transfer to areas A and B, respectively

This equation is based on the assumptions that the volumes of the compartments remain constant, that there is no loss of labeled sodium during the experiment, and that the rates of transfer in and out of the plasma are equal for any one compartment.

Before consideration of the physical meaning of Eq. (1-31) it may be helpful to go through the steps by means of which the numerical values of the equation are derived from the data. The data are taken selectively from the paper of Gellhorn et al. (75). Column 2 of Table 1-6 presents the observed concentration of labeled Na in the plasma as a function of time after injection. It may be noted by inspection that there was a rapid initial drop with a leveling off at the equilibrium value after about 30 min. This gives a value of 1000 for C_{eq}, and column 3 gives the calculated values of $C_p - C_{eq}$ for purposes of plotting. Figure 1-7 presents the plot of $C_p - C_{eq}$ on a log scale vs. t on a linear scale. Extrapolation of

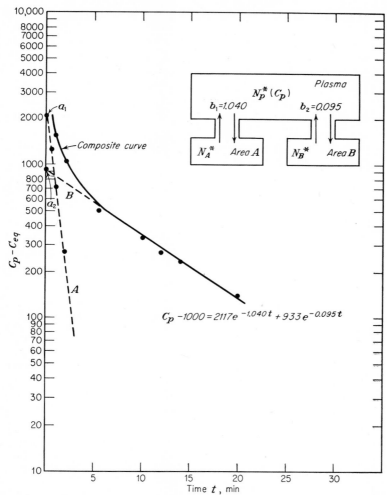

Fig. 1-7. Reversible exchange into more than one compartment.   Removal of labeled sodium from plasma of dog.   [*From Alfred Gellhorn, Margaret Merrell, and Robert M. Rankin, The Rate of Transcapillary Exchange of Sodium in Normal and Shocked Dogs, Am. J. Physiol.*, **142**: 407–427 (1944).]

the linear portion of the curve between 6 and 20 min gives a value of 933 for the intercept on the ordinate; this represents the value a_2.   This straight line represents a simple exponential removal curve whose slope is determined by methods previously described to give the exponential constant 0.095, b_2.   The straight line is subtracted graphically from the original curve to give another straight line that represents the exponential removal to area A.   Column 5 gives the values that are plotted to give

TABLE 1-6. CALCULATION OF TRANSCAPILLARY EXCHANGE OF Na

(1) Time, min	(2) Observed cpm	(3) $C_p - C_{eq}$ ($C_{eq} = 1000$)	(4) Cpm from extrapolated curve B	(5) (3) − (4) Cpm calculated to give curve A
0				
0.5	3162	2162	890	1272
1	2575	1575	848	727
2	2050	1050	772	278
4	1713	713	638	75
6	1508	508		
8	1433	433		
10	1341	341		
12	1271	271		
14	1233	233		
20	1140	140		
30	1113	113		
40	1053	53		
60	1030	30		
120	1000	0		

[From Alfred Gellhorn, Margaret Merrell, and Robert M. Rankin, The Rate of Transcapillary Exchange of Sodium in Normal and Shocked Dogs, *Am. J. Physiol.*, **142**: 407–427 (1944).]

curve A. The intercept and slope of this line give values of 2117 and 1.040, respectively, a_1 and b_1. The equation for this process is then

$$C_p - 1000 = 2117e^{-1.040t} + 933e^{-0.095t} \qquad (1\text{-}32)$$

It must be remembered that the constants in Eq. (1-32) refer to the behavior of labeled sodium ions introduced into the plasma, and since the primary interest is in the behavior of *sodium* ions in the plasma, it is necessary to make conversions:

1. The initial plasma concentration of labeled Na ions =

$$C_{eq} + a_1 + a_2 = 4050.$$

2. (Na in plasma)/(total Na) = $C_{eq}/C_0 = 0.247$.
3. Percentage of Na in plasma transferred per minute from plasma to extravascular fluid, $R_p = (a_1b_1 + a_2b_2)/C_0 \times 100 = 56.6$.
4. Percentage of Na in total body transferred per minute from plasma to extravascular fluid, $R_T = R_pC_{eq}/C_0 = 14.0$.

Further relationships in regard to the rate of transfer to the individual areas A and B and detailed derivations may be found in the original paper (75). Equation (1-32) is expressed in terms of concentration of labeled Na. For purposes of comparison it is convenient to express the constants C_p, C_{eq}, a_1, and a_2 in terms of fractions of the initial labeled Na concentration, and the equation then becomes

$$C_p - 0.247 = 0.522e^{-1.040t} + 0.231e^{-0.095t} \qquad (1\text{-}32a)$$

It is necessary to consider the physiological interpretations possible from this type of information. It is clear that the dynamic state of the various constituents in the body system can be quantitated as far as removal and reentry into plasma are concerned. Although these curves do show one or more characteristic transfer rates, it is recognized that they represent the results of complex processes that cannot be mechanistically interpreted at this time.

In general, there are several possible processes that could account for removal from the plasma at more than one rate. For example, the substance might be present in the plasma in more than one form, each of which might be removed at its characteristic rate, or the substance might pass across the vascular membrane at a different rate than that of the subsequent passage across the cell membrane. On the basis of other observations, it has been suggested that at least Na and K are transported across the capillary wall at different rates in different parts of the system. Thus, on the basis of tissue accumulation of injected labeled sodium, Gellhorn et al. (75) consider that sodium ions in the extravascular system may be divided into two groups, one group being in areas where the rate of exchange with plasma ions is relatively rapid and the other group being in areas where the rate is relatively slow.

Obviously, much more information is needed on the kinetics of accumulation in the various compartments. Subjectively one thinks of the rapid rates of removal as being concerned with mechanical mixing and physical processes such as fixation to proteins and cell surfaces. Sheppard et al. (76) have studied theoretically and experimentally the mixing of K^{42} in the plasma, a process that was shown to be predominantly oscillatory. The next slower rate would probably be concerned with diffusion or filtration into tissues and cells. The slowest rates may represent excretion.

Uncertainties in the method may arise from the existence of removal rates of similar magnitude which therefore cannot be resolved. It has also been pointed out that the mean capillary concentration of an injected substance may not equal that of the arterial blood until some time after injection (77). However, this does not seem to be an important factor in the normal intact animal.

TABLE 1-7. SUMMARY OF EQUATIONS FOR REMOVAL OF SUBSTANCES FROM PLASMA; CONSTANTS FOR EQUATION

$$C_p - C_{eq} = a_1 e^{-b_1 t} + a_2 e^{-b_2 t} + \cdots + a_n e^{-b_n t}$$

Substance	Animal	Physiological factors	C_{eq}	a_1	b_1	a_2	b_2	a_3	b_3	a_4	b_4	%/min removed from plasma	Ref. No.
Na	Dog	Normal	0.247	0.523	1.040	0.230	0.095	.....	.....	.....	.....	56.6	(75)
Na	Dog	Untreated shock	0.118	0.687	0.747	0.195	0.058	.....	.....	.....	.....	52.4	(75)
Na	Dog	Shock and saline	0.224	0.582	0.427	0.194	0.038	.....	.....	.....	.....	25.6	(75)
Na	Dog	Shock and serum	0.224	0.594	0.546	0.177	0.047	.....	.....	.....	.....	33.2	(75)
Na	Dog	Normal	0.217	0.425	0.95	0.251	0.14	0.107	0.021	.....	.....	44.1	(78)
Na	Man	Normal	0.294	0.528	0.582	0.178	0.0644	.....	.....	.....	.....	32	(79)
Cl	Dog	Normal	.....	0.455	2.079	0.247	0.308	0.052	0.0377	0.246	0.000175	102	(80)
Ca	Cattle	10 days old	.....	0.42	2.08	0.32	0.38	0.22	0.070	0.037	0.0039	102	(81)
Ca	Cattle	6 mo old	.....	0.68	1.03	0.17	0.12	0.065	0.033	0.087	0.0033	72	(81)
Ca	Cattle	Aged	.....	0.74	0.35	0.033	0.051	0.23	0.0015	.....	.....	26	(81)
Ca	Dog	Normal	.....	0.491	0.93	0.264	0.22	0.128	0.04	0.117	0.003	52	(78)
Ca	Rabbit	Adult	.....	0.483	1.36	0.26	0.177	0.113	0.024	0.144	0.0024	71	(46)
Ca	Rabbit	Young	.....	0.448	1.76	0.31	0.28	0.166	0.026	0.074	0.0026	88	(46)
Y	Cattle	20 mo old	.....	0.54	0.102	0.40	0.0151	0.064	0.0023	0.0014	0.00011	.....	(82)
Hg-diuretic	Man	.....	.....	0.363	0.603	0.378	0.154	0.259	0.0058	.....	.....	.....	(83)

36

Some typical results have been summarized in Table 1-7 after calculation to a fractional basis. Space will not permit discussion of comparisons but the interested reader may draw his own conclusions as to agreement between investigators and species differences.

Transfer Between Phases—Precursor Relationships. A common rate problem is concerned with the transfer of a labeled substance from a phase into which it is introduced into one or more phases in which the activity may be measured. These rates are often used to give information on the turnover rate and precursors of a substance normally present in the system. The simplest method for determination of turnover by the disappearance of a label has already been discussed (page 25). If it is necessary to determine turnover rate from the appearance of a label in the substance, then information must also be available on the time-activity relationships of the immediate precursor of the substance.

In some cases the specific activity of the precursor can be maintained as a constant over the experimental period. Madden and Gould (84) used this approach to determine the turnover rate of fibrinogen in the dog. The animals were fed daily with sulfur-labeled methionine for about 3 weeks, at which time the specific activity of the fibrinogen reached an equilibrium level. In this case the equation is

$$2.3 \log \frac{S_{eq}}{S_{eq} - S} = kt \tag{1-33}$$

where S_{eq} = specific activity of fibrinogen at equilibrium
S = specific activity of fibrinogen at time t
k = constant = fraction renewed per unit time

This equation can be derived by using the principles already set forth and recalling that the specific activity of the precursor will be equal to S_{eq}. Thus the precursor does not need to be known, nor does its specific activity need to be measured experimentally. Madden and Gould found that the half-turnover time for fibrinogen in dogs averaged about 4 days, and these values checked with observations made by the disappearance method. It was of interest to note that S^{35}-labeled yeast gave just as good results as methionine for the determination of turnover of proteins under certain conditions. It was also pointed out that the reutilization of labeled amino acids was decreased, in the disappearance method, by feeding high levels of inert S-amino acids while following the disappearance.

The general precursor relationships have been developed by Zilversmit et al. (68) and discussed in terms of the incorporation of a phosphate label into phospholipid. It should be noted that there are two main problems, the determination of turnover rate and identification of the precursor. When labeled phosphate is injected into the blood stream, it becomes rapidly mixed with the nonradioactive phosphates of extracellular and intracellular fluids, bone phosphates, etc., so that its specific activity decreases with time. If plasma phosphate is the immediate precursor of phospholipid, the phospholipid that is formed at the earliest intervals will have a high specific activity because the specific activity of the plasma phosphate is high at this time. The specific activity of the total phospholipid phosphorus will increase, but there will be a competing process since the loss of label by breakdown will also increase. At a time when the specific activity of the newly formed phospholipid equals that of the phospholipid breaking down, the tissue phospholipid will have reached its maximum specific activity. It is concluded that, at a time when the specific activity of the tissue phospholipid has reached its maximum, its specific activity will equal that of the precursor. These relationships have been treated mathematically and are presented in Fig. 1-8. The derivations are based on the following assumptions: (a) The rate of appearance equals the rate of disappearance. (b) The rates are constant during the experiment. (c) There is only a single precursor. (d) The appearance and disappearance of all molecules proceed at random; that is, the organism does not distinguish between old and newly formed molecules.

These theoretical curves provide the following criteria for decision as to whether the precursor measured is the immediate precursor: The precursor specific activity must exceed the substance specific activity until the latter reaches its maximum, at which time the two specific activities become equal. Thereafter the specific activity of the substance is greater than that of the precursor.

The turnover time can be estimated graphically (see Fig. 1-8) by determining the shaded area as indicated and dividing by m, the increase in specific activity of the substance between the times t_1 and t_2 (68):

$$t_t = \frac{\text{shaded area}}{m} \tag{1-34}$$

It is noted that the estimation of t_t from the disappearance of the label, as described on page 27, is generally much simpler.

General Considerations. The rate processes discussed up to this point are essentially first-order reactions and as such are probably most widely applicable. For a general mathematical treatment the reader is referred to the more sophisticated papers of Branson (85, 86), Sheppard and Householder (74), Hearon (87), and Reiner (88, 89). The paper of Ussing (29) should be consulted for a detailed review of the use of tracers in exploring the mechanism of permeability.

The classic study of Shemin and Rittenberg (90) on the incorporation of glycine into hemoglobin and the determination of the life span of the red cell represents a nonexponential process that may be described narratively. Glycine labeled with the stable isotope N^{15} was used in the original study, and the findings were later confirmed with C^{14}-labeled glycine. The N^{15}-labeled glycine was administered to a human adult, and the N^{15} concentration was followed as a function of time in the various nitrogenous metabolic constituents. Except for the hemin isolated from the red blood cells, all the constituents reached a peak value at 24 hr after administration with a decline in N^{15} concentration thereafter. The hemin, however, rose rapidly for about 20 days, remained at

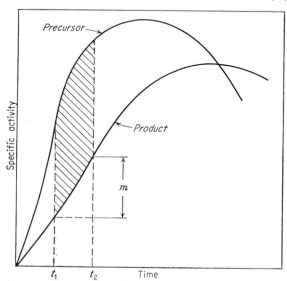

Fig. 1-8. Specific activity–time relations between product and precursor. [*From D. B. Zilversmit, C. Entenman, and M. C. Fishler, On the Calculation of "Turnover Time" and "Turnover Rate" from Experiments Involving the Use of Labeling Agents, J. Gen. Physiol.*, **26**: 325–331 (1943).]

a plateau for the next 70 days, and then fell along an S-shaped curve. These data were interpreted to mean: (*a*) The hemoglobin must have become labeled during the formation of the red blood cell. (*b*) The hemoglobin was not involved in a dynamic process or in the flux of synthesis and degradation. (*c*) The hemoglobin remained in the red cell until the cell disintegrated. (*d*) The heme was not reutilized. (*e*) The red cells were not randomly destroyed, but their destruction was a function of age. It was also possible, from the curve, to estimate the average life span of the red cells, which was found to be 127 days. Further studies on the time course of specific activities demonstrated that glycine was the precursor of the protoporphyrin of hemoglobin. The equations for the kinetics of this system may be found in the original papers.

A critical discussion of red-cell-survival curves has been presented by

Dornhorst (91), and Neuberger (92) has pointed out certain discrepancies between results obtained from the agglutination methods and those obtained from the isotopic labeling methods. Burwell et al. (93) have shown that lower values of red-cell life span in rabbits were found by measurement of erythrocyte iron turnover than by direct measurement of erythrocyte survival; radioiron was employed in these studies. Necheles et al. (94) have described the use of labeled sodium chromate ($NaCr^{51}O_4$) for the estimation of survival of red blood cells.

METABOLIC PATHWAYS

It is not unexpected that the labyrinths of *intermediary metabolism* would offer a most fertile field for radiotracer procedures. The biochemist, organic chemist, and carbon 14 comprise a team that has contributed greatly to elucidation of the various metabolic cycles. The general approach involves the administration of isotopic compounds and the subsequent isolation, purification, and measurement of possible conversion products. Rigorous isolation procedures and the wide application of degradation methods to allow assignment of the label to specific carbon atoms in the molecule have allowed increasingly detailed interpretations of the mechanisms involved. A broad base for advanced experimentation is provided by the chemical synthesis of labeled compounds for use as intermediates and by the biosynthesis of important naturally occurring substances. The scope of investigations actively under way may be gained from a consideration of some of the general fields in which carbon isotopes are extensively used, which sounds like the roll call of the biochemical sciences: animal and plant biochemistry, photosynthesis, microbiological metabolism, carbon dioxide fixation, fatty acid oxidation, glycolysis, fat metabolism, transmethylation, amino acids, and proteins.

The literature dealing with metabolic pathways is already so formidable and the rapid changing of status so overwhelming that no attempt can be made to treat comprehensively even one narrow aspect. Reference to the *Annual Review* type of article, in addition to consultation of standard textual discussions, represents perhaps the best way of keeping abreast of this field (9, 11, 12, 95 to 97). The following discussion on the pathway of carbon in photosynthesis, based primarily on the work of Calvin and coworkers (98, 99), illustrates the power of the method:

Photosynthesis, the process by which green plants convert radiant energy (light) into chemical energy (organic compounds), may be represented by the over-all equation

$$CO_2 + H_2O \xrightarrow{\text{light}} [CH_2O] + O_2 \qquad (1\text{-}35)$$

For an understanding of the mechanism it is necessary to know the pathway by which carbon dioxide is converted to carbohydrate or other organic end products. Early work done with C^{11} was limited by its short half-life. However, the availability of C^{14} now allows detailed experimentation. The procedure is generally to expose the experimental material, usually algae or higher plants, to $C^{14}O_2$ for a predetermined time under specific conditions and then to determine into what organic fraction the labeled carbon has been incorporated. In addition to the conventional methods of organic chemistry, paper chromatography (see Chap. 8 for details) has proved most valuable in this work, which requires the detection and positive identification of the intermediate compounds.

It was very soon shown with C^{14} that algae in the dark were able to fix about twenty times as much CO_2 if they had been previously exposed to light. Furthermore this fixation of CO_2 in preilluminated plants was shown to yield intermediates similar to those produced by reduction of carbon during photosynthesis and different from those fixed in the dark without preillumination. This and other evidence led to postulation of two fairly distinct mechanisms, represented as follows:

$$2H_2O + light \xrightarrow{\text{chlorophyll}} 4[H] + O_2 \qquad (1\text{-}36)$$
$$CO_2 + 4[H] \rightarrow CH_2O + H_2O \qquad (1\text{-}37)$$

Equation (1-36) represents the absorption of light by chlorophyll and the transfer of energy to yield a photolysis of water, forming oxygen and hydrogen, the latter in the form of a reducing agent. This reaction does not seem to involve carbon or CO_2 or the direct reduction of CO_2. Equation (1-37) represents the synthesis of organic intermediates from CO_2, the pathway of which may be traced with radiocarbon.

Experimental observations indicated that C^{14} was incorporated into intermediates within a matter of seconds. At 10 sec after exposure of *Scenedesmus* to C^{14}-labeled bicarbonate, radiocarbon was found in the following compounds: phosphoglycerate, ribulose diphosphate, hexose diphosphate, fructose phosphate, mannose phosphate, glucose phosphate, sedoheptulose phosphate, ribose phosphate, ribulose phosphate, dihydroxyacetone phosphate, phosphoenol pyruvate. First, it may be noted that nearly all the activity was found in phosphorylated compounds, indicating the importance of phosphorus. Secondly, most of the C^{14} was found in the phosphoglyceric acid (see Chap. 2 for reference to experiments showing that this was not due to an exchange reaction). Time studies showed that the percentage of C^{14} to be found in this compound approached 100 at zero time. Thus phosphoglyceric acid was apparently the first product of carbon dioxide reduction detectable under the experimental conditions. Furthermore the other compounds found suggested the formation of hexoses from phosphoglyceric acid by the reversible reactions of glycolysis.

It was then of interest to observe the rate of labeling of the individual carbon atoms of each compound. Thus, if phosphoglyceric acid were formed by a carboxylation reaction, the labeled carbon would probably not be uniformly distributed among the three carbon atoms of the molecule after short exposures to $C^{14}O_2$. Actually, degradation studies of the phosphoglyceric acid indicated that nearly all the C^{14} was found in the carboxyl position when the period of photosynthesis with C^{14} was 5 sec. Table 1-8 presents further data on the distribution of the label in the molecule as a function of time.

TABLE 1-8. PERCENTAGE OF DISTRIBUTION OF RADIOCARBON IN SPECIFIC CARBON ATOMS OF COMPOUNDS LABELED DURING PHOTOSYNTHESIS

Compound	Preillumination, 2 min dark	Photosynthesis, sec		
		4	15	60
Glyceric acid COOH	96.0	87.0	56	44
Glyceric acid CHOH	2.6	6.5	21	30
CH₂OH	1.7	6.8	23	25
Hexose (from sucrose)				
Carbon atoms 3 and 4	....	....	52	
Carbon atoms 2 and 5	....	....	25	
Carbon atoms 1 and 6	....	....	24	

[From Melvin Calvin, Photosynthesis (The Path of Carbon in Photosynthesis and the Primary Quantum Conversion Act of Photosynthesis), UCRL-2040, No. 22, 1952; and J. G. Buchanan, J. A. Bassham, A. A. Benson, D. F. Bradley, M. Calvin, L. I. Daus, M. Goodman, P. M. Hayes, V. H. Lynch, L. T. Norris, and A. T. Wilson, The Path of Carbon in Photosynthesis. XVII. Phosphorus Compounds as Intermediates in Photosynthesis, *Phosphorus Metabolism*, **2**: 440–466 (1952).]

From the data in Table 1-8 it is also clear that the phosphoglyceric acid was formed by carboxylation of a two-carbon compound. This carbon dioxide acceptor is labeled at an equal rate between the two positions, which is slow compared with the rate of primary carboxylation. The fact that no reservoirs of labeled two-carbon compounds have been found after short periods of photosynthesis with C^{14} is further evidence that the two-carbon compound is not formed by the reduction and coupling of two molecules of carbon dioxide.

It is next possible to suggest and confirm a mechanism for the production of a hexose from two molecules of phosphoglyceric acid. A reasonable sequence would be the reduction of the glyceric acid to the aldehyde, some of which would isomerize to give dihydroxyacetone, which could condense to give the hexose. This may be represented schematically as follows:

$$
\begin{array}{c}
\text{C} \\
? \rightarrow \quad | \quad \xrightarrow{\;C*O_2\;} \\
\text{C}
\end{array}
\qquad
\begin{array}{l}
^1CH_2OPO_3H_2 \\
| \\
^2CHOH \qquad \text{phosphoglyceric acid}\\
| \\
^3C*OOH
\end{array}
$$

2-carbon
CO_2 acceptor

$$\Big\downarrow 2H$$

$$
\begin{array}{l}
^1CH_2OPO_3H_2 \\
| \\
^2CHOH \\
| \\
^3C*HO
\end{array}
\quad \rightleftharpoons \quad
\begin{array}{l}
^1CH_2OPO_3H_2 \\
| \\
^2C{=}O \\
| \\
^3C*H_2OH
\end{array}
\qquad
\begin{array}{l}
\text{dihydroxyacetone} \\
\text{phosphate}
\end{array}
$$

$$
\begin{array}{l}
^1CH_2OPO_3H_2 \\
| \\
^2C{=}O \\
| \\
^3C*HOH \\
| \\
^4C*HOH \qquad \text{fructose diphosphate}\\
| \\
^5CHOH \\
| \\
^6CH_2OPO_3H_2
\end{array}
$$

With this sequence carbon atoms 3 and 4 of the hexose must come from carbon atom 3 of the glyceric acid. This is in direct agreement with the 15-sec values from Table 1-8, where carbon atom 3 of the acid was 56 per cent labeled as compared with a 52 per cent label for carbon atoms 3 and 4 of the hexose. Likewise all the other carbon atoms in both compounds were labeled at a level of about 21 to 25 per cent.

It was next necessary to postulate a mechanism to account for a two-carbon acceptor that becomes labeled at a slow rate and for the various specific intermediates that have been observed. As already mentioned, in addition to the hexose, the five- and seven-carbon keto sugars, ribulose diphosphate and sedoheptulose monophosphate, were found to acquire a C^{14} label rapidly during short-term photosynthesis tracer experiments with $C^{14}O_2$. This indicated that they were in the path of carbon during photosynthesis and probably function in regenerating the two-carbon acceptor complex. The exact mechanism for this pathway has not yet been elucidated, but by trace studies ribulose diphosphate has been shown to be directly related to the two-carbon acceptor and is probably the immediate precursor for it in a cleavage into a three-carbon compound and a two-carbon compound.

Biosynthesis. Labeled organic compounds may be prepared by chemical synthesis or biosynthesis. Since many of the important biological metabolites are exceedingly complex, the biological synthesis is often most convenient. The general procedure is to grow the biological material under such conditions that the radioactive label enters into the metabolism and becomes incorporated into the various metabolites produced. One consideration is that with biological synthesis the label usually becomes randomly located at all possible sites. This is especially true for radioisotopes of carbon or hydrogen. However, random labeling is not usually a problem with elements such as phosphorus, cobalt, sulfur, or iodine which are most often located in specific positions in the molecule.

The bibliography in reference (100) may be consulted for a listing of the various labeled compounds that have already been synthesized biologically. Plants, animals, and microorganisms have been utilized for this purpose. Some of the more important types of compounds labeled include sugars from tobacco and crop plants; drugs from medicinal plants; amino acids, nucleic acids, and vitamins from bacteria, yeasts, and molds; fatty acids and pigments from algae; and insulin, cortical steroids, cholesterol, and glycogen from tissue cultures.

These procedures may also be employed to determine whether or not a given element is a constituent of a particular metabolite. For example, Totter et al. (101) showed that molybdenum was a nondialyzable component of xanthine oxidase by administration of radiomolybdenum to a dairy cow and subsequent isolation of the enzyme from the milk. In all the purification steps the ratio of radiomolybdenum to xanthine oxidase did not change; also, when the isotope was merely added to milk, it did not enter the enzyme. From these experiments it was also possible to calculate that there was a molar ratio of flavin to molybdenum of $2:1$. The biosynthesis of a vitamin-B_{12}-like compound in both the gastrointestinal tract and the tissues of sheep was demonstrated by Monroe et al. (102). This was done by administration of inorganic labeled cobalt to the animals and subsequent fractionation of the tissues and excreta for radioassay.

ADVANTAGES OF DOUBLE LABELING

The simultaneous use of two radioisotopes in an experiment is made feasible by the fact that measurements of each in the same sample are possible (see Chap. 5). In general, double labeling offers a means of comparing directly in a biological system the movement, synthesis, or degradation of two substances or the differential behavior of two parts of a given molecule. Double-isotope studies, by allowing two sets of data to be obtained from the same organism, may save considerable time and expense, especially where the experiment involves systems that are difficult to prepare. This is the situation for animals or plants brought to special nutritional status or raised under special environmental conditions.

For example, pairs of elements (C^{14}-P^{32}, P^{32}-K^{42}, P^{32}-Cs^{137}) have been simultaneously traced in the plant to give information on the mechanism of translocation (36, 44). In animal nutrition and physiology the close relationships of calcium and phosphorus have made the use of this pair of elements very fruitful. Simultaneous measurements have been made of the endogenous fecal phosphorus and calcium in cattle (103). By the concurrent measurement of sodium and calcium disappearance from the plasma of dogs, it was shown that the transcapillary movement of the two elements was about the same except for the exchange into bone exhibited by the calcium (78).

The synthesis of nucleic acids has been studied by the simultaneous injection of carbon-labeled glycine and P^{32} into rats (104). The specific activities of the P^{32} and C^{14} in the purine nucleotides from DNA (desoxy-ribosenucleic acid) were similar, indicating that both precursors were incorporated into some intermediate at the same time. However, the specific activity of the P^{32} in the RNA (ribosenucleic acid) purine nucleotides was considerably higher than that of C^{14}, indicating that the P^{32} was incorporated earlier in this case.

A very powerful method is available in those instances where it is possible to use two different radioisotopes of the same element (Na^{22}-Na^{24}, Fe^{55}-Fe^{59}, Sr^{89}-Sr^{90}, Y^{90}-Y^{91}, Ag^{110}-Ag^{111}). A considerable advantage lies in the correction for secondary losses, which is an extension of isotope dilution, as discussed on page 16. For example, assume that radioisotope A is administered to the system and that an unknown amount of it becomes located in a sample. A known amount of radioisotope B is added to the sample, which is then analyzed for both isotopes. It is clear that the following is true:

$$C = A \frac{B_a}{B_r} \qquad (1\text{-}38)$$

where C = amount of radioisotope A in sample
  A = amount of radioisotope A measured in sample or in given portion of sample
  B_a = amount of radioisotope B added to sample
  B_r = amount of radioisotope B measured in same portion of sample in which A is measured

The important thing is that, after radioisotope B has been added, any losses from the sample do not affect the results, since A and B are lost in the same proportion and the value of C can be determined despite such a loss.

This application may be illustrated by the work of Saylor and Finch (105) on the absorption of iron. In a conventional study the isotope is given orally to an animal and the absorption measured by analysis either of the carcass or of the excretions. In human beings or large animals, analysis of the carcass is either impossible or impractical, and the quantitative collection of excretions is always difficult. *By the application of the double-isotope principle it was possible to determine the absorption of orally administered radioiron merely by analyses of a blood sample.* A known amount of Fe^{55} was administered to a rat by stomach tube, and a short time later a known amount of Fe^{59} was intravenously injected into the same animal. After several days a blood sample was taken and analyzed for both isotopes. The percentage of absorption of the orally administered Fe^{55} was calculated as follows:

$$\% \ Fe^{55} \ absorbed \ = \ \frac{100 \times Fe_b^{55} \dfrac{Fe^{59}}{Fe_b^{59}}}{Fe^{55}} \qquad (1\text{-}39)$$

where Fe_b^{55} = amount of Fe^{55} in blood sample
   Fe^{59} = amount of Fe^{59} injected intravenously
   Fe_b^{59} = amount of Fe^{59} in blood sample
   Fe^{55} = amount of Fe^{55} given orally

This calculation is based on the assumption that iron is removed from the blood in the same way whether it reached there by direct injection or by absorption from the gastrointestinal tract. Values obtained by this procedure were in agreement with results from the direct analyses of the carcasses of the rats used. The double-labeling principles were also used in the direct-carcass analyses to correct for manipulative errors. Since no large amounts of intravenously administered iron are lost from the body by excretion, the recovery of the injected Fe^{59} from the whole carcass was assumed to represent also the recovery of Fe^{55} from the carcass and was used to correct the observed Fe^{55} value. Thus absorption from whole-carcass analysis was calculated as follows:

$$Absorbed \ Fe^{55} \ = \ recovered \ Fe^{55} \ \frac{Fe^{59} \ injected}{Fe^{59} \ recovered} \qquad (1\text{-}40)$$

An example of how two radioisotopes of different elements are used to label the same substance is given in the work of Keston et al. (63) on the analysis of amino acids in mixtures. In general, the procedure is as follows: (*a*) The unknown acids are converted to labeled derivatives by reaction with I^{131}–pipsyl chloride. (*b*) A pure sample of each amino acid to be measured is labeled with S^{35}–pipsyl chloride, and a known amount of each derivative is added to the unknown mixture. (*c*) The mixture is separated into components on a paper chromatogram. (*d*) The bands of the paper chromatogram are sectioned, the amino acids eluted from the sections, and the S^{35}/I^{131} ratios determined. The identity of the bands is determined from previous experience with the movement of known amino acids. If a given band is pure, this will be shown by a constant S^{35}/I^{131} ratio in the various sections of the band. Furthermore the original content of the I^{131} derivative of a particular amino acid can be quantitatively estimated from the S^{35}/I^{131} ratio by the same type of calculation as described above for the iron experiments.

MISCELLANEOUS APPLICATIONS

The investigator who thoroughly understands the basic principles of tracer methodology and considers them in terms of his specific problems is in an excellent position to develop novel and useful applications. Following are a few illustrations:

Bioassays. The various techniques available for the assay of vitamin D are not considered entirely satisfactory. Snyder, Eisner, and Steenbock (106) have proposed a method that apparently offers many advantages. It is based upon the effect of the vitamin D status of a test animal upon the uptake of P^{32} as determined by an external measurement. Young rats are fed upon a rachitogenic ration for 16 days and are then given orally an unknown vitamin D preparation in a potency range of $\frac{1}{2}$ to 50 units. After 48 hr the rats are given an intraperitoneal injection of P^{32}, and following 10 days of continued feeding of the rachitogenic ration the animals are anesthetized and an external count taken of the forepaw. A standard reference curve is prepared by the identical treatment of rats receiving doses of known vitamin D potency.

The increase in P^{32} excretion following the administration of parathyroid hormone to thyroparathyroidectomized rats has been used as a basis for the bioassay of parathyroid hormone by Rubin and Dorfman (107). In principle, the hormone and P^{32} in 1.2 mg disodium phosphate were administered about 24 hr after the operation, and the urine then collected for radioassay. Amounts as small as 0.5 USP unit were detectable; this represents a 200-fold increase in sensitivity over the standard USP method. Also the need for tedious chemical estimations of blood phosphate was eliminated.

Steric Relations and Enzyme Action. In a very important paper Ogston (108) postulated that compounds that are chemically symmetrical may exist in two spatial configurations, one of which could combine with an enzyme and undergo certain reactions, whereas the other configuration could not. Support for this concept was found in the studies of Potter and Heidelberger (109), as follows: $C^{14}O_2$ was incorporated into citric acid in a rat liver homogenate, and the citric acid then purified by chromatography and converted to α-ketoglutarate in another rat liver homogenate. This compound was purified and chemically degraded to yield CO_2 and succinic acid. The C^{14} label was found entirely in the CO_2 and not at all in the succinic acid. This reaction may then be represented schematically as follows:

$$
\begin{array}{ccccc}
^1COOH & & ^1COOH & & ^1COOH \\
| & & | & & | \\
^2CH_2 & & ^2CH_2 & & ^2CH_2 \\
| & \xrightarrow[\text{homogenate}]{\text{rat liver}} & | & \xrightarrow{KMnO_4} & | \\
HO-^3C-^4COOH & & ^3CH_2 & & ^3CH_2 + {}^6C^*O_2 \quad (1\text{-}41)\\
| & & | & & | \\
^5CH_2 & & ^5C{=}O & & ^5COOH \\
| & & | & & \\
^6C^*OOH & & ^6C^*OOH & & \\
\text{citric acid} & & \text{α-ketoglutaric} & & \text{succinic acid} \\
& & \text{acid} & &
\end{array}
$$

It is clear from the experimental results that carbon atoms 1 and 6 in Eq. (1-41) were not identical so far as the enzyme action was concerned. However, there was the question as to whether this result may not have been due to the presence of the radioactive carbon atom. In other words, was there an isotope effect? This matter was settled by the work of Wilcox et al. (110), who prepared the L- derivative of an asymmetric compound which was then converted to citric acid and carried through the same procedures as above. The reactions are indicated below, and in this case all the C^{14} was found in the succinic acid, none being present in the CO_2:

$$
\begin{array}{ccc}
Cl & & ^1C^*OOH \\
| & & | \\
^2CH_2 & & ^2CH_2 \\
| & \xrightarrow{KC^{14}N} HO- & | \\
HO-^3C-^4COOH & & ^3C-^4COOH \xrightarrow[\text{homogenate}]{\text{rat liver}} \\
| & & | \\
^5CH_2 & & ^5CH_2 \\
| & & | \\
^6COOH & & ^6COOH \\
& & \text{citric acid}
\end{array}
$$

$$
\begin{array}{c}
^1\text{C*OOH} \\
| \\
^2\text{CH}_2 \\
| \\
^3\text{CH}_2 \\
| \\
^5\text{C}{=}\text{O} \\
| \\
^6\text{COOH} \\
\alpha\text{-ketoglutaric} \\
\text{acid}
\end{array}
\quad \xrightarrow{\text{KMnO}_4} \quad
\begin{array}{c}
^1\text{C*OOH} \\
| \\
^2\text{CH}_2 \\
| \\
^3\text{CH}_2 \\
| \\
^5\text{COOH} \\
\text{succinic} \\
\text{acid}
\end{array}
+ \ ^6\text{CO}_2
\qquad (1\text{-}42)
$$

The implications of this work may be listed as follows: (*a*) The isotope method was able to reveal the two spatial configurations of citric acid and showed that the enzyme can distinguish between them, thus supporting Ogston's concept of a three-point contact between enzyme and substrate. (*b*) The results were not due to an isotope effect (see Chap. 2). (*c*) Earlier studies which were taken to indicate that citric acid could not be a primary condensation product in the Krebs cycle could now be reinterpreted to show that citric acid is indeed an initial product of condensation.

Radiocarbon Dating. The development of the carbon-14 method of age determination by Libby and associates (111 to 114) made an outstanding contribution to the fields of geology, anthropology, archaeology, etc. The procedure is based upon the fact that C^{14} is being continually formed in the atmosphere by cosmic-ray-produced neutrons. All material in the life cycle, as well as all material exchangeable with atmospheric CO_2, is uniformly labeled with C^{14}. At death, plants and animals cease to take up new carbon from the atmosphere, and no C^{14} is produced in the inanimate material. Thus at the time of death, or when material is removed from the carbon cycle, the C^{14} present begins to decrease in amount owing to radioactive decay without replenishment. It is assumed that the cosmic-radiation intensity and therefore the C^{14} specific activity in the biological cycle have been reasonably constant over the past thousands of years. Using the known half-life of C^{14} and comparing the specific activities of a relic and contemporary material, it is possible to calculate the time that has elapsed since the death of the relic. For example, Libby et al. (111) found a value of 12.5 ± 0.2 counts/min/g carbon for contemporary material and 7.04 ± 0.20 for wood samples from ancient Egyptian tombs that were estimated to be 4600 yr old from other considerations. Using a half-life value of 5720 yr for C^{14}, it was calculated that the theoretical specific activity for 4600-yr-old material should be 7.15 ± 0.15, which is in excellent agreement with that observed. Hundreds of samples have now been assayed, and the agreement with independent estimations has supported the basic assumptions.

The primary technical problems are the avoidance of contamination in the handling of samples and the precise measurement of the low levels of carbon 14. Details of procedure have been published by various laboratories (115 to 118). The main considerations may be listed as follows: (a) reduction of background by anticoincidence counters and shields, (b) avoidance of traces of radioactivity in shield and counter materials, (c) correction or elimination of drifts in sensitivity or background, (d) elimination of spurious counts, and (e) cleanliness in handling of samples. Present techniques permit age determinations in the range of 500 to 30,000 yr.

Several laboratories in addition to Chicago are now reporting radiocarbon age results: Lamont (119, 120), Yale (121), Michigan (116, 117, 122), Copenhagen (123, 124), and Mexico (125). The results are usually based on a C^{14} half-life of 5568 ± 30 yr and contain an error term that is calculated from the standard deviation of the counting data. It must be remembered that there may be other errors, both laboratory and nonlaboratory, which may have to be taken into account (121, 122, 126). The nonlaboratory errors are concerned with the mode of deposition of the material to be dated and the circumstances of its preservation. For example, thousands of years after an organic deposit had been laid down, it could be enriched with C^{14} from new organic material such as plant roots and burrowing animals. There are also problems of isotope effects and equilibria in the sea and in carbonates.

Criteria for Blood Preservation. When whole blood or packed red cells are stored for transfusion purposes, the cells tend to lose their capacity for survival in the blood stream of the recipient. It is very difficult to estimate by conventional methods whether or not the stored cells have lost their viability. Procedures have been developed by Ross et al. (127) and Gibson et al. (128), using radioiron, which have been convenient and satisfactory for this determination. In principle, tracer amounts of radioiron are administered to normal individuals so as to label their red cells. Blood samples are then taken from them for storage studies and subsequent transfusion into the recipient. After transfusion the nonviable cells are rapidly removed from the circulation, so that the isotope content or, more particularly, the specific activity of the recipient's blood at various times after transfusion gives a reliable measure of the value of the blood sample for transfusion purposes. The primary practical application has been in the improvement of preservation methods and the determination of maximum storage times.

Study of Rooting Patterns. It is important to have knowledge of the extent and activity of the root systems of crop plants so as to gain an idea of the volume of soil from which the plant can obtain the nutrients and water that it requires. Also, such information is most helpful in determination of the placement of fertilizer for optimum utilization by the growing plant. A simple method for the study of rooting systems and habits, utilizing radiophosphorus, has been described by Hall (129). In essence, the procedure consists in injecting radiophosphorus into the soil at specific locations relative to the plant and then determining the amount taken up by the plant at different times by an analysis of leaf or root tissue. A typical injection pattern as used in the study of cotton and

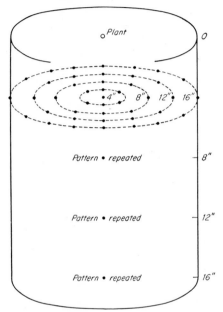

FIG. 1-9. Radiophosphorus injection pattern used for study of the root development of cotton and tobacco. [*From N. S. Hall, The Use of Phosphorus 32 in Plant Root Studies, in "The Role of Atomic Energy in Agricultural Research," Proceedings of the Fourth Annual Oak Ridge Summer Symposium (Sponsored by the Oak Ridge National Laboratory and Oak Ridge Institute of Nuclear Studies, Aug. 25–30, 1952), TID-5115, pp. 435–451, January, 1953.*]

tobacco is shown in Fig. 1-9 (129). This design required 20 different placements and therefore 20 different plants for one complete experiment (see Chap. 5 for experimental details).

The following kinds of information can be obtained: (*a*) the time of arrival of the roots at a given location in the soil, which is a measure of the over-all growth and rate with which the root expands through the soil volume; (*b*) the seasonal and soil effects on the root pattern; (*c*) the time and manner of plant competition, which may lead to spacing recommendations; (*d*) the effects of depth of tillage; (*e*) the relative importance of various root segments for nutrient uptake; and (*f*) the efficiency of the root system of a given species in utilizing added fertilizer under given conditions.

GENERAL REFERENCES

1. Rutherford, Sir Ernest, James Chadwick, and C. D. Ellis: "Radiations from Radioactive Substances," Cambridge University Press, New York, 1951.
2. Bethe, H. A.: "Elementary Nuclear Theory; A Short Course on Selected Topics Given at the Research Laboratory of the General Electric Company at Schenectady," John Wiley & Sons, Inc., New York, 1947.
3. Dushman, Saul: "Fundamentals of Atomic Physics," McGraw-Hill Book Company, Inc., New York, 1951.
4. Lapp, R. E., and H. L. Andrews: "Nuclear Radiation Physics," Prentice-Hall, Inc., New York, 1948.
5. Pollard, Ernest C., and William L. Davidson: "Applied Nuclear Physics," 2d ed., John Wiley & Sons, Inc., New York, 1951.
6. Cork, James M.: "Radioactivity and Nuclear Physics," D. Van Nostrand Company, Inc., New York, 1947.
7. Glasstone, Samuel: "Sourcebook on Atomic Energy," D. Van Nostrand Company, Inc., New York, 1950.
8. Whitehouse, W. J., and J. L. Putman: "Radioactive Isotopes," Oxford University Press, New York, 1953.
9. Kamen, Martin D.: "Radioactive Tracers in Biology," Academic Press, Inc., New York, 1951.
10. Siri, William E.: "Isotopic Tracers and Nuclear Radiations," McGraw-Hill Book Company, Inc., New York, 1949.
11. Hevesy, George: "Radioactive Indicators," Interscience Publishers, Inc., New York, 1948.
12. Sacks, Jacob: "Isotopic Tracers in Biochemistry and Physiology," McGraw-Hill Book Company, Inc., New York, 1953.
13. *Advances in Biological and Medical Physics*, ed. by John H. Lawrence and C. A. Tobias, Academic Press, Inc., New York.
14. *Annual Review of Nuclear Science*, ed. by James G. Beckerley, Annual Reviews, Inc., Stanford, Calif.

CITED REFERENCES

15. Bugher, J. C., and M. Taylor: Radio-Phosphorus and Radio-Strontium in Mosquitoes, *Science*, **110**: 146–147 (1949).
16. Jenkins, Dale W., and Charles C. Hassett: Radioisotopes in Entomology, *Nucleonics*, **6**: 5–14 (1950).
17. Oughton, John: "Tagging" Root Maggot Flies (*Hylemya* spp., Anthomyidae) by Means of Radioactive Phosphorus, *Ann. Rept. Entomol. Soc. Ontario*, **81** (1950).
18. Fuller, R. A., J. W. T. Spinks, A. P. Arnason, and H. McDonald: Use of Radioactive Tracers in Investigations on Soil-inhabiting Insects, *Ann. Rept. Entomol. Soc. Ontario*, **81** (1950).
19. Irwin, R. L. B., J. W. T. Spinks, and T. J. Arnason: Deposition of P^{32} in Developing *Drosophila*, *Can. J. Research*, **D28**: 137–142 (1950).
20. Hassett, C. C., and D. W. Jenkins: The Uptake and Effect of Radiophosphorus in Mosquitoes, *Physiol. Zoöl.*, **24**: 257–266 (1951).
21. Radeleff, R. D., R. C. Bushland, and D. E. Hopkins: Phosphorus-32 Labeling of the Screw-worm Fly, *J. Econ. Entomol.*, **45**: 509–514 (1952).
22. Fredeen, F. J. H., J. W. T. Spinks, J. R. Anderson, A. P. Arnason, and J. G. Rempel: Mass Tagging of Black Flies (*Diptera:* Simuliidae) with Radiophosphorus, *Can. J. Zool.*, **31**: 1–15 (1953).

23. Shemanchuk, J. A., J. W. T. Spinks, and F. J. H. Fredeen: A Method of Tagging Prairie Mosquitoes (*Diptera:* Culicidae) with Radio-phosphorus, *Can. Entomologist*, **85**: 269–272 (1953).
24. Lindquist, Arthur W.: Radioactive Materials in Entomological Research, *J. Econ. Entomol.*, **45**: 264–270 (1952).
25. Buckland, F. E., G. J. Harper, and J. D. Morton: Use of Spores Labelled with Radiophosphorus in the Study of the Respiratory Retention of Aerosols, *Nature*, **166**: 354 (1950).
26. Goldberg, L. J., and W. R. Leif: The Use of a Radioactive Isotope in Determining the Retention and Initial Distribution of Airborne Bacteria in the Mouse, *Science*, **112**: 299–300 (1950).
27. Comar, C. L.: Radioisotopes in Nutritional Trace Element Studies, I–III, *Nucleonics*, **3**(3): 32–45; **3**(4): 30–42; **3**(5): 34–48 (1948).
28. Hansard, Sam L., C. L. Comar, and M. P. Plumlee: Absorption and Tissue Distribution of Radiocalcium in Cattle, *J. Animal Sci.*, **11**: 524–535 (1952).
29. Ussing, Hans H.: Some Aspects of the Application of Tracers in Permeability Studies, *Advances in Enzymol.*, **13**: 21–65 (1952).
30. Pressman, David: Antibodies as Specific Chemical Reagents, *Advances in Biol. and Med. Phys.*, **3**: 99–152 (1953).
31. Dixon, F. J., S. C. Bukantz, G. J. Dammin, and D. W. Talmage: Fate of I131-labeled Bovine Gamma Globulin in Rabbits, in A. M. Pappenheimer, Jr., ed., "The Nature and Significance of the Antibody Response" (Symposium Held at New York Academy of Medicine, Mar. 2–22, 1953), pp. 170–182, Columbia University Press, New York, 1953.
32. Pressman, David: Radioactive Tracers in the Study of Anti-tissue Antibody, in A. M. Pappenheimer, Jr., ed., "The Nature and Significance of the Antibody Response" (Symposium Held at New York Academy of Medicine, Mar. 2–22, 1953), pp. 207–227, Columbia University Press, New York, 1953.
33. Tabern, D. L., J. D. Taylor, and G. I. Gleason: Radioisotopes in Pharmaceutical and Medical Studies, I–III, *Nucleonics*, **7**(5): 3–23 (1950); **7**(6): 40–55 (1950); **8**(1): 60–77 (1951).
34. Tolbert, N. Edward, and Paul B. Pearson: Atomic Energy and the Plant Sciences, *Advances in Agron.*, **4**: 279–303 (1952).
35. Collected Papers, *Soil Sci.*, **68**: 113–197 (1949).
35a. Hendricks, S. B., and L. A. Dean: Radioisotopes in Soils Research and Plant Nutrition, *Ann. Rev. Nuclear Sci.*, **1**: 597–610 (1952).
36. Swanson, C. A., and J. B. Whitney, Jr.: Studies on the Translocation of Foliar-applied P32 and Other Radioisotopes in Bean Plants, *Am. J. Botany*, **40**: 816–823 (1953).
37. Stout, P. R., and D. R. Hoagland: Upward and Lateral Movement of Salt in Certain Plants as Indicated by Radioactive Isotopes of Potassium, Sodium, and Phosphorus Absorbed by Roots, *Am. J. Botany*, **26**: 320–324 (1939).
38. Lindquist, Arthur W., A. R. Roth, and Robert A. Hoffman: The Distribution of Radioactive DDT in House Flies, *J. Econ. Entomol.*, **44**: 931–934 (1952).
39. Winteringham, F. P. W.: Some Aspects of Insecticide Biochemistry, *Endeavour*, **11**: 22–28 (1952).
40. Gjullin, C. M., and Arthur W. Lindquist: Absorption of Radioactive DDT by Resistant and Nonresistant Mosquitoes, *Mosquito News*, **12**: 201–205 (1952).
41. Strajman, Enrique, and Nello Pace: In Vivo Studies with Radioisotopes, *Advances in Biol. and Med. Phys.*, **2**: 193–241 (1951).
42. Everett, Newton B., and Robert J. Johnson: Use of Radioactive Phosphorus in Studies of Fetal Circulation, *Am. J. Physiol.*, **162**: 147–152 (1950).

43. Craig, Roderick, and N. A. Olson: Rate of Circulation of the Body Fluid in Adult *Tenebrio molitor* Linnaeus, *Anasa tristis* (de Geer), and *Murgantia histrionica* (Hahn), *Science*, **113**: 648–650 (1951).

44. Chen, S. L.: Simultaneous Movement of P^{32} and C^{14} in Opposite Directions in Phloem Tissue, *Am. J. Botany*, **38**: 203–211 (1951).

45. Sheppard, C. W.: New Developments in Potassium and Cell Physiology: 1940–50, *Science*, **114**: 85–91 (1951).

46. Thomas, R. O., T. A. Litovitz, M. I. Rubin, and C. F. Geschickter: Dynamics of Calcium Metabolism: Time Distribution of Intravenously Administered Radiocalcium, *Am. J. Physiol.*, **169**: 568–575 (1952).

47. Flexner, Louis B., Dean B. Cowie, and Gilbert J. Vosburgh: Studies on Capillary Permeability with Tracer Substances, in "Biological Applications of Tracer Elements," *Cold Spring Harbor Symposia Quant. Biol.*, **13**: 88–98 (1948).

48. Overstreet, R., and T. C. Broyer: The Nature of Absorption of Radioactive Isotopes by Living Tissues as Illustrated by Experiments with Barley Plants, *Proc. Natl. Acad. Sci. U.S.*, **26**: 16–24 (1940).

49. Visek, W. J., R. A. Monroe, E. W. Swanson, and C. L. Comar: Calcium Metabolism in Dairy Cows as Studied with Ca 45, *J. Dairy Sci.*, **36**: 373–384 (1953).

50. Van Middlesworth, Lester: Personal communication.

51. Edelman, I. S., J. M. Olney, A. H. James, L. Brooks, and F. D. Moore: Body Composition: Studies in the Human Being by the Dilution Principle, *Science*, **115**: 447–454 (1952).

52. Gregersen, Magnus I.: Blood Volume, *Ann. Rev. Physiol.*, **13**: 397–412 (1951).

53. Hansard, Sam L., W. O. Butler, C. L. Comar, and C. S. Hobbs: Blood Volume of Farm Animals, *J. Animal Sci.*, **12**: 402–413 (1953).

54. Storey, R. H., J. Moshman, and J. Furth: A Simple Procedure for Determination of the Approximate Lymph Space, *Science*, **114**: 665–667 (1951).

55. Fried, Maurice, and L. A. Dean: A Concept Concerning the Measurement of Available Soil Nutrients, *Soil Sci.*, **73**: 263–271 (1952).

56. Hendricks, Sterling B.: Radioisotopes in Fertilizer Usage, Soil Fertility and Plant Nutrition, in "Use of Isotopes in Plant and Animal Research" (Conference Sponsored by Kansas State College, Argonne National Laboratory, and Isotopes Division, U.S. Atomic Energy Commission, June 12–14, 1952), TID-5098, pp. 41–47, April, 1953.

57. Kleiber, Max, Arthur H. Smith, N. P. Ralston, and Arthur L. Black: Radiophosphorus (P^{32}) as Tracer for Measuring Endogenous Phosphorus in Cow's Feces, *J. Nutrition*, **45**: 253–263 (1951).

58. Visek, W. J., R. A. Monroe, E. W. Swanson, and C. L. Comar: Determination of Endogenous Fecal Calcium in Cattle by a Simple Isotope Dilution Method, *J. Nutrition*, **50**: 23–33 (1953).

59. Comar, C. L., R. A. Monroe, W. J. Visek, and Sam L. Hansard: Comparison of Two Isotope Methods for Determination of Endogenous Fecal Calcium, *J. Nutrition*, **50**: 459–467 (1953).

60. Rosenblum, Charles: Applications of Isotope Labeled Vitamin B_{12}, in "The Role of Atomic Energy in Agricultural Research," Proceedings of the Fourth Annual Oak Ridge Summer Symposium (Sponsored by the Oak Ridge National Laboratory and Oak Ridge Institute of Nuclear Studies, Aug. 25–30, 1952), TID-5115, pp. 185–212, January, 1953.

61. Gest, Howard, Martin D. Kamen, and John M. Reiner: The Theory of Isotope Dilution, *Arch. Biochem.*, **12**: 273–281 (1947).

62. Keston, Albert S., Sidney Udenfriend, and R. Keith Cannan: Microanalysis of

Mixtures (Amino Acids) in the Form of Isotopic Derivatives, *J. Am. Chem. Soc.*, **68**: 1390 (1946).

63. Keston, Albert S., Sidney Udenfriend, and Milton Levy: Determination of Organic Compounds as Isotopic Derivatives. II. Amino Acids by Paper Chromatographic and Indicator Techniques, *J. Am. Chem. Soc.*, **72**: 748–753 (1950).

64. Wood, John L., and Helmut R. Gutmann: Radioactive *l*-Cystine and *d*-Methionine. A Study of the Resolution of Radioactive Racemates by Isotopic Dilution, *J. Biol. Chem.*, **179**: 535–542 (1949).

65. Solomon, A. K.: Equations for Tracer Experiments, *J. Clin. Invest.*, **28**: 1297–1307 (1949).

66. Solomon, A. K.: The Kinetics of Biological Processes; Special Problems Connected with the Use of Tracers, *Advances in Biol. and Med. Phys.*, **3**: 65–97 (1953).

67. Radin, Norman S.: Isotope Techniques in Biochemistry, IV, *Nucleonics*, **2**: 50–56 (1948).

68. Zilversmit, D. B., C. Entenman, and M. C. Fishler: On the Calculation of "Turnover Time" and "Turnover Rate" from Experiments Involving the Use of Labeling Agents, *J. Gen. Physiol.*, **26**: 325–331 (1943).

69. Chaikoff, I. L., and D. B. Zilversmit: Radioactive Phosphorus: Its Application to the Study of Phospholipid Metabolism, *Advances in Biol. and Med. Phys.*, **1**: 321–352 (1948).

70. Sheppard, C. W., and W. R. Martin: Cation Exchange between Cells and Plasma of Mammalian Blood. I. Methods and Application to Potassium Exchange in Human Blood, *J. Gen. Physiol.*, **33**: 703–722 (1950).

71. Sheppard, C. W., W. R. Martin, and Gertrude Beyl: Cation Exchange between Cells and Plasma of Mammalian Blood. II. Sodium and Potassium Exchange in the Sheep, Dog, Cow, and Man and the Effect of Varying the Plasma Potassium Concentration, *J. Gen. Physiol.*, **34**: 411–429 (1951).

72. Sheppard, C. W., and Gertrude E. Beyl: Cation Exchange in Mammalian Erythrocytes. III. The Prolytic Effect of X-rays on Human Cells, *J. Gen. Physiol.*, **34**: 691–704 (1951).

73. Raker, John W., Isaac M. Taylor, John M. Weller, and A. Baird Hastings: Rate of Potassium Exchange of the Human Erythrocyte, *J. Gen. Physiol.*, **33**: 691–702 (1950).

74. Sheppard, C. W., and A. S. Householder: The Mathematical Basis of the Interpretation of Tracer Experiments in Closed Steady-state Systems, *J. Appl. Phys.*, **22**: 510–520 (1951).

75. Gellhorn, Alfred, Margaret Merrell, and Robert M. Rankin: The Rate of Transcapillary Exchange of Sodium in Normal and Shocked Dogs, *Am. J. Physiol.*, **142**: 407–427 (1944).

76. Sheppard, C. W., R. R. Overman, W. S. Wilde, and W. C. Sangren: The Disappearance of K^{42} from the Nonuniformly Mixed Circulation Pool in Dogs, *Circulation Research*, **1**: 284–297 (1953).

77. Pappenheimer, J. R., E. M. Renkin, and L. M. Borrero: Filtration, Diffusion and Molecular Sieving through Peripheral Capillary Membranes, *Am. J. Physiol.*, **167**: 13–46 (1951).

78. Armstrong, W. D., John A. Johnson, Leon Singer, R. I. Lienke, and M. L. Premer: Rates of Transcapillary Movement of Calcium and Sodium and of Calcium Exchange by the Skeleton, *Am. J. Physiol.*, **171**: 641–651 (1952).

79. Burch, George, Paul Reaser, and James Cronvich: Rates of Sodium Turnover in

Normal Subjects and in Patients with Congestive Heart Failure, *J. Lab. Clin. Med.*, **32**: 1169–1191 (1947).

80. Burch, G. E., S. A. Threefoot, and C. T. Ray: Rates of Turnover and Biologic Decay of Chloride and Chloride Space in the Dog Determined with the Long-life Isotope, Cl³⁶, *J. Lab. Clin. Med.*, **35**: 331–347 (1950).

81. Hansard, Sam L., C. L. Comar, and G. K. Davis: Effects of Age upon the Physiological Behavior of Calcium in Cattle, *Am. J. Physiol.*, **177**: 383–389 (1954).

82. Hood, S. L., and C. L. Comar: Unpublished data.

83. Threefoot, S. A., C. T. Ray, G. E. Burch, J. A. Cronvich, J. P. Milnor, W. Overman, and W. Gordon: Concentration-time Course in the Plasma of Man of Radiomercury Introduced as a Mercurial Diuretic, *J. Clin. Invest.*, **28**: 661–670 (1949).

84. Madden, Robert E., and R. Gordon Gould: The Turnover Rate of Fibrinogen in the Dog, *J. Biol. Chem.*, **196**: 641–650 (1952).

85. Branson, Herman: A Mathematical Description of Metabolizing Systems, I, *Bull. Math. Biophys.*, **8**: 159–165 (1946).

86. Branson, Herman: A Mathematical Description of Metabolizing Systems, II, *Bull. Math. Biophys.*, **9**: 93–98 (1947).

87. Hearon, John Z.: Rate Behavior of Metabolic Systems, *Physiol. Revs.*, **32**: 499–523 (1952).

88. Reiner, John M.: The Study of Metabolic Turnover Rates by Means of Isotopic Tracers. I. Fundamental Relations, *Arch. Biochem. and Biophys.*, **46**: 53–79 (1953).

89. Reiner, John M.: The Study of Metabolic Turnover Rates by Means of Isotopic Tracers. II. Turnover in a Simple Reaction System, *Arch. Biochem. and Biophys.*, **46**: 80–99 (1953).

90. Shemin, David, and D. Rittenberg: The Life Span of the Human Red Blood Cell, *J. Biol. Chem.*, **166**: 627–636 (1946).

91. Dornhorst, A. C.: The Interpretation of Red Cell Survival Curves, *Blood*, **6**: 1284–1292 (1951).

92. Neuberger, A.: Studies on Mammalian Red Cells, in "Ciba Foundation Conference on Isotopes in Biochemistry," pp. 68–85, J. and A. Churchill, Ltd., London, 1951.

93. Burwell, E. Langdon, Barbara A. Brickley, and Clement A. Finch: Erythrocyte Life Span in Small Animals, *Am. J. Physiol.*, **172**: 718–724 (1953).

94. Necheles, T. F., Irwin M. Weinstein, and George V. Leroy: Radioactive Sodium Chromate for the Study of Survival of Red Blood Cells. I. The Effect of Radioactive Sodium Chromate on Red Cells. II. The Rate of Hemolysis in Certain Hematologic Disorders, *J. Lab. Clin. Med.*, **42**: 358–376 (1953).

95. Hevesy, G.: Nucleic Acid Metabolism, *Advances in Biol. and Med. Phys.*, **1**: 409–454 (1948).

96. Heidelberger, Charles: The Application of the Carbon Isotopes to a Study of Animal Metabolism, *Advances in Biol. and Med. Phys.*, **2**: 77–131 (1951).

97. Burris, R. H.: Carbon 14 Studies on Organic Acid Metabolism in Plants, in "The Role of Atomic Energy in Agricultural Research," Proceedings of the Fourth Annual Oak Ridge Summer Symposium (Sponsored by the Oak Ridge National Laboratory and Oak Ridge Institute of Nuclear Studies, Aug. 25–30, 1952), TID-5115, pp. 342–377, January, 1953.

98. Calvin, Melvin: Photosynthesis (The Path of Carbon in Photosynthesis and the Primary Quantum Conversion Act of Photosynthesis), UCRL-2040, Nov. 22, 1952.

99. Buchanan, J. G., J. A. Bassham, A. A. Benson, D. F. Bradley, M. Calvin, L. I. Daus, M. Goodman, P. M. Hayes, V. H. Lynch, L. T. Norris, and A. T. Wilson: The Path of Carbon in Photosynthesis. XVII. Phosphorus Compounds as Intermediates in Photosynthesis, *Phosphorus Metabolism*, **2**: 440–466 (1952).

100. "Isotopes, A Five-year Summary of U.S. Distribution," U.S. Atomic Energy Commission, August, 1951.

101. Totter, John R., William T. Burnett, Jr., Robert A. Monroe, Ira B. Whitney, and C. L. Comar: Evidence That Molybdenum Is a Nondialyzable Component of Xanthine Oxidase, *Science*, **118**: 555 (1953).

102. Monroe, R. A., H. E. Sauberlich, C. L. Comar, and S. L. Hood: Vitamin B_{12} Biosynthesis after Oral and Intravenous Administration of Inorganic Co^{60} to Sheep, *Proc. Soc. Exptl. Biol. Med.*, **80**: 250–257 (1952).

103. Monroe, R. A., W. J. Visek, and C. L. Comar: Unpublished results.

104. Tyner, Evelyn Pease, Charles Heidelberger, and G. A. LePage: Intracellular Distribution of Radioactivity in Nucleic Acid Nucleotides and Proteins Following Simultaneous Administration of P^{32} and Glycine-2-C^{14}, *Cancer Research*, **13**: 186–203 (1953).

105. Saylor, Linda, and Clement A. Finch: Determination of Iron Absorption Using Two Isotopes of Iron, *Am. J. Physiol.*, **172**: 372–376 (1953).

106. Snyder, R. H., H. J. Eisner, and Harry Steenbock: The Determination of Vitamin D with Radiophosphorus, *J. Nutrition*, **45**: 305–318 (1951).

107. Rubin, Betty, and Ralph I. Dorfman: Bioassay of Parathyroid Hormone, *Proc. Soc. Exptl. Biol. Med.*, **83**: 223–225 (1953).

108. Ogston, A. G.: Interpretation of Experiments on Metabolic Processes, Using Isotopic Trace Elements, *Nature*, **162**: 963 (1948).

109. Potter, Van R., and C. Heidelberger: Biosynthesis of "Asymmetric" Citric Acid: A Substantiation of the Ogston Concept, *Nature*, **164**: 180 (1949).

110. Wilcox, Philip E., C. Heidelberger, and Van R. Potter: Chemical Preparation of Asymmetrically Labeled Citric Acid, *J. Am. Chem. Soc.*, **72**: 5019–5024 (1950).

111. Libby, W. F., E. C. Anderson, and J. R. Arnold: Age Determination by Radiocarbon Content: Worldwide Assay of Natural Radiocarbon, *Science*, **109**: 227–228 (1949).

112. Arnold, J. R., and W. F. Libby: Age Determinations by Radiocarbon Content: Checks with Samples of Known Age, *Science*, **110**: 678–680 (1949).

113. Arnold, J. R., and W. F. Libby: Radiocarbon Dates, *Science*, **113**: 111–120 (1951).

114. Libby, W. F.: Radiocarbon Dates, II, *Science*, **114**: 291–296 (1951).

115. Anderson, E. C., J. R. Arnold, and W. F. Libby: Measurement of Low-level Radiocarbon, *Rev. Sci. Instr.*, **22**: 225–232 (1951).

116. Crane, H. R.: Dating of Relics by Radiocarbon Analysis, *Nucleonics*, **9**: 16–23 (1951).

117. Crane, H. R., and E. W. McDaniel: An Automatic Counter for Age Determination by the C^{14} Method, *Science*, **116**: 342–347 (1952).

118. Barker, H.: Radiocarbon Dating: Large-scale Preparation of Acetylene from Organic Material, *Nature*, **172**: 631 (1953).

119. Kulp, J. Laurence, Herbert W. Feely, and Lansing E. Tryon: Lamont Natural Radiocarbon Measurements, I, *Science*, **114**: 565–568 (1951).

120. Kulp, J. Laurence, Lansing E. Tryon, Walter R. Eckelman, and William A. Snell: Lamont Natural Radiocarbon Measurements, II, *Science*, **116**: 409–414 (1952).

121. Blau, Monte, Edward S. Deevey, Jr., and Marsha S. Gross: Yale Natural Radiocarbon Measurements. I. Pyramid Valley, New Zealand and Its Problems, *Science*, **118**: 1–6 (1953).

122. Bartlett, H. H.: Radiocarbon Datability of Peat, Marl, Caliche, and Archaeological Materials, *Science*, **114**: 55–56 (1951).
123. Anderson, E. C., Hilde Levi, and H. Tauber: Copenhagen Natural Radiocarbon Measurements, I, *Science*, **118**: 6–9 (1953).
124. Iversen, J.: Radiocarbon Dating of the Allerod Period, *Science*, **118**: 9–11 (1953).
125. de Terra, Helmut: Radiocarbon Age Measurements and Fossil Man in Mexico, *Science*, **113**: 124–125 (1951).
126. Childe, V. Gordon: Comparison of Archaeological and Radiocarbon Datings, *Nature*, **166**: 1068 (1950).
127. Ross, J. F., C. A. Finch, W. C. Peacock, and M. E. Fammons: The In Vitro Preservation and Post-transfusion Survival of Stored Blood, *J. Clin. Invest.*, **26**: 687–703 (1947).
128. Gibson, John G., II, Wendell C. Peacock, Arnold M. Seligman, and Theodore Sack: Circulating Red Cell Volume Measured Simultaneously by the Radioactive Iron and Dye Methods, *J. Clin. Invest.*, **25**: 838–847 (1946).
129. Hall, N. S.: The Use of Phosphorus 32 in Plant Root Studies, in "The Role of Atomic Energy in Agricultural Research," Proceedings of the Fourth Annual Oak Ridge Summer Symposium (Sponsored by the Oak Ridge National Laboratory and Oak Ridge Institute of Nuclear Studies, Aug. 25–30, 1952), TID-5115, pp. 435–451, January, 1953.

CHAPTER 2

BASIC DIFFICULTIES IN TRACER METHODOLOGY

CHEMICAL EFFECTS. RADIOCHEMICAL PURITY—Extraneous Elements; Chemical State; Radiocolloids; Parent-Daughter Relationships; Detection of Radioactive Impurities; Removal or Elimination of Radioactive Impurities. RADIATION EFFECTS. EXCHANGE REACTIONS. ISOTOPE EFFECTS.

Experiments with radiotracers will be valid and interpretations meaningful only if careful consideration has been given to the behavior that may result from the chemical, radiochemical, physical, and biological properties of the radioisotope preparation used. The listing of precautions may appear formidable indeed at first glance. However, in practice, the difficulties for the specific radioisotope and the specific experiment are usually overcome rather easily. Also, once the necessary conditions have been established for a given line of experimentation, they may suffice over a considerable period of investigation. The important point is that the possibilities for misinterpretation should be recognized at the beginning of the investigation and that the experiment should be planned so as to permit interpretations that are as unequivocal as possible.

CHEMICAL EFFECTS

Except for the principal element, there will usually be no problem of chemical effects due to the radioisotope preparation. An indication of possible contaminating chemicals may be gained from a knowledge of the target material, which is usually analytical reagent grade or purer. If there should be some question, control experiments can be run using appropriate levels of nonirradiated target material. Particularly where materials are to be injected into humans must care be taken to ensure that no pyrogens are present, and normal sterilization procedures should be employed. There are few reports in the literature of difficulties from this source. However, Graham et al. (1) observed a toxic factor in a particular batch of pile-produced P^{32} which increased the death rate of embryos following injection into eggs for the production of labeled viruses. Later preparations did not show this effect.

The amount of the principal element introduced into the system may be an important consideration. The mass that must be employed depends upon the specific activity of the preparation available, the degree of accumulation in the samples to be measured, and the sensitivity of the measurement. These factors may frequently be varied to fit the experimental requirements. The following terminology is often used: *Tracer dose*—the amount of the administered element is small compared with the normal intake or that normally present in the system. *Physiological dose* —the amount of the administered element is of the same order of magni-

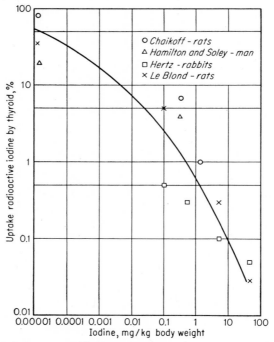

FIG. 2-1. Effect of the mass of iodine administered on the percentage of thyroidal uptake of I¹³¹. (*From J. G. Hamilton, Summary of Iodine Physiology and Metabolic Studies Using Radioactive Isotopes of Iodine*, MDDC-1060, 1944.)

tude as the normal intake. *Massive dose*—the amount of the administered element far exceeds the normal intake. The tracer and physiological doses will usually follow the normal path, since the amount of the element introduced into the system will not be large enough to disturb equilibrium or steady-state conditions. However, a massive dose may well flood the tissues and present an abnormal picture.

The classic example of flooding is the effect of the mass of iodine administered upon the percentage of uptake by the thyroid, as summarized by

Hamilton (2) in Fig. 2-1.   It is apparent that the percentage of collection decreased as the dosage contained increased amounts of iodine and that in any given experiment the results would be primarily a function of the mass of iodine in the range indicated.   In this type of study the dietary and body status of iodine would also have to be taken into account.   For example, Gorbman (3) showed that almost ten times as much I^{131} was required to destroy the thyroids of mice on diets containing moderate amounts of iodide as was required to destroy the thyroids of mice on a low iodide diet.   In some experiments, especially those involving toxicity, large amounts of the element must be used.   This presents no problem, since the dosage can be increased by using additional inert element. Difficulties usually arise when it is necessary to keep the dosage at a minimum.

Physiological concentrations of salts and normal acidities should be used if possible, particularly when solutions are to be administered to animals parenterally.   Some substances are difficult to maintain in solution under such conditions, and these are discussed under the specific elements in Chap. 6.

RADIOCHEMICAL PURITY

In practically all tracer studies it is essential that the radioactivity measured in a system be derived originally from a single known atomic or molecular species.   It is necessary that any radioactivity other than that of the principal species be recognized and eliminated.

Extraneous Elements.   All component atoms of the target material may become more or less radioactive.   Likewise, in isotope production, nuclear reactions may occur other than the one that leads to the principal activity.   The producer of radioisotopes minimizes radiocontamination by choosing a target material which has minimum chemical impurities and which is of such a nature that atomic species prone to activation are not present (e.g., use of the metal or the oxide).   The contribution of each atomic species is not proportional to the amount present, because each species has its characteristic efficiency of production (cross section). Thus a 1 per cent impurity of sodium in a potassium target will result in a 13 per cent contamination after pile irradiation.   Similarly 0.01 per cent calcium phosphate in target $CaCO_3$ may result in a 5 per cent contamination of Ca^{45} with P^{32}, which may lead to difficulties because of the increased sensitivity of counting P^{32} (4).

Chemical State.   Any radioactive atoms that are not in the same valence state or chemical form as the element that is to be followed must be considered as radiocontaminants.   Bombardment of the target material may often produce different forms of the principal activity.   When the target material is processed, however, it usually results in a product containing a single radioactive species.   Special precautions must be taken with unprocessed irradiation units.

A serious and widespread difficulty of this type resulted from the use of P^{32} from pile bombardment of Na_2HPO_4.   In 1940 Libby (5) showed that orthophosphates underwent disruption as a result of neutron bombardment, and found only about 50 per cent of the P^{32} atoms as orthophosphate in the product.   It was suggested that the rest was probably in the form of phosphite.   Thomas and Nicholas (6) in 1949 and Fried and MacKenzie (7) in 1950 confirmed this behavior for pile-bombarded orthophosphate, and the latter workers were thereby able to explain some anomalous fertilizer results.   Borland, MacKenzie, and Hill (8) further characterized this phenomenon and showed that higher temperatures in the pile caused a lower degree of contamination.   The seriousness of this behavior is not so much concerned with studies on orthophosphates as such, since these materials can be obtained in pure form by bombardment of sulfur and processing.   Rather, it is important that certain naturally occurring fertilizers, particularly rock phosphate, be labeled so that the phosphorus availability can be determined directly.   MacKenzie and Borland (9) have investigated the possibilities of removing the contamination from neutron-irradiated rock phosphates and have suggested a satisfactory procedure which consists in heating at 450°C in steam at atmospheric pressure for 168 hr.

Radiocolloids.   It has long been known that some carrier-free tracers in solution behave like colloids rather than true solutes.   Under such conditions these substances have been called *radiocolloids*.   A literature review on radiocolloids has been compiled by Schweitzer and Jackson (10), and Wahl and Bonner (11) have presented tables on the radiocolloid formation of various radioisotopes.   Radiocolloids may be detected by such procedures as dialysis, ultrafiltration, diffusion, electrophoresis, adsorption, and autoradiograms.   The following elements are known to form radiocolloids under appropriate conditions: barium, beryllium, bismuth, cerium, lanthanum, lead, magnesium, niobium, plutonium, polonium, protactinium, scandium, thorium, tin, titanium, yttrium, and zirconium.   Some of the factors tending to promote colloid formation are as follows: (*a*) use of solvents in which the tracer tends to hydrolyze or form an insoluble compound, (*b*) presence of foreign particles in the solution, (*c*) presence of certain electrolytes, and (*d*) increased age of solution (11).

It would be expected that radiocolloids might behave differently in a biological system than do ions of the same radioisotope.   Dobson et al. (12) have shown that the distribution of radiocolloids of zirconium in animals was entirely dependent on particle size.   The localization of radiocolloids in the reticulo-endothelial system, especially the bone marrow, spleen, and liver, has been utilized for the therapeutic delivery of radiation to these sites.   However, interpretations of physiological and metabolic behavior may be made quite difficult by the use of these radio-tracers in an ill-defined physical state.

Parent-Daughter Relationships.   Special attention must be paid to radioisotopes that decay to yield other radioactive species with different chemical or physical properties.   Examples are 20-yr Sr^{90}, which decays to 60-hr Y^{90}, and 65-day Zr^{95}, which decays to 35-day Nb^{95}.   There are two general types of parent-daughter relationships: (a) *Shorter-lived parent*—If the parent is shorter-lived than the daughter, then no equilibrium is reached between the parent and daughter.   Starting with the parent activity initially free of the daughter, as the parent decays, the amount of daughter will increase and eventually decay with the half-life of the daughter.   (b) *Longer-lived parent*—If the parent is longer-lived than the daughter, it becomes possible to use the measured amount of daughter present in a sample as an indication of the amount of parent present. The important point is that, starting with the parent activity, an equilibrium will be reached after a time equal to about 6 to 10 daughter half-lives.   At equilibrium the daughter will be decaying at the same rate at which it is formed, and therefore the amount present will be proportional to the amount of parent present.   Also the apparent half-life of the daughter will be the same as that of the parent.   An illustration of how this behavior is employed in biological studies is presented on page 65. When the parent is being constantly replenished, as in pile bombardment, or is very much longer-lived than the daughter, the term *secular equilibrium* is employed.   In this case the parent does not decay measurably during many daughter half-lives.   When the parent is relatively little longer-lived than the daughter, the term *transient equilibrium* is used. Clearly, secular equilibrium is the limiting case of transient equilibrium, and whether or not the equations for secular equilibrium can be applied depends upon the accuracy desired and the particular experiment.   The text of Cook and Duncan (13) may be consulted for a mathematical treatment of the growth and decay curves of parent-daughter couples.

In many cases the radiation characteristics of the short-lived daughter make radioassay of the daughter much easier than measurement of the parent.   Also, when chemical separations of the daughter are convenient, it may lead to analytical methods that have the following advantages: (a) The radioactivity present in the chemically separated fraction represents only that from the parent activity, and therefore the results are unaffected by any radiocontaminants in the original sample which are not carried through with the daughter fraction.   (b) The separated daughter activity is usually present in a smaller amount of extraneous mass and can therefore be measured with less self-absorption losses than when it is measured in the original sample. (*c*) The radiation character-istics of the daughter serve to identify the parent. (*d*) The original sam-ple can be analyzed many times by allowing time for equilibrium to be reached between successive chemical separations of the daughter. The chemical separation and radioassay of Y^{90} from the samples containing Sr^{90}-Y^{90} is a good illustration of the advantages of this procedure. This method also allows differentiation between Sr^{90} and Sr^{89}, the latter having no radioactive yttrium daughter.

In a few cases a process known as *isomeric transition* (abbreviated IT) occurs in which a radioactive daughter is isotopic with the parent. These types of contamination can be anticipated from the published decay schemes for the radioisotope to be used and are noted in the descriptions of the specific radioisotope in Chap. 6.

Detection of Radioactive Impurities. Knowledge of the nature of the target material may give leads as to possible radiocontaminants. For example, sodium, rubidium, or cesium activities might well be antic-ipated in irradiated potassium. In many cases the determination of the half-life and the absorption curves (see Chap. 5) may provide information as to the presence of extraneous activities. Obviously these methods are of no value if the impurities have half-lives or energies of radiation close to those of the principal activity.

Special tests may be devised to ascertain the absence of radiocontam-inants that may be of particular significance. For example, if a sample of radiocobalt as produced by cyclotron bombardment of iron were to be used in a hematopoietic study, it would be important to be sure that no iron activity was present. This could be determined by incorporating some stable iron in an aliquot of the isotope preparation and then per-forming a chemical separation to recover the iron. If there were no radioactivity in the recovered iron, this would be evidence that there was no significant radioiron in the original radiocobalt preparation. The procedure could then be repeated for manganese, nickel, or any other element that might be a probable and important contaminant.

A demonstration of how a combination of physical and biological factors led to the detection of radiocontaminants in pile-produced radio-copper was reported by Frierson et al. (14). These workers administered Cu^{64}, which showed the expected half-life of 12.9 hr, to swine and rats. The activity collected in the urine consistently gave a half-life of about 28 hr. Paper chromatography and chemical fractionation allowed the identification of two major radiochemical impurities, Zn^{65} and Ag^{110}. The urine measurements were made about twenty half-lives after removal from the pile, so that by this time the ratio of the short-lived Cu^{64} to the radiocontaminants had decreased merely by physical decay. In addition, it was evident that the animals caused a decrease in this ratio by preferential absorption and urinary excretion of the radiocontaminants. The difficulty was eliminated by the electrolytic purification of the original Cu^{64} preparation. These findings emphasize the possibility of unexpected interference from radiocontaminants and the precautions necessary when *very large amounts of a principal activity are used to demonstrate very small accumulation in some parts of a system.*

Removal or Elimination of Radioactive Impurities. If the impurity has a half-life much less than that of the principal activity, then interference is eliminated by allowing a lapse of time sufficient for the impurity to remove itself by decay. Except for parent-daughter isotopes, this period of waiting can come at any time during the experiment just so long as it occurs before the final measurement of the sample. In the case of a short-lived daughter, this method can also be used except that the period of waiting must occur between the time of final sample preparation and the time of measurement.

To illustrate the parent-daughter relationship, let us consider the couple 20-yr Sr^{90}–60-hr Y^{90}, in which the daughter is relatively short-lived as

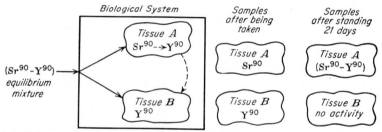

FIG. 2-2. Schematic illustration of the method of handling parent-daughter isotopes in which the daughter is relatively short-lived, by allowing a lapse of time between taking the sample and the radioassay.

compared with the parent. In an equilibrium mixture one normally measures the energetic beta ray of Y^{90}, which is then a direct measure of the Sr^{90} content. If one has pure Sr^{90}, it will take about 21 days for equilibrium to be attained, after which the Y^{90} will be decaying at the same rate as it is being produced. After this mixture is placed in a biological system, as illustrated in Fig. 2-2, let us postulate that the Sr^{90} goes to tissue A and that the Y^{90} goes to tissue B. As the Sr^{90} deposited in tissue A gives rise to Y^{90}, the latter may either stay there or be continually removed for deposition in tissue B. After sample A is taken and processed, there can be no further removal of Y^{90} by translocation, and after waiting for about 21 days, there will again be a Sr^{90}-Y^{90} equilibrium, and the measurement of the Y^{90} will indicate how much Sr^{90} was present in sample A. Likewise, after sample B is taken and set aside for 21 days, the Y^{90} activity will have decayed, and the measurements will indicate that no Sr^{90} had been deposited there.   In other words, if an equilibrium mixture of this type is placed in the system and the samples taken therefrom are allowed to stand for about 6 to 10 half-lives of the daughter, then the measurement of the activity of the daughter will give a direct measure of the amount of parent in the sample.

Interference by radiocontaminants may often be eliminated by appropriate radioassay procedures.   If the radioisotope is separated as a specific chemical compound, then any substance that did not follow it through the chemical reactions would not be counted.   For example, Ca^{45} is often precipitated as calcium oxalate for measurement—a procedure which would automatically eliminate radiocontaminants that did not precipitate or adsorb on the precipitate under the conditions used. Depending upon the comparative radiation characteristics, it is often possible to screen the contaminant activity from the counter while measuring that of the principal activity by gamma or hard-beta counting (see Chap. 5).

Chemical methods may be used for purification but are usually more tedious than physical procedures.   The classical separation techniques may be used such as coprecipitation, ion exchange, solvent extraction, and electroplating.   If the contaminants are not isotopic with the principal activity and are not daughters, then purification can be performed at any stage prior to measurement.   If the contaminants are nonisotopic daughters, then the removal must be effected after the samples have been taken and treated so that translocation cannot occur.

RADIATION EFFECTS

It is essential that the experimental results not be affected by any response of the system to radiation from the isotope used.   The amount of radioactivity employed should be the minimum necessary to permit reasonable counting rates in the samples to be measured and will be a function of accumulation in the sample and of the sensitivity of the radioassay.   The possibilities of interference due to physiologic response to radiation are minimized by the extreme sensitivity of the activity measurements, plus the fact that most studies are of short term and are completed before latent effects come into play.

It is possible to calculate the radiation dosage delivered to a tissue of known isotope concentration for comparison with known effects from external radiation.   However, such comparisons should be accepted with reserve because the radioisotope may become deposited within the cells of a tissue or even incorporated into the metabolic constituents.   This may result in a greater biological effectiveness than otherwise anticipated. For example, evidence is now accumulating that P^{32} internally located in tissues is mutagenically effective (15, 16).   Some of the factors responsible are as follows: (*a*) The P^{32} becomes incorporated in the nucleic acids and nucleoproteins of the chromosome, and the probabilities are high that single and multiple "hits" on chromosomes will result from the beta particles emitted. (*b*) The recoiling atom nucleus will probably have enough energy to break a chemical bond. (*c*) The P^{32} is converted to S^{32}, so that there is some molecular rearrangement at the point of decay. There may also be effects in tissue from activity located nearby, but these will usually be of secondary importance.

It is obvious that each radioisotope, having characteristic radiation properties and specific behavior in the biological system, must be considered as an individual case. Thus direct evidence on internal radiation effects should be sought. But this type of experimentation is usually uninspiring, and very few data are available.

Let us then examine the literature primarily from the standpoint of the lowest levels of radioisotope dosage at which there have been indications of pathology or dysfunction. For practical purposes, the information will be considered on the basis of the amounts of radioisotope used in the system rather than the radiation dosage delivered to the tissue. Amounts of radioisotope are expressed in microcuries (μc), where 1 μc corresponds to an amount of radioactivity undergoing 3.7×10^4 dis/sec (see Chap. 3 for a definition of the *curie* unit).

An extensive compilation by Bloom (17) has included histologic observations in laboratory animals after administration of various levels of certain radioisotopes. Although these studies were aimed primarily at the LD_{50} range, nevertheless they serve to establish a starting point. A liberal interpretation of some of the data is presented in Table 2-1. It is

TABLE 2-1. SUMMARY OF ADMINISTERED LEVELS OF RADIOISOTOPES AT WHICH INJURY OR NO INJURY WAS OBSERVED IN MICE AND RATS[a]

	Effect	Sr^{89}	Radium	Ba^{140}-La^{140}	Na^{24}	P^{32}
$LD_{50/30}$		7	1	4	30	4
Bone	No effect	0.5	0.005	1.4	32	2.5
	Injury	0.86	0.02	4.0	..	9.2
Bone marrow	No effect	0.2	0.005	0.5	..	0.6
	Injury	0.5	0.02	1.4	47	2.5
Spleen	No effect	0.2	0.02	0.5	..	2.5
	Injury	0.5	0.06	1.4	47	
Lymph nodes	No effect	0.86	0.02	4	..	2.5
	Injury	2.0	0.06	14	47	
Testis	No effect	....	0.005	1.4	..	2.5
	Injury	2.9	0.02	14	47	9.2

[a] All values in microcuries per gram body weight administered parenterally.

(Compiled from William Bloom, ed., "Histopathology of Irradiation," McGraw-Hill Book Company, Inc., New York, 1948.)

clear that a given dosage of an alpha-emitting bone seeker such as radium would produce more radiation response in the tissue than would a dosage of the beta-emitting bone seeker Sr^{89}. It is interesting to note that, although Sr^{89} was less effective lethally than P^{32}, the former produced more response in the tissues studied. Observe that radiosodium, which is generally distributed throughout the body, had the lowest lethal action. It must be remembered that these are histologic observations only, and it is probable that physiologic dysfunctions could occur at lower levels. Although the time factor is an important one, it is not practical to discuss the observations of Bloom as a function of time after dosage, which varied from a day up to several months. In any event, it would be wisest, where possible, to use amounts of radioisotopes well below those known to have produced injury, as reported in Table 2-1. Care must be taken particularly in connection with bone studies if the experiments are to be prolonged. In this laboratory there was a suggestion of bone pathology in a 700-lb steer sacrificed 1 yr after having ingested about 600 μc Sr^{90}.

Bloom and Bloom (18) have described definite bone overgrowths in mice at 5 months after intraperitoneal injection of 0.03 μc radium per gram body weight. Similarly, as little as 0.003 μc plutonium per gram body weight administered intravenously produced marked bone changes. Moses et al. (19) reported that ingestion by rats of 0.1 μc P^{32} per gram body weight caused a temporary decrease in total white count but produced no histologic or rate-of-growth changes in the kidneys, liver, adrenals, and testes. Warren, MacMillan, and Dixon (20, 21), using mice, have described the effects of subcutaneous injection of various levels of P^{32}. Their observations on the lowest level, about 0.8 μc/g body weight, showed significant changes in lymphoid tissue, spleen, lymph nodes, thymus, and ovaries. It has been reported that in man the threshold dose of P^{32} is 0.006 to 0.009 μc/g body weight so far as effects on the formation of blood corpuscles are concerned (22).

Considerable attention has been given to responses to I^{131} on account of the importance of this isotope in medical and physiological studies. Maloof, Dobyns, and Vickery (23) have reviewed earlier work and demonstrated that as little as 0.045 μc/g body weight administered to rats caused a definite impairment of function even though there was no histologic evidence of radiation damage in the thyroids of these animals. No functional abnormalities were noted in animals receiving about 0.009 μc/g. The functional changes with the dose of 0.045 μc/g were as follows: (a) The thyroid lost ability to respond to a low iodine diet. (b) The ability of the thyroid to enlarge in response to low iodine stimulus was decreased. (c) The capacity of the thyroid to hypertrophy was impaired. Skanse (24) reported dysfunction of the chick thyroid after administration of 10 μc radioiodine. As indicated earlier, particularly with iodine, the physiological response will be greatly dependent upon such factors as the amount of dietary and carrier iodine and the functional state of the thyroid.

Peacock et al. (25) reported that human donors who had carried of the order of 4800 disintegrations of Fe^{59} (or 40,000 disintegrations of Fe^{55}) per minute per milliliter of blood showed no clinical radiation effects when observed over periods of several years. Considerations in regard to the use of radioactive iron in human beings have been reviewed by McFarlane (26).

Hassett and Jenkins (27), using larvae of yellow-fever mosquitoes, noted radiation effects at concentrations of 0.05 μc/ml of P^{32} in the rearing medium with early instars. Resistance increased with age, but at concentrations above 5.0 μc/ml practically no adults emerged. Retardation or inhibition of growth, and death occurred at high concentrations. Mating and egg laying occurred normally in adults reared from larvae in P^{32} solutions of 1.0 μc/ml or less.

Phosphorus 32 has been and is being widely used for important agronomic and plant physiological studies. Early workers observed no differences in the yields of plants grown with and without radiophosphorus, and little consideration was given to radiation effects. In 1949 Russell and Martin (28) reported that barley plants grown in nutrient solution containing 10 μc/liter of P^{32} showed a reduction in the weight of roots produced which was accentuated at the lower total-phosphate levels. At 50 μc/liter there was also a change in the phosphorus content of the roots. Shoot changes were equivocal. Dion et al. (29) reported no injury to wheat when applications of P_2O_5 were made at 12, 24, and 48 lb/acre, with P^{32} being incorporated at 26 μc/g phosphorus. Russell, Adams, and Martin (30) grew barley in pots containing 1500 g of soil plus the equivalent of 8 lb of total phosphorus per acre and varying amounts of P^{32}. Although neither shoot nor root weight was affected, there was a depressed phosphorus absorption.

Blume and coworkers (31) have reported extended observations on radiation effects and histologic changes induced in barley plants grown in nutrient solution. It was clear that injury to the plant primarily depended on the accumulation of P^{32} in the tissues. Injury to the root by external radiation from the solution was minor. It was shown that the specific activity of the solution was the determining factor rather than the level of P^{32} in the solution. Obviously at high specific activities the plant absorbs more P^{32}. The damage occurred only in zones of active division, and the measurement of arc lengths of shoot-tip cells was used as an indication of radiation damage. Some of these points are self-explanatory from the data in Table 2-2 (32). Evidence was presented for radiation effects at as low as 2 μc/liter at a total phosphorus concentration of 2×10^{-5} M. In contrast to other work mentioned, no changes were found in the absorption of phosphate from solution.

Bould, Nicholas, and Thomas (33) and Blume (34) have reported further observations of the effects of P^{32} on plants grown in soil. It was the consensus that the intake of phosphorus and the radiation effects are not large enough to preclude radiotracer fertilizer studies, provided that reasonable concentrations of P^{32} are used. Blume found no significant changes in plants grown in soils receiving surface applications of KH_2PO_4 containing up to 12,500 μc P^{32} per gram of total phosphorus.

TABLE 2-2. SHOOT-TIP CELL LENGTHS AS RELATED TO SPECIFIC ACTIVITY

P^{32} μc/liter	Specific activity, μc/g P	Average cell length[a]
0	0	7.20 ± 0.27
50	0.32	7.74 ± 0.26
200	1.29	7.66 ± 0.42
0	0	7.98 ± 0.41
50	3.22	7.97 ± 0.22
200	12.90	8.59 ± 0.32
0	0	7.72 ± 0.29
50	32.25	10.00 ± 0.27
200	129.0	12.46 ± 0.40
0	0	8.36 ± 0.51
50	322.5	12.02 ± 0.56
200	1290.0	12.98 ± 0.30

[a] Arbitrary units plus or minus standard error.
[From Ruth W. Mackie, James M. Blume, and C. E. Hagen, Histological Changes Induced in Barley Plants by Radiation from P^{32}, *Am. J. Botany*, **39**: 229–237 (1952).]

Goring and Clark (35) have reported that the levels of P^{32} necessary to effect changes in the soil bacterial population are above those normally used in fertilizer studies. If high levels of P^{32} are to be used, then the specific activity should not exceed 50 μc P^{32} per milligram of total phosphorus. Clark and Goring (36) grew bacteria in a broth containing 0.2 ppm inorganic P and 0.6 ppm organic P, which was enriched with 4 ppm P as KH_2PO_4 at levels of 0 to 5000 μc P^{32} per milligram of total phosphorus. Deleterious effects were observed at levels higher than 100 μc. It was pointed out that, although individual cells were affected by the P^{32}, the surviving cells continued to multiply, so that there were no differences in such measurements as turbidity and substrate transformation.

Giles and Bolomey (37) found that P^{32} and C^{14} in solution produced chromosomal changes in *Tradescantia* at levels of 100 and 900 μc/liter, respectively.

In retrospect, it must be emphasized that the radiation effect is important here only inasmuch as it directly or indirectly affects the experimental observation. As a trivial example, if an insect labeled with a radioisotope is physically affected so that it will not cover its normal distance, then this is important in flight-range studies. If it is not so affected, then it makes little difference if the insect becomes sterile or undergoes other metabolic changes, particularly if this occurs after the experiment has been completed. Of course, with human beings any possible latent effects must be avoided. It is apparent that generalizations are impossible as to the radioisotope levels that can or cannot be used, since there are too many variables. Some of the values quoted above will give indications as to when the danger levels may be reached. *In practice, one may usually determine whether radiation effects are significant by performing replicate experiments using graded levels of radioactivity.* In some cases duplicate experiments in part can be undertaken with stable isotopes or chemical indicators.

The chemical effects of radiation have been reported in connection with the radiation decomposition of some C^{14}-labeled compounds (38). It is recommended that frequent checks be made of labeled organic compounds to exclude the possibility of the presence of decomposition products.

EXCHANGE REACTIONS

An isotopic exchange reaction as a special case of exchange may be defined as a chemical reaction in which the atoms of a given element interchange between two or more chemical forms of the element. Wahl and Bonner (11) may be consulted for a detailed treatment of this subject, and Edwards (39) has reviewed chemical-exchange studies. References (40, 41) may be consulted for collections of papers and references on this subject.

Examples of isotopic exchange reactions are as follows:

1. Simple exchange due to electrolytic dissociation (ionization):

$$2PbCl_2 + 2Pb^*(NO_3)_2 \rightleftharpoons 2Pb^{++} + 4Cl^- + 2Pb^{*+++} + 4NO_3^-$$
$$\updownarrow$$
$$PbCl_2 + Pb^*Cl_2 + Pb(NO_3)_2 + Pb^*(NO_3)_2 \tag{2-1}$$

If lead chloride and labeled lead nitrate are dissolved in solution, the free ions will be present. It is clear that, if lead chloride were separated from such a solution, it would contain an equivalent amount of labeled lead atoms that were present in the original lead nitrate.

2. Electron transfer:

$$Fe^{++} + Fe^{*3+} \rightleftharpoons Fe^{*++} + Fe^{3+} \qquad (2\text{-}2)$$

This type of exchange is known to occur by the transfer of electrons from one substance to another.

3. Atom transfer:

$$I^{*-} + CH_3I \xrightarrow{\text{ethyl} \atop \text{alcohol}} I^- + CH_3I^* \qquad (2\text{-}3)$$

This reaction involves the Walden inversion mechanism, which has been widely studied.

4. Solid-fluid reaction:

$$\text{Bone crystal--Ca} + Ca^{*++} \rightarrow \text{Bone crystal--Ca}^* + Ca^{++} \qquad (2\text{-}4)$$

The implications of the exchange of ions between plasma and bone are discussed in detail later.

5. Solid-gas reaction:

$$BaCO_3 + C^*O_2 \xrightarrow{\text{H}_2\text{O} \atop \text{vapor}} BaC^*O_3 + CO_2 \qquad (2\text{-}5)$$

Carbon 14 from experimental material is often converted to $BaC^{14}O_3$ for radioassay. The loss of activity from such $BaC^{14}O_3$ samples by exchange with the CO_2 of the air may be serious (42). Similar exchange may interfere with various degradation procedures carried out to assign the C^{14} label to particular locations in the organic molecule (43).

6. Reversal of a degradation reaction:

$$\text{Organic phosphate} \xrightleftharpoons{\text{inorganic} \atop \text{phosphate}^*} \text{organic residue} + \text{inorganic phosphate} \qquad (2\text{-}6)$$

Even though a substance may be undergoing degradation, there is the possibility that the reverse reaction may occur to a slight degree. This might result in the appearance of the label in the substance under study but could not be interpreted as metabolic incorporation.

Although these types of reactions have provided much valuable information on reaction rates, bond strengths, and molecular rearrangements and structure, the interest here is in connection with their disadvantages in tracer studies. In problems of intermediary metabolism, radiotracers are used to provide information on the processes involved in the biological synthesis of important metabolic compounds. If the radioactive element becomes incorporated in the metabolic product merely by exchange, which requires no energy production, then these experiments are of no value in that there is no evidence for synthesis of the product.

It is usually possible, however, to carry out studies that can show whether or not exchange has occurred by allowing the precursors and product to react under conditions where the biological or energy-producing system is interfered with.   For example, animal tissues are known to convert inorganic phosphate into phospholipid.   This is probably not an exchange process, because experimental observations showed that (a) inorganic phosphate does not exchange with the phosphate radical of phospholipid when sodium phosphate is shaken with a phospholipid solution, (b) homogenized liver failed to form radioactive phospholipid from inorganic P^{32}, and (c) respiratory inhibitors such as cyanide and carbon monoxide interfered with the formation of the tagged phospholipid (44).

It will be recalled from Chap. 1 that the pickup of C^{14} in the carboxyl group of phosphoglyceric acid was interpreted to mean that this compound was the first stable site of CO_2 fixation in photosynthesis.   It was necessary, however, to show that this pickup is not merely due to an exchange reaction.   Fager and Rosenberg (45), by comparing simultaneously the kinetics of total fixation of CO_2 and fixation in the phosphoglyceric acid, were able to provide support for the postulation that the labeling of PGA does indeed represent a step in the photosynthetic process and not just an unrelated exchange reaction.

A detailed listing of exchange reactions, particularly in organic systems, has been compiled by Wahl and Bonner (11).   It has been shown (22) that no exchange occurs between inorganic phosphate ions in solution and hexose monophosphate, glycerophosphate, lecithin, casein, nucleic acid, pyrophosphate, and metaphosphate.   No exchange was found between the sulfur atoms of cysteine, thioglycolic acid, or urea and those of H_2S, $S^=$, or SH^-, respectively.   In general, where the atom is tightly bound in an organic molecule, there will be little opportunity for exchange (e.g., hydrogen in benzene, carbon in the chain).

Care must be taken to prevent the loss of the label from the molecule under study.   The H^+ of —OH, —COOH, —NH_2, for example, is known to exchange readily with the H^+ of water.   A tritium or deuterium label in such a position would become widely distributed in an aqueous medium and would no longer be indicative of the labeled molecule.   A tritium or deuterium label for an aldehyde might be stable under some conditions but would be lost if the aldehyde underwent oxidation.

Important considerations resulting from the exchange reaction that occurs between certain ions in blood and those in the bone crystal have been largely overlooked in the interpretation of studies of labeled calcium and phosphate in animals.   It is well recognized that fresh bone suspended in a solution containing Ca^{45} ions can incorporate these ions by the process of exchange (46 to 48).   Phosphate, strontium, and radium ions can likewise be incorporated.   Experiments have shown that 10 to 20 per cent of the calcium in bone is exchangeable, depending on the part of the bone and the age of the animal from which it is taken.   There is little question that this exchange occurs in vivo between these ions in blood and bone, and the evidence from blood disappearance curves indicates that the reaction is a rapid one (47).   The result of this rapid exchange reaction is that the Ca^{45} ions introduced into the blood are accumulated almost quantitatively in bone.   This is primarily due to the fact that the exchangeable-calcium concentration in bone is at least a hundred times the normal calcium concentration in plasma.   Thus at equilibrium the specific activity in bone will equal that in plasma, or

$$\frac{\text{Activity in bone}}{100} = \frac{\text{activity in blood}}{1}$$

This means that, shortly after the activity enters the blood, the concentration of Ca^{45} in the bone will be at least a hundred times that in the

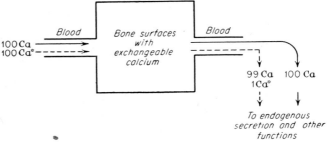

FIG. 2-3. Schematic illustration of how the exchange of calcium ions between blood and bone causes an apparent difference in the behavior of Ca^{45} and stable calcium ions in the system.

plasma.   The relative accumulation in bone may exceed this value, because some of the Ca^{45} entering the bone may be rendered less available for exchange by new growth covering the crystal surfaces or by such processes as recrystallization.

A direct effect upon tracer studies may be illustrated by Fig. 2-3.   If 100 units of stable calcium ions enters the blood, by injection or absorption from the gastrointestinal tract, it will come in contact with bone surfaces and undergo exchange.   If there is no bone accretion, 100 stable calcium ions will be contained in the blood leaving the bone to go through the process of endogenous excretion or recycling for other metabolic uses. However, if 100 units of labeled calcium ions enters the blood, it will be accumulated in the bone surfaces and, for the most part, replace stable calcium ions, which then follow the same path as do all the Ca ions in the blood leaving the bone.   This behavior is not based on any "isotope effect" due to a differential behavior of Ca^{45} ions in blood or bone.   It merely results from the attainment of equilibrium in a system of high calcium concentration in bone and low concentration in blood; or, expressed mechanistically, the stable calcium ions contact the bone and replace like calcium ions, whereas the labeled calcium ions contact the bone and replace unlike stable calcium ions, because there are so few, if any, labeled calcium ions in the bone to be replaced. Support for this concept has been found in measurements with more than 40 cattle in which the retention of dietary calcium as shown by calcium balance was significantly lower than the retention of dietary labeled calcium (49). This behavior has been utilized to determine endogenous fecal calcium (50). The importance of this reaction in evaluation of the health hazards from bone-seeking radioisotopes will be discussed in Chap. 3.

The implications, which may also apply to other elements, are summarized for calcium as follows: (a) The appearance of administered labeled calcium ions in bone is not necessarily a measure of bone accretion. (b) After contact with bone, the Ca^{45} ions in blood are no longer a true tracer for the original calcium ions. (c) Small physiological differences in calcium behavior between control and treated animals may be masked by the large changes in concentration of Ca^{45} ions due directly to physical processes. As discussed in Chap. 1, this situation applies also to elements such as Na and K which interchange between compartments. However, the effects are not so marked, since the compartments do not have concentrations differing so widely as in the case of calcium, and equilibrium is reached much sooner.

An example of exchange reactions in plant-nutrition studies is given by Overstreet and Broyer (51), who measured the absorption of stable and radiopotassium ions by barley roots. When plants with a high level of potassium were used, there was an inward movement of radiopotassium into the roots, but there was no simultaneous entry of stable potassium ions. It was concluded that the colloidal phases of the protoplasm and cell wall contained potassium that was capable of rapid exchange with the ions in the culture medium. Under these conditions the movement of radiopotassium into the plant did not represent a net absorption of potassium by the plant.

It should be emphasized that, if the system has reached equilibrium, then the isotope will act as a true tracer, and the above considerations no longer apply. However, many experimental observations are made before equilibrium is attained. When bone and bone minerals are involved, equilibrium may not be reached for considerable lengths of time, unless the experiment is one in which the animals have been raised on a diet of experimental isotopic composition. Such experiments, based on continuous administration of the radioisotope as opposed to single dosage, offer great possibilities.

ISOTOPE EFFECTS

The term *isotope effect* is used to denote the influence upon reactions due to the presence of a radioisotope label or of an abnormal mixture of stable isotopes. Effects resulting from the physiologic response of tissues to the radiation are not considered in this category. Since isotopes of the same element differ in mass and thus in mobility, it is expected that there would be some differences in physical and chemical behavior. As the extreme case, the differences between normal hydrogen (H^1), deuterium (H^2 or D), and tritium (H^3 or T) are large and well recognized, because the actual mass difference represents an appreciable fraction of the atomic weight of the element. Thus one scarcely considers H_2O, D_2O, and T_2O as the same substance from any point of view. In fact, optical activity has been detected in molecules with no centers of asymmetry except those created by the substitution of deuterium for hydrogen (39). In general, the higher the atomic weight of the element, the less will be the fractional mass difference between isotopes, and the magnitude of the isotope effect will be correspondingly decreased. From the standpoint of tracer experiments, it is important to anticipate the occurrence and magnitude of these effects.

The mass differences may exert their effect either upon the equilibrium constant of a reaction or upon the rate of a reaction. An example of the former is as follows:

$$C^{13}N^- + HC^{12}N \rightleftharpoons C^{12}N^- + HC^{13}N \qquad (2\text{-}7)$$
$$\text{gas} \qquad \text{solution} \qquad \text{gas} \qquad \text{solution}$$

If there were no isotope effect, the equilibrium constant for this reaction would be unity, whereas it is actually 1.012 at 25°C (52). This means that the amount of C^{13} in gaseous HCN is slightly greater than that in the ion CN^-, with which it is in equilibrium. It is thus shown that the mass-difference effect is not the same for different chemical combinations of the isotope. However, the effect on reaction rates is perhaps of more importance and will be illustrated later.

It should be noted that many elements occur naturally as mixtures of isotopes and that the radioisotope is often of intermediate mass. For example, stable copper consists of two isotopes of mass numbers 63 and 65 with relative abundances of 70.1 and 29.9 per cent, respectively. The experimental behavior of radiocopper of mass 64 in a biological system would not be expected to be greatly different from the over-all behavior of the naturally occurring mixture, so far as mass effects are concerned. In accurate measurements of some processes such as diffusion, however, differential behavior at this level of mass difference may be observed. Thus, after 16 hr of contact between solid copper metal and silver sulfide at high temperatures, the isotopic constitution of copper atoms diffused into the silver sulfide was found to be 71.2 per cent Cu^{63} and 28.8 per cent Cu^{65} (52). This indicated a higher rate of diffusion for the lighter isotope. The practical application of this behavior is seen in the large-scale separation of the uranium isotopes.

The possibility of isotope effects with carbon is of major interest. There are six isotopes of carbon: C^{10}, C^{11}, C^{12}, C^{13}, C^{14}, and C^{15}. However, the discussion will be limited to C^{12} and C^{13}, which are stable isotopes normally present in nature in a ratio of about 90:1, respectively, and to C^{14}, which is the long-lived radioisotope most widely used experimentally. It has been shown that living organisms, plants, and animals, together with their geological remains, contain less C^{13} than does limestone (53). Also algae have been found to contain 2.97 per cent less C^{13} than did the CO_2 in the solution in which the plants grew (54). In studies of photosynthesis with barley seedlings, it was definitely shown by California workers that the assimilation of $C^{14}O_2$ was about 17 per cent slower than that of $C^{12}O_2$ (55). Buchanan et al. (56), in a series of detailed experiments in which biological material was grown for about 3 yr exposed to a known specific activity of C^{14}, were able to confirm the general finding that plants tended to reject the heavier isotope in favor of C^{12}. The differences in isotope concentration were approximately twice those found with C^{13}, as estimated from kinetic studies during the growth of algae. These results were in disagreement with those of the California group, who reported much higher C^{14} effects. It was also of particular interest that, whereas the organic matter of snails appeared to reject the heavier isotope, the carbonate of the shell tended to concentrate C^{14}. This is consistent with the results on the natural occurrence of C^{14}, as discussed in the section on radiocarbon dating in Chap. 1. Although there is little evidence to indicate the mechanism involved, it seems clear that there is an isotope effect in nature by means of which plants discriminate against the heavier isotopes of carbon.

The effect of isotope substitution on organic reaction rates has been reviewed by Ropp (57). These studies have led to some understanding of the mechanism of carbon isotope effects as well as to quantitative expressions for the magnitude of these effects. The effects may be classified as *intermolecular* or *intramolecular*. An example of an intermolecular process is as follows:

$$HC^{12}OOH \xrightarrow[H_2SO_4]{k_{12}} C^{12}O_2 + H_2O$$
$$HC^{14}COOH \xrightarrow[H_2SO_4]{k_{14}} C^{14}O_2 + H_2O$$

(2-8)

The symbol k represents the specific rate constant for the reaction as designated. The magnitude of the isotope effect may be expressed as some relationship of the k values: $(k_{12} - k_{14})/k_{12}$, k_{12}/k_{14}, or k_{14}/k_{12}.   It was shown that $k_{14}/k_{12} = 0.8889$ for the above reactions carried out at 0°C.   Thus, in a sample of C^{14}-labeled formic acid undergoing removal of H_2O, the CO_2 evolved at first will have a lower specific activity than that of the carboxyl carbon of the acid.   However, it is important to note that, if the reaction is carried to completion, the specific activity of all the CO_2 evolved will be equal to that of the parent carboxyl carbon, and there will be no observed isotope effect.   This "disappearance" of the isotope effect if the measurements are made at completion is characteristic of inter-molecular reactions.

An example of intramolecular isotope effects is the well-known decarboxylation of malonic acid:

$$\begin{array}{l} C^{14}OOH \\ \diagup \\ CH_2 \quad\quad \xrightarrow{k_{14}} C^{14}O_2 + CH_3C^{12}OOH \\ \diagdown \\ C^{12}OOH \end{array}$$

$$\begin{array}{l} C^{14}OOH \\ \diagup \\ CH_2 \quad\quad \xrightarrow{k_{12}} C^{12}O_2 + CH_3C^{14}OOH \\ \diagdown \\ C^{12}OOH \end{array}$$

(2-9)

As the decarboxylation of singly labeled malonic acid proceeds, the concentration of C^{14} in the CO_2 is less than that in the original label, and the concentration of C^{14} in the carboxyl of the acetic acid is greater.   This may be expressed by the statement that the C^{12}—C^{12} bonds are broken with a frequency 1.12 times greater than are the C^{12}—C^{14} bonds.   It should be noted that the maximum isotope effect is measured if the reaction goes to completion.   This is characteristic of the intramolecular as contrasted with the intermolecular processes.   In general, the molecule bearing the heavier isotope will react more slowly.   The reverse of this behavior was reported for the decomposition of urea by urease (58). However, more recent experimental data indicated that the k_{12}/k_{14} value was 1.032 at 30°C.   An excellent general review of isotope effects in chemical reactions has been presented by Yankwich (59).

A few generalizations may now be stated.   Isotope effects may be anticipated in experiments involving diffusion-like processes, especially when lighter elements are used and accurate measurements are made. Effects may also be seen in processes based on organic reactions of the intermolecular type if these cannot be forced to essential completion. With intramolecular reactions, these effects may also be of significance regardless of the degree of completion of the reaction.   On the optimistic side, it should be recalled that the magnitude of the effect, depending upon the isotopic composition and the system, will most probably be less than 15 per cent and usually less than 5 per cent. Thus these effects will pass undetected in most biological experiments. Where the interest is primarily concerned with the behavior of the radioisotope itself, it is not necessary to take the isotope effect into account. This is the situation in health-physics studies of the retention and excretion of radiotoxic substances. Also the isotope effect will usually be negligibly small when the isotopic atom is not involved in bond making or breaking. Thus deuterium or tritium can be used satisfactorily in many cases for labeling large molecules or for studies involving body-water determinations, and C^{14} can be used for labeling almost any organic molecule provided the label is located in a nonfunctional part of the molecule. It should be noted that there are many organic reactions in which, contrary to expectation, no isotope effects have been noted (57). As yet, empirical working rules are not available, but as more data are accumulated, it may be possible to predict the extent of isotope fractionation under specified conditions.

CITED REFERENCES

1. Graham, A. F., G. Dempster, and Barbara Buchner: The Toxicity of P^{32} for Normal and Influenza Virus Infected Embryos, *J. Bacteriol.*, **63**: 426–427 (1952).
2. Hamilton, J. G.: Summary of Iodine Physiology and Metabolic Studies Using Radioactive Isotopes of Iodine, MDDC-1060, 1944.
3. Gorbman, Aubrey: Functional and Structural Changes Consequent to High Dosages of Radioactive Iodine, *J. Clin. Endocrinol.*, **10**: 1177–1191 (1950).
4. Cohn, Waldo E.: Radioactive Contaminants in Tracers, *Anal. Chem.*, **20**: 498–503 (1948).
5. Libby, W. F.: Reactions of High Energy Atoms Produced by Slow Neutron Capture, *J. Am. Chem. Soc.*, **62**: 1930–1943 (1940).
6. Thomas, W. D. E., and D. J. D. Nicholas: Radioactive Phosphorus in Biochemical Research, *Nature*, **163**: 719 (1949).
7. Fried, Maurice, and Arnold J. MacKenzie: Contamination in Orthophosphates Irradiated in a Neutron Pile, *Science*, **111**: 492–493 (1950).
8. Borland, J. W., A. J. MacKenzie, and W. L. Hill: Characterization of Nonorthophosphate P^{32} in Neutron-irradiated Potassium Dihydrogen Phosphate, *Ind. Eng. Chem.*, **44**: 2726–2728 (1952).
9. MacKenzie, A. J., and J. W. Borland: Nonorthophosphate Contaminant of Neutron-irradiated Rock Phosphates, *Anal. Chem.*, **24**: 176–179 (1952).
10. Schweitzer, George K., and Morrison Jackson: Radiocolloids, ORO-48.
11. Wahl, Arthur C., and Norman A. Bonner, eds.: "Radioactivity Applied to Chemistry," John Wiley & Sons, Inc., New York, 1951.
12. Dobson, Ernest L., John W. Gofman, Hardin B. Jones, Lola S. Kelly, and Leonard A. Walker: Studies with Colloids Containing Radioisotopes of Yttrium, Zirconium, Columbium, and Lanthanum, *J. Lab. Clin. Med.*, **34**: 305–312 (1949).
13. Cook, G. B., and J. F. Duncan: "Modern Radiochemical Practice," Oxford University Press, New York, 1952.
14. Frierson, W. J., Sam L. Hood, Ira B. Whitney, and C. L. Comar: Radiocontaminants in Biological Studies with Copper-64, *Arch. Biochem. and Biophys.*, **38**: 397–404(1952).

15. Arnason, T. J.: Chromosome Breakage Induced by Absorbed Radioactive Phosphorus, in "Biological Applications of Tracer Elements," *Cold Spring Harbor Symposia Quant. Biol.*, **13**: 1–5 (1948).
16. King, Robert C.: Studies with Radiophosphorus in Drosophila. I. The Mutagenic Effectiveness of Radioactive Phosphorus in Adult Male *Drosophila melanogaster*, *J. Exptl. Zool.*, **122**: 541–575 (1953).
17. Bloom, William, ed.: "Histopathology of Irradiation," McGraw-Hill Book Company, Inc., New York, 1948.
18. Bloom, Margaret A., and William Bloom: Late Effects of Radium and Plutonium on Bone, *Arch. Pathol.*, **47**: 494–511 (1949).
19. Moses, Campbell, Joseph B. Boatman, Robert S. George, and Agatha M. DeLacio: Toxicity of Radioiodine and Radiophosphorus in Rats in Doses Comparable to Those Used Clinically, *Proc. Soc. Exptl. Biol. Med.*, **79**: 343–344 (1952).
20. Warren, Shields, Jane C. MacMillan, and Frank J. Dixon: Effects of Internal Irradiation of Mice with P^{32}. I. Spleen, Lymph Nodes, Thymus, Bone and Bone Marrow, *Radiology*, **55**: 375–389 (1950).
21. Warren, Shields, Jane C. MacMillan, and Frank J. Dixon: Effects of Internal Irradiation of Mice with P^{32}. II. Gonads, Kidneys, Adrenal Glands, Digestive Tract, Spinal Cord, Lungs, and Liver, *Radiology*, **55**: 557–570 (1950).
22. Hevesy, George: "Radioactive Indicators," Interscience Publishers, Inc., New York, 1948.
23. Maloof, Farahe, Brown M. Dobyns, and Austin L. Vickery: The Effects of Various Doses of Radioactive Iodine on the Function and Structure of the Thyroid of the Rat, *Endocrinology*, **50**: 612–638 (1952).
24. Skanse, Bengt N.: The Biologic Effect of Irradiation by Radioactive Iodine, *J. Clin. Endocrinol.*, **8**: 707–716 (1948).
25. Peacock, Wendell C., Robley D. Evans, John W. Irvine, Jr., Wilfred M. Good, Arthur F. Kip, Soma Weiss, and John G. Gibson, 2d: The Use of Two Radioactive Isotopes of Iron in Tracer Studies of Erythrocytes, *J. Clin. Invest.*, **25**: 605–615 (1946).
26. McFarlane, A. S.: Considerations Governing the Use of Radioactive Iron in Humans, in A. Haddow, ed., "Biological Hazards of Atomic Energy" (Conference Convened by the Institute of Biology and the Atomic Scientists' Association, October, 1950), pp. 139–143, Oxford University Press, New York, 1952.
27. Hassett, C. C., and D. W. Jenkins: The Uptake and Effect of Radiophosphorus in Mosquitoes, *Physiol. Zoöl.*, **24**: 257–266 (1951).
28. Russell, R. Scott, and R. P. Martin: Use of Radioactive Phosphorus in Plant Nutritional Studies, *Nature*, **163**: 71–72 (1949).
29. Dion, G., C. F. Bedford, R. J. St. Arnaud, and J. W. T. Spinks: Plant Injury from Phosphorus-32, *Nature*, **163**: 906–907 (1949).
30. Russell, R. Scott, S. N. Adams, and R. P. Martin: Radiation Effects Due to Phosphorus-32 in Fertilizer Experiments, *Nature*, **164**: 993 (1949).
31. Blume, James M., C. E. Hagen, and Ruth W. Mackie: Radiation Injury to Plants Grown in Nutrient Solutions Containing P^{32}, *Soil Sci.*, **70**: 415–426 (1950).
32. Mackie, Ruth W., James M. Blume, and C. E. Hagen: Histological Changes Induced in Barley Plants by Radiation from P^{32}, *Am. J. Botany*, **39**: 229–237 (1952).
33. Bould, C., D. J. D. Nicholas, and W. E. E. Thomas: Radiation Effects in Plant Nutrition Experiments with Phosphorus-32, *Nature*, **167**: 140 (1951).
34. Blume, James M.: Radiation Effects on Plants Grown in Soil Treated with Fertilizer Containing P^{32}, *Soil Sci.*, **73**: 299–303 (1952).

35. Goring, C. A. I., and Francis E. Clark: Radioactive Phosphorus and the Growth and Metabolic Activities of Soil Microorganisms, *Soil Sci. Soc. Amer. Proc.*, **16**: 7–9 (1952).
36. Clark, Francis E., and C. A. I. Goring: Growth of Bacteria in the Presence of Radioactive Phosphorus, *J. Bacteriol.*, **62**: 352–354 (1951).
37. Giles, Norman H., and Rene A. Bolomey: Cytogenetical Effects of Internal Radiations from Radioisotopes, in "Biological Applications of Tracer Elements," *Cold Spring Harbor Symposia Quant. Biol.*, **13**: 104–112 (1948).
38. Lemmon, Richard M.: Radiation Decomposition of Carbon-14-labeled Compounds, *Nucleonics*, **11**: 44–45 (1953).
39. Edwards, R. R.: Isotopic Tracers in Chemical Systems, *Ann. Rev. Nuclear Sci.*, **1**: 301–342 (1952).
40. Conference on Isotopic Exchange Reactions and Chemical Kinetics, Dec. 1–3, 1948, Chemistry Conference No. 2, AECU-226 (BLN-C-8).
41. Isotope Separation and Isotope Exchange, A Bibliography of Unclassified Literature, compiled by G. M. Begun and Robert E. Allen, TID-3036, Jan. 23, 1953.
42. Samos, George: Some Observations on Exchange of CO_2 between $BaCO_3$ and CO_2 Gas, *Science*, **110**: 663–665 (1949).
43. Calvin, Melvin, Charles Heidelberger, James C. Reid, Bert M. Tolbert, and Peter F. Yankwich: "Isotopic Carbon," John Wiley & Sons, Inc., New York, 1949.
44. Chaikoff, I. L., and D. B. Zilversmit: Radioactive Phosphorus: Its Application to the Study of Phospholipid Metabolism, *Advances in Biol. and Med. Phys.*, **1**: 321–352 (1948).
45. Fager, E. W., and J. L. Rosenberg: Exchange Reactions and Phosphoglyceric Acid in Photosynthesis, *Arch. Biochem. and Biophys.*, **37**: 1–4 (1952).
46. Hodge, Harold C.: The Role of Exchange in Calcium and Phosphate Adsorptions by the Calcified Tissues, in Edward C. Reifenstein, ed., "Metabolic Interrelations," Transactions of the Third Conference, Jan. 8–9, 1951, Josiah Macy, Jr., Foundation.
47. Comar, C. L., W. E. Lotz, and G. A. Boyd: Autoradiographic Studies of Calcium, Phosphorus and Strontium Distribution in the Bones of the Growing Pig, *Am. J. Anat.*, **90**: 113–129 (1952).
48. Neuman, W. F., and M. W. Neuman: The Nature of the Mineral Phase of Bone, *Chem. Revs.*, **53**: 1–45 (1953).
49. Hansard, Sam L.: The Effects of Age upon Calcium Absorption, Deposition and Exchange in Animals, Thesis submitted to the University of Florida, June, 1953.
50. Comar, C. L., R. A. Monroe, W. J. Visek, and Sam L. Hansard: Comparison of Two Isotope Methods for Determination of Endogenous Fecal Calcium, *J. Nutrition*, **50**: 459–467 (1953).
51. Overstreet, R., and T. C. Broyer: The Nature of Absorption of Radioactive Isotopes by Living Tissues as Illustrated by Experiments with Barley Plants, *Proc. Natl. Acad. Sci., U.S.*, **26**: 16–24 (1940).
52. Yankwich, Peter E.: Radioactive Isotopes as Tracers, *Anal. Chem.*, **21**: 318–321 (1949).
53. Nier, Alfred O., and Earl A. Gulbransen: Variations in the Relative Abundance of the Carbon Isotopes, *J. Am. Chem. Soc.*, **61**: 697–698 (1939).
54. Urey, Harold C.: Oxygen Isotopes in Nature and in the Laboratory, *Science*, **108**: 489 (1948).
55. Weigl, John W.: The Relation of Photosynthesis to Respiration, UCRL-590, Apr. 27, 1950.

56. Buchanan, D. L., Akira Nakao, and George Edwards: Carbon Isotope Effects in Biological Systems, *Science*, **117**: 541–545 (1953).
57. Ropp, Gus A.: Effect of Isotope Substitution on Organic Reaction Rates, *Nucleonics*, **10**: 22–27 (1952).
58. Myerson, Albert L., and Farrington Daniels: Relative Rates of Hydrolysis of Urea Containing C^{12} and C^{14}, *Science*, **108**: 676 (1948).
59. Yankwich, Peter E.: Isotope Effects in Chemical Reactions, *Ann. Rev. Nuclear Sci.*, **3**: 235–248 (1953).

CHAPTER 3

HEALTH PHYSICS AND RADIATION PROTECTION

Nomenclature and Units: *Specific ionization; Energy of radiation; Alpha rays; Beta rays; Gamma rays; Absorption of radiation; Units of radioactivity; Units of radiation dose;* External Hazards: *Maximum permissible levels; Shielding;* Internal Hazards: *Maximum permissible levels; Avoidance of internal hazards; Classification of radioisotopes;* Decontamination: *General hand washing; Rigorous hand washing; Clothing; Laboratory tools and glassware; Various surfaces;* Waste Disposal: *Isotopes with a half-life not greater than 2 weeks; Isotopes of intermediate half-life used in small quantities; Carbon 14;* Instrumentation for Radiation Protection. Summary and Suggested Working Rules.

In 1896, shortly after the discovery of X rays, the damaging properties of ionizing radiation were recognized as manifested by epilation, dermatitis, and ulceration of the skin. The more insidious aspects—the long latent period, the production of malignancies, the possible shortening of the life span, the extreme sensitivity of the developing embryo, and the genetic effects—were to be observed later as more and more people were to work with X-ray machines and radioactive materials and as animal experiments were undertaken. In the early 1920's various national and international committees established permissible levels of exposure to ionizing radiation from X rays and radium. As a result of the production of large amounts of radioactive materials by particle accelerators and nuclear reactors, it became evident about 1942 that special attention should be given to the hazards of radiation. The science of *health physics* thus came into being, with the development of philosophies, personnel, and procedures aimed at the prevention of radiation damage to man. References (1 to 11) may be consulted for a historical account of radiation effects and for a listing of various committees and their recommendations as published by the National Bureau of Standards. The handbooks from the Bureau should be readily available to all persons working with radioactive material.

The practical utilization of atomic energy will be governed to a large extent by the establishment of reasonable but adequate tolerances and procedures. Safety must be the first consideration. Very few investigations would be worth the risk of injury to the experimenter. Similarly,

83

if the procedures must be prohibitively expensive or cumbersome, then full benefits will not be realized. Experience in operations of the U.S. Atomic Energy Commission and in private laboratories has shown that almost any level of radioactive material can be handled without damage to personnel provided adequate precautions are taken. The extent of these precautions primarily depends upon the amount of radioactivity used. This discussion will be limited primarily to the lower levels of operation most customary for biological experiments. Only such considerations will be treated as are necessary for the intelligent application of measures for radiation protection.

The ultimate basis for protective measures will undoubtedly result from fundamental studies of radiation biology. However, at the present time and probably for some time to come it will be necessary to rely upon empirical considerations. The problems of the action of radiation on the living cell are so complex as to fall beyond the scope of this text. The interested reader may consult references (12 to 23a) for a general treatment of this subject.

Nomenclature and Units. In order to discuss problems of radiation protection, it is first necessary to establish the meaning of certain units of measurement and to outline some aspects of the interaction of radiation with matter and with biological systems. We are not particularly interested in formal definitions or in the precise values of various constants. Rather it is important to understand the interrelationships between the units, the characteristics of the radiation, and the biological response.

Specific Ionization. The radiation from radioactive materials, as well as X rays, is characterized by its ability to produce ionization, that is to say, the removal of electrons from certain atoms and their attachment to other atoms, thus forming pairs of positive and negative ions. Such radiation is therefore called *ionizing radiation*. It is generally accepted that the biologic effects of radiation are primarily due to the ionization produced in the tissues. The number of ions formed per unit length of path is called the *specific ionization* and is a characteristic of the radiation. In higher plants and animals, at least, the amount of injury generally increases with the specific ionization, because the more densely ionizing radiation releases more of its energy in localized regions.

Energy of Radiation. It is necessary to have a unit of energy to describe in part the radiation emitted by radioisotopes. The *Mev* (*million electron volts*) has been found convenient to use. It is equal to the amount of work done when an electron is accelerated by a potential of a million volts. Other fractions and multiples of this unit are often employed, such as the *ev* (*electron volt*), *kev* (*kilo-electron-volt*), and *Bev* (*billion electron volts*). The energies involved in ordinary chemical reactions range up to 10 ev, whereas those encountered in nuclear interactions are enormously higher—of the order of millions of electron volts. The higher the energy of a given type of radiation, the greater is its penetrating power. This property is of importance in shielding considerations and in the use of detection and measurement instruments.

Alpha Rays. Radioisotopes emitting alpha rays will not normally be used in biological research. However, because of the health hazards from internally deposited alpha emitters, brief mention of them is made here. Alpha rays are swiftly moving stripped atoms of helium and are emitted chiefly by the heavier elements with initial energies of 2 to 8 Mev. Their outstanding characteristic is the ability to ionize intensely and to penetrate only short distances. Thus sources outside the body constitute no hazard, because the rays are stopped by a few centimeters of air or by the dead layer of skin. Once inside the body, however, alpha emitters constitute a considerable hazard, since the energy of the radiation is dissipated in such a small volume of tissue, thus producing an intense localized effect.

Beta Rays. Beta rays are most generally the ones measured in radioisotope work and are also important as a radiation hazard. They are high-speed electrons emitted from the nucleus of an unstable atom at the instant of disintegration. Unlike alpha rays, beta rays emitted from a given substance have energies ranging from zero up to some maximum, characteristic of the particular radioisotope. The value listed usually refers to the maximum energy. Thus, for example, P^{32} is listed as a 1.7-Mev beta emitter, which means that this isotope yields beta rays of all energies up to 1.7 Mev, the average being about one-third of the maximum, or 0.6 Mev.

Beta rays have a lower specific ionization and greater penetrating power than do alpha rays. When beta rays pass through matter, the rapid deceleration causes the production of gamma rays, called *bremsstrahlung*, which, however, is small in amount compared with the original beta radiation. The higher the atomic number of the absorber, the more bremsstrahlung is produced.

Gamma Rays. Unlike alpha and beta rays, which are particulate in nature, gamma rays are electromagnetic radiations (photons). They arise from the atomic nucleus and are similar to light except that they are of much shorter wavelength. Gamma rays are characterized by high penetrating power. X and gamma rays have identical properties and differ only in their mode of origin.

Absorption of Radiation. Knowledge of the absorption properties of the various ionizing radiations is of importance from the point of view of shielding against external radiation, penetration into tissues, and the characteristics of detection instruments. It is often convenient to express the thickness of absorbing material in terms of *mass per unit area* instead of units of length.   A common unit is the milligram per square centimeter (mg/cm^2).   The primary advantage is that the mass per unit area is more directly related to the absorbing process than is the thickness.   Furthermore the range expressed as mass per unit area will be independent of the density for all practical purposes and will therefore be essentially the same for various materials.   For example, if the range of a given alpha particle is 3.8 mg/cm^2 of aluminum, it will also be 3.8 mg/cm^2 of air.   However, the particle will traverse only 0.014 mm aluminum as compared with about 25 mm air.   Alpha and beta rays have definite ranges; they can be stopped completely by relatively small amounts of material.   Gamma-ray intensity, on the other hand, is decreased exponentially according to the following equation:

$$I = I_0 e^{-kt} \tag{3-1}$$

where I_0 = intensity of incident radiation
I = intensity of radiation after passage through thickness t of absorbing material
k = constant for material which represents fractional change of intensity with thickness of absorber

Equation (3-1) will be recognized as identical with Eq. (1-15), which was discussed in detail.   The relationships presented in Chap. 1 hold also for this case.   Thus gamma rays may be characterized by the half-value layer, which is the thickness or the mass per unit area required to reduce the initial intensity to one-half its value.   This will be recognized as analogous to the half-life of a radioactive material or to the half-value time of an exponential removal process.   It should be noted that beta rays, because of a combination of circumstances, follow Eq. (3-1) fairly closely in the middle of the absorption curve.

Table 3-1 presents a comparison of some of the characteristics of alpha, beta, and gamma radiation.

Units of Radioactivity.   The amount of radioactive material is conveniently expressed in terms of a disintegration rate, since this is more closely related to the properties of interest than is the mass of the radioisotope. The *curie* (c), named in honor of the discoverers of radium, has been adopted as the unit of radioactivity.   The curie was originally defined in terms of radium decay, and Evans (24) may be consulted for a discussion of the difficulties in the use and misuse of the term.   However, the following definition has now been established (4): *A curie is the amount of any radioactive material in which* 3.7×10^{10} *atoms disintegrate per second.* Smaller fractions of the curie are commonly used—*millicurie* (mc) = 10^{-3} c, or *microcurie* (μc) = 10^{-6} c.   The magnitude of the curie unit in terms of instrumental detection and biological response will be apparent in other parts of the text.   Another unit, the *rutherford* (rd), has been proposed but does not appear destined to gain wide usage. A rutherford represents that amount of radioactive material in which 10^6 atoms disintegrate per second.

Units of Radiation Dose. It is necessary to have a unit to denote the energy absorbed by material from the radiation that passes through it. The *roentgen* (r), named after the discoverer of X rays, has been formally defined as *that quantity of X or gamma radiation such that the associated corpuscular emission per 0.001293 g of air produces, in air, ions carrying*

TABLE 3-1. SUMMARY OF CHARACTERISTICS OF ALPHA, BETA, AND GAMMA RADIATION

	Alpha rays	Beta rays	Gamma rays
Nature.....................	$[He^4]^{++}$	High-speed electrons from radioactive transformations	Electromagnetic radiations (photons) from atomic nuclei
Specific ionization, ion pairs per centimeter track in tissue	4×10^7 (for 5 Mev)	6×10^4 (for 1 Mev)	
Range in air, cm			
0.5 Mev................	0.3	140	Infinite
2 Mev..................	1	840	Infinite
4 Mev..................	2.5	1600	Infinite
Range in tissue, cm			
1 Mev..................	0.0006	0.42	Infinite
5 Mev..................	0.0037	2.2	Infinite
Range in Al, mg/cm²			
0.5 Mev................	0.5	111	Infinite
2 Mev..................	1.6	926	Infinite
4 Mev..................	3.8	2010	Infinite
Half-value layer in tissue, cm			
1 Mev..................	....	0.04	10
5 Mev..................	....	0.4	24

one electrostatic unit of quantity of electricity of either sign. A smaller unit is often used—*milliroentgen* (mr) = 10^{-3} r.

For practical purposes, it is necessary to understand the physical significance of the unit and its relationship to biological effects. The roentgen represents a certain amount of energy absorbed in a certain amount of air. If a beam of radiation passes through a layer of air, it will have a certain intensity which represents all the energy that passes through. However, only a fraction of this energy may be absorbed and is thus able to produce the ionization that is measured in roentgens. Thus the roentgen does not tell us how much radiation passed through the air but does give a measure of how much was absorbed. For comparison, remember that the curie is a measure of how much radiation is emitted by a source and may therefore reach the absorbing material, whereas the roentgen indicates the amount of energy dissipated in the absorbing material. It must also be noted that the roentgen is a unit of quantity of dosage. The number of roentgens per unit time is necessary to express the dosage rate. For example, if 100 r/hr is delivered for 8 hr, the total dose delivered would be 800 r.

Another concept that is confusing but must be understood is that the roentgen refers to energy absorbed per unit volume of air. Thus, if a man receives the equivalent of 1000 r just on his hand, there would be no serious effects. However, if the same dosage, 1000 r, were delivered to the entire body, there would be considerably more energy absorbed, undoubtedly enough to produce death. To evaluate the dosage received, one must therefore take into account the dosage rate, the time, and the volume irradiated.

From the biological standpoint the interest is primarily in the energy absorbed by tissue rather than by air. Also there is an interest in radiation other than gamma rays or X rays (e.g., beta rays, alpha rays, and neutrons). An unambiguous unit for tissue dose that has been officially adopted (4) is the *erg per gram*. However, the roentgen has been so widely used that there is some merit in having a unit for dose which is related to the roentgen. This is feasible because with photon energies below 3 Mev there is an essentially constant factor of proportionality between the exposure of biological tissues as expressed in roentgens and the energy absorption. The International Commission on Radiological Units in 1953 proposed a new unit for absorbed dose called the *rad, which is equal to* 100 *ergs/g* (25). A similar unit that appears in the literature had previously been proposed by Parker (26); this was called the *roentgen-equivalent-physical* (rep), which corresponded to the amount of ionization that would bring about the same absorption of energy per unit of air or tissue as would be caused by 1 r of gamma or X rays. It should be noted that the roentgen actually corresponds to the absorption of 83 ergs/g of air and about 93 ergs/g of tissue. The use of the rad avoids confusion as to the actual erg-per-gram value that has been used for any particular reported value. Another unit proposed by Parker which appears in the literature is the roentgen-equivalent-man (or -mammal) (rem). This is the amount of energy absorbed in tissue which is biologically equivalent in man to 1 r of gamma or X rays.

In regard to relative biological effectiveness (RBE), it is considered that gamma and beta rays are equivalent and that alpha rays are twenty times more effective. References (27 to 29) are of interest in connection with units and dosimetry.

To give an idea of the magnitude of the roentgen unit in terms of radiation commonly encountered and also in terms of biological response, Tables 3-2 and 3-3 present some illustrative values.

TABLE 3-2. APPROXIMATE RADIATION DOSAGES COMMONLY ENCOUNTERED

Source	Dosage
Cosmic and natural radioactivity	0.0003 r/day
Back of luminous-dial watch	0.02 r/day
Diagnostic X ray, chest	0.05 r per film
Fluoroscopy	0.3 r/sec
Dental film	5 r
Diagnostic X ray, pregnancy, lateral	9 r
X-ray shoe-fitting machine	10–15 r per fitting

[From Frederick P. Cowan, Everyday Radiation, *Phys. Today,* **5**: 10–16 (1952); C. F. Behrens, Permissible Dosage and Considerations of Calculated Risk, Naval Medical Research Institute, NP-3546, July 2, 1951; Harold H. Plough, Radiation Tolerances and Genetic Effects, *Nucleonics,* **10**: 16–20 (1952).]

External Hazards. *Maximum Permissible Levels.* There is need to know the amount of radiation that may be received without harmful consequence by human beings during their daily work. The term *tolerance,* which is often used, implies that there is a radiation level that can be tolerated with complete safety. Since there is as yet no substantial evidence to support this concept of a threshold response to radiation, the adjectives *maximum permissible* are commonly used to indicate a reluctance to guarantee freedom from damage. When reliable clinical or experimental data are available, the practice has been to set the permissible levels about ten times lower than those known to have produced minimal effects. References (4, 6, 19, 26, 30 to 32, 35 to 38) may be consulted for a general discussion of the philosophy of the tolerance concept.

On the basis of extensive experience of radiologists and technicians in work with X rays and radium therapy, as well as more limited animal experimentation, the U.S. National Committee on Radiation Protection has recommended the *tolerance dose, or maximum permissible dose, of X and gamma rays to be* 0.3 *r/week.* This applies to absorption over the whole body. In the case of exposure of the hands and forearms to X, gamma, and beta radiation, the maximum permissible dose is recommended as 1.5 r/week or its energy equivalent (4). It is known that a given dose of radiation will produce more damage if delivered over a shorter period of time. Consequently it is not good practice to accept routinely high dosages which are then balanced by an appropriate radiation-free period. (See note added in proof, page 113.)

Spalding et al. (39) have recently surveyed typical radiation dosages as received by X-ray technicians and isotope users employing less than

TABLE 3-3. EXAMPLES OF PHYSIOLOGICAL RESPONSE TO X OR
GAMMA RADIATION

Organism	Dosage, r	Effect
Rat	5	Decreased uptake of Fe^{59} by red blood cells
Mouse	30	Doubled spontaneous-mutation rate
Man	50	Reduction of lymphocytes
Rat	50–100	Embryonic changes
Man	100	Nausea, vomiting, fatigue
Man	200	Reduction of all blood elements
Swine	420	LD_{50}^a
Dog	300–430	LD_{50}
Man	400	Estimated LD_{50}
Man, gonads	500	Sterilizing dose
Monkey	500	LD_{50}
Rat	590	LD_{50}
Mouse	650	LD_{50}
Rabbit	790	LD_{50}
Chicken	1,000	LD_{50}
Man, skin	1,060	Mean skin erythema dose
Turtle	1,500	LD_{50}
Trichinella spiralis	3,500	Prevented reproduction
Trichinella spiralis	5,000	Prevented maturation in vitro
Sea urchin sperm	7,800	Delayed cleavage
Trichinella spiralis	15,000	Rendered pork noninfective
Bacteria	40,000	Killed 90 per cent of bacteria in milk
Glycine	160,000	Caused deamination
Bacteria	200,000	Destroys colonies
Frog sperm	400,000	Prevents fertilization
Bacteria	500,000	Sterilized spores
Milk	750,000	Completely sterilized
Beef	1,600,000	Prevented bacterial spoilage
Tobacco mosaic virus	1,800,000	Inactivated
Ascorbic acid, niacin, vitamin B_{12}	1.99×10^9	Inactivated

[a] LD_{50} refers to the dosage necessary to kill 50 per cent of the organisms irradiated.
[Compiled primarily from A. H. Sparrow and B. A. Rubin, Effects of Radiations on Biological Systems, in George S. Avery, Jr., ed., "Survey of Biological Progress," vol. 2, pp. 1–52, Academic Press, Inc., New York, 1952; Tabulation of Available Data Relative to Radiation Biology, NEPA-1019, 1949; Harold H. Plough, Radiation Tolerances and Genetic Effects, *Nucleonics*, **10**: 16–20 (1952); S. E. Gould, James G. Van Dyke, and Henry J. Gomberg, Effect of X-rays on Trichina Larvae, *Am. J. Pathol.*, **29**: 323–337 (1953); John P. O'Meara, Radiation Chemistry and Sterilization of Biological Materials by Ionizing Radiations, *Nucleonics*, **10**: 19–23 (1952).]

15 mc of radioactive material for procedures in any one week. The data are summarized in Table 3-4. It is clear that the isotope users were receiving less radiation than the X-ray workers and were well below the maximum permissible level. Knisely et al (40) have described the problems in the medical use of radioisotopes employing of the order of 30 c of radioactivity for internal use per year. Even under these conditions the acceptable weekly dose was rarely exceeded.

TABLE 3-4. SURVEY OF RADIATION EXPOSURES DURING 1950, 1951, AND 1952

	Isotope laboratories	X-ray laboratories
Total No. of films.....................	28,947	12,225
No. of workers......................	580	275
Percentage of films reading, r/week:		
0–0.05........................	99.56	65.5
0.05–0.1........................	0.22	26.7
0.1–0.2........................	0.08	5.8
0.2–0.3........................	0.06	1.4
>0.3........................	0.08	0.56

[Compiled from Charles K. Spalding, Egilda Deamicis, and Russell F. Cowing, Radiation Exposure Survey of X-ray and Isotope Personnel, *Nucleonics*, **11**: 46–47 (1953).]

It is emphasized that the maximum permissible level should not represent an invitation to accept this dosage. Nor should the individual or institution assume the attitude that precautions can be neglected so long as this level is not exceeded. Rather, it is advisable to strive for the lowest possible exposure at all times. Exposures as high as 0.3 r/week are entirely unnecessary if the radioisotope procedures are properly undertaken. The reader interested in genetic effects should consult the review of Plough (32) and the article of Muller (41), who argues that the exposure of large numbers of the population to 0.1 r/day may lead to obvious damage in future generations, since the radiation dosage appears to be cumulative. To repeat, however, radioisotope studies can be carried out readily with exposures acceptable to the extreme pessimist.

The external irradiation hazard for a given isotope is governed by (a) quantity of active material, (b) distance from the material, (c) duration of exposure, and (d) absorption of radiation between the source and the worker. At low levels of radioactivity the hazard may be controlled by a, b, or c above. However, at levels of about 1 mc, especially with high-energy gamma rays, some shielding protection is required, and the following are some practical considerations in regard to this matter:

Shielding. It should first be stated that, even though shielding is used which by calculation should be adequate, instrumental measurements should always be made as an added guarantee. Morgan (42) has published a very useful bulletin on the practical problems of shielding.

Beta-ray shielding is a relatively simple matter. The data from Fig. 3-1 may be used to estimate the thickness of shielding to stop completely beta rays of the maximum energy being used. In the case of large

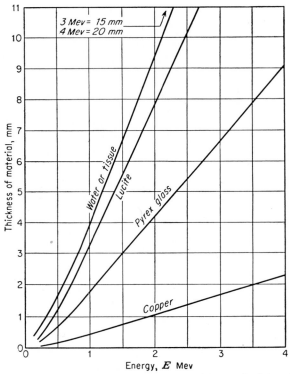

3 Mev = 15 mm
4 Mev = 20 mm

Water or tissue

Lucite

Pyrex glass

Copper

Thickness of material, mm

Energy, E Mev

FIG. 3-1. Thickness, in millimeters, of typical materials required to stop completely beta rays of maximum energy E, in millions of electron volts. (*From "Safe Handling of Radioactive Isotopes," Natl. Bur. Standards Handbook* 42, September, 1949.)

sources, however, attention must be given to the occurrence of bremsstrahlung. As will be noted, the thickness of glass in the usual bottle or container will often provide adequate shielding. It must be remembered that, although there may be no radiation through the walls of an open beaker or bottle, the area above the open top might be quite hazardous.

Gamma-ray shielding is somewhat more complicated, but the requirements may be readily estimated with adequate precision by certain approximate relationships, namely, (a) the roentgens produced per amount of radioactivity, (b) the reduction of intensity in terms of half-layers of absorber, (c) the reduction of intensity as a function of distance (inverse-square law), and (d) the half-layer of absorber as a function of energy.

The following equation gives a relationship between milliroentgens and millicuries which holds fairly well for gamma energies from 0.3 to 3 Mev:

$$R_f = 6CE \qquad (3\text{-}2)$$

where R_f = dosage rate, mr/hr at 1 ft
C = number of millicuries of activity
E = average quantum energy per disintegration, Mev
Values for R_f per millicurie will be listed for the individual isotopes in Chap. 6. It should be noted that, if more than one gamma ray is emitted per disintegration, the calculation is more involved. If the radiations are emitted in cascade, the two energy values are added to give the value of E; for Co^{60}, $E = 1.1 + 1.3 = 2.4$. If there are several modes of disintegration, then the weighted fractions of the energy values are used. Attention is called to the fact that uncertainties in the decay scheme may introduce errors in the calculated R_f values.

In order to calculate the thickness of a given absorber required to reduce an intensity by a certain factor, it is convenient to use the half-value layer according to the following equation:

$$N = 3.32 \log X \qquad (3\text{-}3)$$

where N = number of half-value layers required to reduce the intensity by a factor of X.

One other relationship must be employed: the application of the *inverse-square law*, which states that the radiation intensity varies inversely as the square of the distance. Thus a dosage rate of 100 mr/hr at 1 ft would be reduced to $100 \times 1^2/3^2 = 11$ mr/hr at 3 ft.

Table 3-5 presents some half-value layers for various materials as a function of the gamma-ray energy.

These data and relationships may be very easily used to estimate the shielding required for any particular circumstance. The following is an illustration:

A sample containing 50 mc I^{131} is received and is to be shielded in steel so that the radiation does not exceed 2 mr/hr at 6 in. From Chap. 6 it is seen that I^{131} has an R_f-per-millicurie value of about 2.5, which by Eq. (3-2) gives a dosage of 125 mr/hr at 1 ft for the 50 mc. From the inverse-square law this would be 500 mr/hr at 6 in. Therefore, sufficient shielding is required to reduce the intensity by a factor of $^{500}/_2 = 250$. From Eq. (3-3) it is calculated that the number of half-layers required would be

3.32 log 250 = 8.   From Table 3-5, since the gamma energy is less than 0.5, it can be calculated that about $0.43 \times 8 = 3.4$ in. steel is required. Generally, shields are constructed of lead or steel bricks that can be conveniently arranged so as to give 2, 4, or 6 in. of protection and thus provide adequate shielding for most purposes.   For example, it requires less than 4 in. lead to reduce the intensity of 100 mc Na^{24} to 6.25 mr/hr at 36 in. from the source; Na^{24} has one of the highest R_f-per-millicurie values, about 25.   References (3, 26, 42, 43) may be consulted for various

TABLE 3-5. HALF-VALUE LAYERS FOR GAMMA RADIATION

Energy, mev	Inches			
	Water	Concrete	Steel	Lead
0.5	2.9	1.5	0.43	0.16
0.6	3.2	1.6	0.46	0.19
0.8	3.6	1.8	0.53	0.27
1.0	4.0	2.0	0.60	0.35
1.2	4.4	2.2	0.66	0.41
1.4	4.7	2.4	0.72	0.46
1.6	5.0	2.6	0.77	0.50
1.8	5.3	2.8	0.84	0.54
2.0	5.6	3.0	0.89	0.57
2.2	5.9	3.1	0.95	0.60
2.4	6.2	3.2	0.99	0.61
2.6	6.5	3.4	1.0	0.62
2.8	6.7	3.5	1.1	0.63
3.0	7.0	3.6	1.1	0.63

(From Simon Kinsman and Donald J. Nelson, Jr., eds., "Radiological Health Handbook," Radiological Health Training Section, Environmental Health Center, Cincinnati, Ohio, March, 1953.)

tables and graphs that are useful for the estimation of gamma shielding requirements.

In practice, the external hazard will usually be at the time of opening the original shipment and during the manipulations necessary to prepare it for use in the biological system.   In the biological experiment most work involving less than 1 mc can be handled by the use of distance to reduce the radiation intensity, the so-called *tongs-and-tweezers* technique. A great many operations can be performed using the various tongs available from laboratory supply houses.   It is advisable to cover the tips or jaws with rubber or asbestos, which provides a firm grip on the object being handled.

The operations can be carried out either by *close* shielding of the individual containers or by the use of barriers.   The former is practical for

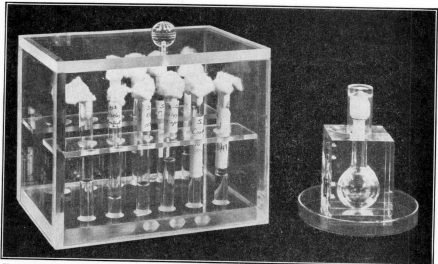

FIG. 3-2. Use of plastic for close shielding of glassware when working with relatively high levels of energetic beta emitters. (*Courtesy of Atomic Energy Commission.*)

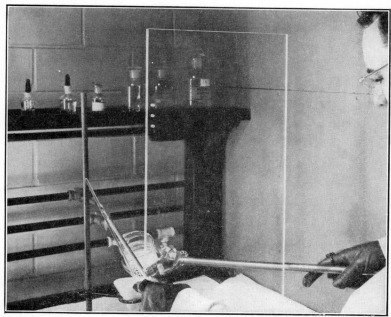

FIG. 3-3. Use of simple plastic barrier for chemical operations with beta emitters. (*Courtesy of Atomic Energy Commission.*)

beta emitters, since plastic shields can be constructed for beakers, flasks, and other apparatus.   Figure 3-2 shows some typical shielded glassware. The use of plastic sheets for barrier shielding with beta emitters offers considerable advantage in that the operations are easily visible at all times (Fig. 3-3).   Lead or iron shielding is usually required for more than 1 mc of the energetic gamma emitters.   Figure 3-4 shows a simple barrier

Fig. 3-4. Simple barrier-and-mirror arrangement for handling low-level gamma emitters. Note simple pipette filler constructed from syringe and rubber tubing. (*Courtesy of Atomic Energy Commission.*)

for low levels, and Fig. 3-5 a more elaborate barrier for higher levels. The bricks and remote-control pipetters are available commercially. Measurements and provisions must be made to ensure that hazardous levels of radiation do not pass between cracks in the shield or in any direction to the room above, through the desk top to the feet of the worker and the room below, or to the room on the other side of a wall.

Internal Hazards.   *Maximum Permissible Levels.*   A detailed review of internal radioisotope hazards is available in *National Bureau of Standards Handbook* 52 (8).   The problem of internal hazards is tremendously complex, with very little guidance available of any sort.   At least in the external radiation problem there are records of numerous individuals who have been exposed at low levels as part of their daily work and who have

shown no effects.   Little or no such information is available for internally
deposited radioactivity.   Perhaps the only clear-cut knowledge is based
on the damage incurred by numerous individuals from ingestion of radium
(44).   On the basis of the application of a safety factor to these data, the
maximum permissible amount of radium 226 in the body has been set at
0.1 μc.   Since strontium is fixed in the bones similarly to radium, maximum permissible body burdens have been stated as 1 μc Sr^{90} and 2 μc

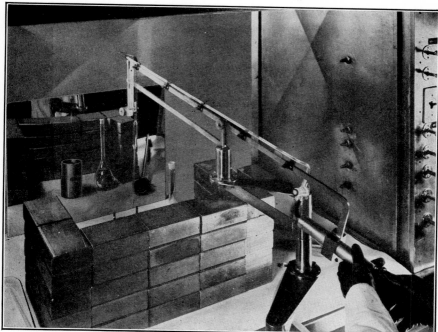

Fig. 3-5. Elaborate barrier-and-mirror arrangement for handling relatively high levels
of gamma emitters.   Note remote-control pipetter.   (*Courtesy of Atomic Energy
Commission.*)

Sr^{89}, which take into account the decreased biological effectiveness of the
Sr beta rays as compared with the Ra alpha rays.
    Although animal experiments have given considerable information as
to the pattern of distribution and removal of radioisotopes from the body,
they have contributed little directly to the basic problem of potential
damage.   This is primarily because the delayed effects may not become
evident for years and most animal experiments have not been carried out
long enough, partly because of the short life span of the usual laboratory
animal.   In this connection, the very important question as to whether
the induction period is a function of life span is still to be answered.   That

is, if a given body burden of radium takes 15 yr to produce a malignancy in man, does it take 15 yr or 1 yr to produce the same effect in the rat? The usefulness of radiotoxicity experiments with laboratory animals will depend to a large extent upon such matters.

Investigations of this sort, which are critically needed, require large numbers of animals and long periods of time and most often will lead to negative results. These considerations have discouraged the undertaking of such studies, which, however, must eventually serve as a basis for tolerance or maximum permissible values.

The complexity of the problem may be indicated by the following: (a) Internally deposited radioisotopes irradiate the body continuously until they are eliminated. (b) The pattern of absorption and behavior in the body is characteristic for each element and is even dependent upon the chemical form of the element; in addition, the behavior pattern may depend upon the age or rate of growth of the individual. (c) The distribution may not be homogeneous even in a given tissue, as demonstrated in Chap. 7 for the bone seekers. (d) The radioisotope may become an integral part of an important metabolite or structure, and thus the radiation may have a greater effect than anticipated, as discussed in Chap. 2.

The National Committee on Radiation Protection has calculated, from available data on various isotopes, the maximum permissible amount of radioisotopes in the total body and the maximum permissible concentrations in air and water for continuous exposure (8). These values, except for radium and strontium as noted above, are based upon an estimation of the uniform concentration of the radioisotope in the critical organ which will irradiate it at a dose rate of 0.3 rep/week, corrected for the biological efficiency of the particular radiation. The *critical organ* is that which receives radiation damage that results in the greatest insult to the total body. It is usually but not always the organ of greatest concentration of the radioisotope. Values are listed in Chap. 6 for the individual radioisotopes. It must be emphasized that, on account of the many assumptions necessary in calculations of this type, the values must be considered only as approximations—even though they are the best available and probably on the conservative side. It is to be hoped that support for these values will be forthcoming from experiments of a toxicologic nature.

Avoidance of Internal Hazards. Radioisotopes may enter the body by ingestion with food and water, by inhalation, through wounds and abrasions, or even by absorption through intact skin. The basic protection lies in good housekeeping and good work habits. In general, procedures should be such as to eliminate any possibility of accidental ingestion. Volatile or dusty materials should be handled in a closed system. Special care should be taken to clean up spills immediately so that the radioactive material does not dry down and become disseminated by air currents or contamination of the surfaces of shoes or equipment. Some specific suggestions will be found at the end of this chapter.

Classification of Radioisotopes. Table 3-6 presents a listing of various radioisotopes subdivided according to the relative internal hazard (5). The relative radiotoxicity was obtained from a consideration of the following factors: (a) half-life, (b) energy and character of radiation, (c) degree of selective localization in the body, (d) rate of elimination, and (e) quantities usually employed and modes of handling.

TABLE 3-6. HAZARD FROM ABSORPTION INTO THE BODY

Group I Slight hazard	Group II Moderately dangerous	Group III Very dangerous
Na^{24},[a] K^{42}, Cu^{64}, Mn^{52},[a] As^{76},[a] As^{77}, Kr^{85}, Hg^{197a}	H^3, C^{14}, P^{32}, Na^{22},[a] S^{35}, Cl^{36}, Mn^{54},[a] Fe^{59},[a] Co^{60},[a] Sr^{89}, Nb^{95},[a] Ru^{103},[a] Ru^{106}, Te^{127}, Te^{129}, I^{131}, Cs^{137},[a] Ba^{140},[a] La^{140},[a] Ce^{141}, Pr^{143}, Nd^{147},[a] Au^{198},[a] Au^{199},[a] $Hg^{203,205}$	Ca^{45}, Fe^{55}, Sr^{90}, Y^{91}, Zr^{95},[a] Ce^{144}, Pm^{147}, Bi^{210}

[a] Principal gamma emitters.

(From "Control and Removal of Radioactive Contamination in Laboratories," *Natl. Bur. Standards Handbook* 48, Dec. 15, 1951.)

Decontamination. The use of rubber gloves and individual pans underneath all equipment will usually eliminate the necessity for rigorous decontamination procedures on either skin or laboratory surfaces. However, the following suggestions, taken mainly from (5), are listed for purposes of reference: If the exact nature of the contaminant is known, some specific reagent may be chosen for the most effective decontamination. In general, with a Geiger-Müller counter of about 2-in.^{2} flat window area placed as close as possible to the contaminated area or to the contaminated skin, group I and II radioistopes should be reduced to a level of less than 1000 counts/min, and group III to less than 100 counts/min. It is sometimes helpful to wipe a suspected surface with slightly moistened filter paper that can then be counted to test for removable contamination.

General Hand Washing:

1. Wash for not less than 2 min or more than 3 min by the clock with a mild pure soap in tepid water with a good lather, covering the entire affected area thoroughly. Give special attention to areas between the fingers and around the fingernails. The outer edges of the hands are readily contaminated and often neglected in washing. Do not use highly alkaline soaps or abrasives. Rinse thoroughly and repeat, as monitoring indicates, until the desired degree of decontamination is achieved, but not exceeding three or four times.

2. If the above procedure is not sufficient to remove the contamination,

scrub the hands with a soft brush using a heavy lather and tepid water. This scrubbing is primarily to agitate the cleansing agent, and hence prolonged scrubbing without change of reagent is of questionable value. For this reason, at least three washes, including rinses, should be made within 8 min of which at least 6 min should be devoted to scrubbing. Only light pressure should be applied to the brush—not sufficient to bend the bristles out of shape or to scratch or erode the skin. Rinse thoroughly and monitor.

3. Apply lanolin or hand cream to prevent chapping.

Rigorous Hand Washing. Mix precipitated titanium dioxide (a very thick slurry, never permitted to dry) with a small amount of lanolin. Apply a liberal portion to the hands. Work this paste over the affected surface and adjacent areas of the skin for at least 2 min. Use water, sparingly, to keep the paste moist. Rinse with warm water, and follow by thorough washing with soap, brush, and water. Be sure that no paste is allowed to remain around the nails. Monitor. Repeat the entire process if necessary.

If this procedure is unsuccessful, the following two-step method may be used:

Step 1. Mix equal volumes of a saturated solution of potassium permanganate and 0.2 N sulfuric acid. Pour this over the wet hands, rubbing the entire surface and using a hand brush for not more than 2 min. (NOTE: This application will remove a layer of skin if allowed to remain in contact with the hands too long. Consequently the times stated here should not be exceeded for any single application.) Be sure that all areas are thoroughly covered. Rinse with warm water and proceed as follows:

Step 2. Apply a freshly prepared 5 per cent solution of sodium acid sulfite ($NaHSO_3$) in the same manner as above, using a hand brush and tepid water for not more than 2 min. Wash with soap and water, and rinse thoroughly.

The above two-step procedure may be repeated several times so long as the permanganate solution is not applied for more than 2 min during any one washing. Applications to other parts of the body than the hands may be facilitated by the use of swabs steeped in the solutions. Lanolin or hand cream should be applied after washing.

Clothing. Contaminated laboratory coats or coveralls should not be worn in clean areas, nor should they be sent to public laundries if they exceed the above-mentioned levels of activity. They may be stored for removal by radioactive decay or laundered in laboratory facilities. A 3 per cent citric acid rinse in addition to regular laundering procedures is sometimes effective.

Rubber goods are easily decontaminated by ordinary washing or by using dilute nitric acid. Leather is notoriously hard to decontaminate.

Laboratory Tools and Glassware. Decontamination of equipment is necessary from the point of view both of health protection and of the elimination of cross-contamination, which will interfere with the experiment. For low-level work it is good practice never to use glassware that has been employed with the relatively high-level activity in the original preparations. The conventional methods of cleaning solution, nitric acid, ammonium citrate, or trisodium phosphate may be used for washing glassware. When experiments are performed in which the counting samples are expected to be low, then special care must be taken to avoid contamination by glassware in any part of the operation. Either new glassware should be used or the vessels should be carefully monitored.

Various Surfaces. The following is a list of agents that have been found effective for the general decontamination of some common surfaces:

PAINT. Water, steam, steam with detergent, soapless detergents, complexing agents such as oxalates or Versenes, organic solvents, caustics, abrasion (wet sandblasting).

METAL. Water, detergents, organic solvents, complexing agents, dilute nitric acid or 10 per cent sodium citrate, abrasion (buffers), abrasion (wet sandblasting).

CONCRETE AND BRICK. Hydrochloric acid (32 per cent), abrasion (vacuum blasting), mechanical removal, flame cleaning.

PLASTICS. Ammonium citrate, dilute acids, organic solvents.

LINOLEUM. Carbon tetrachloride, kerosene, ammonium citrate, dilute mineral acids.

Waste Disposal. It is important that radioactive materials be disposed of in such a way that there will be no hazard to the general public or to sanitation workers or sewage-plant personnel. Consideration must also be given to interference with experimental procedures. For instance, the background count from drainpipes must not interfere with radioassay measurements. Likewise, experimentally grown plants should have no access to radioactive materials that may have been buried nearby. Reviews of the literature dealing with the problem of disposal of radioactive waste to public sewers are available (45 to 48). Various subcommittees of the National Committee on Radiation Protection are developing recommended practices for waste disposal (6, 9). The following remarks are drawn in major part from these reports and are not to be considered as official.

Possible routes of disposal are sewage, garbage, incinerators, ground burial, disposal at sea, and return to the Atomic Energy Commission. The primary consideration is that no one should receive an appreciable dose of radiation from exposure to waste material. The convenience and expense of the disposal procedure are secondary but nonetheless important. The half-life of the isotope and the ease of isotope dilution determine to a large extent the difficulty of the problem. If the half-life is short, the waste can be stored until it has decayed to an acceptable level. It is convenient to consider the specific details of waste disposal in terms of isotopes classified as follows:

Isotopes with a Half-life Not Greater Than 2 Weeks (Such as K^{42}, Na^{24}, I^{131}, P^{32}. Guidance for isotopes in this category may be obtained from the official recommendations for P^{32} and I^{131} (6). Disposal into the sewage system is usually most convenient, and greatest consideration has been given to this route. The value for maximum short-period contamination of P^{32} or I^{131} in sewage has been set at 0.1 mc/liter. Dilutions are estimated for the discharge point from the institution into the sewage system into which the radioactive wastes are discharged (i.e., for the institutional treatment plant or the main sewer outfall). No account is taken of hazards that may develop in private drainpipes owing to the concentration of radioactive wastes or to the use of certain pipes exclusively for the discharge of these materials. This depends on local conditions, which are best controlled by monitoring the plumbing. The single-batch disposal has been limited to 10 mc when the expected water flow through the sewage plant is 1,000,000 gal/day. Under such conditions, as much as 100 mc/day may be disposed of if the waste is discharged uniformly during a 6-hr period.

Solid combustible wastes and small animal carcasses containing tracer levels of these isotopes may be incinerated without special precautions.

An interesting study of the behavior of radioisotopes in the typical institutional incinerator has been reported by Kruse et al. (49). The recovery distribution was found to be as follows:

	Recovery, % of charge incinerated		
	Stack gas	Stack wall	Ash
P^{32}	2	12	86
I^{131}	80	11	9
Sr^{89}	1	9	90

This demonstrates the difference in behavior of the various elements. The recommended maximum charge, in microcuries per pound of refuse per hour, was 4 for P^{32} and 2 for I^{131}. Large animal carcasses present a difficult problem due to the bulk of material, and discussion is deferred until the next classification.

It is apparent that there will be no appreciable difficulties in the disposal of these short-lived isotopes, certainly not at tracer levels (<1 mc) or even at levels of about 100 mc which are useful mainly for producing irradiation effects.

Isotopes of Intermediate Half-life Used in Small Quantities (Such as Ca^{45}, $Fe^{55,59}$, S^{35}). No recommendations have been formulated for radioisotopes in this category. If these materials are to be put into the sewer, it has been suggested by Quimby (50) that they be diluted with enough of the stable isotope in the same form to give a dilution such that a constant intake could not give more than the maximum permissible body burden. This may be theoretically calculated from the maximum permissible body burden and the total amount of the element in the body. However, this approach should be used with caution, especially in the case of the bone-seeking radioisotopes that may be accumulated in the skeleton by the exchange process under nonequilibrium conditions. Quimby has also suggested that water dilution to a concentration ten times that permitted for constant ingestion would be a realistic and adequate procedure.

Especially for the remains and excretions of large animals, it would seem that burial in soil offers the most practical approach. Most agricultural institutions where this type of work is done would have some small areas of land that could be set aside for the purpose. The burial ground should be under the long-term control of the institution, and permanent records should be kept of the amounts and materials buried. The area should be fenced off and plainly marked. Such factors as the level of the water table, the final pathways of wastes, and the burial capacity will be of importance in the choice of the site. For specific elements the exchange capacity and nature of the soil may be used to estimate the amount of diffusion to be expected. The behavior of elements incorporated in soils has been the subject of much study by soil scientists, who may be called on to offer specific recommendations for local conditions. Soil and vegetation samples can be measured occasionally to determine the possibility of the spread of radioactive material. The radioactive wastes may be buried in pits or trenches, either with or without prior enclosure. If the waste is contained in a relatively small volume, enclosure may be preferred. This may be accomplished by using a pipe of appropriate diameter, sealed at one end and set vertically in the ground.

Burial at sea after incorporation in concrete or return to the Atomic Energy Commission is possible but will usually not be necessary under ordinary conditions.

Longer-lived isotopes in sealed sources used chiefly for external irradiation (such as Co^{60}, Sr^{90}, and Ta^{182}) should be returned to the supplier for disposal.

Carbon 14. General recommendations have been proposed for the disposal of wastes containing carbon 14 which are considered to be very conservative with respect to the health hazards involved, and at the same time very liberal in regard to the needs of the users (9). The tremendous dilution of the disposed C^{14} with the carbon of the biological cycle makes it possible to have such liberal recommendations. There are two cases, however, which are not covered by the general proposals and to which the following precautions are directed: (*a*) Insoluble particles containing C^{14} should not be discharged into the air, since there may be considerable lung retention of particle sizes of the order of microns. (*b*) The contamination of wounds with insoluble C^{14} particles should be avoided.

The general disposal recommendations for carbon 14 are as follows:

1. *Isotopic dilution.* Carbon 14 may be disposed of in any manner provided it is intimately mixed with stable carbon, in the same chemical form, in a ratio that never exceeds 1 μc C^{14} for every 10 g of stable carbon.

2. *Sewers.* Carbon 14 may be discharged to sewers in amounts that do not exceed 1 mc/100 gal of sewage based on the sewage flow available to the disposer within his own institution.

3. *Incineration.* Combustible material containing C^{14} may be incinerated if the maximum concentration does not exceed 5 μc/g of carbon. (In animal carcasses, this requirement would usually be met by an average concentration not exceeding 0.2 μc/g of tissue.) Sufficient fuel should be employed to make sure that there is not more than 5 μc C^{14} per pound of total combustible material.

4. *Atmospheric dilution.* $C^{14}O_2$ from carbonates may be discharged in the exhaust system of a standard chemical-laboratory hood that has a lineal air flow of at least 50 ft/min, at a rate not to exceed 100 μc/hr/ft^2 of air-intake area in the face of the hood as operated.

5. *Garbage.* Carbon 14 may be disposed of with garbage in amounts that do not exceed 1 μc/lb of garbage available to the disposer within his own institution.   Approximate equivalents of this requirement are stated here for convenience:

$$1 \ \mu c/\text{lb of garbage} = 20 \ \mu c \text{ per 10-gal garbage can (allowing for 50 per cent voids)}$$
$$= 800 \ \mu c/\text{yd}^3 \text{ of garbage}$$
$$= 0.5 \ \mu c/\text{day per person contributing garbage}$$

6. *Burial.* Carbon-14-containing material may be buried provided it is covered with at least 4 ft of well-compacted earth and does not exceed the following limits:

a. The maximum permissible concentration of C^{14} in biological material (plant or animal) for burial shall not exceed 5 μc/g.

b. The maximum permissible amount of C^{14} in chemical compounds mixed with 1 ft^3 of soil shall not exceed 10 mc.

In summary, it may again be stated that the disposal of radioisotopes used in metabolism studies will not be a serious problem.   The Isotopes Division of the Atomic Energy Commission is cognizant of the amounts of radioactivity allocated to each community and will be in a position to advise when the burden may become significant.   The present outlook indicates that the use of radioisotopes will not approach these levels for some time. The attention given to radioactive-waste disposal has been due to its uniqueness rather than its magnitude.

Instrumentation for Radiation Protection. All discussions of instruments will be limited to those commercially available. There are a considerable number of manufacturers now supplying a great variety of instruments for radioactivity measurements, and listings and catalogues are available through the usual channels (51). The uninitiated should purchase instruments from a reliable manufacturer. It will be assumed

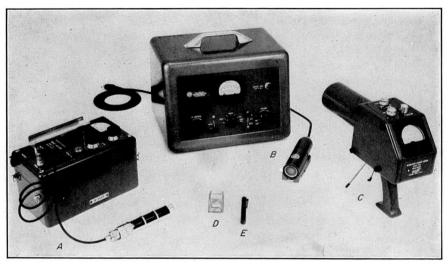

FIG. 3-6. Typical health-physics instruments: *A*, portable beta-gamma count-rate meter with glass counter tube of about 30-mg/cm² thickness; *B*, line-operated beta-gamma count-rate meter with thin-mica-window tube; *C*, Cutie Pie ionization survey meter; *D*, film badge; *E*, pocket dosimeter.

that no particular experience on the part of the investigator will be required to operate the instrument following the manufacturer's directions. Electronic instruments will get out of order. Minor adjustments and the replacement of tubes or batteries may be undertaken by the investigator, depending on his aptitude. The necessity for more complex electronic repair should be anticipated, and it is wise to have at least two of each of the major units so that the work can be carried on during the time required for repair.

For simplicity, only one of each type of instrument required for a particular job will be mentioned—one that has been found adequate in our personal experience. This is not meant to disapprove or cast aspersion on any other type or specific instrument. Figure 3-6 shows several typical survey instruments. Other equipment for monitoring radiation has been described in references (7, 53).

Perhaps the most important point is to ensure that the instrument is operating properly before use. As a practical procedure, each instrument when first received should be checked at a standard distance from some source, and a record made of the reading. It will then take just a few seconds each day to check it against the same source so that any loss of sensitivity will be noted. After the use of two or three instruments, the order of magnitude of the readings can be anticipated.

Cutie Pie. This instrument is battery-operated and has an ionization chamber and usually three scale ranges of 25, 250, and 2500 mr/hr. It usually has a 2- to 3-mg/cm^2 window, so that it is suitable for monitoring the soft-beta emitters such as C^{14}, S^{35}, and Ca^{45}. It is primarily of value at the higher levels of radiation, as indicated by the scale ranges, and is not suitable for low-level scanning for surface contamination.

Portable Beta-Gamma Count-rate Meter. This instrument is a battery-operated Geiger-Müller counter and is useful when the radiation field is less than 20 mr/hr. Thus, in contrast to the Cutie Pie, it is ideal for scanning surfaces and is not suitable at the higher levels of radiation. At high levels it will "jam" and show a zero reading, which must not be interpreted as indicative of zero radiation under such conditions. These instruments can be used with glass counter tubes of about 30-mg/cm^2 window thickness or thin-mica-window counters up to about 4 mg/cm^2. The latter must be used for the soft-beta emitters.

Line-operated Beta-Gamma Count-rate Meter. This instrument performs the same function as the above and is similar except that it is not dependent upon batteries and is therefore not so portable. It is very convenient for scanning desk tops or material that can be brought to it. These instruments usually read in counts per minute. In addition to survey work, they can often be used for special types of quantitative studies.

Pocket Dosimeter. This instrument is about the size of a fountain pen and is designed to be worn upon the person. It is self-reading, has a scale of 200 mr, and gives the total dose received from the time of charging to the time of reading. An auxiliary charging unit is required which suffices for any number of dosimeters. It is sensitive only to gamma and high-energy beta rays. The advantage of this instrument is that it can be read by the wearer at any time to give the dose received. It can be conveniently placed within the gloved palm of the hand for an estimation of the hand dose during a given operation.

Ionization pocket meters of a condenser type are similar to the above but must be read on another instrument. These may be more economical when large numbers of personnel are involved, but the dosimeter is more convenient. All these personnel meters have a tendency for spurious readings due to spontaneous discharge, and it is advisable to wear two of them if possible.

Film Badges. Film-badge service is commercially available. The developed film serves as a permanent record of the individual's exposure and may thus be of legal value. The film packet usually contains a sensitive and an insensitive film which cover the gamma dosage in the range of 30 to 20,000 mr. The primary disadvantage is the time lag between the exposure and the evaluation of the film. The film badge is also insensitive to soft-beta radiation. The value of the film badge is questionable in the small laboratory doing tracer work when adequate monitoring is available by other methods and detailed records are kept of instrument readings and amounts of activity.

SUMMARY AND SUGGESTED WORKING RULES

It is clear that the careless handling of radioactive materials may create a health hazard and may cause serious interference in experimental work on account of cross-contamination. Adequate control will primarily depend upon the actions and integrity of the individual engaged in the work. In perspective, it seems agreed that the inconveniences caused by necessary health-physics practices are seldom unduly restrictive and, in any event, are far outweighed by the productivity of the radioisotope procedures.

There can be no substitute for experience. In general, the inexperienced worker will and should take more stringent measures than may be required later on as the actualities become apparent. It is suggested that the initial experience be gained with the group I or II isotopes, which present little or no hazard when used in small amounts (e.g., P^{32}, I^{131}, K^{42}). Any activity to be employed for the first time should be used at the lowest levels feasible. This gives a "feel" for the handling procedures and contamination control that will be required.

Persons who are naturally neat and careful are to be preferred for radioisotope work. Individuals should be informed of the known dangers that may be involved and should be adequately supervised and instructed as to local rules. It is advisable that medical examinations be made before employment. However, the actual value of such routine examinations for the detection of overexposure is highly questionable. For example, exposure to about 25 r is required before effects on the blood count are noted. Such exposures in a radioisotope laboratory would be unlikely and occur only as the result of gross negligence.

If internal exposure is suspected, analysis of urine, feces, nasal smear, or sputum may be helpful depending upon the metabolism of the particular element involved. External measurements over the thyroid may be used to estimate body burdens of radioiodine.

General requirements for radiation control may be stated as follows:

(*a*) knowledge of the amount and nature of the radioactivity received; (*b*) understanding of the chemical and physical behavior of the radioactive material in the experiment to be performed; (*c*) repeated performance of "dummy runs" to eliminate unforeseen difficulties; (*d*) forethought in planning of operations; (*e*) proper use of suitable instruments; and (*f*) common sense, vigilance, good housekeeping, and good work habits.

In the Radiochemical Laboratory. It is not reasonable to set forth rules and regulations applicable to all situations. Any rigid set of recommendations would be unnecessarily stringent for some operations and inadequate for others. The regulations required will depend upon the amount and kind of radioisotopes employed and the number of people involved. When only a few individuals are working with tracer amounts of group I and II radioisotopes, the restrictions required will be minimal. With larger operations it may be advisable to have definite regulations and policies. The following are some illustrative recommendations (52 to 54) which may be used selectively as a guide for setting up working rules:

General:

1. No unnecessary materials should be brought into the laboratory. No unnecessary work should be done there.

2. Eating, drinking, smoking, and the use of cosmetics in the laboratory should be forbidden. Radioactive materials should not be placed in milk bottles, soft-drink bottles, or other vessels that might be inadvertently used for food purposes.

3. Records should be kept of radioactivity brought into the building and of its disposition.

External Hazards:

4. Radioactivity should be stored so that the general background is less than of the order of 1 mr/hr.

5. Work should be planned so as to minimize exposure to external irradiation. In no case should the hands receive more than 1 r/week, nor the whole body more than 300 mr/week. Pocket ionization chambers and survey meters should be employed to estimate the dosages received, and these values should be recorded.

Contamination and Internal Hazards:

6. Laboratory protective clothing (laboratory coats, gloves, goggles, and shoe covers) should be employed as needed, but these items should not be taken outside the laboratory and worn in clerical offices, rest rooms, counting rooms, etc. No person who has breaks in the skin on his hands should work with radioactive materials without using rubber

gloves.   Gloves should always be handled so as to avoid contamination of the inside surfaces.

7. Operations involving radioactive materials higher than counting levels should be performed over trays bedded down with disposable absorbent paper (diaper paper).   Radioactive solutions should be handled in double containers so as to avoid spread of contamination in case of breakage.

8. Pipetting or the performance of any similar operation by mouth suction should be prohibited.   Glass blowing in the laboratory should be discouraged.

9. Hoods should be used when radioactive solutions are to be distilled or heated or when there is formation of volatile compounds or spray. Hood fans should not be turned off while the hood contains radioactive materials.

10. When dusty radioactive materials are handled, a dry box should be employed, or if the operation is performed in a hood, the worker should wear a face mask.

11. If, in the course of the work, personal or laboratory contamination is suspected, a survey with a suitable instrument should be made immediately, to be followed by required cleansing.   Group I and II radioisotopes should be reduced to a level of less than 1000 counts/min, and group III to less than 100 counts/min, as measured with a Geiger counter of about 2-in.^{2} flat window area.

12. In the event of a spill, the liquid should be blotted up with absorbent paper.   When the surface is dry, a survey should be made with an appropriate survey meter and the surface then cleaned until the permissible level is reached.

Disposal:

13. Solid waste and contaminated materials should be placed in properly labeled trash cans for disposal according to regulations.

14. Radioactivity should not be put into the drain or contaminated apparatus washed in the sink unless the levels have been calculated as appropriate for disposal by this route.   Rubber tubing attached to the faucet should not be allowed to dip below the surface of the waste in the sink and thus allow the waste to be siphoned back into the water lines in the event of water-pressure failure.

15. Contaminated glassware or equipment should not be returned to central stores for general use or sent away from the laboratory for repair.

Upon Leaving Laboratory:

16. Open radiation sources should be plainly marked for the protection of custodial or repair men.

17. Before the laboratory is left, the hands should be washed and checked with a suitable low-level scanning instrument.

In the Chemical Laboratory.   It is perhaps not out of place to list a few safety precautions which apply to all chemical-laboratory operations but which may become of increasing importance when radioactive materials are involved (53):

1. Everyone in the laboratory should familiarize himself with the types, locations, and use of fire extinguishers.   Sand should be available for putting out metal or metal hydride fires.

2. When flammable solvents are in use, smoking and open flames are forbidden.   All electrical equipment should be sparkproof or explosion-proof.   A warning sign should be posted in the doorway.

3. Flammable or highly volatile solvents should not be stored in any laboratory room in greater than 10-gal quantities, with no more than 5 gal to a container.   (This refers to the total quantity of all solvents in the room.)

4. Large quantities of flammable waste liquids that are not miscible with water should be collected in closed metal cans.

5. The contact of boiling, undiluted perchloric acid or hot vapors of perchloric acid with organic matter or easily oxidized inorganic matter results in serious explosions.   Consequently such materials must be destroyed before an evaporation with perchloric acid is carried out. Evaporation should always be done in a hood with a good draft.   Perchloric acid should never be fumed in hoods made of wood or similar organic material.   The quantity of perchloric acid stored in the laboratory should be kept to an absolute minimum and should be stored in such a manner that there is no possibility of contact with organic materials.

6. Concentrated acids and alkalies should be stored below bench-top level in bottles set in lead or enamelware trays.

7. Cleaning solution should be kept covered at all times.   Location near the sink should be avoided if possible.

8. An intensive effort should be made to avoid mercury spills and to keep mercury from collecting in various corners of the table.

9. Both liquid oxygen and liquid nitrogen are often stored in the same type of Dewar flask.   Obviously care should be taken not to confuse the two, since serious explosions may result from the contact of liquid oxygen with organic matter.

10. Safety glasses or shields should be worn for all vacuum-line work.

11. All Dewar flasks should be wrapped with tape.

12. All gas cylinders should be securely chained in place to avoid any possibility of upsetting.

13. Lead bricks and other heavy objects should not be stored in elevated positions.

14. Any operations in which high pressures might develop should be carried out behind explosion shields.

15. All moving parts of heavy equipment, such as vacuum-pump motors, should be so braced and protected that there can be no danger of catching a person's clothing.

GENERAL REFERENCES

1. Morgan, Karl Z.: Health Physics and Its Control of Radiation Exposures at Clinton National Laboratory, *Chem. Eng. News*, **25**: 3794–3798 (1947).
2. Morgan, Karl Z.: Historical Sketch of Radiation Protection Experience and Increasing Scope of Radiation Protection Problems, *Ind. Med. Surg.*, **20**: 148–156 (1951).
3. "Safe Handling of Radioactive Isotopes," *Natl. Bur. Standards Handbook* 42, September, 1949.
4. "Recommendations of the International Commission on Radiological Protection and of the International Commission on Radiological Units (1950)," *Natl. Bur. Standards Handbook* 47, June 29, 1951.
5. "Control and Removal of Radioactive Contamination in Laboratories," *Natl. Bur. Standards Handbook* 48, Dec. 15, 1951.
6. "Recommendations for Waste Disposal of Phosphorus-32 and Iodine-131 for Medical Users," *Natl. Bur. Standards Handbook* 49, Nov. 2, 1951.
7. "Radiological Monitoring Methods and Instruments," *Natl. Bur. Standards Handbook* 51, Apr. 7, 1952.
8. "Maximum Permissible Amounts of Radioisotopes in the Human Body and Maximum Permissible Concentrations in Air and Water," *Natl. Bur. Standards Handbook* 52, Mar. 20, 1953.
9. "Recommendations for the Disposal of Carbon-14 Wastes," *Natl. Bur. Standards Handbook* 53, Oct. 26, 1953.
10. "Safe Handling of Cadavers Containing Radioactive Isotopes," *Natl. Bur. Standards Handbook* 56, Oct. 26, 1953.
11. Morgan, Karl Z., et al.: Health Physics Insurance Seminar, TID-388, Mar. 12, 1951.
12. Hollaender, Alexander, ed.: "Radiation Biology," vol. 1, pts. 1 and 2, McGraw-Hill Book Company, Inc., New York, 1954.
13. Spear, F. G.: "Radiations and Living Cells," John Wiley & Sons, Inc., New York, 1953.
14. Lea, D. E.: "Actions of Radiations on Living Cells," The Macmillan Company, New York, 1947.
15. Curtis, Howard J.: The Biological Effects of Radiations, *Advances in Biol. and Med. Phys.*, **2**: 1-51 (1951).
16. Certain Aspects of the Action of Radiation on Living Cells, Report of London Conference Held May 13–14, 1946, *Brit. J. Radiol.*, Supplement No. 1, 1947.
17. Sparrow, A. H., and B. A. Rubin: Effects of Radiations on Biological Systems, in George S. Avery, Jr., ed., "Survey of Biological Progress," vol. 2, pp. 1–52, Academic Press, Inc., New York, 1952.
18. Sparrow, Arnold H., and Frederick Forro, Jr.: Cellular Radiobiology, *Ann. Rev. Nuclear Sci.*, **3**: 339–368 (1953).
19. Brues, Austin M.: Carcinogenic Effects of Radiation, *Advances in Biol. and Med. Phys.*, **2**: 171–191 (1951).

20. Furth, J., and A. C. Upton: Vertebrate Radiobiology: Histopathology and Carcinogenesis, *Ann. Rev. Nuclear Sci.*, **3**: 303–338 (1953).
21. Bloom, William, ed.: "Histopathology of Irradiation," McGraw-Hill Book Company, Inc., New York, 1948.
22. Tabulation of Available Data Relative to Radiation Biology, NEPA-1019, 1949.
23. Selle, W. A.: Attempts to Prevent and Counteract Effects of Ionizing Radiations by Chemical and Pharmacological Means, NEPA-1127, Sept. 15, 1949.
23a. Stephens, S. V., and R. D. Boche: Annotated Bibliography in Radiobiology, ANL-5111, December, 1953.

CITED REFERENCES

24. Evans, Robley D.: Fundamentals of Radioactivity and Its Instrumentation, *Advances in Biol. and Med. Phys.*, **1**: 151–221 (1948).
25. International Commission Recommendations on Radiological Units, *Nucleonics*, **12**: 11 (1954).
26. Parker, H. M.: Health-Physics, Instrumentation, and Radiation Protection, *Advances in Biol. and Med. Phys.*, **1**: 223–285 (1948).
27. Marinelli, Leonidas D.: Radiation Dosimetry and Protection, *Ann. Rev. Nuclear Sci.*, **3**: 249–270 (1953).
28. Mayneord, W. V., and W. K. Sinclair: The Dosimetry of Artificial Radioactive Isotopes, *Advances in Biol. and Med. Phys.*, **3**: 1–63 (1953).
29. Glasser, Otto, Edith H. Quimby, Lauriston S. Taylor, and J. L. Weatherwax: "Physical Foundations of Radiology," 2d ed., Paul B. Hoeber, Inc., New York, 1952.
30. Cowan, Frederick P.: Everyday Radiation, *Phys. Today*, **5**: 10–16 (1952).
31. Behrens, C. F.: Permissible Dosage and Considerations of Calculated Risk, Naval Medical Research Institute, NP-3546, July 2, 1951.
32. Plough, Harold H.: Radiation Tolerances and Genetic Effects, *Nucleonics*, **10**: 16–20 (1952).
33. Gould, S. E., James G. Van Dyke, and Henry J. Gomberg: Effect of X-rays on Trichina Larvae, *Am. J. Pathol.*, **29**: 323–337 (1953).
34. O'Meara, John P.: Radiation Chemistry and Sterilization of Biological Materials by Ionizing Radiations, *Nucleonics*, **10**: 19–23 (1952).
35. Cantril, S. T., and H. M. Parker: The Tolerance Dose, MDDC-1100, Jan. 5, 1945.
36. Ingram, M.: Health Hazards in Radiation Work, *Science*, **111**: 103–109 (1950).
37. Warren, Shields, and Austin M. Brues: Protection against Radiation Hazards, *Nucleonics*, **7**: 70–76 (1950).
38. Brues, Austin M., Hermann Lisco, and Miriam P. Finkel: Biological Hazards and Toxicity of Radioactive Isotopes, AECU-525 (UAC-93), May 13, 1949.
39. Spalding, Charles K., Egilda Deamicis, and Russell F. Cowing: Radiation Exposure Survey of X-ray and Isotope Personnel, *Nucleonics*, **11**: 46–47 (1953).
40. Kniseley, Ralph M., Gould A. Andrews, and Marshall Brucer: Radiation Problems in the Pathology Laboratory of a Hospital Using Radioisotopes, *Lab. Invest.*, **1**: 447–455 (1952).
41. Muller, H. J.: Radiation Damage to the Genetic Material, *Science in Prog.*, 7th ser. (1951).
42. Morgan, G. W.: Some Practical Considerations in Radiation Shielding, U.S. Atomic Energy Commission, *Isotopes Division Circular* B-4, November, 1948.

43. Kinsman, Simon, and Donald J. Nelson, Jr., eds.: "Radiological Health Handbook," Radiological Health Training Section, Environmental Health Center, Cincinnati, Ohio, March, 1953.

44. Aub, Joseph C., Robley D. Evans, Louis H. Hempelmann, and Harrison S. Martland: The Late Effects of Internally-deposited Radioactive Materials in Man, *Medicine*, **31**: 221–329 (1952).

45. Shannon, R. L.: Radioactive Waste Disposal, A Bibliography of Unclassified Literature, TID-375, August, 1950.

46. Sanitary Engineering Conference Held at South District Filtration Plant, City of Chicago, WASH-129, Sept. 11, 1952.

47. Kittrell, F. W.: Radioactive Waste Disposal to Public Sewers, *Sewage and Ind. Wastes*, **24**: 985–993 (1952).

48. Ruchhoft, C. C., and Sergei Feitelberg: Estimates on the Concentration of Radioiodine in Sewage and Sludge from Hospital Wastes, *Nucleonics*, **9**: 29–34 (1951).

49. Kruse, C. W., P. V. Freese, A. Machis, and V. C. Behn: Behavior of Institutional Incinerators When Used to Burn Radioactive Wastes, NYO-4517, Nov. 1, 1952.

50. Quimby, Edith H.: Disposal of Radioactive Waste from Hospital Laboratories, *Lab. Invest.*, **2**: 49–55 (1953).

51. "*Nucleonics* Annual Buyers' Guide," McGraw-Hill Publishing Company, Inc., New York.

52. Morgan, G. W.: Surveying and Monitoring of Radiation from Radioisotopes, *Nucleonics*, **4**: 24–37 (1949).

53. Guide to Special Chemicals Handling, Kellex Corporation, Research and Development Division, KLX-08, Feb. 23, 1951.

54. Introductory Manual on the Control of Health Hazards from Radioactive Materials, Prepared for the Medical Research Council by the Ministry of Supply, Atomic Energy Research Establishment, Harwell, England, NP-921, January, 1949.

(NOTE ADDED IN PROOF: Additional details in regard to the permissible external dose and rules for protection may be found in "Permissible Dose from External Sources of Ionizing Radiation," *Natl. Bur. Standards Handbook* 59, Sept. 24, 1954.)

CHAPTER 4

FACILITIES AND HANDLING OF RADIOISOTOPES
WITH ANIMALS AND PLANTS

LABORATORY DESIGN AND EQUIPMENT—General Features; Typical Floor Plans; Specifications; Hoods; Isotope Storage; Laboratory Equipment. PROCEDURES WITH ANIMALS—The Small-animal Colony: *General specifications; General management; Management of radioactive animals;* Metabolism and Collection Methods for Farm Animals: *Cattle; Sheep, goats, and small calves; Swine;* Administration of Radioisotopes to Animals: *Oral dosage; Subcutaneous, intramuscular, or intraperitoneal injection; Intravenous injection; Inhalation and intratracheal dosage;* Collection of Blood Samples. PROCEDURES WITH PLANTS AND SOILS—Closed System for C^{14} Studies; Plant Injection: *Interveinal leaf injection; Leaf-tip injection; External application to the leaf; Leafstalk injection; Shoot-tip injection; Stem or branch injection;* Miscellaneous Methods with Plants; Soil, Plant, and Fertilizer Methods.

Most biological tracer work will not require the handling of more than a few millicuries of activity. Furthermore it is usual that in any given study only a few operations will be carried out at the millicurie level as compared with the large number of samples to be handled in microcurie amounts. Therefore the context of this chapter, drawn heavily from the general references (1 to 18), will be directed to the minimum facilities necessary for the handling of low to medium levels of radioactivity. In the planning of facilities the following considerations, in order of importance, must be kept in mind: *safety, economy, convenience.* The design should take into account a number of factors such as (*a*) budgetary limitations, (*b*) nature of experimental program, (*c*) floor space available or required, (*d*) characteristics and amounts of radioactivity to be used, and (*e*) frequency of handling radioisotopes.

It will be obvious that the suggestions in this discussion, presented perhaps in an arbitrary manner for convenience, represent very often only one adequate method, not necessarily any better than alternative ones. The individual should make adaptations to fit specific experimental needs and of course should not abandon any practice that is giving satisfactory results.

LABORATORY DESIGN AND EQUIPMENT

General Features. It has been found entirely satisfactory for the most part to convert existing facilities rather than to construct new labora-

114

tories, and the discussion is predicated on this basis.   Certain features are generally applicable: The rooms of a radioisotope unit should be grouped together to minimize the spreading of radioactivity to other areas not involved in the work.   Locating the laboratory on the top floor offers the practical advantage of requiring short exhaust ducts leading from the fume hoods to the roof.   The laboratories should not be located in the vicinity of X-ray machines, radium sources, or accelerators which may interfere with the counting procedures.   Separate areas and separate facilities should be provided for high- and low-activity work to reduce the possibilities of cross-contamination.   If all the work is relatively low-level, these various areas may be accommodated in the same room.   The counting area, especially, should be isolated if possible.

The flow of ventilating air in the radioisotope unit should be from areas of low activity to areas of high activity.   This pattern will help prevent the spread of radioactivity to the counting rooms or offices in the event of accidental spills.   The air in radioactivity rooms should not be recirculated.   Since fume hoods remove considerable air, it is generally not economical or essential to air-condition laboratory rooms containing hoods.   Fume hoods will also place a drain on the heating system.

It is essential that all surfaces be accessible and cleanable so that radioactive material spilled or deposited gradually over a period of time can be removed without difficulty.   The proper choice of surface materials, as discussed later, is of prime importance.

Typical Floor Plans.   It is convenient to discuss the laboratory layout in terms of areas set aside for specific purposes, which may or may not require separate rooms depending upon the magnitude of the experimental work.

The *hot laboratory* is used primarily for unloading the radioisotopes and preparing the dilutions necessary for radiochemistry or for administration to the biological system.   It should be located near the isotope-storage room, which may be used for storing both isotope shipments and radioactive wastes.   Likewise the hot laboratory should be located near the *injection area* in which the radioisotopes are administered to animals.   There is often the likelihood of spillage in this area.   The *hot animal* or *plant room* is used to house biological specimens that have received radioactivity.   The *medium-level laboratory* is used for dissection of active biological material, ashing procedures, and radiochemical operations at intermediate levels.   At this stage care must be taken to avoid the cross-contamination of samples, which will lead to counting errors.   As the name implies, the *low-level laboratory* will be used for operations in which the materials have radioactivity at about the counting level.   The *counting room* is used for the quantitative measurements of radioactivity in samples, and in this area stray radiation or radioactive contamination cannot be tolerated. Other facilities will be required for nonradioactive operations such as utility and storage rooms, a darkroom, animal or plant rooms, and offices; these present no special problems and will not be considered further.

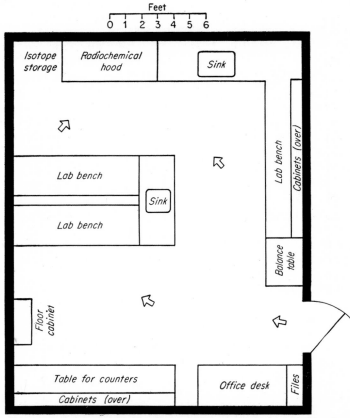

FIG. 4-1. Typical one-room radiochemical laboratory of about 400 ft². Arrows indicate air-flow pattern.

Figure 4-1 illustrates a one-room laboratory of about 400 ft² that would be suitable for handling several millicuries of a soft-beta emitter or microcurie quantities of more energetic emitters. The counting is done as far as possible from the chemical operations, and the use of a shielded counter tube is very helpful under these conditions. A two-room laboratory of about 700 ft² is shown in Fig. 4-2. The main feature is the use of a separate room for counting procedures. The higher-level work in the main laboratory would be performed in the hoods and adjacent laboratory benches. A typical six-room laboratory is shown in Fig. 4-3.

Separate rooms or areas are provided for counting, animal quarters, monitoring, medium-level work, and high-level work.   The main features are proper air flow and provision for monitoring at entrances to the medium- or high-level areas, which should serve to control the spread of contamination to the low-level areas.   The hot laboratory should be

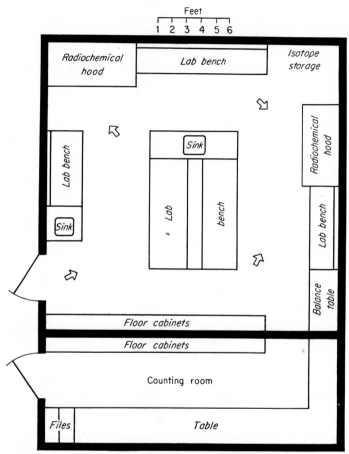

FIG. 4-2. Typical two-room radiochemical laboratory of about 700 ft². Arrows indicate air-flow pattern.

equipped with only that furniture which is necessary for the operations; there should be room for flexibility in the construction of barricades and shielding.   Some suggested minimum floor-space requirements are as follows: counting room, 70 ft²; low-level laboratory, 180 ft²; monitoring room, 80 ft²; medium-level laboratory, 150 ft²; hot laboratory, 130 ft².

A satisfactory arrangement for the use of radioisotopes with farm

animals is shown in Fig. 4-4.   The isotope preparations are performed in
the high-level (hot) laboratory.   The animals to be treated are held in
stanchions in the metabolism (hot animal) room or in the operating room,
usually the former.   The radioactive solutions are then wheeled on a
shielded cart to the animal.   The metabolism room provides space for
various stalls and cages which can be arranged at will.   The concrete
pad adjacent to the metabolism room is a very convenient location for

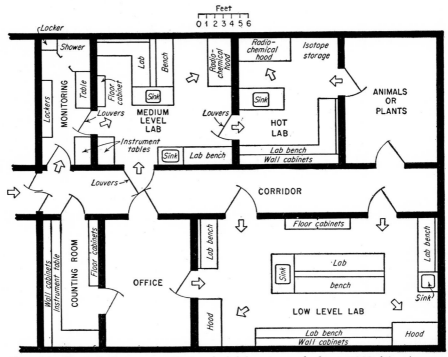

FIG. 4-3. Typical six-room radiochemical laboratory of about 1300 ft². Arrows
indicate air-flow pattern.

washing large objects such as the collection trays.   The rest of the barn
is of conventional design since no significant amounts of radioactivity are
used therein.

Specifications.   Floors should be covered so that radioactive liquids
cannot soak into wood or concrete, which are most difficult to decontaminate.   Asphalt tile, rubber tile, vinyl tile, and linoleum have been
found suitable, with the primary advantage that contaminated sections
can be removed and readily replaced.   Cracks between squares can be
satisfactorily filled by heavy waxing of the surface.

Walls and ceilings are less likely to become contaminated than floors.

Nevertheless the surfaces should be smooth, crack-free, and nonporous. Porous wall materials should be coated with a nonporous, washable paint and preferably with a final layer of strippable coating. If physically possible, the walls may be finished with a hard-surfaced Masonite or

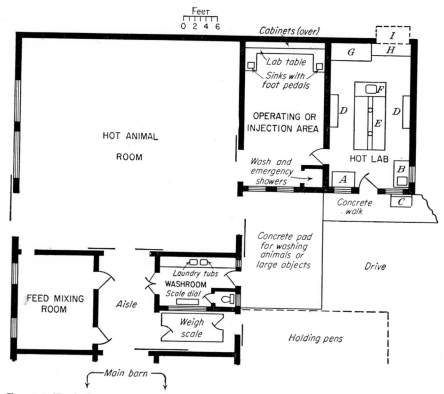

FIG. 4-4. Typical arrangement in barn for the use of radioisotopes with farm animals. *A*, office desk; *B*, hot sink; *C*, hot-waste drum from *B*; *D*, storage cabinets; *E*, laboratory bench; *F*, sink; *G*, radiochemical hood; *H*, worktable; *I*, cave with drawer-type isotope units.

Transite sheeting laid over suitable furring. Stainless-steel plywood-laminate panels or coated mild-steel panels have been used for this purpose but are somewhat more expensive than the simple lath-and-plaster wall.

The wall and ceiling coating should have the following properties: ease of decontamination by washing, chemical resistance, and ease of removal and replacement in case of severe contamination. For low- and medium-level rooms, nonporous paints or hard-surface enamels should be adequate. In general, the vinyl paints show good chemical resistance.

Where there is a greater possibility of contamination, strippable films are recommended, preferably a vinyl type. Care must be taken to provide a good base for the strippable film. Cracks between wall panels may be sealed by using polyethylene or vinyl tapes.

The usual laboratory utilities such as gas, air, vacuum, water, and electrical outlets will be required. Adequate circuits should be available to provide for hot plates, water baths, heat lamps, and muffle furnaces, which require considerable current. Fluorescent lighting is generally recommended because of lower operating cost and less heat production. It is advantageous to use a voltage-stabilizing unit for the counting room to avoid errors due to fluctuations in the line supply, and a ground wire should be installed.

For the most part, conventional laboratory benches may be used, with emphasis on the elimination of dust-catching protrusions or cavities and the use of cup sinks rather than open troughs. The decontamination properties of the bench top are not particularly important, since most operations are carried out over trays bedded down with absorbent paper. Continuous stainless-steel bench tops are not necessary. Drains should be as short as possible and located so as to permit ready access for monitoring or repair. The use of flanged joints in the drainage system will permit the easy removal of pipes. Cast-iron drains and piping should be adequate, although silicon iron, at a higher initial cost, will be most acid-resistant.

Stainless-steel sinks, commercially available, offer certain advantages over those of soapstone or porcelain. The sink should not have sharp corners, which are difficult to clean. In sinks to be used for routine dishwashing, conventional hand controls are preferred. However, in locations where the faucets must be operated intermittently during a period when the hands and gloves are contaminated, elbow or foot controls have been found convenient. Ample drainboard space is very helpful. Pegboards for drying glassware are not recommended; rather, arrangements can be easily devised so that the glassware can be drained without contact between the inside of the vessel and a supporting structure. Grilles of stainless steel or parallel stainless-steel rods are very handy for this purpose. Small cup sinks are recommended for the reception of radioactive wastes, since they have a minimum of exposed surface to become contaminated.

Adequate ventilation is of utmost importance and is directly related to the air flow of the hoods. The continuous supply of free air can often be made available by the use of simple door louvers. The removal of air by hoods must also be taken into account in calculating the heating capacity required and the placement of the heating units. Unit blowers offer some advantage over radiators in that the latter take up floor space and are hard to keep clean; however, blowers spread dust, so that the choice is a difficult one.

Hoods. The purpose of the hood is to prevent contamination—such as volatile compounds, spray, or dust—from escaping into the laboratory. At low levels of the nonhazardous radioisotopes, work may be done on the open bench if it is known that no air-borne contamination is being produced.   Under slightly more hazardous conditions the ordinary chemical fume hood may suffice, although tests have shown that it is usually inefficient in preventing the spread of fumes into the laboratory.   For general purposes, and in order to anticipate future work, it is desirable, if economically possible, to install a *radiochemical* fume hood, which is now available commercially.   Figure 4-5 presents a schematic diagram of a radiochemical fume hood with mention of special features (3).   If necessary to

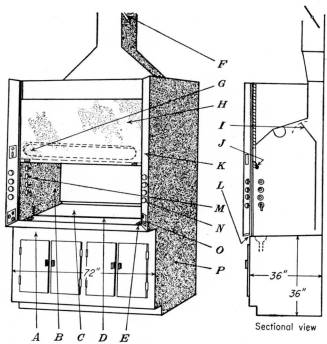

Sectional view

FIG. 4-5. Radiochemical fume hood.   Special features: *A*, the hood should be resistant to heat and chemical action and may be made of stainless steel or of less expensive material such as Masonite, Transite, or furniture steel covered with the proper paint. *B*, the interior of the hood may be given a final coating of washable, strippable paint, which may be peeled off and replaced with a fresh coat if it becomes badly contaminated.   *C*, a layer of replaceable absorbent paper with waterproof backing may be used to cover the working surface of the hood; trays, preferably of stainless steel, may be used for additional spillage protection.   *D*, for proper fume control, all operations should be performed beyond a safety line painted 8 in. inside the face of the

economize, the more expensive stainless-steel construction need not be used, since protective coatings can be employed. Strippable films are very helpful in reducing acid corrosion of the exposed areas of the hood. Also it is advisable to coat the interior of the duct work with acidproof paint before it is put in place. In practice, there is usually more difficulty from acid corrosion of metal parts than from contamination with radio-active materials.

A hood should not be placed near doorways or windows or in the vicin-ity of strong air currents, which may tend to draw fumes from the hood. All the hoods in any one room should be controlled by the same switch. This will avoid the chance that air flow from an operating hood will bring contamination into the room from a nonoperating hood. The exhaust air should be discharged so as not to contaminate surrounding facilities; a point of discharge 5 to 10 ft above the roof is usually satisfactory. The blower should be mounted so that the motor does not become contam-inated. Also the blower should be located near the top of the exhaust duct so as to minimize the escape of active material caused by positive pressure within the duct. Usually it will not be necessary to filter the hood output. The performance of the hood may be readily evaluated by setting off commercial smoke bombs and observing the distribution of smoke both within the hood and from the hood stack.

For work in the gas phase, particularly with carbon 14, a specially designed hood is desirable which permits ready access to a vacuum rack (see Fig. 4-6).

---

hood. *E*, easily cleaned-up sinks, located near the front of the hood, are recom-mended in place of less accessible trough sinks located at the back. *F*, an air velocity of 50 to 80 linear feet per minute at the face of the hood, with the sash wide open, is recommended; an exhaust-duct damper can be set as required. *G*, the lintel behind the sash contains an air bypass opening which becomes exposed when the sash is lowered; this bypass prevents excessive air velocity at the work surface when the sash is nearly closed. *H*, the counterbalanced hood sash may be made of tempered safety glass. *I*, the withdrawal of both light and heavy fumes may be achieved by the proper adjustment of a movable section of the back baffle. *J*, in accordance with general practice, a trough is located behind the bottom edge of the lintel to carry any condensate to the ends of the hood. *K*, turbulence of the air entering the hood should be reduced as much as possible; this may be accomplished by the use of a 6-in. "picture-frame" airfoil at the sides and bottom of the hood. *L*, the air-flow char-acteristics will be improved by the use of a vent space between the bottom airfoil and the hood body. *M*, service outlets (gas, water, vacuum, etc., as required) should be located near the front of the hood so that the operator will not have to reach into the hazardous zone to make hose connections. *N*, service handles and electric outlets should be located outside the hood. *O*, there should be plenty of 110-volt electric outlets, connected to two or more laboratory circuits to minimize the likelihood of circuit overloading. *P*, the base structure should be strong enough to support a ton of shielding, but it is not recommended that shielding be incorporated in the hood structure. (*From Donald R. Ward, Design of Laboratories for Safe Use of Radio-isotopes, AECU-2226, November, 1952. Courtesy of Atomic Energy Commission.*)

Experience has shown that the best of fume hoods cannot guarantee absolute freedom from laboratory contamination.   In dealing with particularly hazardous materials, the *gloved box*, illustrated in Fig. 4-7, should be used.   A small blower maintains the box at a slightly reduced pressure, and the exhausted air may be filtered before being passed into the

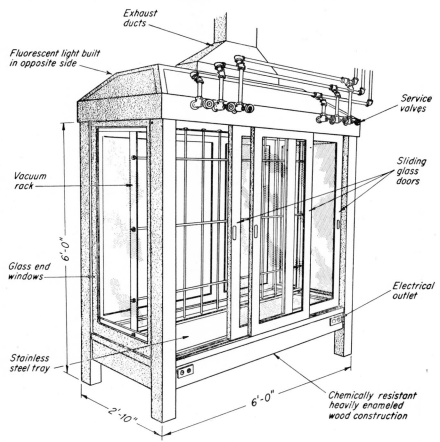

FIG. 4-6. Typical hood for C^{14} or work requiring vacuum-line technique.   (*From Donald R. Ward, Design of Laboratories for Safe Use of Radioisotopes, AECU-2226, November*, 1952.   *Courtesy of Atomic Energy Commission.*)

main hood stack.   For some types of work a simple box without a blower may be satisfactory.   Depending upon the type and amount of work to be done, the gloved-box system may be used as an economical replacement for the fume hood.

Isotope Storage.   Radioisotopes must be stored so as to present no hazard to personnel and so as not to interfere with counting or photographic procedures.   In general, they should be stored well away from the counting room and near the laboratory where the initial radiochemical work is to be done.

Beta emitters present no particular problem.   As a matter of fact, the nonreturnable containers in which they are shipped are entirely suitable

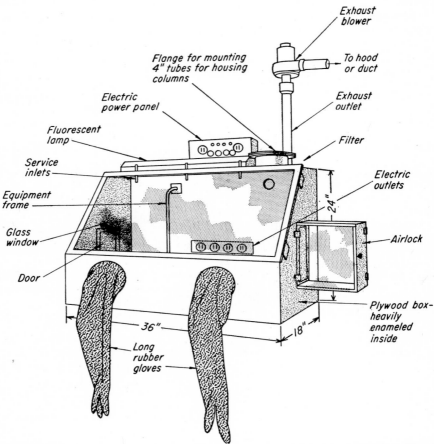

FIG. 4-7. Gloved box.   (*From Donald R. Ward, Design of Laboratories for Safe Use of Radioisotopes, AECU-2226, November, 1952.   Courtesy of Atomic Energy Commission.*)

for routine storage.   Special provision must be made for the gamma emitters, however, since the shipping containers must be returned to the supplier.   A simple vault for this purpose may consist of a bank of holes, cast in a concrete block, which accommodate the bottled isotopes and are plugged with shielding blocks of iron or lead; or a barrel of sand containing a pipe and shielding plug may be employed.   Simple barricades of lead or iron bricks are often adequate and have the advantage of flexibility.   Perhaps of most convenience for small laboratories is the system whereby the individual shipments are placed in lead or iron pots which can then be stored on the floor or on the bench, in which case no additional shielding is required.   In any event, the shielding material may place a considerable weight load on the floor of the room, which must be taken into account.

Laboratory Equipment.   A listing of specialized equipment for a small- to moderate-sized radioisotope laboratory follows:

Item	*Suggested quantity*	*Remarks*
Radiochemical fume hood..........	1–2	
Chemical fume hood..............	1–2	
Gloved box.....................	1	Two or more may be needed if used instead of hoods
Isotope storage pots..............	4	Depends on amount of gamma activity to be stored
Laboratory cart..................	1–2	Handy for transport of shielded radioactivity
Shielding bricks (iron or lead).......	20–80	Few needed if work is confined to beta emitters
3-ft tongs.......................	3	
Various small tongs...............	10	
Pantograph or remote-control pipetter........................	1	
Scalers (see Chap. 5 for discussion of counting equipment)	2–4	May need more if repair facilities are not handy
Automatic sample changer.........	1	Only if money is to be traded for technician's time in counting large numbers of samples
Extra Geiger-Müller counters.......	6	A variety should be maintained to anticipate needs
Scintillation counter..............	1	A "must" for gamma counting
Internal counter.................	1	May need more than one if most of work is to be done with soft-beta emitters
Vibrating-reed electrometer and ionization chamber	1	Only if high-sensitivity C^{14} assays are required
Lead counter shield...............	1–2	Can use lead bricks if necessary to economize
Cutie Pie (ion-chamber survey instrument).....................	1	
Portable Geiger-Müller survey instrument	1	Two of these preferable if finances permit
Line-operated Geiger-Müller survey instrument....................	1	
Pocket dosimeter.................	6	
Charging box for above...........	1	
Absorber sets....................	1	Cover range from 0 to 1500 mg/cm²
Syringe shields..................	2	Lucite for beta emitters, lead for gamma emitters

PROCEDURES WITH ANIMALS

To obtain meaningful results from animal experimentation, it is well recognized that normal healthy subjects must be used and must be maintained in this condition for the duration of the study. It may not be so apparent that in many types of investigation the animal should be conditioned to the handling it is to receive. For example, frequently we see experiments where rats that have been raised in lots in an air-conditioned colony room are fasted for a short time, excessively handled prior to and during the administration of the radioisotopes, and placed in a different type of individual cage in a different environment for the study. Do these animals eat and react normally, especially during the time immediately after dosage when the major metabolic handling of the isotope may be taking place?

These uncertainties can be minimized by taking the time and effort to condition the animal properly. For at least 2 to 3 weeks before the experiment, the laboratory animal should be kept in a cage similar to that which is to be used, and should be handled in the same way that will be necessary during the experiment. When farm animals are brought in from the pasture for study, they likewise should be accustomed to handling in the lot and be trained to the metabolism stanchion; this may require one to several months. With dogs, there is always the controversial issue of runs vs. cages. Certainly the dog confined to a cage for a long period of time differs physiologically from the dog allowed to exercise. Unfortunately, most radioisotope work has to be done in a metabolism cage on account of contamination problems, whereas it is usually most convenient to keep the dogs in outside runs. The management in this case will largely depend on the specific study, particularly as to cage space available and as to how soon the excretion falls low enough to permit return of the animal to the run.

Needless to say, it is most helpful if the animals are handled by men who understand and sincerely like them. The scientist has a moral obligation to practice the highest degree of humaneness with respect to experimental animals. Such endeavors automatically improve the reliability of the results obtained.

The Small-animal Colony. In small-animal work a most important factor in regard to the suitability of experimental animals will be the maintenance of environmental conditions so as to minimize infection, disease, epidemics, and physiological changes. Discussion of biological and dietary causes of variation is beyond the scope of this text. The management of animals until such time as they are treated with radioisotopes is no different from that in any conventional colony, as detailed in general references (11 to 14, 16). However, a brief summary of management practice is presented, since the data may be helpful in the estimation of space requirements.   The use of radioisotopes imposes additional needs for the avoidance of cross-contamination of animals and the elimination of radioactive dust hazards from diets, shed hair, dried excreta, and bedding.

General Specifications. The following discussion applies primarily to the laboratory rodent: Animal-colony rooms should have surfaces that are verminproof and easily cleaned.   Hard tile, glass bricks, or gloss-painted surfaces are suitable for the walls, and concrete floors are satisfactory, especially if sealed with suitable paint.   Floor drains may become a source of vermin and are therefore not usually recommended. Incandescent lamps are generally used for lighting, which may be critical in certain types of nutritional studies.   Temperature control is generally required, at least to an extent that will avoid sudden changes.   It is also desirable that the humidity be controlled if practicable.   If the studies are such that the animals become experimentally valuable, it may be wise to have an auxiliary source of heat for emergency use.   The ventilating system should be designed so that the animals are not exposed to direct drafts.

Simple rectangular cages of wire mesh mounted on movable racks are widely used.   A popular design is a drawer-type cage supported from runners placed on the underside of a solid shelf which forms the top of the cage.   The excreta and spilled food fall through the mesh floor onto a catch pan placed so that the animal cannot touch any of the material collected in it.   Sheets of waxed kraft paper or similar paper may conveniently be used for the collection of fecal material.   Cages are generally constructed of galvanized iron wire and sheet metal.   Stainless steel is more durable and easier to clean but is considerably more expensive. Wooden or plastic cages are well liked for mice.   All cage equipment in the nonradioactive area should be interchangeable, but not with that coming in contact with radioisotopes.

General Management. It is helpful to have one or two substantial tables available.   These are used for handling animals while administering the radioactivity or collecting blood samples.   Also they can hold the scales for weighing the animals.   Reasonably accurate weights can be obtained using a scale of about 1000 g capacity.   Often it is very handy to have a table mounted on casters so that it can be moved to service colony cages or metabolism cages that are themselves not movable.

For routine maintenance of the colony, pelleted commercial diets are adequate, and several days' supply may be made available at one time, thus reducing labor.   Feed cups about 4 in. diameter and 3 in. deep or open mesh hoppers should be used in preference to dropping the food on the bottom of the cage.   Animals are usually watered from an inverted bottle fastened to the outside of the cage and fitted with a rubber stopper through which passes a glass tube with a fire-polished opening of about 3 mm at the licking end; this is extended into the cage so that the rat may conveniently reach it. Aluminum tubes are often used to avoid the high breakage of glass, and large-size water bottles have been found easier to clean and also to require less frequent filling.

Cages are customarily washed once every 2 or 3 weeks. They are usually soaked in hot water containing soaps or detergents, followed by hand scrubbing, washing, and air-drying. Steam sterilization or a 2 per cent cresol dip is often employed. The possibility of infection may be reduced by the following practices: sterilization of bedding and litter, exclusion of wild mice and rats from the colony, vermin and insect control with insecticides, and the quarantining of animals before their introduction into the colony.

Brief mention is made of facilities required for the domestic fowl, which is becoming increasingly important as an experimental subject (12, 13). Chicks are inexpensive and can be obtained in large numbers with reasonable uniformity at any season of the year. For embryological studies, fertile eggs can be obtained from commercial hatcheries and incubated in small cabinet-type incubators. These hold about 500 eggs and are available commercially at reasonable cost. Electric brooders can be purchased which are quite suitable for laboratory use. The main points are that there should be space for the chicks away from the heated compartment and that the unit may be easily cleaned. To avoid problems that may result from the chicks' eating their excreta, it is advisable to use screen floors; $\frac{1}{2}$-in. mesh is suitable for young chicks, and coarser screens as the birds get larger. Up to 50 chicks can be placed in the 6 to 8 ft^2 of the usual brooder compartment. The chicks are kept at 90 to 95°F during the first week and then at about 85°F with gradual reduction. At 3 to 5 weeks it will be necessary to reduce the number of birds per compartment by about one-half. From 6 to 12 weeks they can be kept in a broiler battery at a temperature not below 60°F. Thereafter the birds should be placed in individual laying cages. In general, excellent commercial equipment and feed are available. Sanitation is not a particularly difficult problem; with most arrangements the droppings can be collected on paper for convenient disposition. The dustiness of the feed may become a hazard and require special precautions if radioactive materials are incorporated in the feed.

Table 4-1 summarizes some approximate housing and management requirements for the various laboratory animals. The values given are representative of typical conditions and of course may be varied widely depending on the size of the animal to be maintained, the number of animals per cage, etc. The general references may be consulted for specific details.

TABLE 4-1. APPROXIMATE MANAGEMENT REQUIREMENTS FOR VARIOUS LABORATORY ANIMALS

	Cage area per animal, in.²	Cage cubage per animal, in.³	No. of cages in room 7½ × 20 ft	Labor requirement, animals per person	Temp., °F	Daily[a] food consumption, g
Mice............	6	30	560 (5 mice per cage)	3000	73–78	5
Rats.............	70	500	240	500	72–78	15
Guinea pigs.......	100	700	220	500	70–80	25
Baby chicks.......	20	200	20 (50 chicks per cage)	2000	95	15
Month-old chicks..	50	500	20 (12 chicks per cage)	1000	70–80	25
Hens.............	200	3400	72	500	Outside temp.	85
Rabbits...........	440	6400	64	250	65–75	150
Monkeys..........	600	20,000	16	50	80–90	300
Small dogs........	600	20,000	16	75	70–85	300

[a] Complete dry ration.

Management of Radioactive Animals. After the administration of radioactivity the animal must be considered as a source of external radiation and as an origin of excreted and expired radiomaterials that will contaminate the surroundings. Only after the use of relatively large amounts of radioactivity will there be a significant hazard to personnel from external radiation. However, the possibility of the effects of one animal on another should be taken into consideration where they are housed close together over prolonged periods of time. The hazard from excreta again depends upon the levels used, but more particularly upon the physical and metabolic characteristics of the radioactive element or compound.

The features already described for radiochemical laboratories and the small-animal colony are generally applicable to the hot animal room (15, 16).

If considerable numbers of animals are to be maintained continuously on an intake of radioactive materials and if excreta collections are not required, then the commercial cage units as already described will probably be used. They may need thorough decontamination at the end of the experiment. Often, however, the studies may require only a single dosage. In this case, the animals may be kept in inexpensive, disposable cages or in regular metabolism cages until most of the excretion has occurred.   They can then be replaced in the regular units, which will be exposed to little or no contamination.   To facilitate decontamination the cages may be dipped in paraffin, or the flat metal surfaces can be coated with strippable film.

MICE, RATS, AND GUINEA PIGS.   When quantitative separate collection of urine and feces is not required, home-made racks and cages described as follows have been found adequate: Hardware cloth of about $\frac{1}{2}$-in. mesh is attached to a wooden frame about 2 by 3 ft to form the floor for six cages.   The cages themselves are simply constructed from a single length of $\frac{1}{4}$-in. hardware cloth to give a cylinder about 10 in. in diameter and 7 in. high.   A 10-in. cake pan serves as a cover and supports the water bottle.   Feces and urine pass through the wire mesh for collection and disposal.

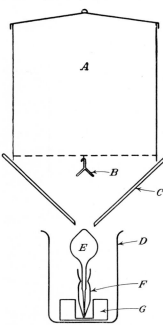

FIG. 4-8. Unit for quantitative separate collection of feces and urine from rats. *A*, wire-mesh rat cage with removable bottom. *B*, small funnel.   *C*, large funnel cut off to give 1¼-in. bottom hole.   *D*, two-liter beaker.   *E*, glass bulb with long stem.   *F*, centrifuge tube.   *G*, wood block. The urine flows down into the centrifuge tube, and the feces bounce off into the beaker.

Numerous methods have been proposed for quantitative separate collections of feces and urine (15).   A simple arrangement that has been satisfactory for most studies is illustrated in Fig. 4-8.   A commercial rat-metabolism cage of 8-in. diameter is used.   The cage has a removable wire-mesh bottom and brackets so that it can be supported on a 9-in.-diameter funnel.   A small inverted funnel is suspended by a wire from the center of the cage bottom to direct the urine and feces to the sides of the large supporting funnel. The neck of the supporting funnel is cut off at the base to provide a 1- to 1½-in. opening.   The separating unit is comprised of a 5-in. piece of 3-mm glass tubing which has a 3- to 5-cm bulb at one end and is drawn to a closed point at the other, a 15- to 30-ml centrifuge tube which has indentations near the top to fit the neck of the bulb and keep it centered, a block of wood with a hole to support the centrifuge tube, and a 2-liter beaker.   The unit is assembled as indicated in Fig. 4-8, with the bulb centered about 5 mm beneath the large funnel opening.   In operation, the urine flows around the bulb into the centrifuge tube, and the feces strike the bulb and bounce into the beaker.   All surfaces that have contact with urine may be coated with silicone to increase water repellency and expedite the flow of urine droplets; also the hairs and skin platelets will stick to the coating and not be washed into the urine (19).

After the administration of some radioisotopes to animals, particularly carbon 14, tritium, or radium, there may be radioactivity in the expired air. Even where the levels are so low that no health hazard exists, there may still be the possibility of cross-contamination of animals housed

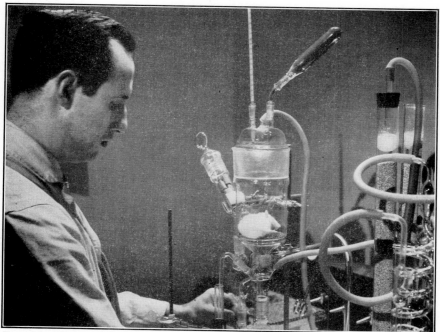

Fig. 4-9. Glass metabolism cage for the collection of feces, urine, and expired CO_2 from small animals. (*Courtesy of Atomic Energy Commission.*)

close together; this could interfere with the interpretation of experimental observations.   Where it is necessary only to dispose of expired gases, ordinary cages may be employed utilizing hoods or other means of effective ventilation.   If the animals are to be maintained for only 1 to 3 days, an ordinary vacuum desiccator can be used with a pump for supplying air and a collection device for trapping the expired gas for subsequent measurement.   For longer-term studies where excreta collections are also required, more elaborate cages are necessary, such as that illustrated in Fig. 4-9.

A useful cage has been described by Bollman (20) for restraining a rat over several days while an indwelling tube is in place.   It has proved satisfactory for injection through a venous catheter, collection of urine from a cystostomy tube, or collection of lymph from an indwelling tube in a lymphatic vessel. The cage is made of two endpieces of Lucite plastic, 3 by 6 in. Each endpiece has a $5/8$-in. hole, one to accommodate a drinking tube and the other for the rat's tail. The floor and sides of the cage are comprised of 14 steel rods, $6\frac{1}{2}$ in. long and $\frac{1}{8}$ in. in diameter, set about $\frac{1}{2}$ in. apart. These rods fit into slots drilled in one endpiece and into holes in corresponding positions in the other endpiece. A 200-g rat is accommodated with the dimensions given. Additional holes or slots may be made for larger or smaller animals.

RABBITS. Rabbits consistently ingest their own fecal material directly from the anus; this interferes greatly with any study of the absorption or utilization of materials that are administered. This is avoided by collaring the animal. Commercial metabolism cages are available which operate on the usual principle of having a wire-mesh floor through which the feces and urine pass onto a finer mesh screen that catches the feces but permits the urine to flow into a funnel arrangement for collection. This type of cage has the inherent disadvantage that some of the feces may not pass through the floor and may be ingested as well as contaminate the skin of the animal. There is also opportunity for considerable cross-contamination between urine and feces. It is helpful to place a raised strainer (made out of hardware cloth) over the urine outlet; this serves to keep the feces from collecting around the outlet.

DOGS. Conventional metabolism units are available for the dog similar to those described for the rabbit except that the feces are retained on the floor of the cage. These cages are fairly satisfactory, especially if the animal habitually defecates in one particular area and is on a diet that produces firm stools. Hansard (21) has described a cage which has a circular false floor that supports the animal satisfactorily but still allows the urine and feces to pass through for separate collection. A metabolism mask for dogs has been described by Gaebler (22) which may be suitable for the collection of expired radioactive gases.

Metabolism and Collection Methods for Farm Animals. Domestic animals will normally be managed under farm conditions until used in the radioisotope studies. The primary problem will be the separate quantitative collection of urine and feces for one to several weeks, with the animal subject to a minimum of discomfort. Also metabolism units should allow convenient feeding and watering of the animal and permit the administration of radioisotopes as well as the routine sampling of blood. The units should be relatively inexpensive so that they can be discarded if necessary. However, in several years' experience with the facilities here described, very little if any contamination has occurred. A literature review and detailed discussion of adequate metabolism stands for this purpose have been presented by Hansard, Comar, and Plumlee (17) which may be consulted for details that are not included below.

In general, the animal is maintained in a stanchion so that the feces are dropped directly into a collection pan. Urine is collected from males directly or by a rubber funnel which is attached to the animal by a harness. Collection of urine from females is accomplished by an indwelling

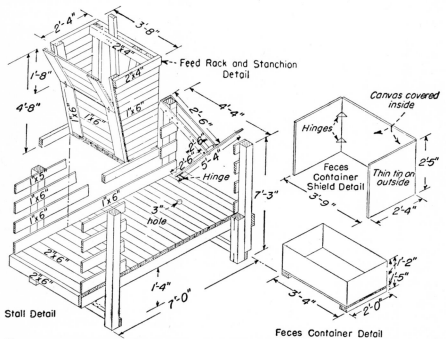

FIG. 4-10. Schematic diagram of metabolism stall for the collection of excreta from cattle. With given dimensions, this will accommodate 1200-lb animals (for smaller animals it can be scaled down). [*From Sam L. Hansard, C. L. Comar, and M. P. Plumlee, Radioisotope Procedures with Farm Animals, Nucleonics*, **9:** 13–25, 38–45 (1951).]

catheter or by cementing 3-in. Gooch tubing around the vulva which directs the flow of urine into a collection bottle. The animals can stand or lie down at will, and after they have become accustomed to confinement, they will eat normally. They soon learn not to step back off the stand into the feces pan.

Cattle. Figure 4-10 shows the details of the metabolism stand, including the feedbox and stanchion, the feces collection pan made of sheet metal, and the splatter shield. The stanchion as shown may be replaced by a commercial metal stanchion which is easier to operate and allows the animal greater freedom of movement. A 5-gal carboy is placed alongside the feces pan for the collection of urine from females and beneath the stand for collection from males. In practice it is convenient to tape heavy paper inside the feces pan; in this way the inside of the pan seldom becomes contaminated with feces, and the cleaning problem is greatly simplified. A heavy matting can be used on the floor area under the animal's feet to minimize slipping.

For collection from males a soft rubber funnel can be constructed from wire and rubber sheeting as follows (Fig. 4-11): A piece of steel wire about 36 in. long is inserted into rubber tubing, and a ring is formed by braising or taping together the ends of the wire. By gluing or vulcanizing sections of thin rubber sheeting, a funnel is made so as to be about 13 to 14 in. in diameter at the top, 3 in. in diameter at the bottom, and about 10 in. long. The wire ring is attached to the top of the funnel to provide rigidity; to do this, the rubber sides are turned down over the ring and glued so as to hold the ring firmly in place. To hold the funnel in place on the animal, another wire ring, called the *supporting ring*, is constructed about 10 to 11 in. in diameter. The supporting ring is held in place on the animal by 2-in. webbing straps which are attached to the ring and pass up the side and buckle over the back of the animal. Movement of the harness can be prevented by cementing it at various places to the skin; branding cement (from Nebraska Salesbook Co.)

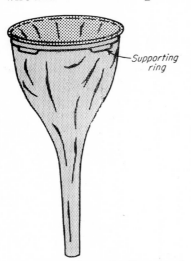

FIG. 4-11. Schematic diagram of steer urinal and supporting ring. [*From Sam L. Hansard, C. L. Comar, and M. P. Plumlee, Radioisotope Procedures with Farm Animals, Nucleonics*, **9**: 13–25, 38–45 (1951).]

is suitable for this purpose. If necessary, additional webbing straps can be employed. The rubber funnel is then simply placed in the supporting ring. The main advantage of this arrangement is that the funnel can be removed and replaced in position without the necessity of removing the harness. The bottom of the funnel is attached to 3-in. rubber tubing which directs the urine to the collection carboy. The funnel is protected from the rear feet of the animal by a heavy canvas apron supported between the funnel and the rear feet. The bottom end of the apron is tacked to the floor and is held in position against the animal's belly by a rope that ties over the back.

The urine conduits for the female are made from a 4-ft length of 3-in. seamless rubber tubing. One end is slit about 5 in., and a cold rubber patch is used to prevent further tearing. A wire ring is attached to the outside about 4 in. below the slit to hold the conduit open. By the use of webbing straps attached to the conduit and a thin metal strip attached to the outside top of the conduit, the split end of the conduit is secured around the vulva and sealed with branding cement. The arrangement can perhaps best be visualized by reference to Fig. 4-15, which illustrates

FIG. 4-12. Cow in metabolism stall. Note tail held up, rubber urinal, feces pan lined with paper, and galvanized tray under whole unit to prevent contamination of the concrete floor. (*Courtesy of Atomic Energy Commission.*)

its use with swine. The conduit is given additional support by means of a small cord attached to the side of the stand, and a small weight attached to the bottom of the tube serves to keep it in the carboy (see Fig. 4-12). The tail is prevented from interfering by a pulley arrangement that holds it out of the way. Figure 4-12 illustrates the metabolism stand in use with the female, and the features described may be noted. The side partitions are removable to provide access to the udder for the routine milking of dairy cows. Observe that the entire stand is placed on sheet metal; this serves to reduce the possibility of contamination of the concrete floor.

A respiration apparatus has been described by Kleiber and Edick (23) which allows simultaneous measurements of the metabolic rate and the radioactivity in the expired CO_2 of cows injected with C^{14}-labeled compounds. Its unique feature is a face mask that is sufficiently tight yet comfortable enough to be used for 3 hr at a time. Absolute tightness is not essential, since the apparatus operates with open-air circulation. By the use of gas-sampling devices, representative samples of the expired air

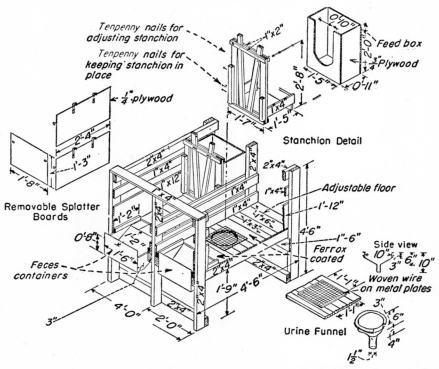

FIG. 4-13. Schematic diagram of two-unit metabolism stall suitable for sheep, goats, or small calves. [*From Sam L. Hansard, C. L. Comar, and M. P. Plumlee, Radioisotope Procedures with Farm Animals, Nucleonics,* **9**: 13–25, 38–45 (1951).]

can be taken to allow measurements of expired $C^{14}O_2$ at varying times after dosage of the animal. The health or cross-contamination hazard is not a particular problem with farm animals, since they can be maintained out in the open, where the expired C^{14} will be diluted in the atmosphere.

Sheep, Goats, and Small Calves. Figure 4-13 (17) presents the details of a two-stall metabolism unit which is satisfactory for these animals. The procedures for the females are essentially the same as described above for cattle. With the males it is convenient to provide a grille and urine funnel in the stall so that it is not necessary to attach a funnel to the

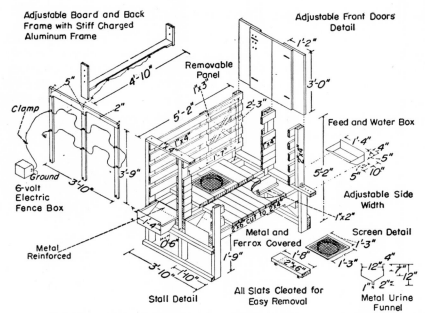

FIG. 4-14. Schematic diagram of two-unit metabolism stall for swine. [*From Sam L. Hansard, C. L. Comar, and M. P. Plumlee, Radioisotope Procedures with Farm Animals, Nucleonics,* **9**: 13–25, 38–45 (1951).]

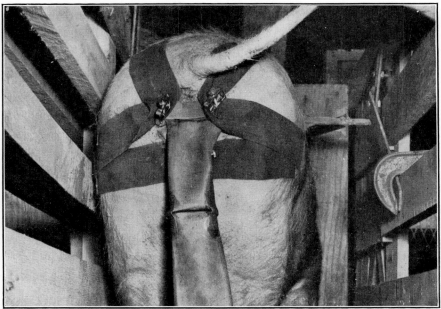

FIG. 4-15. Method of attachment of urinal around vulva of swine for quantitative collection of urine. [*From Sam L. Hansard, C. L. Comar, and M. P. Plumlee, Radioisotope Procedures with Farm Animals, Nucleonics,* **9**: 13–25, 38–45 (1951).]

137

animal. This may result in some splattering of urine, which, however, has not been found serious.

Swine. Swine present a more difficult problem than the animals discussed so far in that they cannot be held in place by means of a stanchion. This difficulty was overcome by the use of a swine metabolism stall which

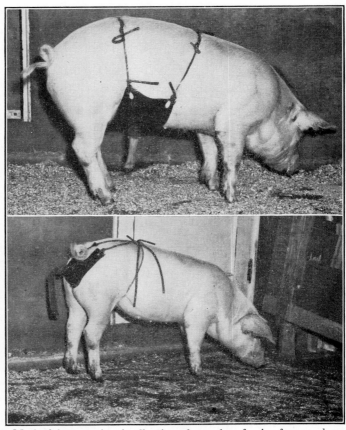

FIG. 4-16. Method for occasional collection of samples of urine from male and female swine requiring no restraint of the animal. The rubber tubing is sealed at the end. (*Courtesy of L. K. Bustad, Biology Section, Radiological Sciences Department, General Electric Company, from work performed under AEC Contract W-31-109-Eng-52.*)

was too narrow to permit the animal to turn around and in which an electrically charged wire was employed to keep the animal in the proper position. The hog soon learns how to avoid contact with the charged wire and becomes reasonably comfortable and perhaps even mentally at rest in the unit. A schematic diagram is presented in Fig. 4-14 (17). The unit as described will accommodate animals from about 100 to 350 lb.

For smaller or larger animals the dimensions should be adjusted. The combination feedbox and waterer is easily removable and is located, when in position, slightly below floor level.   The removable panel, as indicated, provides ready access for the injection of solutions or the withdrawal of blood samples.

When the animal is first placed in the unit, it is usually necessary to use iron pipe in place of the charged wire to prevent him physically from backing out.   As soon as the animal becomes used to the surroundings, the

FIG. 4-17. Simple holder for swine which affords restraint for bleeding or thyroid monitoring.   (*Courtesy of L. K. Bustad, Biology Section, Radiological Sciences Department, General Electric Company, from work performed under AEC Contract W-31-109-Eng-52.*)

charged wire will suffice.   Urinary collections from males are made as described above for sheep.   The urinary collection from females is accomplished as described for cattle and is illustrated in Fig. 4-15.

A method for occasional collection of samples of urine from the male and female is illustrated in Fig. 4-16.   Figure 4-17 shows a holder for swine that affords restraint for such operations as bleeding or thyroid monitoring.

Administration of Radioisotopes to Animals.   Almost any study will require the quantitative administration of radioisotopes to the animal by some route. Unless quantitative delivery is assured, the experimental results will have little or no meaning. Often, if the dose is only partially delivered, the animal will be unsuitable for further work. Thus it is very important that the radioactivity be quantitatively administered in a high proportion of the animals, especially if the individuals have been on treatment and there are only limited numbers available. It is emphasized that only extensive practice, which can be done with inert solutions and cull animals, will result in satisfactory proficiency. Descriptions of conventional methods of administration, especially to laboratory animals, may be found in references (11, 13, 18).

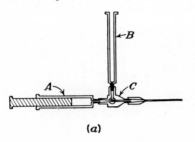

(a)

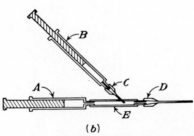

(b)

FIG. 4-18. Two methods for the quantitative delivery of radioactive solutions. [*From Sam. L. Hansard, C. L. Comar, and M. P. Plumlee, Radioisotope Procedures with Farm Animals, Nucleonics,* **9**: 13–25, 38–45 (1951).]

Two methods for the quantitative delivery of a radioactive solution are illustrated in Fig. 4-18 (17). The apparatus in (a) is assembled from a metal three-way stopcock and two syringes. In operation, the solution to be administered is measured into the open syringe B, is drawn into the horizontal syringe A, and, with manipulation of the stopcock C, it is delivered to the site of injection. Wash solution is placed in the open syringe, and the procedure is repeated. The advantages of this method are that small amounts of the active solution, delivered to the syringe by a micropipette, can be injected quantitatively, since it is not necessary to measure the volume by the syringe markings. Also the rinsing of the system is conveniently accomplished without removing the needle from the site of injection, and the system can be well shielded if required, since it is never necessary to read the syringe markings. A useful modification is to use syringe A for the dosing solution and to replace syringe B with rubber tubing that dips into wash solution.

Another method that has been found convenient is illustrated in Fig. 4-18b. In this procedure, syringe A, which is used for the wash solution, is connected to the injection needle or stomach tube by a convenient length of soft rubber tubing E. In operation, the radioactive solution is injected into the lumen of the connecting tube, both the dosing and wash syringes being operated simultaneously. The dosing syringe B can be calibrated so that an accurately known volume of solution is administered.   In some instances it may be desirable to deliver all the radioactivity contained in the syringe rather than a predetermined amount.   This can be done without removing the syringe from the site of injection by rinsing it repeatedly with the wash solution, supplied under slight positive pressure from the wash syringe.

Shielding requirements are easily met for pure beta emitters by simple Lucite shields that cover the body of the syringe (Fig. 4-19).   When

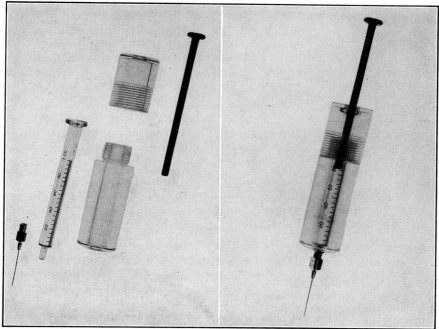

FIG. 4-19. Simple Lucite shield for 1-ml syringe; very convenient for beta emitters.

gamma emitters are used, the shielding requirements are increased.   A syringe shield is available commercially which provides 1/4-in. lead shielding and which has been satisfactory in operation at the multimillicurie level.   Its features are scale reflection and internal lighting which enable one to read the liquid level in the syringe or check for air bubbles without direct exposure to the radiation.   The syringe can be handled without the hand's coming in contact with the shielding directly over the barrel of the syringe.   The weight of this unit, however, makes it difficult to do injections requiring a delicate touch.

Oral Dosage.   For studies involving ingestion, the radioisotope can be administered in the feed, in the drinking water, by capsule, or by stomach tube.   Administration in the feed of mice and rats, etc., is avoided whenever possible because of the likelihood of spreading contamination around the cage area and because it is difficult to get a good measure of actual intake.   However, in some cases this route of administration is necessary, for example, when the experiment calls for a continual intake with a constant ratio of radioactivity to some dietary constituent.   In this situation the feed should be given in slightly moist condition so as to minimize dusting, and localized barriers can be put around the cages.   Also the cage and floor areas should be monitored to give an indication of any contamination as soon as it occurs.   Incorporation in the drinking water can be accomplished fairly well and is perhaps the method of choice for studies involving the daily dosing of considerable numbers of animals over long periods of time.   By the use of commercial graduated drinking tubes, which can be conveniently filled by vacuum devices, it is possible to accomplish a known daily administration with a minimum of contamination.

The use of the stomach tube is ideal for single dosage to all except the largest species and can even be carried out semiautomatically for routine daily force feeding (24).   A convenient semiautomatic arrangement for the routine administration of plutonium solution to rats has been described by Katz et al. (25).   For rats, mice, and guinea pigs, small catheter tubing or, even better, a ball-pointed hypodermic needle is suitable for intubation.   A procedure with rats is as follows: The stomach tube is attached by a short piece of rubber tubing to a syringe containing wash solution, as illustrated in Fig. 4-18b.   The rat is placed on the table with its head facing the operator's right, and the left hand of the operator is spread across the back firmly pressing the animal to the table; the thumb and index finger are placed at the angle of the mouth, giving these two fingers control of the head.   Slight pressure by the thumb and index finger will tend to open the jaws, and the stomach tube, moistened with saline, is inserted over the tongue and passed into the stomach, keeping as close to the cheek as possible.   If any resistance to the passage of the tube is encountered, it should be withdrawn and reintroduced.   When the tube is properly in place, the radioactive solution in the dosing syringe is injected by another person directly into the rubber connection, and the dose is then washed into the stomach with the solution in the wash syringe.   The stomach tube is then withdrawn.   The length of stomach tube required is determined by the size of the animal.   If the animal is vicious, it may be wrapped in a towel for easier handling.

With larger animals both the diameter and the length of the stomach tube to be used are determined by the size of the animal.   Stiff-walled plastic or rubber tubing or conventional animal or human stomach tubes may be used.   With small volumes it may be convenient to insert and clamp a small-diameter catheter inside the stomach tube to carry the activity and wash solution, thus decreasing surface area and adsorption. The animal is restrained, the mouth spread, and the moistened tube inserted gently over the back of the tongue and into the esophagus as the animal swallows.   A commercial mouth spreader is available for use with swine and sheep.   For cattle and horses a stomach-tube speculum can be employed which keeps the animal from biting the tube and directs the tube into the esophagus.   With horses, the tube may also be passed through the nostril.   After insertion it should be determined that the tube is actually in the stomach and not in the lungs.   Frequently the passage of the tube through the esophagus can be directly observed.   The animal will usually cough if the tube has gone into the lungs.   As an additional criterion, the open end of the inserted tube can be placed underwater, and bubbles will be seen if it is in the lungs.   Upon assurance that the tube is correctly located, a large syringe filled with wash solution is attached to the open end, and the radioactive solution is injected into the lumen of the stomach tube or insert.

In general, for the farm animals, the capsule method offers an advantage over the stomach tube.   The stomach tube requires thorough washing to ensure quantitative delivery of the activity, and there is a greater possibility of spread of contamination.   The capsule can be used only when the volume of the radioactive solution to be administered is compatible with the capsule size for the given animal.   It is necessary to prevent softening of the gelatin capsule between the time when the solution is placed therein and the time when the capsule is administered. This may be done either by placing an inert absorbent such as filter paper in the capsule prior to addition of the solution or by using two capsules, the smaller containing the solution being placed within the larger.   These procedures will allow 5 to 10 min working time.

The balling gun is customarily used for oral administration.   It is convenient to place the capsule, ready to be loaded, in the gun and to add the radioactivity by pipette.   The cover can then be placed on the capsule with tongs, and the gun handled directly with the gloved hand at a distance of 10 to 15 in. from the activity, which reduces exposure.   In the case of beta emitters the walls of the balling gun serve as an effective shield.   The mouth of the immobilized animal is opened, the balling gun inserted, the capsule delivered in back of the tongue, the gun removed, and the animal's mouth held closed until the capsule is swallowed.   A gamma emitter can be followed with a monitor to indicate when the capsule has moved into the stomach.

If an animal can be trained to consume completely a small amount of feed, this offers a convenient method for oral administration.   For example, a hole can be drilled into a food pellet into which the radioactivity can be placed (26). An animal consuming the entire pellet will get a quantitative dose.

Subcutaneous, Intramuscular, or Intraperitoneal Injection. These procedures offer no particular difficulty and are made on the immobilized animal. Subcutaneous injections are usually given in the median line of the abdominal wall or in the groin. A fold of skin is pinched up between the forefinger and thumb, and the needle inserted therein. Intramuscular injections are usually made into the posterior muscles of the thigh or into the lateral thoracic or abdominal muscles. For intraperitoneal injection of smaller animals, the wall of the abdominal cavity is pinched up, care being taken that no intestinal coils are included, and the needle is inserted until it pierces the peritoneum, when the abdominal muscles will be felt to relax. In cattle, sheep, and swine the best point of administration is 6 to 8 in. anterior and ventral to the point of the right hip.

Intravenous Injection. The lateral tail veins of the mouse are suitable for injection. The tail is immersed in warm (50°C) water for about 30 sec. The animal may be conveniently held in a small mailing tube, one end of which is perforated to admit air, the other end being fitted with a cork notched so that the tail can protrude through it. After the mouse is in the tube, the tail is straightened by gentle traction, and the needle (No. 26) is pushed through the skin over one of the lateral veins and then downward into the vein. The radioactive solution can be delivered in the usual way, already described.

Although many workers use the tail vein and some the jugular for the injection of rats, in our hands the femoral vein has proved most satisfactory (Fig. 4-20). The animal is lightly anesthetized and placed on its back. The hair of the hind leg is shaved over the area covering the vein, and a ½-in. incision made slightly to the right of and parallel to the vein. The skin is rolled over to the left to bring the vein into view. The vein is dilated by compression, and the needle (No. 26 gauge) is passed through the fascia about ⅛ in. to the left of and parallel to the vein; the needle is then inserted into the vein from the side. After the injection the skin is released and returns to its position covering the vein. Usually suturing is not needed, and the incision may be covered with collodion.

In guinea pigs a large superficial vein on the medial surface of the hind leg is suitable for injection. Karlson and Feldman (27) have described a technique by means of which it was possible to make daily injections into the ear veins of the guinea pig for 60 successive days. The important feature was transillumination of the ear by means of a Lucite rod with polished ends. A 27-gauge needle was used, and injections were made at the rate of two per minute when the volume injected did not exceed 0.2 ml. The vein along the outer margin of the ear of the rabbit is well adapted for this purpose. It is convenient to immobilize the rabbit by confinement in a tight-fitting box.   An ear vein can also be used satisfactorily in young pigs.   The dog, under restraint, may be injected in the jugular or saphenous vein.   There is also a lingual vein underneath the tongue which may be used for injection when the animal is under anesthesia.

With small animals, which can be completely immobilized, the direct insertion of the needle into the vein is satisfactory.   With larger animals, however, this method is made difficult because a slight movement of the animal may cause the needle to go through the wall of the vein or be pulled out of the vein.   There is no way of knowing just when this may occur.

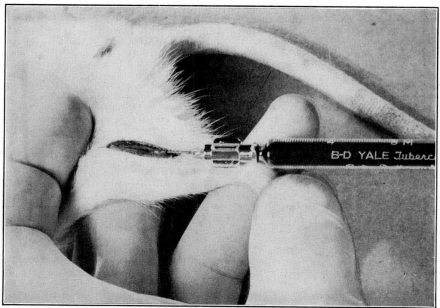

FIG. 4-20. Intravenous injection of solution into femoral vein of rat.   (*Courtesy of U. S. G. Kuhn III and W. E. Lotz.*)

In such case an unknown portion of the radioactivity may be delivered in the tissues external to the vein.   To avoid this possibility, the technique of venous catheterization can be employed.   This technique has been widely used for man and animals (17), and suitable catheter tubing is available from surgical supply houses.   The usual procedure is to insert the needle into the vein and then to thread at least several inches of the catheter tubing through it.   The needle is then withdrawn.   The catheter is immediately washed out with heparinized normal saline (4 mg of heparin per 100 ml of saline).   The radioactive solution is then delivered in the usual way through the catheter.   The catheter may be left in place for several days; however, under such conditions there is a strong probability of thrombosis or embolism (28). Detrick and Rhodes (29) have described a modified injection needle that facilitates insertion of the catheter. They have also suggested that a length of nylon fishing leader be used as a stylet to prevent blood from entering and blocking the catheter between periods of use.

Catheterization has proved satisfactory with sheep, cattle, and horses; the jugular vein is convenient, and a 16-gauge needle is customarily employed. Pressure over the base of the neck will distend the vein and

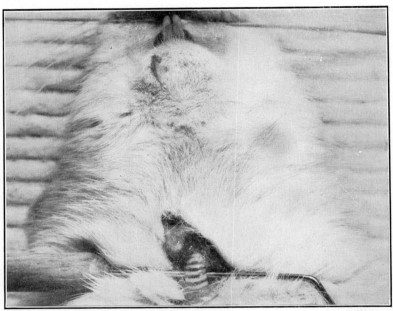

Fig. 4-21. Exposure of trachea of rat for the insertion of a hypodermic needle between the rings for intratracheal administration. (*Courtesy of R. W. Wagner, Biology Section, Radiological Sciences Department, General Electric Company, from work performed under AEC Contract W-31-109-Eng-52.*)

make it easier to locate and pierce. Kainer and Dickson (30) have pointed out that the external jugular vein of cattle has several valves that interfere with venipuncture. It was recommended that the anterior 10 to 12 cm of the vein be employed, since this region was found to be free of valves. Livestock can be adequately restrained for this procedure in the regular metabolism units or stanchions.

Procedures with swine for injection into the anterior *vena cava* have been described by Carle and Dewhirst (31). Small animals are restrained manually in a dorsal recumbent position. A 20-gauge $1\frac{1}{2}$-in. needle is inserted about 2 cm on either side of the point of the cariniform cartilage on a line drawn from the point of the cartilage to the base of the ear. The needle is guided inward, downward, and backward to the entrance of the thorax between the first pair of ribs to pierce the *vena cava* at the convergence point of the jugular and brachial veins. Large swine are restrained in a standing position, and the same procedure is followed, but with a 2½-in. needle. Catheterization can be accomplished as already described.

Inhalation and Intratracheal Dosage. One of the more difficult procedures is the quantitative administration of radioactive materials by the inhalation route. Such procedures are needed to supply important information on the relative toxicities and absorption from the lungs of insoluble dust suspensions, sprays, volatile compounds, and gases. The apparatus for inhalation studies is specialized and fairly complicated. Various chambers have been described for exposure of laboratory rodents to airborne contamination (32), exposure of rabbits to hydrogen fluoride (33), and exposure of rabbits to uranium dioxide dust (34).

Introduction of material directly into the trachea does allow estimation of pulmonary toxicity and removal rate from the lungs. However, such data are not directly applicable to behavior after inhalation. Tracheal administration is relatively simple. The trachea of the animal is surgically exposed, and the hypodermic needle is inserted between the rings (Fig. 4-21). The solution should be carefully injected into the lumen of the trachea in rhythm with inhalation by the animal.

Collection of Blood Samples. In many studies it is necessary to have blood samples for measurement. The following are descriptions of some of the methods:

A jugular technique for the bleeding of mice has been described by Kassel and Levitan (35). The animal is held by the loose skin of the back to expose the neck and upper thorax. Several threads of a gauze sponge are caught on the upper incisors, and the sponge is used to hold the head in hyperextension. Depilation from the chin to mid-thorax exposes both external jugulars. A 26-gauge needle is introduced over the sternum, puncturing the skin 1 to 2 mm below the sternoclavicular junction, and the vessel is approached in a caudocephalic direction.

With rats, blood may be satisfactorily drawn from the heart. The animal is maintained in a light surgical anesthesia, and the heart is located as the point of maximum palpitation beneath the fourth to sixth ribs. A ½-in. No. 26 gauge needle and 5-ml syringe are pushed into the thoracic cavity toward the point of throb at an angle of about 45° with the long axis of the body. As the heart is pierced, the plunger is pulled out to draw the blood into the syringe. Amounts of blood up to 1 or 2 per cent of the body weight can be obtained without serious harm to the animal. Smaller amounts may be obtained by free bleeding from a puncture of the tail vein or by cutting the tail.   To obtain blood at the time of sacrifice, the thorax can be opened and the heart exposed for direct puncture.

With the guinea pig, from 5 to 15 ml of blood may be obtained by heart stab as described above for the rat.   For collection at sacrifice the animal is anesthetized or stunned, and the large vessels of the neck are exposed by incision and then severed.

Up to 20 ml of blood may be obtained from a 5-lb rabbit by heart stab. About 2 or 3 ml can be collected by free bleeding from a marginal ear vein after puncture with a large needle.   It helps if the ear is flipped with the hand and treated with xylene and alcohol before puncture.

Blood can be collected from dogs, swine, sheep, cattle, and horses by the same methods as employed for injection.   One advantage in the use of farm animals in experimentation is that relatively large quantities of blood can be drawn frequently during the course of the study.   In many studies, blood samples must be taken frequently and in large numbers, in which case considerable injury to the vein will result if a puncture is made for each sample.   Under these conditions there is considerable advantage in the use of a catheter that is inserted as previously described.

PROCEDURES WITH PLANTS AND SOILS

Plant-nutrition research with radioisotopes may range from laboratory studies with excised roots through greenhouse work with potted plants to full-scale field applications of labeled fertilizers.   In general, conventional techniques are adequate, and mention will be made only of some typical adaptations for work with radioactive materials.

Closed System for C^{14} Studies.   It is necessary to grow plants in a closed system in which the atmosphere can be altered for the investigation of carbon fixation or for the biosynthesis of carbon-labeled compounds. Simple methods have been described by Burris et al. (36), and their procedure as reported below represents the basis of other, more elaborate arrangements.

Figure 4-22 (36) shows the simple chamber that permits the internal generation of CO_2.   The plant is grown under ordinary conditions in a porous pot and is placed in a glass jar when ready for experiment. Another glass jar of equal diameter is drilled near the bottom to furnish a hole for the generating test tube.   This jar is placed over the first one and fastened to it with adhesive tape, after which the joint is painted with a 50:50 beeswax-rosin mixture to make it airtight.   A hole is blown in the side near the bottom of the test tube to be used for the generation of the CO_2.   The $BaC^{14}O_3$ is placed in the test tube, which is then closed at the top with a serum-vial rubber stopper and sealed into the upper glass jar with beeswax-rosin.   If desired, a small vial of indicator solution can be attached to the generating tube which will show when the CO_2 supply has been exhausted.   Carbon dioxide is produced in the system by the injection of 30 per cent perchloric acid through the serum-vial stopper with a hypodermic needle.   The $BaCO_3$ should be moistened before acid treatment to avoid particles being blown from the generating tube into the chamber.   If several additions of CO_2 are required, the generating tube can be removed and replaced with a charged tube.   It may be convenient to seal into the jar a ground-glass joint to accommodate a vessel that mixes acid and $BaC^{14}O_3$ upon rotation. Quantitative CO_2 generation can be obtained, if desired, by the use of known amounts of carbonate or acid.

The jars should be opened in a well-ventilated hood.   However, if the plant is allowed to photosynthesize for some time after completion of the $C^{14}O_2$ generation, the radioactivity will be almost entirely removed from the gas phase of the system. The use of small systems to produce compounds of relatively high specific activity seems to offer some advantage in the control of radioactivity over facilities for the production of large quantities of plants with low specific activities.

A single leaf of the intact plant may be enclosed in a glass photosynthetic chamber for exposure to $C^{14}O_2$. Chen (37) has described a 9.5-liter chamber into which the leaf blade of a geranium plant was inserted through a hole and sealed.   The $BaC^{14}O_3$ was placed in a beaker at the bottom of the chamber, and the acid introduced through a separatory funnel at the top of the chamber.

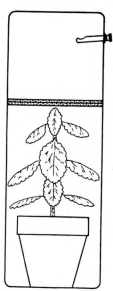

FIG.   4-22.   Closed plant-culture chamber for the internal generation of CO_2. [*From R. H. Burris, P. W. Wilson, and R. E. Stutz, Incorporation of Isotopic Carbon into Compounds by Biosynthesis, Botan. Gaz.,* **111:** 63–69 (1949).]

In short-term studies of photosynthesis the excised leaf may be used to synthesize C^{14} carbohydrates from $C^{14}O_2$.   The leaf is simply removed from the plant and the petiole is immersed in a solution containing C^{14}- labeled bicarbonate.   Dubbs (38) has described a simplified photosynthesis apparatus by means of which a detached leaf can be exposed to an atmosphere of $C^{14}O_2$ to carry on photosynthesis for as long as 24 hr.

A typical procedure for the tagging of aquatic algae with C^{14} has been reported by Clendenning and Gorham (39).   The plant material, 2 to 5 g, was distributed in 150 ml of distilled water that had been aerated with 5 per cent CO_2 in air.   A Waring Blendor jar was used for the tagging vessel.   Under the desired conditions of illumination a dilute $NaHC^{14}O_3$

solution was introduced rapidly, the vessel sealed with a glass plate, and the contents agitated gently throughout the tagging period.   At termination, the lights were extinguished, and the plants were killed by 5 min maceration at top speed in the Blendor and were then prepared for fractional analysis.

Plant Injection.   A detailed review of methods of plant injection has been compiled by Roach (40).   The procedures, although designed for general plant physiological and nutritional studies, may be useful for radioisotope administration and are therefore briefly outlined.   In botanical work the term *injection* refers to the introduction of a liquid into a plant through a cut or hole in an organ or by other methods without wounding, even though no force is used.   This is contrasted with the medical or veterinary use of the term to indicate the forcing of a fluid into the body.   Consideration of the point of application in relation to plant anatomy and the subsequent transport of material is treated excellently by Roach (40) and is beyond the scope of this text, so that only the mechanics of making the solution available to the plant will be covered.

Interveinal Leaf Injection.   A small incision is made in the leaf at a chosen point.   The liquid is contained in a reservoir and is drawn up a filter-paper wick or a darning-cotton wick which passes through and makes contact with the lips of the incision.   The wick can be sealed into the bottom of the reservoir with paraffin wax and can thereby support the vessel.

Leaf-tip Injection.   The tip of a leaf or leaflet is cut off at right angles to the midrib and immediately submerged in the liquid to be injected. The liquid is drawn in through the cut edge of the leaf as a result of transpiration and travels along the veins and veinlets to replace the tissue transpiration losses.

External Application to the Leaf.   It is often of interest to apply radioactive materials to the leaf and measure the rate of translocation to other parts of the plant.   It is difficult, however, to accomplish quantitative administration.   Swanson and Whitney (41) overcame this difficulty by application of the radioisotope to the leaf surface (usually a 0.01-ml drop) and calculation of movement from a ratio of the activity at some distant part to that in the petiole of the treated leaf.   The results showed that a reliable measure of rate of transport was obtained even though there was considerable variability between plants as to the actual amount of isotope absorbed into the leaf.   With P^{32} it was found that a pH of about 3 gave good absorption and that the uptake was greatly diminished with solutions of pH higher than 4.

Leafstalk Injection.   This method was used very satisfactorily with apple trees (40).   The leaf is cut off so as to leave a short length of stalk which is connected by rubber tubing to the drawn-out end of a test tube.

The tube is filled with solution, care having been taken to wet the cut end of the leafstalk and to expel all air from the rubber tubing.   With plants that have grooved leafstalks this method is inapplicable, and the cut end of the stalk must be bent over for submergence in a reservoir.

Shoot-tip Injection.   The tip of the shoot is cut off, and the cut end is kept wet with the liquid.   The cut should be made far enough from the growing point to permit access of solution to the differentiated conducting tissues.   If the shoot is stiff, it is convenient to use a rubber connection and reservoir as described for the apple leafstalk.   If not, the shoot can be bent over for submergence in a reservoir.

Stem or Branch Injection.   Introduction of solutions into the stem or branch may be accomplished as indicated in Fig. 4-23.   A small vial is attached to the stem by tape, and the radioactive solution placed therein.   An ordinary sewing needle attached to a heavy thread is passed through the stem, the needle removed, and both ends of the thread immersed in the solution.   The solution moves into the plant by capillary action.   Of course, it is difficult to know just which transport systems are making contact with the thread.   However, the results are indicative of transport in the plant uncomplicated by considerations of root absorption.

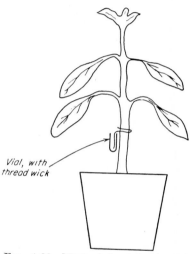

FIG. 4-23. Method for injection of radioactive solution into plant stem.

Branches may be injected independently of the rest of the tree through suitably placed diametrical holes.   Trees may also be injected through single diametrical holes or multiple radial holes (40).   Graham (40a) has described a convenient technique for introduction of radioactive solutions into tree stems.   The radioactivity contained in 1 ml solution is placed in a shell vial 25 mm long with a 12-mm outside diameter, which is then stoppered with a No. 3 cork of 14-mm diameter at the larger end. At the desired location on the tree trunk or branch, a 13-mm hole is bored with a slight upward slant to a depth of 50 mm.   The vial is placed in the hole and its cork firmly seated.   A dissecting needle is forced through the center of the cork and the vial is pushed off the cork inside the tree.   The needle is withdrawn, with care being taken to hold the cork in place.   The cork and surrounding area are immediately covered with a sealing substance such as a 1:1 mixture of grafting wax and mineral oil.   An advantage is that handling of the radioisotopes can be done in the laboratory.

Also, the upward slant of the hole causes the isotope to be concentrated in the regions from which it is most readily translocated.

Miscellaneous Methods with Plants. A typical procedure for studies of ion absorption with excised barley roots of high capacity for ion accumulation has been described by Epstein and Hagen (42). Twenty grams of barley seed was suspended in 10 per cent H_2O_2 for 20 min, the H_2O_2 solution then decanted, and the seeds soaked for 24 hr in 1 liter of continuously aerated distilled water. After several rinsings they were planted on cheesecloth supported by a stainless-steel screen about 2 cm above the surface of a solution of 10^{-4} M $CaSO_4$. The corners of the cheesecloth were dipped into the solution. Another screen was placed on top of the seeds and covered with cheesecloth which also dipped into the solution. The solution was continuously aerated, and the seedlings were grown in the dark at 24°C. At 44 hr after planting, the top screen was removed, and at 72 hr the solution was renewed, at which time the roots were dipped into distilled water at 24°C. The roots were then removed and blotted on dry cheesecloth, and 1.00-g portions were placed in pyrex test tubes, 250 by 22 mm, containing 50 ml of distilled water at 24°C. Each tube was equipped with a 3-mm aerating tube held in place by nonabsorbent cotton. Just prior to the start of the experiment, the water was decanted and replaced by distilled water. The tubes were transferred to a 30°C water bath, the aerators were connected, and the solutions of salts and radioactivity were added. After 3 hr the solutions were decanted, and the roots rinsed with distilled water and prepared for measurement of radioactivity. The standardization of conditions yielded excellent reproducibility in the absorption values.

Pollen of Douglas fir was labeled by Colwell (43) with P^{32} in order to study spore distribution patterns. Three methods were compared: dipping of basal ends of male cone-bearing branches into P^{32} solution; direct soaking of pollen grains in P^{32} solution; and soaking of pollen grains with alternate application and release of suction. The latter procedure was found to be the best, and the results indicated that the distribution characteristics were unaffected by the labeling treatment.

Soil, Plant, and Fertilizer Methods. Conventional greenhouse or pot techniques are entirely satisfactory provided that care is taken to prevent the spread of contamination. In studies utilizing nutrient solutions there are usually no difficulties, since the radioisotope can be uniformly mixed for presentation to the root surfaces. Figure 4-24 shows a typical arrangement in which the roots of the peanut plant were held in 4-gal glazed crocks, whereas the fruiting zone was maintained separately in sand in an asphaltum-coated metal pan (44). A complete nutrient solution was applied to each zone, and it was possible to study the relative absorption and distribution of radiocalcium by the root and the fruit.

When soils are used in pots or lysimeters, the radioactive preparation can be thoroughly mixed, distributed throughout the top layer, and applied as a band or in any other way, depending on the information desired.   The procedure of Ulrich et al. (45) will illustrate a simple placement study with grapevines in the field.   A square ridge of soil 6 to 8 in. high was built 2 ft from the base of each vine.   For the surface application 10 gal of water was added, followed by 5 gal of the P^{32} solution; after

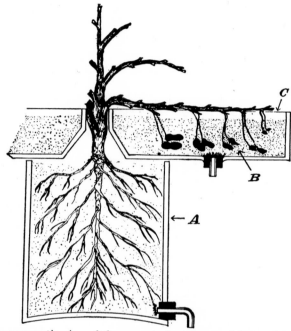

Fig. 4-24. Diagrammatic view of the peanut plant arranged for study of the independent root and fruit uptake, showing A, rooting medium, B, fruiting medium, and C, wire-mesh support to prevent the branches and foliage from touching the sand of the fruiting medium.   [*From Roger W. Bledsoe, C. L. Comar, and H. C. Harris, Absorption of Radioactive Calcium by the Peanut Fruit, Science,* **109**: 329–330 (1949).]

the solutions had penetrated the soil, another 25 gal of water was added. For the deep placement a hole $1\frac{1}{2}$ in. wide and 15 in. deep was drilled in each corner of the square.   The P^{32}, in about 600 ml of solution, was distributed in equal portions to the four holes around each vine.   Immediately thereafter 40 gal of water was added to each vine.

It is very important that field studies be undertaken with labeled fertilizers that are as similar as possible to those commercially available. The method of preparation of radioactive phosphate fertilizers has been described by Hill et al. (46).   The U.S. Department of Agriculture Bureau of Plant Industry, Soils, and Agricultural Engineering has developed facilities and methods for the production of a variety of labeled commercial phosphate fertilizers—normal phosphates, concentrated and ammoniated superphosphates, and various combinations of calcium and phosphates. The individual laboratory should attempt to obtain its labeled fertilizers from the Department of Agriculture before making its own preparations. Differential fertilizer placement machines have been developed which are adequate for the field application of radioactive fertilizers (47, 48).

It will be recalled from Chap. 1 that important studies of rooting patterns have been made possible by the delivery of radiophosphorus to

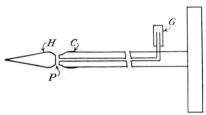

Fig. 4-25. Schematic diagram of probe for placement of P^{32} solution at specified locations in soil. Typical dimensions: length, 3 ft; outside diameter, $\frac{3}{8}$ in.; head, $1\frac{1}{4}$ in. from ports to tip. (*From N. S. Hall, W. V. Chandler, C. H. M. van Bavel, P. H. Reid, and J. H. Anderson, A Tracer Technique to Measure Growth and Activity of Plant Root Systems, N. Carolina Agr. Expt. Sta. Tech. Bull.* 101, October, 1953.)

known locations in the soil around the plant. The technique of delivery has been described by Hall et al. (49). Figure 4-25 presents a schematic diagram of the probe employed. It is important that the diameter of the collar C be slightly larger than that of the shaft, and that the head H and the shaft be of the same diameter. The shaft should have a small diameter but should be sufficiently rigid to withstand bending upon insertion into the soil. Usually $\frac{3}{8}$-in. pipe is satisfactory, but greater rigidity would be desirable in heavy soils. The rubber cap G provides a seal for the hypodermic needle and allows pressure to be applied to clear the outlet ports P.

The probe is usually inserted to the required depth and then pulled back about $\frac{1}{2}$ in. The solution containing the tracer is drawn into a hypodermic syringe with a No. 22 needle and then injected through the rubber cap G. The injection rate should be such that the liquid penetrates the surrounding soil and is not forced back up the channel made by the probe.

GENERAL REFERENCES

1. Coleman, H. S., ed.: "Laboratory Design," Reinhold Publishing Corporation, New York, 1951.
2. Manov, George G.: Radioisotope Laboratories for Animal and Agricultural Research, in "The Role of Atomic Energy in Agricultural Research," Proceedings

of the Fourth Annual Oak Ridge Summer Symposium (Sponsored by the Oak Ridge National Laboratory and Oak Ridge Institute of Nuclear Studies, Aug. 25–30, 1952), TID-5115, pp. 81–116, January, 1953.

3. Ward, Donald R.: Design of Laboratories for Safe Use of Radioisotopes, AECU-2226, November, 1952.
4. Preuss, Luther E., and John H. L. Watson: Design and Construction of a Small Radioactivity Laboratory, *Nucleonics*, **6**: 11–26 (1950).
5. Levy, Henri A.: Some Aspects of the Design of Radiochemical Laboratories, *Chem. Eng. News*, **24**: 3168–3173 (1946).
6. Levy, Henri A.: Remodeling a Laboratory for Radiochemical Instruction or Research, *Ind. Eng. Chem.*, **41**: 248–250 (1949).
7. Rice, C. N.: Laboratory for Preparation and Use of Radioactive Organic Compounds, *Ind. Eng. Chem.*, **41**: 244–248 (1949).
8. Tompkins, P. C., O. M. Bizzell, and C. D. Watson: Practical Aspects of Surface Decontamination, *Nucleonics*, **7**: 42–54 (1950).
9. Eaton, S. E., and R. J. Bowen: Decontaminable Surfaces for Millicurie-level Laboratories, *Nucleonics*, **8**: 27–37 (1951).
10. Bizzell, Oscar M.: Equipment for Radioisotope Laboratories, in "Isotopics," pp. 21–37, U.S. Atomic Energy Commission, Isotopes Division, Oak Ridge, April, 1951.
11. Farris, Edmond J., and John Q. Griffith, Jr., eds.: "The Rat in Laboratory Investigation," 2d ed., J. B. Lippincott Company, Philadelphia, 1949.
12. Farris, Edmond J., ed.: "The Care and Breeding of Laboratory Animals," John Wiley & Sons, Inc., New York, 1950.
13. Guerrant, N. B.: General Aspects of Small Animal Experimentation, in Paul Gyorgy, ed., "Vitamin Methods," vol. 2, pp. 1–40, Academic Press, Inc., New York, 1951.
14. Herrlein, Harry G.: "A Practical Guide on the Care of Small Animals for Medical Research," Rockland Farms, New City, N.Y., 1949.
15. Hansard, Sam L., and C. L. Comar: Radioisotope Procedures with Laboratory Animals, *Nucleonics*, **11**: 44–47 (1953).
16. Qualitative Specifications for Animal Laboratories for Experimental Work with Radioactive Materials (Report to the Brookhaven National Laboratory, Associated Universities, Inc., Upton, L.I., N.Y., from Arthur D. Little, Inc., Cambridge, Mass.), ALI-8 (AECU-298), Dec. 8, 1948.
17. Hansard, Sam L., C. L. Comar, and M. P. Plumlee: Radioisotope Procedures with Farm Animals, *Nucleonics*, **9**: 13–25, 38–45 (1951).
18. Kolmer, John A., and Fred Boerner: "Approved Laboratory Technic," 4th ed., Appleton-Century-Crofts, Inc., New York, 1945.

CITED REFERENCES

19. Helvey, T. C.: Improved Metabolism Cage for Small Animals (In press).
20. Bollman, Jesse L.: A Cage Which Limits the Activity of Rats, *J. Lab. Clin. Med.*, **33**: 1348 (1948).
21. Hansard, Sam L.: A Metabolism Unit Designed for Radioisotope Balance Studies with Dogs, *Science*, **117**: 301–302 (1953).
22. Gaebler, O. H.: Metabolism Masks for Dogs, *Proc. Soc. Exptl. Biol. Med.*, **31**: 500–502 (1934).
23. Kleiber, Max, and Melvin Edick: A Respiration Apparatus for C^{14} Studies with Cows, *J. Animal Sci.*, **11**: 61–71 (1952).

24. Talalay, P., and G. M. V. Takano: Apparatus for Tube-feeding Rats, *J. Lab. Clin. Med.*, **40**: 486–488 (1952).
25. Katz, Joseph, Harry A. Kornberg, and Herbert M. Parker: Absorption of Plutonium Fed Chronically to Rats. I. Fraction Deposited in Skeleton and Soft Tissues Following Oral Administration of Solutions of Very Low Mass Concentration, HW-28991, Aug. 10, 1953.
26. Bustad, Leo K.: Personal communication.
27. Karlson, Alfred G., and William H. Feldman: Method for Repeated Intravenous Injection into Guinea Pigs, *Lab. Invest.*, **2**: 451–453 (1953).
28. Rust, John H., Robert A. Monroe, and W. E. Lotz: Venoclysis by Catheterization; Some Pathologic Observations, *Cornell Vet.*, **63**: 193–198 (1953).
29. Detrick, Lawrence A., and Bonnie Rhodes: A Note on an Apparatus for Prolonged and Repeated Intravenous Infusions in Large Animals, *J. Am. Pharm. Assoc. Sci. Ed.*, **41**: 283 (1952).
30. Kainer, R. A., and W. M. Dickson: An Examination of the Valves of the External Jugular Veins of the Ox with Reference to the Selection of a Site for Venipuncture, *J. Am. Vet. Med. Assoc.*, **122**: 523–526 (1953).
31. Carle, B. N., and William H. Dewhirst: A Method for Bleeding Swine, *J. Am. Vet. Med. Assoc.*, **101**: 495–496 (1942).
32. Baurmash, L., F. A. Bryan, R. Dickinson, and W. C. Burke, Jr.: A New Exposure Chamber for Inhalation Studies, UCLA-231, Oct. 22, 1952.
33. Smith, F. A., and D. E. Gardner: A Preliminary Investigation of Blood Fluoride Levels Following Exposure to Hydrogen Fluoride at a Concentration of Approximately 29 Mg/m³, UR-77, Aug. 16, 1949.
34. LaBelle, Charles, Clarence Booth, and Robert Barrett: The Retention of Uranium Dioxide in Rabbits, AECD-2028, June 3, 1948.
35. Kassel, Robert, and Seymour Levitan: A Jugular Technique for the Repeated Bleeding of Small Animals, *Science*, **118**: 563–564 (1953).
36. Burris, R. H., P. W. Wilson, and R. E. Stutz: Incorporation of Isotopic Carbon into Compounds by Biosynthesis, *Botan. Gaz.*, **111**: 63–69 (1949).
37. Chen, S. L.: Simultaneous Movement of P^{32} and C^{14} in Opposite Directions in Phloem Tissue, *Am. J. Botany*, **38**: 203–211 (1951).
38. Dubbs, Clyde A.: Improved Apparatus for Radiobiological Syntheses, *Science*, **109**: 571–572 (1949).
39. Clendenning, K. A., and P. R. Gorham: Intracellular Distribution of Assimilated C^{14} in Briefly Exposed Aquatic Plants, *Arch. Biochem. and Biophys.*, **37**: 56–71 (1952).
40. Roach, W. A.: Plant Injection for Diagnostic and Curative Purposes, *Imp. Bur. Hort. Plantation Crops, East Malling, Kent, Tech. Commun.* 10, October, 1938.
40a. Graham, Ben F., Jr.: A Technique for Introducing Radioactive Isotopes Into Tree Stems, *Ecology*, **35**: 415 (1954).
41. Swanson, C. A., and J. B. Whitney, Jr.: Studies on the Translocation of Foliar-applied P^{32} and Other Radioisotopes in Bean Plants, *Am. J. Botany*, **40**: 816–823 (1953).
42. Epstein, Emanuel, and C. E. Hagen: A Kinetic Study of the Absorption of Alkali Cations by Barley Roots, *Plant Physiol.*, **27**: 457–474 (1952).
43. Colwell, Robert N.: The Use of Radioactive Isotopes in Determining Spore Distribution Patterns, *Am. J. Botany*, **38**: 511–523 (1951).
44. Bledsoe, Roger W., C. L. Comar, and H. C. Harris: Absorption of Radioactive Calcium by the Peanut Fruit, *Science*, **109**: 329–330 (1949).
45. Ulrich, Albert, Louis Jacobson, and Roy Overstreet: Use of Radioactive Phos-

phorus in a Study of the Availability of Phosphorus to Grape Vines under Field Conditions, *Soil Sci.*, **64**: 17–28 (1947).

46. Hill, W. L., E. J. Fox, and J. F. Mullins: Preparation of Radioactive Phosphate Fertilizers, *Ind. Eng. Chem.*, **41**: 1328–1334 (1949).

47. Cumings, Glenn A., Walter C. Hulburt, and Dale B. Eldredge: Development of a Dispenser for Applying Radioactive Phosphatic Fertilizer, *Agr. Eng.*, **31**: 275–277 (1950).

48. Anderson, James H., W. C. Hulburt, E. N. Scarborough, and R. W. Wilson: Differential Fertilizer Placement Machine, *N. Carolina Agr. Expt. Sta. Dept. Agr. Eng. Inform. Circ.* 6, October, 1951.

49. Hall, N. S., W. V. Chandler, C. H. M. van Bavel, P. H. Reid, and J. H. Anderson: A Tracer Technique to Measure Growth and Activity of Plant Root Systems, *N. Carolina Agr. Expt. Sta. Tech. Bull.* 101, October, 1953.

CHAPTER 5

GENERAL PROCEDURES FOR RADIOASSAY

PRETREATMENT OF SAMPLES—Collection; Weighing and Drying; Ashing: *Pseudo wet-ashing; Wet-ashing; Dry-ashing; Oxidation for* C^{14} *assay;* Preparation of Sample for Counting: *Direct evaporation; Filtration; Settling and centrifugation; Electroplating; Briquet formation.* SOME CONSIDERATIONS IN COUNTING PROCEDURES—Statistical Evaluation of Counting Errors; Comparison of Counter Sensitivities; Instrumental Counting Losses; Calibration Curves and Standards; Self-absorption of Beta Particles: *Thin samples; Samples of standard thickness; Empirical relationships; Infinitely thick samples.* INSTRUMENTATION AND METHODS—The Scaling Unit; Soft-beta Counting; Hard-beta Counting; Gamma Counting; Assay of Radioisotope Mixtures: *Differential decay; Differential absorption; Different radiations; Chemical separation methods;* In Vivo Measurements. EXPRESSION OF DATA.

The methods suitable for a specific analysis will be dependent upon the element involved, the nature of the sample, and the degree of accuracy and precision required. The present discussion will be concerned with some of the basic techniques that serve as the keystone for the radioassay of biological material, and the application to individual radioisotopes will be illustrated in Chap. 6.

Whenever it is necessary to measure only radioactivity, the problem is often simplified and becomes a matter of presenting a uniform sample to the radiation-detecting device. However, in many experiments it is essential to have chemical values in addition to radioassays so that turn-over rates can be calculated. In any event, recourse should be made to the extensive literature on chemical analysis, as indicated in general references (1 to 5). The methods to be used should be planned so as to give both chemical and radioactivity values with the minimum number of steps. Usually the standard chemical procedures can be employed, and somewhere in the operation an aliquot taken for radioassay. In some cases it may be necessary to use a different sample or aliquot for the chemical and radioactivity determinations because of the necessity of adding carrier to improve the recovery of the radioisotope.

It may be obvious, but there is one good way of testing an over-all method: the addition of a known amount of radioactivity to a typical biological sample and the determination of recovery after processing.

PRETREATMENT OF SAMPLES

Collection. The proper collection of samples is just as important as the reliability of subsequent analysis. The sample should be truly typical of the material that it represents. There may be many biological factors that can be taken into account only by the investigator. For instance, special consideration may be given to the sampling of pasture to simulate the grazing animal, or if an animal is being fed hay, it may selectively reject the stemmy portions, which must then be analyzed separately to give a true measure of the nutrient intake. Care must be taken to mix feces well before sampling, because successive increments may differ widely in activity, especially at short times after administration of the radioisotope. Sampling of bone presents a particularly difficult problem which will be discussed in Chap. 7. Conventionally, large samples of dried material are often reduced by grinding to allow selection of representative subsamples. This poses considerable difficulties with radioactive material on account of the dust produced, and grinding is not usually recommended unless precautions are taken against this hazard. Analysis of numerous small samples may overcome this problem, especially where the analytical procedure is simple. With plants, excessive separation of leaf, stem, and seed should be prevented; otherwise it becomes difficult to subsample the material.

In radioisotope studies, cross-contamination must be particularly guarded against on account of the extremely high dilutions that are often measured. For example, care must be taken to avoid adhering soil particles on plant material taken from radioactive soil. In animal studies, precautions must be observed to ensure that the tissue samples do not become contaminated by the original dose or active excreta. Any radioactivity found at the site of administration may well have arrived there mechanically rather than metabolically; after intraperitoneal injection, activity found in the liver or other abdominal organs may also have been deposited there mechanically. If the radioisotope has been given orally and the animal sacrificed shortly thereafter, it is essential that the tissue samples not be allowed to come into contact with intestinal contents. As a further illustration, in tissue distribution studies with elements like calcium or strontium which selectively deposit in bone, soft-tissue samples that become contaminated with bone particles may give erroneous measurements.

Weighing and Drying. When fresh weights are necessary for concentration calculations on this basis, the samples should be weighed before any appreciable moisture loss has occurred. If they cannot be weighed immediately, they should be kept in closed containers to minimize weight loss. With some small samples such as adrenals, thyroids, or pituitaries of laboratory animals, it becomes almost impossible to get accurate fresh weights, and it is usually better to express the results on a dry-weight basis. Depending on the experiment, samples should be dried as soon as possible after collection to minimize chemical and biological changes such as dry-weight losses due to respiration. Material should be dried in a well-ventilated oven at 60 to 70°C. Good ventilation tends to reduce decomposition of organic constituents, and in special cases it may be necessary to dry under vacuum. If dry weights are required, the samples should be finished at 100 to 110°C. If the dried material is hygroscopic, weighing bottles may be needed for the drying and weighing.

Ashing. Depending upon the characteristics and amount of radioactivity present, fluid samples such as blood, plasma, urine, bile, or milk may be assayed directly by liquid counting. Also, as discussed later, it is sometimes feasible to count solid samples directly. However, it is often necessary to reduce solid samples to a homogeneous-solution phase for liquid counting, and sometimes large samples of milk, blood, etc., must be ashed to permit concentration. Where simultaneous chemical analyses or chemical separations are required, it is frequently necessary to oxidize completely the organic matter of the sample.

Pseudo Wet-ashing. This method is convenient when the only requirement is the production of a homogeneous solution. Small samples of plant or animal tissue may be placed in a graduated test tube, concentrated nitric acid added to dissolve the tissue, and the solution diluted to volume for direct liquid counting. For larger samples, a typical procedure is as follows (13): A representative sample, up to 50 g, is cut into small pieces and placed in a 400-ml beaker, to which about 40 ml concentrated nitric acid is added. The tissue is allowed to soak 10 min, after which gentle heat is applied. It there is not too much fat or particulate material at this stage, the acid solution can be made to volume for direct solution measurement. If there is appreciable fatty material present, it is better to make a solvent extraction. In this case the original acid digest is evaporated to about 15 ml on a hot plate and then transferred to a steam bath for continued evaporation to remove the acid. The residue is washed into a separatory funnel with small amounts of warm water. The beaker is rinsed with two 10-ml portions of isoamyl alcohol which are in turn transferred to the separatory funnel. The separatory funnel is shaken gently, and the two solutions are separated and made to volume for measurement with a Geiger counter. The activities as measured in each solution are added to give the total for the sample. Isoamyl alcohol is a suitable general solvent chiefly because of its high boiling point.

Certain tissues may require slight modifications of this procedure, and the following suggestions are offered: When it is necessary to pseudo-ash more than 35 g of whole blood, it has been found advantageous to slow down the initial reaction by using increased amounts of acid and applying heat very cautiously with frequent stirring. In the case of teeth, bone, or cartilage samples, care must be taken not to reduce the acid solution to the point where the salts start to precipitate; it is very difficult to get the precipitated salts back into solution. In handling samples such as white bone marrow, lymph glands, and adipose tissue, which contain large amounts of fat, there is a tendency for bumping and spattering, so that it is advisable to heat them gently at all times, preferably on a water bath. With this type of sample, a solvent mixture of 10 parts ethyl alcohol, 25 parts diethyl ether, and 25 parts petroleum ether may be more efficient than isoamyl alcohol.

Some feces samples, depending on the nature of the diet, may require more than the usual amount of nitric acid for complete digestion. It has been observed that, if these samples are evaporated to dryness, it is very difficult to get the residue into solution again. In some experiments, collections are made on filter paper, and in such cases wet-ashing may be carried out as follows: The filter paper is first dampened with water, and 4 to 5 ml concentrated sulfuric acid is added. About 10 ml nitric acid is then added, and the beaker is heated gently until the violent reaction has subsided, then heated further until the contents are charred. At that stage 25 to 30 ml nitric acid is added, and the digestion continued as previously described.

Bahner et al. (14) have suggested a modification of this procedure which is based on the use of acetone or dioxane to bring both the fat and the water into a single phase. The tissue sample is heated with a minimum amount of concentrated nitric acid until all particulate matter is dissolved and most of the excess acid boiled away. The solution is cooled and diluted with acetone or dioxane and a little water to form a clear solution. The optimum mixture contains 60 to 80 per cent dioxane or acetone depending on the relative amounts of fat and inorganic salts. Howarth (15) was able to obtain satisfactory tissue suspensions for radioassay by boiling under reflux with a solution of lithium hydroxide containing 20 per cent alcohol. Tabern (16) has proposed the disintegration of tissue in a Waring Blendor or Potter Elvejhem homogenizer followed by treatment with formamide to give a concentration of at least 40 per cent; this produced a homogeneous colloidal solution suitable for liquid counting.

Wet-ashing. Conventional wet-ashing procedures have been adequately described in the literature (4, 5, 17 to 21). The Kjeldahl procedure, using concentrated H_2SO_4 as the oxidizing agent and various catalysts, is widely employed. Various combinations of nitric, sulfuric, hydrochloric, and perchloric acids and hydrogen peroxide have been successfully used. A typical procedure for plant samples has been described by Piper (4): One to five grams of the finely ground sample is transferred to a 300-ml flat-bottomed Kjeldahl flask.   Four milliliters perchloric acid (sp. gr. 1.54) is added, also about 7 ml nitric acid for each gram of sample, followed by 2 to 5 ml of sulfuric acid.   The solution is swirled and heated gently for 3 to 5 min or until the first appearance of dense brown fumes. The flask is removed from the heat for about 5 min, and thereafter the digestion is continued slowly until the appearance of dense white fumes of sulfuric acid.   The digestion is continued at low heat for another 5 to 10 min and then at full heat for a further 1 to 2 min.   If the liquid is not colorless, 1 to 2 ml nitric acid is added, and the solution again digested to fuming.   *The individual should be aware of the explosive potentialities of perchloric acid before using it.*

Lindner and Harley (22) suggested a simple method for wet digestion of small amounts of plant material which has also been found satisfactory for animal tissues.   About 100 mg of dry material is placed in a 50-ml Erlenmeyer flask or beaker, 2 ml concentrated H_2SO_4 added, and the solution heated gently until the sample is partially dissolved.   If nitrates are present, the digestion is continued for about a minute after the appearance of dense fumes.   After cooling, 0.5 ml of 30 per cent H_2O_2 is added, and the solution heated gently until dense fumes are given off.   After cooling, another few drops of H_2O_2 is added, and the solution heated as before.   If the solution does not become clear and colorless after the continued heating, the addition of H_2O_2 is repeated.   With liver samples, for example, 7 to 10 additions of H_2O_2 were found necessary.

Dry-ashing.   When the conventional method of dry-ashing in the muffle furnace is used, care must be taken to avoid losses due to volatilization, incorporation of the radioisotope into solid carbon particles, or adsorption onto the walls of the crucible.   Platinum, fused-silica, and porcelain crucibles are widely employed, the last being considerably cheaper than the others.   The porcelain crucibles can be economically discarded when the glaze has been lost or the residual activity becomes high.   Platinum should be used if hydrofluoric acid is to be employed for dissolution of the ash, but porcelain or silica must be employed if aqua regia is required.   Muffle furnaces with automatic temperature controls are highly recommended.   Also it is preferable if the heating elements are not exposed.

A general procedure is as follows: The dried tissue is weighed into a tared crucible, which is then placed in a cold muffle furnace.   Samples such as bone or ground grain do not need to be dried before ignition.   The furnace temperature is raised slowly to about 250°C and held there for several hours, after which the temperature is raised to 500 to 600°C for completion of the ashing, which may take several hours more.   If the temperature is raised too rapidly, volatile gases may be produced which will carry material out of the crucible with resultant cross-contamination.

When seeds or other material low in basic content is ashed, the sample should be mixed with calcium or magnesium acetate or nitrate prior to ashing. These salts give increased oxidation activity, minimize the fusion of ash to crucible, and increase the amount of ash for easier handling. Samples like blood and liver often tend to "boil" over, and these must be watched carefully, especially in the preliminary heating from 150 to 300°C. It is helpful if small samples are used relative to the crucible size. If the ash does not appear white, it can be treated with a few drops of distilled water, moistened with nitric or perchloric acid, heated to drive off the acid, and re-ashed in the muffle furnace; this also permits the use of a lower maximum temperature. The crucibles are usually allowed to cool in the furnace and then transferred to desiccators to reach room temperature prior to weighing. Care must be taken to avoid blowing of the friable ash, especially in the removal of the desiccator cover, if the pressure within has not been equalized. The ash may then be dissolved in HCl solution for further operations. With plant material there is always an acid-insoluble siliceous residue which may retain many of the elements like manganese, copper, or zinc (4). It may be necessary to recover such elements by alkaline fusion or hydrofluoric acid treatment.

Advantages of wet- over dry-ashing are that more samples can be handled in a shorter time with less equipment required. There are also fewer chances for loss due to volatilization, fusion with crucibles, adsorption onto silica residues, blowing of ash, etc. Dry-ashing requires patience and experience. With some radioisotopes that show losses in transfer, it is convenient to dry-ash small samples directly in porcelain milk-ashing dishes, after which the ash can be spread with a little acid, dried, and counted directly.

Oxidation for C^{14} Assay. Very frequently biological samples cannot be assayed directly for C^{14} on account of self-absorption (see page 177) or the physical nature of the sample. It then becomes necessary to oxidize the sample for production of CO_2, which may be measured as a gas or absorbed in alkali for conversion to barium carbonate for solid counting. Various oxidation methods have been employed such as Liebig combustion, sodium peroxide fusion, persulfate wet oxidation, or Van Slyke–Folch wet oxidation. The text of Calvin (6) and the original papers of Van Slyke and associates (23 to 25) may be consulted for details. Fresh tissues can be oxidized by any of the methods, and dry tissues can be used with any except the persulfate procedure.

The Van Slyke–Folch method appears to be most generally applicable and convenient. The oxidation reagent suitable for use in the procedure to be described may be prepared as follows (6, 24): In a 1-liter Erlenmeyer flask equipped with a ground-glass stopper are placed 25 g chro-

mium trioxide, 167 ml phosphoric acid (density 1.7), and 333 ml fuming
sulfuric acid containing 20 per cent free sulfur trioxide.   The mixture is
heated and swirled occasionally, and heating is discontinued when the
temperature reaches 150°C.   A beaker is inverted over the mouth of the
flask during cooling.   Care is taken to keep dust out of the solution during
subsequent storage and use.   A modification of the combustion procedure
as described by Claycomb, Hutchens, and Van Bruggen (26) is presented
below.

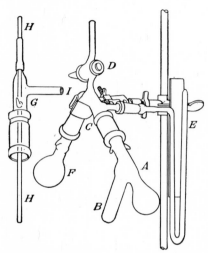

The apparatus is shown and described in Fig. 5-1.   It is essential
that all components of the oxidation
apparatus be initially cleaned in a
hot bath of Van Slyke–Folch oxidation mixture.   After initial assembly
and use, routine cleaning of flask A
with this reagent is strongly recommended.   Such treatment destroys
all organic contaminants including
trace amounts of the silicone lubricant used, thus assuring low blank
values.   After cleaning, the equipment is thoroughly rinsed and
oven-dried.

Delivery tube C is solidly clamped
to a movable ring stand, the mercury
manometer being attached and
fastened to the same stand.   A
minimal amount of silicone lubricant
is used on stopcock D and all other
glass-to-glass connections.

FIG. 5-1. Combustion assembly for C^{14}
assay. [*From   Cecil   K.   Claycomb,
Tyra T. Hutchens, and John T. Van
Bruggen, Techniques in the Use of C^{14}
as a Tracer.   I. Apparatus and Technique for Wet Combustion of Non-volatile
Samples, Nucleonics,* **7**: 38–41 (1950).]

The sample to be combusted, containing 5 to 10 mg carbon, is placed
in the bulb of A.   Solutions may be pipetted into the flask, or solids may
be introduced in a porcelain boat of suitable dimensions.   Solutions in A
are taken to dryness by attaching the flask to the evaporation sleeve G
and immersing flask A in a hot water bath, with the empty oxidant tube
B in an upright position.   Dry CO_2-free air is drawn in through tube H
by applying a minimal vacuum via the side tube I.   To minimize bumping and splattering, drying is accomplished largely by the air stream from
H rather than by strong vacuum distillation.   When the sample appears
dry, flask A is removed from G, and with side arm B directed downward,
5 ml of the Van Slyke–Folch reagent is carefully added to B with a bent-
tip pipette.   The flask is attached to tube C, care being taken not to spill
any of the oxidant onto the sample to be combusted.   The absorption

flask F, containing a measured amount of standard CO_2-free NaOH (usually 2 mmoles), is also connected to C, the system evacuated through D to about 20 mm, and stopcock D closed. Since maintaining adequate reduced pressure is essential, the apparatus is allowed to stand for a few minutes, and the manometer observed for pressure changes.

Flask A is rotated 180°, bringing the side arm B upright and spilling the oxidant onto the sample. The bulb of flask A is now immersed in the 160°C bath, preferably by manipulating the entire ring stand to which the assembly is attached. An ice-water bath is then placed so as to cool absorption flask F. After 10 min flask A is removed from the hot bath, the apparatus is allowed to stand an additional 5 min, and F remains in the ice bath. If no leakage has occurred and CO_2 absorption is adequate, the manometer reading returns to 20 to 30 mm. CO_2-free air or purified nitrogen is admitted through stopcock D to equalize the pressure.

Absorption flask F is removed, and its contents titrated with 0.2 N HCl to a faint but definite phenolphthalein pink. From the titration figures obtained, the amount of CO_2 liberated by combustion is determined, one equivalent of base being used per mole of CO_2. Care is taken to avoid excess acid, which would cause CO_2 loss. After the titration is complete, 1.5 to 2.0 mmoles of excess base is added to ensure CO_2 retention and to furnish base for the subsequent use of $BaCl_2$-NH_4Cl precipitating reagent.

The entire alkaline carbonate solution may now be used for $BaCO_3$ plating, but usually aliquots of the homogeneous solution are taken, since absorption of CO_2 in NaOH instead of $Ba(OH)_2$ permits the use of aliquots for plate preparation.

Typical procedures for precipitation of the $BaCO_3$ from the samples of Na_2CO_3 contained in the NaOH solutions are as follows (27): The entire sample or aliquots are transferred to a heavy-walled 40-ml centrifuge tube. If the total carbonate present, as determined by titration, is not adequate to give a satisfactory $BaCO_3$ plate (approximately 16 mg $BaCO_3$ is required), aliquots of a standard Na_2CO_3 (0.5 to 0.75 N) may be added. Phenolphthalein indicator is added, and the tube placed in a 45 to 55°C water bath. About 5 ml of 0.5 N $BaCl_2$ in 0.4 N NH_4Cl is added forcefully to the sample by a syringe fitted with a fine needle. Additional NaOH must be added quickly if the reagent decolorizes the solution. The tubes should be kept covered as much as possible to minimize CO_2 contamination. The precipitated sample is allowed to remain at 45°C for at least 10 min. The sides of the tube are washed down with a few milliliters of 3:1 alcohol-ether, and the solution centrifuged at about 2500 rpm. The supernatant liquid is removed by aspiration, the precipitate suspended in 15 ml of distilled water, and the suspension centrifuged again. The wash water is removed by aspiration, and the $BaCO_3$ is suspended in 10 to 15 ml of the alcohol-ether and transferred to the plastic-tube-and-cup assembly, as illustrated in Fig. 5-5 and described on page 170. After centrifugation the supernatant is siphoned off carefully, the cup is removed, and the precipitate is carefully dried for weighing and counting.

When manometric measurement of evolved CO_2 is desired, the procedure of Van Slyke, Steele, and Plazin (25) may be followed. Reference (25) may also be consulted for details of combustion and handling of

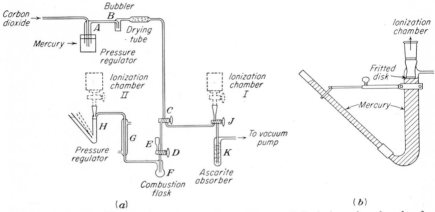

(a) (b)

FIG. 5-2. (a) Assembly for wet combustion and collection of $C^{14}O_2$ in an ion chamber for measurement. [*From O. Kenton Neville, Carbon 14 Sample Preparation and Counting Techniques (Gas Counting), in "The Role of Atomic Energy in Agricultural Research," Proceedings of the Fourth Annual Oak Ridge Summer Symposium (Sponsored by the Oak Ridge National Laboratory and Oak Ridge Institute of Nuclear Studies, Aug. 25–30, 1952), TID-5115, pp. 126–150, January, 1953.*] (b) Details of pressure regulator employed in combustion assembly. (*Courtesy of O. K. Neville and W. B. Leslie.*)

samples to be measured in the Bernstein and Ballentine (44) counter, which is a gas-phase proportional counter now commercially available.

Figure 5-2a, taken from Neville (28), shows a schematic diagram of a wet-combustion apparatus which may be used for larger samples than above and which illustrates the collection of CO_2 in an ion chamber. The ion chamber, placed in position I, can be evacuated and flushed with nonradioactive carbon dioxide which is passed from a cylinder through the bubbler B and drying tube. At the beginning of an assay the ion chamber is evacuated in position I and moved to position II. The organic sample of 2 to 20 mg (or larger if relatively more solution is used) is weighed into the combustion flask F together with 200 mg potassium iodate. A 15- to 20-ml portion of combustion fluid is released into the flask, and the chamber stopcock is opened. The combustion fluid is heated to boiling and allowed to stand for about 5 min. At the end of this time the stopcock connecting the nonradioactive carbon dioxide supply with the combustion flask is opened, and the gas is allowed to sweep through the solution for several minutes. The chamber is moved to position I, where carbon dioxide is admitted rapidly to bring the gas to atmospheric pressure. The use of the pressure regulator H between the combustion flask and the ion chamber obviates liquid-nitrogen traps and permits the oxidation to be carried out at atmospheric pressure. At the beginning of the determination, when the evacuated chamber is opened to the regulator, the mercury seal prevents the entrance of gas through the disk. When carbon dioxide is evolved with consequent increased pressure on the right arm of the mercury, the mercury column is depressed, and gas is allowed to flow through the sintered disk until the pressure on the right side is again equal to atmospheric pressure. Since the rate of gas evolution is relatively low, all that is observed is a slight flutter of the mercury surface. Figure 5-2b shows the details of the pressure regulator.

With this very simple apparatus, which can be mounted on one ring stand, samples may be combusted in 10 to 15 min with very good precision. Whenever materials containing halogen or nitrogen are burned, a U tube containing 5 to 10 g hydrated stannous chloride is inserted between the water condenser and the pressure regulator. Small amounts of these gases interfere with the operation of the regulator but do not affect the ion-chamber performance.

Preparation of Sample for Counting. The form of the sample required will be determined primarily by the energy of radiation emitted, and this matter will be discussed in detail in later sections. In general, samples must be geometrically and physically uniform, these requirements being more rigorous for the lower-energy beta emitters. If liquid counting is feasible, the ash solutions or aliquots thereof may be used directly. A combination of wet-ashing and liquid counting makes a very convenient and simple procedure.

Direct Evaporation. A radioisotope in solution may be converted to a solid sample by direct evaporation. However, most biological samples will require a preliminary separation of unwanted soluble matter because of crystallization and creeping, which may result in nonuniform deposits. Nevertheless direct evaporation is widely used, especially for the preparation of calibration standards, since these solutions usually have very little soluble material. The texts of Cook and Duncan (8) and Calvin et al. (6) have described some of the various procedures for the preparation of samples in this manner.

The sample is mounted on the same material of the same geometric shape as will be used for all later samples that are to be compared with it. The mount may be a flat metal or plastic disk, a planchet, a glass surface, etc. Lens paper may be used as an auxiliary to promote even spreading, but this introduces additional uncertainties. Burch (29) has described a method in which about 0.3 ml of biologic fluid is spread upon a filter-paper disk which is dried and then cemented to a metal disk.

Usually a small volume of the liquid is added to the mount and evaporated on a hot plate or water bath or by infrared lamp. Care must be taken to avoid mechanical loss by spluttering. However, the main problem is to get coverage of some uniform area. The source area may be defined by a mark made with a wax pencil or by the use of lacquer. There may be considerable creeping, especially with volatile liquids; this may be avoided by the addition of a less volatile solvent before the final addition to the mount. When cups are used, there is a tendency for excessive deposition around the edges; this may be minimized by having the cup supported on the hot plate by a hollow metal cylinder which selectively heats the edges and causes the solids to be drawn to the center of the mount. Devices are commercially available which provide a slowly revolving turntable on which the mount is placed. The solution is added slowly in a spiral line, and a continuous source of heat causes rapid evaporation of solvent.

The investigator can determine for himself whether standards prepared by direct evaporation give sufficiently reproducible and comparable results for the evaluation of biological samples prepared by another method. For example, we have found that aliquots of Ca^{45} solutions directly evaporated in metal cups gave essentially the same counts with about the same error as when the activity was precipitated as calcium oxalate, counted, and corrected for self-absorption. Thus it was possible to save time, since it was not necessary to carry standards routinely through the same precipitation procedure as used for the samples.

McKay and Zilversmit (30) have described a procedure for P^{32}, a hard-beta emitter, which has considerable merit. Rectangular strips of Reynolds household aluminum foil $2\frac{1}{2}$ by $1\frac{3}{4}$ in. are made into cups by folding the edges manually or by using the sample press. This cup is placed on a thermostatically controlled hot plate. Radioactive samples in aqueous solutions are added to the aluminum cup in toto or dropwise. When the radioactivity is present in alcohol or ether, the sample is always added dropwise. In order to prevent creeping of the nonaqueous solvents, a piece of filter paper $1\frac{3}{4}$ by $1\frac{1}{2}$ in. is placed in the cup before addition of the radioactive solvent. When the radioactivity is present in dilute sodium hydroxide or hydrochloric acid, lead foil is used instead of aluminum foil. When the sample is thoroughly dry, the edges are unfolded, and the sample is covered with 3-in.-wide scotch tape. After the corners are cut, the tape is folded over the edges to prevent escape of the radioactive material. The sample is now ready for counting. When counting is done manually, it is put around a cylindrical thyrode Geiger tube and held in place with a wire test-tube clamp. An automatic sample changer is also described to handle this form of sample.

In these operations the accuracy of pipetting is a major factor. Following is a procedure found satisfactory for the use of micropipettes to handle volumes from 0.01 to 0.5 ml: A simple pipette filler is assembled from a 1-ml syringe fitted with a rubber stopper which is bored to accommodate the pipette (Fig. 5-3). The pipette is filled with the test solution and brought to the mark, the tip wiped with cleaning tissue, and the solution delivered onto the mount. The pipette is filled with water, which is added to the mount. This procedure is repeated twice. The pipette is rinsed once or twice each with water, alcohol, and acetone, is then dried with an air current, and is ready for the next sample. Macropipettes and larger volumes of solution should be used for regular dilutions, and the ordinary analytical use of the pipette is prescribed. Pipetting in a radio-chemical laboratory is *never* done by mouth, and although commercial pipetters are available, a simple device described by Hood (31) has been most satisfactory for routine use (Fig. 5-3). The pipetter consists of a 10- to 30-ml

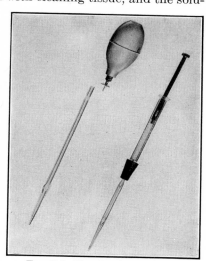

Fig. 5-3. Simple pipette fillers.

rubber bulb into which is inserted the shank of a No. 18-23 hypodermic needle that has been broken off to $\frac{3}{16}$-in. length. A rubber disk is pierced by the needle and in use serves to make a seal on the pipette. The needle is inserted into the bore of the pipette, and the solution drawn up by suction using the bulb. The pipetter is removed, and the meniscus level thereafter controlled by finger in the usual way.

Filtration. It is often necessary to prepare solid counting samples from suspensions, for instance, $BaCO_3$ for assay of C^{14} or CaC_2O_4 for assay of Ca^{45}. Comar et al. (32) have reviewed the various methods that have been suggested for this purpose. Many filtration devices have been developed for the purpose of quantitative collection of precipitates for radioassay. Techniques involving the use of filter paper suffer from the general disadvantages of variable texture, difficulty in reproducing constant weights, tendency of the paper and precipitate to buckle, and necessity for careful handling of the final sample to avoid damaging the precipitate. Although some of the methods eliminate certain of these disadvantages, there has been a tendency toward use of the sintered-glass Gooch crucible.   In this case, however, there is the need for thorough decontamination of the crucible before reuse, and it is not practical to hold a large number of samples until the results have been studied.

A typical commercially available filter assembly is shown in Fig. 5-4. The filter paper is placed over the top of the lower section, and when pressed together the barrel of the assembly makes a tight fit, holding the

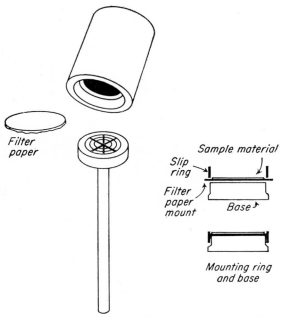

Fig. 5-4. Filter assembly for collection of precipitates on filter paper.

filter paper in place.   After filtration the paper with precipitate is transferred to a mounting block.

Settling and Centrifugation.   Many of the difficulties encountered in the use of filtration technique have been eliminated by the development of settling and centrifugation methods.   Greenberg (33), working with C^{14}, has found it very satisfactory to evaporate acetone suspensions of protein onto aluminum disks.   He used a simple device consisting of an inverted mayonnaise jar from which the bottom had been removed, with the aluminum disk held in place by the screw cap of the jar.

A simple device that has been used in this laboratory for the large-scale routine collection of calcium oxalate precipitates is illustrated in Fig. 5-5. The apparatus consists of a tapered-end plastic pipe with a nickel-steel, or preferably stainless-steel, cup forming the bottom.   The cups and tubing are commercially available, but the tubing has to be machined to fit. The 4-in. plastic tubes are cut to a taper on each end so that a tight inside fit is made when the tube is pressed into the cup. Worn tubes may be reversed and the other end used. This apparatus is accommodated by the regular 50-ml centrifuge-tube carriers. The plastic tube is sufficiently resilient so that a reasonably tight fit is obtained. To ensure that no leakage occurs, water is placed between the plastic tube and the carrier; this serves to equalize the centrifugal pressure. The cups and precipitate can readily be brought to constant weight by drying. Since the cups are inexpensive and used only once, the samples can be kept for reference purposes as long as necessary. The method has given good reproducibility.

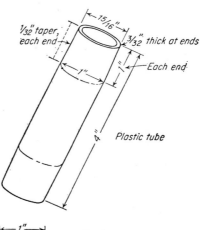

Electroplating. Electroplating is an excellent method for the preparation of uniform thin films of many of the metals, and a general discussion has been presented by Dunn (9). The chemical literature should be consulted for the specific conditions required for each element. Many types of electrolysis cells have been described. However, a commercial unit is available for general isotope work. This apparatus consists of a leak-proof cell formed by a glass cylinder, a rubber gasket, and a flat metal disk which serves as the cathode and bottom of the vessel. The unit is easily assem-

Fig. 5-5. Plastic-tube-and-cup apparatus for collection of precipitates by centrifugation.

bled or disassembled. Platinum wire is usually employed as the anode, and copper disks are often satisfactory for the cathodic deposition of the film. The copper surface must be thoroughly cleaned for satisfactory film formation; this can be done by degreasing in organic solvents, followed by final cleaning in cold dilute HCl or HNO_3. The power supply is conveniently furnished from ordinary 6-volt storage batteries, although commercial power supplies are available for this purpose and are convenient for the investigation of various voltage-current relationships.

In general, the biological material must be ashed prior to the electroplating procedure. The ash solution will usually contain large amounts of sodium, potassium, and phosphate, etc., compared with the element to be determined. If less than 10 mg of ash is used, it may not be necessary to employ a separation procedure before electroplating. Usually 1 to

10 mg of the stable element is added to serve as a carrier. This can be added to any stage.   However, if it is added to the original sample and the final plate is weighed, it becomes possible to estimate the recovery of the over-all procedure. Specific methods will be given in Chap. 6 for some of the radioisotopes. The primary disadvantage of electroplating as compared with some of the direct methods is the time and labor required.

Briquet Formation. Dry powders may be pressed into shallow dishes with a spatula or may be formed into briquets with a laboratory press and piston-cylinder apparatus. The latter method has been used successfully for the convenient measurement of P^{32} in plant material (34). These procedures, however, would not be satisfactory where thin samples are required, as in the assay of soft-beta emitters.

SOME CONSIDERATIONS IN COUNTING PROCEDURES

The term *count* is used to designate the response of a measuring device to an ionizing event. Thus the counting rate, that is to say, the counts measured in a given time by the Geiger counter, is directly proportional to the amount of radioisotope in the sample. The counting rate is here expressed as counts per minute (counts/min; cpm). The Geiger-Müller counter tube, which contains the sensitive volume responding to the radiation, is variously referred to by the following terms: *Geiger counter tube, Geiger counter, Geiger tube, counter tube,* or *counter.* The last two terms may also be used for other types of detectors, such as the proportional counter and the scintillation counter. Discussion of auxiliary electronic equipment and particularly of different types of counter tubes is deferred to page 183, since it seems most logical to describe the detection devices in terms of the measurement for which they are best suited.

Statistical Evaluation of Counting Errors.   There will always be some degree of error in the observed counting rate on account of the statistical fluctuations inherent in a random process such as radioactive decay. References (6, 8, 9, 11, 35) may be consulted for a detailed discussion of counting statistics. The investigator interested in extremely low-level counting will want to study this matter at some length. The primary interest here is to establish the order of magnitude of the errors in terms of the counting rates usually encountered. It has been shown that the accuracy, assuming no abnormalities in the instrument, depends only upon the total number of counts taken and that for practical purposes *the standard deviation will equal the square root of the number of counts.* Thus, in samples that have total counts of 100, 1000, and 10,000, the standard deviations are 10, 32, and 100 counts, respectively. It requires about 1000 total counts to yield a standard deviation of about 3 per cent.

To express the deviation in terms of counting rate, the square root of the total counts is divided by time. Thus if 1000 counts were measured in 5 min, the deviation would be $\sqrt{1000}/5 = 6$ counts/min, and the counting rate would be expressed as 200 ± 6 counts/min. This means that there is a 68.3 per cent probability that the counting-rate error is less than 6 counts/min in this sample. Other error terms may be used. However, in this text the standard deviation will be employed unless otherwise noted.

The counting rate when there is no radioactive source present is called the *background* and is due to cosmic radiation and radioactivity in the air and surrounding materials. The counting rate of a sample is equal to the observed rate minus the background rate. When the sample count is large compared with the background, the standard deviation can be estimated with little inaccuracy by taking the square root of the total counts as indicated. However, when the background and sample counts are not greatly different, it becomes necessary to take into account the deviation in the background as well as in the sample count. This can be done by use of the following formula:

$$\text{Standard deviation of sample counting rate} = \left[\frac{C_s}{T_s^2} + \frac{C_b}{T_b^2}\right]^{\frac{1}{2}} \quad (5\text{-}1)$$

where C_s = total counts for sample in time T_s

C_b = total counts for background in time T_b

A typical illustration is presented in Table 5-1. In this case it will be noted that the standard deviation as calculated from the sample plus background was $3.5/60 \times 100 = 5.8$ per cent, whereas the actual standard deviation was $4/40 \times 100 = 10$ per cent. With weak samples the background contribution to the counting error becomes of increasing importance. In practice this may be overcome somewhat by the reduction of background by shielding or other methods, and by utilizing spare time to give long background counting periods. Of course, the weak samples will also have to be counted for long periods of time.

TABLE 5-1. CALCULATION OF STANDARD DEVIATION FOR SAMPLE CONTAINING LOW ACTIVITY

	Total counts	Time, min	Standard deviation		Counting rate and standard deviation, cpm + SD
			Counts	Cpm	
Sample plus background....	300	5	± 17.3	± 3.5	60 ± 3.5
Background...............	100	5	± 10	± 2	20 ± 2
Sample, using Eq. (5-1).....	...	..	$\left[\frac{300}{5^2} + \frac{100}{5^2}\right]^{\frac{1}{2}} = 4$		40 ± 4

The usefulness of rigorous statistical treatment of counting procedures in most biological studies is open to question because (a) the errors in other parts of the study usually exceed those of counting, (b) there is generally time to count the samples to give reasonable total counts, and (c) very often the experiment can be performed so as to have relatively high counting rates in the samples.   Where the samples have low counts, less than background, one must always bear in mind the possibility of contamination before assigning significance to the results, even though this may be warranted by the counting statistics.

Comparison of Counter Sensitivities.   In comparing counter tubes, attention may be given to such operating characteristics as the change of counting rate vs. voltage, the resolution time, and the number of spurious pulses.   However, most commercial counters are satisfactory in this regard, and perhaps a more important factor is the sensitivity of the tube for the radiation to be measured.   Thomas (36) has presented equations for the calculation of counter sensitivities and has discussed some of the factors that must be taken into account for a rigorous comparison, such as the counting rates involved and the optimum time allocation to sample and background measurement.   The important point is that the over-all sensitivity of the counter is largely dependent upon its sensitivity to the radiation of the source as compared with the background.   As already indicated, with weak samples the time required for reduction of background error may be considerable.

In this text comparisons will be simply expressed in terms of the microcuries of a given radioisotope required to give a count equal to the background, which we shall designate as the *minimal detectable activity*.   For example, if the MDA of a given counter with a background of 20 counts/min is listed as 1.8×10^{-4} μc for Co^{60}, this means that 1.8×10^{-4} μc Co^{60} would give a net count of 20 counts/min when measured.   The microcurie values are usually derived from the supplier of the isotope, and although they may be slightly in error, the comparisons between the instruments listed in Chap. 6 will still be valid, because the same shipment of isotope was used to make the comparison, and any errors would cancel.   Expression of sensitivities in this manner, as is done for the individual isotopes in Chap. 6, gives a fairly good picture of the abilities of different counters and also allows estimation of the amount of activity that will be required in the samples.   It should be noted that with this method of expression the higher the MDA value, the less sensitive the instrument.

The term *geometry* is often used in connection with counting-tube arrangements and refers to the percentage of rays leaving a sample which reach the sensitive volume of the counter.   Thus a gas sample contained within a counter would have 100 per cent geometry, whereas a solid sample in the usual internal counter might approximate 50 per cent geometry

Standard mounts, which are used for end-window counters, have shelves with definite geometrical relationships between them, usually so arranged that each shelf has one-half the geometry of that above it. The geometry, which primarily depends on the distance between source and counter and the size of the source, is an important factor in the over-all sensitivity.

Instrumental Counting Losses. When two particles arrive at a Geiger counter tube within a time interval less than the resolving time of the tube, they will be counted only as one, giving low results. This is called the *coincidence loss* and increases as the counting rate increases. There may also be losses in the electronic circuits and the mechanical register, but these are not usually important if a high enough scaling factor is employed.

The over-all instrumental counting losses can be estimated in a practical manner by preparing a series of sources of known radioisotope content relative to each other. These samples should be measured under identical conditions and should not differ between themselves in self-absorption due to varying mass. The "true" value at each counting rate can be calculated from the observed value at the low counting rate and the known dilution. This is illustrated in Table 5-2 for a typical

TABLE 5-2. DETERMINATION OF COUNTING LOSS IN COMMERCIAL SCALER
AND END-WINDOW COUNTER

Aliquot of P^{32} solution	"True" counting rate, cpm	Observed counting rate, cpm	Correction factor
0.1	520	520	1.000
0.3	1,560	1,551	1.006
0.5	2,600	2,576	1.009
0.8	4,160	4,100	1.015
1.2	6,240	6,090	1.025
2.0	10,400	10,050	1.035
3.0	15,600	14,780	1.055

commercial scaler and end-window counter; the measurements were made with P^{32}. It will be noted that the correction at 10,000 counts/min was only 3.5 per cent and, of course, was smaller at the lower counting rates. As a rule of thumb, a correction of 0.5 per cent per 1000 counts/min is often used. At counting rates lower than 10,000 counts/min, then, the coincidence correction can usually be neglected. Proportional counters have the advantage that no such corrections are needed until counting rates approach 100,000 counts/min. The data in Table 5-2 actually represent a calibration curve, and, as will be pointed out in the next section, it is possible to use a calibration procedure that minimizes still further the need for coincidence corrections.

Calibration Curves and Standards. Determination of the true disintegration rate of a radioactive sample is not generally required in biological studies except where quantitative data are needed on the radiation dose to the tissues. The true disintegration rate can be estimated from the observed counting rate with an end-window counter, but the complexity of such *absolute beta counting* precludes the use of these methods in the ordinary laboratory (37 to 39). If absolute values are needed, it is recommended that known standards be obtained from the National Bureau of Standards or elsewhere which can then be employed to calibrate the

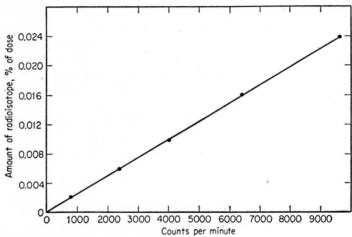

FIG. 5-6. Typical calibration curve for comparison of amounts of radioisotope in standard and sample.

specific-counting assembly by simple measurements under normal conditions. Manov (40) has summarized the status of standardization of radioisotopes as of 1953. Working standards are available for C^{14}, Co^{60}, I^{131}, P^{32}, and Ra D-E. Additional experimental work needs to be done on Fe^{55}, Fe^{59}, Au^{198}, Na^{24}, and H^3. Progress on the establishment of British standards has been recorded by Perry (41).

The primary problem is to evaluate the amount of radioactivity in a given sample in terms of the amount that was originally introduced into the biological system. One way of doing this is described here. With a new counting assembly or tube, a series of dilutions of the radioisotope should be measured to cover the normal counting range, as in Table 5-2. A linear plot of some function of the radioactivity vs. the counting rate should result in a straight line passing through the origin, as illustrated in Fig. 5-6. If such a straight line is obtained with the deviations at the higher counting rates within an acceptable error, then a single point can thereafter be used for the actual calibration, as follows: At the time of administration of radioactivity to the plant or animal, a known aliquot is diluted to enable the preparation of a standard sample of about 3000 to 4000 counts/min. In practice it is wise to prepare such standards in replicate. These standards are counted in exactly the same way as the biological samples. This means that the standard and biological samples must be mounted in the same type of container and measured at the same distance from the counter tube. If the biological samples are to be counted in solid form and have appreciable mass, then self-absorption corrections may also have to be made, as indicated in the next section. If solution counting is used, the calibration and biological samples must consist of the same volume in the same size vessel.

If, for example, it is known that 0.01 per cent of the dose administered to the animal has 4000 counts/min, then the biological-sample count $\times$ 0.01/4000 will give the percentage of dose in the measured sample. By using a calibration sample of this counting rate, which in itself has a small coincidence loss, it is usually not necessary to apply coincidence corrections below counting rates of 10,000 to 12,000 counts/min.

The calibration standard can be counted as often as necessary during the sample measurements, and this compensates for decay or for changes in sensitivity of the counter. With short-lived isotopes it is usually more convenient to record the time of measurement and correct by calculation to the reference time at which the calibration standard was counted. It is clear that sample counting rates should not be used in excess of those known to be acceptably linear. If a sample has too high a counting rate, the measurement can be made with a suitable absorber placed between the sample and the counter tube. This count has to be evaluated with the calibration standard counted in the same way. Serious errors may result if the absorber is not located in the identical geometric position for both standard and sample.

Self-absorption of Beta Particles. A large proportion of radioisotope measurements are based on the counting of beta particles emitted. It will be recalled from Chap. 3 that beta particles have a definite range and are stopped by relatively small amounts of material. In the radioactivity measurements of a sample, many of the beta particles originating from within the sample will be absorbed by the mass of the sample itself and therefore will not be counted. This behavior is called *self-absorption* and is so important, especially with the lower-energy beta emitters, that it is often the determining factor in the sample preparation. To indicate an order of magnitude of this effect, it takes about 6 mg/cm^2 of sample to cause a 50 per cent reduction in the counting rate of C^{14} (0.155 Mev), whereas for Ca^{45} (0.254 Mev) about 15 mg/cm^2 produces a 50 per cent reduction. Actually the beta counting rate of a given sample will be dependent upon many factors, such as (a) relative placement of counter and sample, (b) absorption by counter-tube window and air space between tube and source, (c) air scattering of beta particles into the counter, (d) effect of backscattering from source support, (e) scattering from source support structure and wall housing, and (f) mass of source in causing both scattering and absorption. By the use of standard counting conditions, all the above factors except the last can be easily maintained constant and therefore need not be further considered. However, it is necessary to consider in some detail the effects of self-absorption on the counting rate.

The self-absorption effect can, of course, be approximated from the beta energy of the particular isotope (Chap. 6) for the preliminary planning of sample preparation. However, it is necessary to obtain quantitative data for the actual application of correction factors. The most widely used method for evaluation of the observed activity is to convert this value to the activity that would have been observed at some specified thickness.

The most commonly used thicknesses for reference are zero thickness or infinite thickness (maximum observed activity for increasing amounts of a sample of constant specific activity). In the preparation of a set of standards of constant specific activity, the determination of the infinite-thickness value is difficult because the observed activity increases in the following manner:

$$\frac{N}{N_\infty} = 1 - e^{-\mu T_c} \tag{5-2}$$

where N = observed activity
N_∞ = activity at infinite thickness
T_c = sample thickness, mg/cm^2
μ = self-absorption coefficient, cm^2/mg

Figure 5-7 shows such a constant-specific-activity curve for S^{35}. The slope at thickness equal to zero, which is represented by the broken line N_0, represents the relationship between activity and weight of sample if no self-absorption has occurred. Uncertainties in the determination of this slope are due to self-scattering of the beta particles by the thin samples and to the difficulties in obtaining a uniform spread of the thin samples. Uncertainties in determination of activity at infinite thickness N_∞ are due to the nature of the curve as it approaches zero slope, which may be complicated by the fact that the surface gets closer to the window as the sample thickness is increased.

The equation for self-absorption, where N_0 is the true activity of the sample and T represents the sample thickness, in milligrams per square centimeter, there being a constant amount of sample activity, is

$$\frac{N}{N_0} = \frac{1 - e^{-\mu T}}{\mu T} \qquad (5\text{-}3)$$

If a set of self-absorption standards is prepared using a constant amount of activity for each sample, the resultant self-absorption curve may be used to correct the observed activity to the activity that would be measured if the samples were weightless. In this method the reference point (activity of a weightless sample) is well defined and not artificial. This

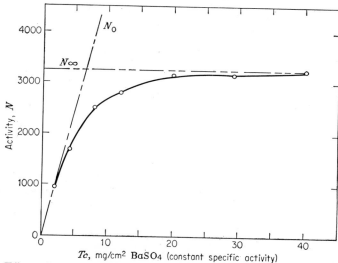

FIG. 5-7. Effect of self-absorption on measured activity of S^{35} in barium sulfate of constant specific activity. [*From Walter L. Graf, C. L. Comar, and Ira B. Whitney, Relative Sensitivities of Windowless and End-window Counters, Nucleonics,* **9**: 22–27 (1951).]

widely used procedure, designated as the *constant-activity method*, is as follows: A series of samples is prepared, each containing the same amount of radioactivity but with different masses. It will be necessary that one sample be essentially weightless so that the counting rate with zero loss due to mass can be determined. In the other samples the radioactivity should be uniformly distributed throughout the mass of the sample. If the measurements are usually to be made on a given compound, then this material should be used to supply the mass.

Some typical data for Ca^{45} are listed in Table 5-3, and Fig. 5-8 shows typical self-absorption curves for Ca^{45} in calcium oxalate as measured in two different types of counters (42). The fraction counted N/N_0 is plotted against the number of milligrams per square centimeter in the sample (N_0 = true activity of sample as measured with zero mass, and N = measured activity of sample).

TABLE 5-3. DATA FOR PREPARATION OF CA^{45} SELF-ABSORPTION CURVE^a

Mass of sample, mg	Mg/cm^2	Cpm	$N/N_0{}^b$
0.5	0.11	7800	1
4.0	0.84	7330	0.94
7.25	1.53	6850	0.88
20.0	4.21	6080	0.78
36.4	7.68	5380	0.69
50.0	10.5	4600	0.59
73.0	15.4	3820	0.49
100.0	21.0	2960	0.38
146	30.7	2260	0.29

^{a} Standard amount of Ca^{45} incorporated into calcium oxalate; precipitate collected in metal cups of 4.75-cm^2 area.

^{b} N = observed activity with indicated mass.

N_0 = observed activity with essentially weightless source.

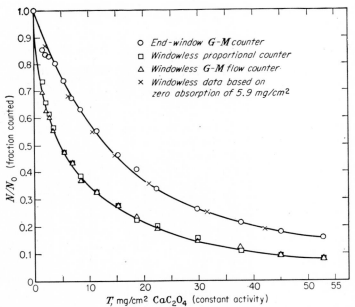

FIG. 5-8. Self-absorption curves for Ca^{45} in calcium oxalate as measured with end-window and windowless counters. [*From Walter L. Graf, C. L. Comar, and Ira B. Whitney, Relative Sensitivities of Windowless and End-window Counters, Nucleonics,* **9**: 22–27 (1951).]

With this information it becomes possible to choose between different methods for estimation and application of the self-absorption correction.

Thin Samples. The self-absorption loss may be insignificant if the sample mass is sufficiently low. As may be noted from Fig. 5-8, the self-absorption loss from Ca^{45} amounts to about 5 per cent at a sample thickness of 1 mg/cm^2. This means that, depending on the accuracy required, the Ca^{45} samples must not exceed about 0.5 mg/cm^2 when it is desired to neglect the self-absorption loss. This method can therefore be employed only when the specific activity of the sample is high enough and the measurement sufficiently sensitive so that a reasonable count can be obtained with the limited mass of the sample. At thicknesses of less than 0.5 mg/cm^2, there are uncertainties in the curve due to self-scattering phenomena. However, these errors are within the usual biological uncertainties, so that the limiting factor in the use of this procedure is the specific activity obtainable in the sample to be measured.

Samples of Standard Thickness. Self-absorption corrections can be eliminated if it is possible to prepare all the samples and standards of identical thickness and area. This may often be accomplished for routine methods by using standardized amounts of carrier that are large compared with the amount of the element in the original samples. With calcium in animal samples, for example, this would be satisfactory for the soft tissues but not generally for skeletal tissues or feces, which themselves contain large amounts of this element. This procedure could also be accomplished by preliminary chemical analysis, the results therefrom being used to choose a specific sample aliquot to yield the standard thickness.

Empirical Relationships. The most general and widely used procedure is based on the empirical relationship between the thickness of the sample and the degree of self-absorption under the conditions of measurement. This relationship is expressed for Ca^{45} in Fig. 5-8. Thus, for instance, a sample of 10 mg/cm^2 would register about 58 per cent of its counts under an end-window counter as compared with a standard of zero mass. A table of correction factors can be prepared from the curve, and each sample can be corrected on the basis of its mass. Although it is recommended that each individual investigator prepare his own self-absorption curves, Comar et al. (32) pointed out that with Ca^{45} such curves for end-window counters were similar as determined in different laboratories. Furthermore the curves were relatively unaffected by the shelf position, the composition of the sample, or the window thickness between 1.8 and 3.5 mg/cm^2. This is of practical importance in the laboratory, since it means that some of the unavoidable variations in procedure (e.g., replacing a worn-out counter tube) will not necessitate the establishment of a new self-absorption curve. However, as shown in Fig. 5-8, larger corrections for self-absorption are required if a windowless counter is used (42).   This is primarily because of the window and air-space attenuation in the case of the end-window counter.   It may be noted in Fig. 5-8 that, if the values for the internal counters are calculated on the basis of an N_0 value of 5.9 mg/cm^2, which represents the air and window thickness, then the self-absorption correction is the same for both types of counters.

It must be emphasized that this type of curve cannot be used as the mass increases to the point where there is little change of N/N_0 with sample mass, because, as the sample gets thicker and thicker, the radiation from the lowest layer is essentially absorbed completely by the upper layers.   Such a sample is called *infinitely thick.*   The curve decreases from that point on simply because of dilution of the activity by the mass and not at all because of self-absorption.

Infinitely Thick Samples.   If the sample measured is sufficiently thick so that the radiation from the lower layer is completely absorbed by the upper layers, then self-absorption corrections are not necessary.   Furthermore the counting rate depends only upon the concentration of activity in the sample and not at all upon the amount of sample measured.   This may simplify the procedure, since it will not be necessary to know how much sample is actually being measured.   In this case, however, it is necessary to construct a standard curve in which the counts are plotted against the known concentration of radioactivity, all measurements being made at infinite thickness.   As a rule of thumb, infinite thickness, so far as activity measurements are concerned, approximates 0.75 times the range, which is $0.75 \times 64 = \sim 50$ mg/cm^2 for Ca^{45}.

It is important to remember that, although under these conditions the counting rate is unaffected by the thickness, the surface of the sample should always be about the same distance from the window of the counter; this becomes increasingly critical at shorter distances.   Disadvantages of this method are that the over-all sensitivity is decreased, because there are portions of each sample which are being counted inefficiently or not at all, and there are often difficulties in handling the large amounts of sample necessary to give infinite thickness.   It will be noted that most solution measurements actually fall in the category of infinitely thick samples.

In summary, the primary considerations in the choice of chemical treatment of the biological sample are as follows: (*a*) ratio of activity to mass of sample as measured, (*b*) physical uniformity of sample, and (*c*) amount of activity in sample.   Table 5-4 illustrates some calcium/mass ratios for typical biological materials.   It is clear that there would be a considerable gain in sensitivity by separation of calcium oxalate from samples such as urine, soft animal tissues, feces, and plant material, whereas there would be no particular advantage in making such separation from bone.   Obviously, if there were enough activity present, direct measurements could be made even on dried urine, provided the physical nature of the sample were satisfactory. Likewise, satisfactory direct measurements on bone would be contingent upon the preparation of suitable uniform samples. The lower the beta energy, the more critical the physical nature of the sample. When possible, it is always most convenient to make direct measurements on the biologic material, and this possibility should always

TABLE 5-4. RATIOS OF CALCIUM TO SAMPLE MASS FOR TYPICAL BIOLOGICAL MATERIALS

Sample	Ca/mass
Bone ash (acid-treated)	0.2
Soft-tissue ash (acid-treated)	0.005
Rat feces ash (acid-treated)	0.015
Plant ash (acid-treated)	0.07
Urine ash (acid-treated)	0.0006
Dried urine	0.0002
$CaC_2O_4 \cdot H_2O$	0.27
$CaCO_3$	0.4

[From C. L. Comar et al., Use of Calcium-45 in Biological Studies, *Nucleonics*, **8**: 19–31 (1951).]

be considered. For example, direct measurement of C^{14} in organic compounds with a high carbon/mass ratio has been found satisfactory (43). Whenever direct measurements of low-counting biological material are made, one must consider the possibility that the radiation measured may be due to naturally occurring K^{40} (see Chap. 6 under Potassium). If the samples are hygroscopic (and this is often the case with biological material), the absorption of water may produce serious counting losses. This can be avoided by keeping the sample in a desiccator until use or by heating just before measurement. In the latter case it must be ascertained that volatilization does not occur.

INSTRUMENTATION AND METHODS

As indicated in Chap. 3, all discussions of instruments will be limited to those commercially available and will for the most part be restricted to a particular type found adequate for each purpose. The manufacturer's catalogues can be consulted for specific items (12). It is suggested that, whenever possible, all units that are operated together be purchased from the same manufacturer so that there will be no difficulties in making the connections. The choice as to type of equipment will mainly depend upon the radiation characteristics of the isotope, and these considerations will be discussed below. The decision as to the advantages of the more

expensive automatic equipment will be based on the number of samples
to be counted and the technician time available. It must also be remembered that the more complicated the equipment, the greater the chances
of its getting out of order. The general references may be consulted for
detailed descriptions and explanations of principles of operation.

Commercial electroscopes can be used for measurement of radioisotopes
and are simple, reliable, and modestly priced. However, they are not
widely used, possibly because of the time required for each measurement,
and will not be discussed further. Conventional instrumentation consists
of the detecting device (e.g., counter tube, ionization chamber) and the
required electronic circuits. The electronic equipment is common to
most of the detecting devices and is discussed below, whereas the detectors are described in later sections.

The Scaling Unit. The scaling unit, or scaler, is the basic electronic
item for radioassay and supplies the voltage for operation of the counter
tube and the circuits for registering the counts. The most expensive
units usually have a built-in timer and register, and it is necessary only
to connect the counter tube. With the simpler units it may be necessary
to use an external timer and register. The scaler has an electronic circuit which totalizes the individual counts received and trips the mechanical register after some given total. With a *scale of* 64, for example, each
unit recorded on the mechanical register indicates that 64 counts have
been received. The most popular circuits operate with scale multiples
of 2. However, many instruments on the market are decade scalers
(multiples of 10). The latter have more complicated circuits to be kept
in order, but the readings are somewhat easier to totalize, although in
practice this does not appear to offer much advantage. It is recommended that the unit have at least a scale of 64 and, for more flexibility,
a scale of 256. The decade units usually have a scale of 100 or 1000.

With a scale of 64 there will be interpolation lights labeled 1, 2, 4, 8,
16, 32. The number of pulses received by the circuit will be the sum of
the numbers of the lights that are glowing. For example, if 63 counts
have been received, all the lights will be on, and the next impulse will
extinguish them and actuate the mechanical register. With decade circuits the total is read directly from the lights and register without the
necessity of addition. Depending upon the instrument, the measurements can be made for a *predetermined count* or a *predetermined time*.
In the former method, all samples are measured to the same number of
total counts, and therefore all values will have the same counting accuracy; also there will be no interpolation lights to totalize. Basic scaling
units, however, can usually be more easily adapted for predetermined
time measurements. In practice, there seems to be little choice between
the procedures.

The general procedure for operation of the scaling unit is as follows: (a) connect the counter tube to the unit and, if necessary, also connect the timer and register; (b) see that all switches are off and the high-voltage adjustment set at zero, since damage may result if the high voltage is turned on before warmup of the circuit; (c) plug the unit into the regular 110-volt receptacle; (d) turn on the master switch and allow the circuit to warm up for at least 30 sec; (e) place a source of radioactive material under the counter tube; (f) set the count-stop switch on count and set the automatic timer, if there is one, to the count position; (g) turn on the high voltage; (h) increase the high voltage slowly until the interpolation lights begin to register; (i) adjust the high voltage to about 50 volts above the starting voltage. Accurate measurements should not be attempted until the instrument has been in operation for about 30 min, at which time the operating voltage should again be determined as above. In practice, the instrument should be left on at all times.

Before the high voltage is adjusted, the approximate operating voltage of the counter tube should be noted from the specifications, and if the unit does not operate when this voltage is reached, all switches should be checked to make sure that the counting circuit is on. This may prevent the application of excess voltage to the counter which may cause damage. A background count in the normal range is the first criterion of correct operation of the assembly. The actual background will vary with the size of the tube, location, etc. However, an ordinary end-window counter will run about 20 counts/min shielded and about 60 unshielded. If the background is extraordinarily high, one should look for contaminating activity in the area, light sensitivity, or spurious counts due to loose cable connections. During a background count it is possible to follow the individual pulses through the interpolation lights and ascertain if the scaling circuits are functioning properly. Very often a simple tube replacement will correct any difficulty in this part of the circuit. If the background is normal, then a standard source should be measured to make sure that the counter sensitivity is in the expected range. By keeping records of background and standard-source measurements from day to day, it becomes easy to detect a counter tube that is going bad or any other malfunction.

In the procurement of scaling units it is wise to ensure that the equipment as obtained will accommodate the particular types of detection devices which are to be employed.

Instead of scaling units, count-rate meters may be employed. These have the advantage of giving direct readings of the counting rate and are useful for in vivo or other studies where quantitative results are not required. However, the scaling unit still appears to be the instrument of choice for general radioassay.

Soft-beta Counting. In order to avoid loss of sensitivity by absorption of soft-beta particles in the window of the counter tube, it is essential that the window have a thickness not greater than 2 to 4 mg/cm². Thus for radioisotopes such as C^{14} or S^{35}, the thin-mica-end-window counter is used. Commercial counters of this sort are now relatively rugged. However, it must be remembered that the thinner the window, the more fragile it will be.

Increased sensitivity with the soft-beta emitters can be obtained by the use of windowless gas-flow counters operating in either the Geiger or proportional region. Essentially these are shielded counters into which solid samples are inserted directly and through which there is a gas flow to prevent air contamination. Comparative sensitivities for the various radioisotopes are listed in Chap. 6. However, in general, the windowless counter is several times more sensitive for C^{14} and S^{35} than the end-window counter is. These units may be operated with the regular scalers, although some are supplied complete with electronic circuits, timer, and register. The increased sensitivity results from the fact that there is no loss due to air and window absorption and also that the geometry factor is high. In purchasing these units one should inquire as to the size of sample that can be accommodated, since this is restricted in many cases. Measurements with the internal counter are not so simple as with the ordinary Geiger counter. The sample must be thoroughly dry and must not contain any pockets of entrapped air or solvent which may poison the counting atmosphere. In many cases a static charge tends to build up which decreases the counting rate and may even cause particles of sample to jump onto the walls and electrode. This becomes especially troublesome if the mount is a nonconductor such as porcelain, and it is therefore recommended that metal cups be used. In making measurements with these instruments it is wise to make a mental note of the count at the end of each minute so that any decrease in counting rate due to the factors just mentioned can be detected. This type of instrument is also difficult to clean in the event of contamination of the counting chamber.

If high sensitivity is required for the counting of C^{14}, then the vibrating-reed electrometer (a type of dynamic condenser electrometer) in combination with an ionization chamber for gas counting is perhaps the method of choice. This equipment is expensive and should not be considered unless large numbers of low-activity samples will have to be measured (see Chap. 6 under C^{14}). Auxiliary apparatus for handling the $C^{14}O_2$ will also be required. A more inexpensive gas-counting apparatus, after that of Bernstein and Ballentine (44), is now in commercial production. Geiger counting tubes employing the $C^{14}O_2$ as part of the counting gas have been devised but have not found widespread use.

Hard-beta Counting. The more energetic the beta particle, the easier the counting measurement. With energies higher than 1 Mev, very convenient methods may be used without any great loss of sensitivity. At energies between 0.5 and 1 Mev the choice of method will usually be the most convenient one that will still give adequate counts for the particular samples being used.

If soft-beta measurements are being made in the laboratory, then the thin-mica-window tube can also be used for the hard-beta emitters. Otherwise it is preferable to use a more rugged counter tube. Solid samples can be prepared and counted in the usual way. Although sample uniformity is not so critical as for the soft-beta emitters, nevertheless a reasonably flat and uniform surface is required, and self-absorption must be taken into account.

Solution counting offers many advantages (13, 45). The preparation of the sample for assay is simple, and the geometry is easily reproducible. Many biological liquids can be measured directly. If the samples contain too much activity, they can be diluted or an aliquot taken for assay. Solution counting may be accomplished either with a tube that dips into the solution (dipping counter) or by an external measurement from the surface of the liquid. Dipping measurements are usually more sensitive but have the disadvantage that the counter tube comes in contact with the radioactivity and must be cleaned and brought to background between each measurement. In some cases the radioisotope tends to be adsorbed onto the glass surface of the tube, and cleaning becomes a difficult problem, especially if there are both high- and low-counting samples in a series of measurements. This difficulty, however, may be overcome to a large extent by the use of a silicone coating on the counter. Special-purpose counter tubes are available which can be used for continual measurement of flowing liquids.

The thin-mica-window counter can be used for external measurement of the liquid surface. However, these measurements cannot usually be made with such a counter inside a closed shield because of vapor effects. The usual cylindrical counters having glass walls of about 30 mg/cm^2 are also convenient for this purpose. Attention is called to a cylindrical metal thyrode tube which is rugged and inexpensive. The solution can be placed in any suitable dish, although various sizes of petri dishes have been found convenient. The thickness of the solution layer in relation to the surface area will have a considerable bearing upon the sensitivity obtained. Some comparisons with various isotopes have been reported by Comar (13). In general, with beta energies greater than 1 Mev the sensitivity of a solution count compared favorably with that of a solid count.

With aqueous solutions there is usually no difficulty due to evaporation

losses during the measurements.   With organic solvents this may become
a problem.   The effect of solids content and density of the liquid may
have to be taken into account, although in our hands the counting rate
of P^{32} was little affected by these variables.   In any event, the standards
should be measured under identical conditions in typical sample solutions,
which will eliminate these variables unless there is a great difference
among samples.   Care must be taken that there is no significant phase
separation during the measurement, e.g., the settling of red blood cells or
the layering of fat globules.   Samples should not be allowed to stand for
long periods in the measurement container before being counted.   Serial
counts should be made on typical samples to ensure that there is no significant change with time.

Any of the counter tubes mentioned may be used for counting solid
samples of hard-beta emitters.

Gamma Counting.   It will be recalled from Chap. 3 that gamma rays
are very penetrating.   This gives a real advantage in gamma counting
because the counting rate is essentially independent of the sample mass,
and therefore the fresh tissue can often be counted as is without the need
of any pretreatment.   A word of caution—the sensitivity of the scintillation counter to low-energy, scattered radiation may introduce errors
with some isotopes if the samples and standards are not similar in mass
and geometry.   On account of the high penetrating power and low
specific ionization, the ordinary Geiger counter tubes are relatively insensitive to gamma rays.   Special *gamma counters* are available, however,
which give a 6- to 10-fold increase in sensitivity over the ordinary Geiger
counters.

The development of the *scintillation counter* has provided a most useful
instrument for efficient measurement of gamma rays, and this detector
is now considered the instrument of choice (46 to 49).   In principle, the
radiation produces light in a suitable crystal which in turn is collected by
photomultiplier tubes to create a pulse that can be recorded.   Commercial
units now available can be used with most of the modern scalers and have
proved satisfactory in practice.   The sample can be presented to the flat
surface of the crystal just as to a counter tube.   A very sensitive unit
utilizes a crystal containing a well which can accommodate a small test
tube holding about 2 or 3 ml of solution.   In this case the sample is surrounded by crystal surface except for the top; this results in very efficient
collection of the gamma rays emitted.   Unlike a Geiger counter; the
response as a function of voltage is dependent upon the gamma-ray
energy and will differ among isotopes.   The operating characteristics of
the instrument should therefore be studied for each activity used.

Before the advent of the scintillation counter it was necessary, with
many isotopes, to measure the beta particles emitted in order to attain

reasonable sensitivity of measurement. For example, the minimal detectable activity of Co^{60} with an end-window counter, which measures mainly the beta rays, was found to be 1.8×10^{-4} μc, whereas a scintillation counter, which measures mainly the gamma rays, was about half as sensitive, requiring 3.6×10^{-4} μc to give a count equal to that of the background. The scintillation counter would usually be the instrument of choice despite the lesser sensitivity, because if the gamma rays are measured, there would be no need to digest the tissues, separate out the cobalt, and correct for self-absorption. All these operations require considerable time and labor as well as provide opportunity for losses. As another example, the scintillation counter has enabled the use of Cr^{51} for routine blood-volume determinations where otherwise it would not be feasible.

The scintillation counter is also of advantage for in vivo directional detection, as will be discussed later. The possibilities of liquid scintillation counters are exciting, because the sample may be intimately mixed with the scintillation liquid to give 100 per cent geometry and zero absorption losses even with weak radiations. This method should be especially advantageous for carbon 14 and tritium (50 to 52). Although the procedures have yet to reach the practical stage, it is anticipated that they will eventually become of considerable importance.

Assay of Radioisotope Mixtures. As indicated in Chap. 1, there are many studies in which it is of considerable advantage to use two radioisotopes simultaneously. This poses the problem of the measurement of each when both are present in a single sample. The same problem arises, as mentioned in Chap. 2, when it becomes necessary to eliminate or evaluate the contribution that may be made by a radioactive impurity. Of the four methods discussed below, the chemical separation procedures are limited to isotopes of different elements, whereas the others may, in addition, be used with isotopes of the same element.

The decay, absorption, and differential radiation methods are similar in principle, and certain aspects apply to all three. A mathematical treatment has been presented by Tait and Williams (53) which may be consulted especially for its discussion of optimum conditions. A most important consideration is the error that may result on account of subtractive procedures. This is illustrated for the decay method in Table 5-5. The term count, as it is used here, refers to counts per unit time. Assume in case 1 that a mixture of isotopes A and B counts 10,200 at zero time and 5000 at time t, during which A has decayed one-half and B has decayed to below detection. The amount of A originally present is $2 \times (5000 \pm 71) = 10,000 \pm 142$, and the amount of B is then the difference between $10,200 \pm 100$ and $10,000 \pm 142 = 200$. Obviously the value of B has little significance because of the errors in the two large numbers. In case 2, where B is in excess, values for both A and B are relatively accurate. In cases of this sort, B (the activity which is reduced most by the second measurement) must usually be equal to or greater than A if reliable results are to be expected. In general, the greater the difference in the decay rates or absorption, the more successful the method.

TABLE 5-5. ILLUSTRATION OF ERRORS AS A FUNCTION OF COMPOSITION OF ISOTOPE MIXTURE IN A SUBTRACTIVE PROCEDURE

	Measured counts at zero time	Measured counts at time t	Calculated counts at zero time
Case 1			
A (half-life $= t$).........	....	5000 ± 71	$2(5000 \pm 71) = 10,000 \pm 142$
B (half-life very short)....	....	0	$(10,200 \pm 100) - (10,000 \pm 142) = 200$
Total..................	$10,200 \pm 100$		
Case 2			
A (half-life $= t$).........	....	100 ± 10	$2(100 \pm 10) = 200 \pm 20$
B (half-life very short)....	....	0	$(10,200 \pm 100) - (200 \pm 20) = 10,000$
Total..................	$10,200 \pm 100$		

The general formulas apply to all three cases, but the specific symbolic notation will be given for purposes of clarity.

Differential Decay. In this method the two isotopes have different half-lives, and a count is taken before and after the passage of time. The general equations for calculation of the composition from the two counts and the known half-lives are as follows:

$$A + B = C_0 \qquad\qquad (5\text{-}4)$$

$$\frac{B}{A} = \frac{F_A - C_t/C_0}{C_t/C_0 - F_B} \qquad\qquad (5\text{-}5)$$

where C_0 = count at zero time
C_t = count at time t
A = count of isotope A at zero time
B = count of isotope B at zero time
F_A = fraction of isotope A present at time t
F_B = fraction of isotope B present at time t

The use of these equations may be illustrated as follows: Assume that a sample containing S^{35} (half-life, 87 days) and P^{32} (half-life, 14.3 days) counts 3000 at some given time and 2085 at 20 days later. F_A and F_B are calculated from decay Eq. (1-17) as 0.853 and 0.379. Substituting in Eq. (5-5),

$$\frac{B}{A} = \frac{0.853 - 0.695}{0.695 - 0.379} = 0.5$$

From Eq. (5-4) it is then calculated that in the original sample there were 2000 counts of S^{35} and 1000 counts of P^{32}. In practice, these counts would be converted to amounts by calibration standards and self-absorption corrections, as already described.

Differential Absorption. In a mixture of two beta emitters of different energies, the assay is performed by measurement with and without an absorber. The ideal situation occurs when the beta particles from one of the isotopes can be completely absorbed. This was illustrated in studies reported by Comar et al. (32) on the simultaneous measurement of Ca^{45} and P^{32}. The mixed source was measured with a thin-mica-window counter and then with an absorber of about 55 mg/cm² which essentially stopped all the Ca^{45} beta rays but reduced the P^{32} contribution by a factor of only 1.5. In line with the previous discussion, accurate results were obtained only when the Ca^{45}/P^{32} activity ratio was 1 or higher. Tait and Williams (53) assayed Na^{24} and K^{42} and reported that the optimum conditions were obtained with a sample thickness of 10 to 12 mg/cm² and an absorber of about 300 mg/cm².

Equations (5-4) and (5-5) also apply for differential absorption, but the symbols have the following meaning:

C_0 = count with no absorber
C_t = count with absorber
A = count of isotope A with no absorber
B = count of isotope B with no absorber
F_A = fraction of isotope A counted with absorber
F_B = fraction of isotope B counted with absorber

Different Radiations. An important example of the use of different radiations for double counting is afforded by the work of Peacock et al. (54) and Saylor and Finch (55) with Fe^{55} and Fe^{59}. The sample was electroplated in the usual way, and measurements were made with an argon-filled Geiger counter with a beryllium filter that responded to the X rays from Fe^{55} and with a helium-filled counter that responded to the beta rays from Fe^{59}. Since there was less than 3 per cent cross-counting in either direction, there were no subtractive errors; this represents the ideal situation. The gamma-beta scintillation spectrometer may become very useful for analysis of mixtures (56).

Chemical Separation Methods. With isotopes of different elements, conventional chemical separations may be employed. This has been used with Ca^{45} and P^{32} (32). Where calcium oxalate is separated as part of the regular procedure, it is a simple matter to determine chemical phosphorus and P^{32} on the supernatant or filtrate. Usually there is no contamination of the calcium oxalate with residual P^{32}. However, this can be checked with the absorber method as described above, and corrections

made if necessary.   Ennor and Rosenberg (57) have described a method
for estimation of P^{32} and Na^{24} from a mixture of each in body fluids and
tissues.   The P^{32} was extracted as a molybdate complex into isobutanol,
and the Na^{24} remained in the aqueous phase.

In Vivo Measurements.   The advantages of in vivo measurements have
been mentioned in Chap. 1, and an excellent review of this subject has
been compiled by Strajman and Pace (58).   The locations within a tissue
from which radiation will be detected by a device at the tissue surface will
be determined primarily by the solid angle subtended by the counter tube,
the scattering in the tissue, and the energy of radiation.   If dynamic factors are involved, the measurements may be dependent upon such factors
as blood perfusion of tissues, mixing of substances with blood, and penetration into cells.   These complicating considerations have virtually
precluded development of absolute quantitative relationships, and reliance has been placed on standardization of conditions and comparative
measurements.

It is usually helpful to reduce as much as possible the tissue volume
from which radiation is received, in order to increase the resolving power
of the instrument.   This is accomplished by shielding the counter and
especially by providing considerable collimation.   Such assemblies are
called *directional counters*.   The limiting factor to the amount of collimation that can be employed is the reduction of sensitivity.   Gamma-ray-
emitting isotopes are primarily employed on account of their penetrating
power.   However, in some cases P^{32}, a beta emitter, has been used.   As
a matter of fact, it is often necessary in this type of measurement to shield
out the beta rays so that the surface contribution will not be magnified.
Since the sensitivity of response to gamma rays is so important, it is clear
that the development of the scintillation counter has been of particular
value in this connection.   MacIntyre (59), for example, reported that,
for measurements of I^{131} uptake in human beings, the scintillation counter
was 30 to 50 times more sensitive than the Geiger counter and that the
use of the former allowed a reduction of the tracer dosage from 100 to
about 25 μc.   Allen and Goodwin (60) were able to do thyroid-function
studies with a scintillation counter (150 times more sensitive than a Geiger
counter) after administration to patients of as little as 1 μc I^{131}.

The in vivo method has perhaps been most widely applied using I^{131} in
the study of thyroid function in human beings.   This is due to the selective
accumulation of iodine in a gland of small proportions, the information on
pathological states which may be gained from thyroid studies, the need for
information on which to base therapeutic I^{131} treatment for malignancies,
and the possibility of using I^{131} uptake as a reliable measure of basal
metabolic rate.   The general procedure is to administer I^{131} and some
time later to make an in vivo measurement over the thyroid, usually at a

distance of 17 to 20 cm so that the tube will "see" all the gland. A background reading is taken over the thigh which is used to compensate for any contribution to the thyroid measurement which was not due to the gland itself. Comparisons are made with phantoms, most often with I^{131} solutions in bottles measured at the same distance. Uncertainties in this method may amount to ± 20 per cent (61). Freedberg et al. (61) proposed a method which reduced the error to ± 5 per cent and which consisted of using four Geiger tubes arranged horizontally in a circle around the patient's neck. With this arrangement the effects of absorption, scatter, and geometry caused the values to be about 7 per cent high, and this correction factor was applied. The thyroid uptake was calculated by relating the in vivo measurement to the measurement of an aliquot from the solution given to the patient. Fields and LeRoy (62), using a single Geiger tube, obtained reliable values for the amount of I^{131} in the gland by making measurements at three known distances and eliminating backscatter by a lead absorber of at least 1.5 g/cm². Calculations were made on the basis of the inverse-square law.

It should be pointed out that scintillation counters especially, by virtue of their great efficiency, tend to give high results on account of scattered gamma rays of reduced energy. This error can be corrected by one of the following methods: (a) use of a lead absorber in front of the detector, (b) use of a comparison standard that consists of an I^{131} dose in a volumetric flask submerged in a suitable water phantom, or (c) use of an electronic circuit that will discriminate against the lower-energy gamma rays.

Cassen et al. (63) and Bauer et al. (64) have described an instrument that produces a visual delineation of the thyroid gland. The device consists of a scintillation counter, a visual recorder, and an automatic scanner. The pictures obtained are called *scintigrams*. This automatic method provides valuable information as to the size of the gland and localization of pathologic tissue. This type of apparatus has been successfully used to estimate the weight of the human gland (60, 65). Anger (66) has described a scanning device employing 10 scintillation counters by means of which human subjects can be scanned from head to foot in about 45 min, and laboratory animals in a shorter time. This procedure, in combination with roentgenograms, was most helpful in the location of thyroid metastases.

There has been considerable interest in the determination of I^{131} uptake in the thyroid of livestock because of the importance of thyroid function in animal growth and production. The procedures that are suitable for human subjects are not practical for domestic animals, which cannot cooperate. It is desirable to use only the restraint to which the animals are accustomed and to avoid exciting the animal. It is impractical to make measurements at a fixed distance from the gland because of unavoidable movement by the animal and great variation among animals in the thickness of tissue covering the thyroid. Also it is not practical to use multiple-counter arrangements. With cattle the absence of anatomical landmarks in the region of the thyroid requires the use of a trial-and-error method of measurement. A technique described by Blincoe (67) for in vivo measurements with dairy cattle is as follows: Instrumentation consisted of a 1-in.-diameter end-window Geiger tube, the window of

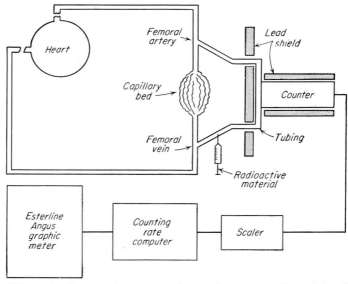

Fig. 5-9. Schematic diagram of apparatus for continuous recording of the disappearance of radioactive materials from the circulating blood of dogs. (*From William J. MacIntyre and Jack R. Leonards, A Continuous Recording Determination of Radioactive Tracers from Circulating Blood, NYO-4029, Apr. 21, 1953.*)

which was shielded with 1.27 mm aluminum and the body of which was surrounded by $\frac{1}{2}$ in. lead. The tube was connected to a conventional count-rate meter. With the cow in the stanchion, the dewlap was drawn to one side, and the counter placed against the skin with light pressure in the region of the gland. The counter was moved about to determine the maximum counting rate attainable. The procedure was then repeated on the other side of the neck. A phantom was used for standardization purposes.

MacIntyre and Leonards (68) have described a method for continuous recording of the disappearance of radioactive materials from the circulating blood of dogs (Fig. 5-9). The right femoral artery was cannulated through rubber tubing to a 3-mm-diameter stainless-steel tube, and the complete circuit established by return to the right femoral vein. The stainless-steel tube was held rigidly in a lead shield and mounted flush against the crystal of a scintillation counter. A volume of 0.6 ml was thereby exposed to the counter at any one time. A concentration of 0.01 μc/ml of I^{131} in the circulating blood gave a reading of 1000 to 1500 counts/min. The injection was made on the venous side of the external loop, so that the first concentration recorded was diluted by cardiac mixing. For work with beta emitters, a thin-mica-window tube was substituted for the scintillation counter, and a thin rubber tubing was used in place of the stainless steel. This method eliminated errors due to timing of samples, withdrawal of samples, or geometric variations.

There are studies that require needle-type detection devices so that they may be inserted into a tissue or vein. Such Geiger counters have been made but usually suffer from poor operating characteristics. Kohl (69) has compared a Geiger probe with a scintillation probe for localization of brain tumors. The Geiger needle was 2 mm in diameter and 10 cm long, whereas the scintillation needle was 3 mm in diameter and 8 cm long. The scintillation device was judged the most suitable for the purpose on the basis of stability when subjected to physical shock or change of temperature. Jonas (70) used a scintillation crystal of about 42-mm² detection area to study the pattern of uptake of K^{42} from sunflower plants in nutrient solution.

In general, commercial Geiger or scintillation counters are satisfactory for most in vivo studies. It is pointed out that adequate supports should be available, since otherwise a heavily shielded counter tube is awkward to handle. Special apparatus such as automatic scanning devices or multicounter arrangements still have to be assembled by the investigator.

EXPRESSION OF DATA

Data in the literature from radioisotope studies have been reported in various ways. In most cases the reported values do serve the purpose of permitting interpretation. Sometimes, however, the expressed results have not included all the factors required for complete comparisons. In any event, intercomparisons between laboratories often become an exercise in the juggling of units. It cannot be hoped that a standard usage will be generally adopted. However, it will be most helpful if the results are presented unambiguously with sufficient information to permit comparisons. A review of conventions in radiotracer studies has been compiled by Schulman and Falkenheim (71).

The fundamental property involved is the amount of radioactivity. This can be expressed in various ways, such as millicuries, microcuries, counts per minute, counts per second, or percentage of dose. It is always understood that radioactivity when expressed as counts refers to some specific arbitrary counting arrangement at some reference time. The concentration found in a tissue is a direct function of the dose administered to the biological system. For example, if 100 counts/min is given to a 100-g animal and becomes uniformly distributed, the concentration would be 1 count/min/g of tissue. If 200 counts/min had been given, it would act in the same way, and in this instance the concentration would be 2 counts/min/g. Yet the metabolic behavior is the same in both cases. Therefore it is recommended that concentrations be expressed in terms of *percentage of dose*, which in the above example would be 1 per cent per gram of tissue for each animal. In all cases the approximate dose should be stated in terms of both radioactivity and mass. This enables the reader to judge whether there might be radiation effects or mass effects and also gives a lead as to the amounts of activity that might be required for similar experiments.

Another problem that is not so straightforward and touches upon experimental procedure is concerned with the ratio of dose to body weight or, more precisely, to the size of the biological system through which the isotope is distributed. For example, if 100 counts/min is given to a 100-g animal and becomes uniformly distributed, the concentration is 1 per cent of dose per gram of tissue. If a comparative study is made with another animal of 200-g body weight, the concentration becomes 0.5 per cent of dose per gram of tissue for the same metabolic behavior. Therefore it would be desirable to take into account the body weight. This may be done by multiplication of the percentage of dose per gram of tissue by the body weight in grams, which would give a value of 100 for each of the above animals. This expression has been called the *biological concentration coefficient*. The same result can be accomplished by using the simple concentration value of percentage of dose per gram if the dose is adjusted to the body weight of all animals to be compared. Where the tissues are to be analyzed by radioassay, it is usually simpler to use a standard dose and compensate by calculation of the biological concentration coefficient or some other value that takes the body weight into account. However, if quantitative autoradiographic comparisons are to be made (see Chap. 7), it is mandatory that in all such cases a constant dose per unit of body weight be used subject to the following consideration:

The above example has been cited in terms of body weight. However, a difficulty arises as to whether the actual dilution of the isotope administered (and this must include excretion losses) is a linear function of the body weight. This can be considered only in terms of the specific metabolic behavior of the radioisotope and the effect of body weight on the organs primarily involved. If possible, these uncertainties can be eliminated by the use of animals of the same body size. However, the experimental variables, e.g., age, nutrition, or pathological condition, may often influence the body size. The investigator will have to decide on the basis of biological knowledge whether taking the body size into account will produce more error in the results than neglecting it. Unless there is information available upon which a decision can be based, it may be wiser to neglect this correction factor. In studies with radioisotopes of Na, Ca, etc., which may be distributed in proportion to body weight, this correction is justified. However, in an iodine distribution study, for example, the size of the thyroid gland will probably be the governing factor, and the gland size may well be inversely related to the body size. In cases where excretion values are known, a partial correction can be made with confidence by calculation of the tissue concentrations in terms of the percentage that was absorbed. Similarly, if there is retention at a site of injection, this may be measured and corrections applied. These considerations have been illustrated for animal studies but might well apply to plants also.

So far the discussion has been concerned with the expression of results for gross tissue distribution. It is often desirable, especially in turnover comparisons, to express results in terms of specific activities. It will be recalled from Chap. 1 that *specific activity* was used to designate the amount of radioactive element per unit weight of the element present, this weight to include both active and stable isotopes. Specific activity may then be expressed in terms of percentage of dose per unit mass of element. In comparisons between tissues of the same animal, the body-weight factor does not enter. However, in comparisons between animals the same considerations as discussed for concentration values of dose and body weight apply also to the specific-activity values. If various elements are to be compared, the specific activity may be expressed as percentage of dose per millimole of element. Specific activity may also be used for pure compounds isolated from the tissue, in which case the specific activity is expressed as percentage of administered activity per millimole or per milligram of compound.

In some experiments it may be of value to make comparisons such as tissue concentration vs. average concentration in the whole animal, or tissue concentration vs. some reference tissue concentration. In many such cases the units cancel out and are unimportant.

GENERAL REFERENCES

1. Furman, N. Howell, ed.: "Scott's Standard Method of Chemical Analysis," 5th ed., vols. 1 and 2, D. Van Nostrand Company, Inc., New York, 1939.
2. Sandell, E. B.: "Colorimetric Determination of Traces of Metals," 2d ed., Interscience Publishers, Inc., New York, 1950.
3. Winton, Andrew L., and Kate Barber Winton: "The Analysis of Foods," John Wiley & Sons, Inc., New York, 1945.
4. Piper, C. S.: "Soil and Plant Analysis," Interscience Publishers, Inc., New York, 1947.

5. "Methods of Analysis of the Association of Official Agricultural Chemists," 6th ed., Association of Official Agricultural Chemists, Washington, D.C., 1945.

6. Calvin, Melvin, Charles Heidelberger, James C. Reid, Bert M. Tolbert, and Peter F. Yankwich: "Isotopic Carbon," John Wiley & Sons, Inc., New York, 1949.

7. Friedlander, Gerhart, and Joseph W. Kennedy: "Introduction to Radiochemistry," John Wiley & Sons, Inc., New York, 1949.

8. Cook, G. B., and J. F. Duncan: "Modern Radiochemical Practice," Oxford University Press, New York, 1952.

9. Siri, William E.: "Isotopic Tracers and Nuclear Radiations," McGraw-Hill Book Company, Inc., New York, 1949.

10. Korff, Serge A.: "Electron and Nuclear Counters," D. Van Nostrand Company, Inc., New York, 1946.

11. Bleuler, Ernst, and George J. Goldsmith: "Experimental Nucleonics," Rinehart & Company, Inc., New York, 1952.

12. "Nucleonics Annual Buyers' Guide," McGraw-Hill Publishing Company, Inc., New York.

CITED REFERENCES

13. Comar, C. L.: Radioisotopes in Nutritional Trace Element Studies, I, *Nucleonics*, **3**: 32–45 (1948).

14. Bahner, Carl T., D. B. Zilversmit, and Etta McDonald: The Preparation of Wet Ashed Tissues for Liquid Counting, *Science*, **115**: 597–598 (1952).

15. Howarth, Frank: Tissue Suspensions for Estimations of Radioactivity, *Nature*, **163**: 249 (1949).

16. Tabern, D. L.: Personal communication.

17. Middleton, G., and R. E. Stuckey: The Preparation of Biological Material for the Determination of Trace Metals. I. A Critical Review of Existing Procedures, *Analyst*, **78**: 532–542 (1953).

18. Cotton, Robert H.: Determination of Nitrogen, Phosphorus, and Potassium in Leaf Tissue, *Ind. Eng. Chem. Anal. Ed.*, **17**: 734–738 (1945).

19. Kelley, Omer J., Albert S. Hunter, and Athan J. Sterges: Determination of Nitrogen, Phosphorus, Potassium, Calcium, and Magnesium in Plant Tissue, *Ind. Eng. Chem. Anal. Ed.*, **18**: 319–322 (1946).

20. Wolf, Benjamin: Rapid Photometric Determination of Total Nitrogen, Phosphorus, and Potassium in Plant Material, *Ind. Eng. Chem. Anal. Ed.*, **16**: 121–123 (1944).

21. Parks, R. Q., S. L. Hood, Charles Hurwitz, and G. H. Ellis: Quantitative Chemical Microdetermination of Twelve Elements in Plant Tissue, *Ind. Eng. Chem. Anal. Ed.*, **15**: 527–533 (1943).

22. Lindner, R. C., and C. P. Harley: A Rapid Method for the Determination of Nitrogen in Plant Tissue, *Science*, **96**: 565–566 (1942).

23. Van Slyke, Donald D., and Jordi Folch: Manometric Carbon Determination, *J. Biol. Chem.*, **136**: 509–541 (1940).

24. Van Slyke, Donald D., John Plazin, and James R. Weisiger: Reagents for the Van Slyke–Folch Wet Carbon Combustion, *J. Biol. Chem.*, **191**: 299–304 (1951).

25. Van Slyke, Donald D., Robert Steele, and John Plazin: Determination of Total Carbon and Its Radioactivity, *J. Biol. Chem.*, **192**: 769–805 (1951).

26. Claycomb, Cecil K., Tyra T. Hutchens, and John T. Van Bruggen: Techniques in the Use of C^{14} as a Tracer. I. Apparatus and Technique for Wet Combustion of Non-volatile Samples, *Nucleonics*, **7**: 38–41 (1950).

27. Hutchens, Tyra T., Cecil K. Claycomb, William J. Cathey, and John T. Van Bruggen: Techniques in the Use of C^{14} as a Tracer. II. Preparation of $BaCO_3$ Plates by Centrifugation, *Nucleonics*, **7**: 41–44 (1950).
28. Neville, O. Kenton: Carbon 14 Sample Preparation and Counting Techniques (Gas Counting), in "The Role of Atomic Energy in Agricultural Research," Proceedings of the Fourth Annual Oak Ridge Summer Symposium (Sponsored by the Oak Ridge National Laboratory and Oak Ridge Institute of Nuclear Studies, Aug. 25–30, 1952), TID-5115, pp. 126–150, January, 1953.
29. Burch, George: A Method of Preparing Biologic Fluids for Counting of Radioelements, *J. Lab. Clin. Med.*, **35**: 626–630 (1950).
30. McKay, B. P., and D. B. Zilversmit: An Automatic Sample Changer and Recorder for Dipping Counters, *Nucleonics*, **11**: 58–60 (1953).
31. Hood, S. L.: Simple Pipetter, *Anal. Chem.*, **24**: 2020 (1952).
32. Comar, C. L., Sam L. Hansard, S. L. Hood, M. P. Plumlee, and B. F. Barrentine: Use of Calcium-45 in Biological Studies, *Nucleonics*, **8**: 19–31 (1951).
33. Greenberg, D. M.: Personal communication.
34. MacKenzie, A. J., and L. A. Dean: Measurement of P 32 in Plant Material by the Use of Briquets, *Anal. Chem.*, **22**: 489–490 (1950).
35. Elmore, W. C.: Statistics of Counting, *Nucleonics*, **6**: 26–34 (1950).
36. Thomas, Alexander: How to Compare Counters, *Nucleonics*, **6**: 50–53 (1950).
37. Gleason, G. I., J. D. Taylor, and D. L. Tabern: Absolute Beta Counting at Defined Geometries, *Nucleonics*, **8**: 12–21 (1951).
38. Burtt, Benjamin P.: Absolute Beta Counting, *Nucleonics*, **5**: 28–43 (1949).
39. Zumwalt, Lloyd R.: Absolute Beta Counting Using End-window Geiger-Mueller Counters and Experimental Data on Beta-particle Scattering Effects, AECU-567 (1950).
40. Manov, George G.: "Status Report on Standardization of Radionuclides in the United States," National Academy of Sciences—National Research Council, Nuclear Science Series Preliminary Report No. 13, July, 1953.
41. Perry, W. E.: "Standardization of Radioactive Isotopes" (A Report on Progress towards the Establishment of British Standards of Radioactive Isotopes), National Physical Laboratory, Department of Scientific and Industrial Research, May 20, 1953.
42. Graf, Walter L., C. L. Comar, and Ira B. Whitney: Relative Sensitivities of Windowless and End-window Counters, *Nucleonics*, **9**: 22–27 (1951).
43. Entenman, C., S. R. Lerner, I. L. Chaikoff, and W. G. Dauben: Determination of Carbon 14 in Fatty Acids by Direct Mount Technic, *Proc. Soc. Exptl. Biol. Med.*, **70**: 364–368 (1949).
44. Bernstein, W., and R. Ballentine: Gas Phase Counting of Low Energy Beta-emitters, *Rev. Sci. Instr.*, **21**: 158–162 (1950).
45. Solomon, A. K., and Hillard D. Estes: The Measurement of Radioactivity in Solution, *Rev. Sci. Instr.*, **19**: 47–50 (1948).
46. Anger, H. O.: Scintillation Counters for the Measurement of Radioactive Samples, UCRL-886, Feb. 14, 1951.
47. Davison, P. W., M. W. Green, M. H. Greenblatt, G. A. Morton, K. W. Robinson, and A. L. Solomon: Scintillation Counters for Radiation Instrumentation, NP-4650, Dec. 15, 1951.
48. MacIntyre, W. J., W. F. Wirth, and T. E. Fessler: The Performance of Clinical Scintillation Counters, NYO-4018, Aug. 17, 1953.
49. Birks, J. B.: "Scintillation Counters," McGraw-Hill Book Company, Inc., New York, 1953.

50. Farmer, Earle C., and Irving A. Berstein: Determination of Specific Activities of Tritium-labeled Compounds with Liquid Scintillators, *Science*, **117**: 279–280 (1953).
51. Roucayrol, Jean-Claude: A Scintillation Counter for the Measurement of Weak β Rays, *Science*, **118**: 493 (1953).
52. Rosenthal, Donald J., and Hal O. Anger: The Liquid Scintillation Counting of Tritium and C^{14}-labeled Compounds, UCRL-2320, Aug. 21, 1953.
53. Tait, J. F., and E. S. Williams: Assay of Mixed Radioisotopes, *Nucleonics*, **10**: 47–51 (1952).
54. Peacock, Wendell C., Robley D. Evans, John W. Irvine, Jr., Wilfred M. Good, Arthur F. Kip, Soma Weiss, and John G. Gibson, 2d: The Use of Two Radioactive Isotopes of Iron in Tracer Studies of Erythrocytes, *J. Clin. Invest.*, **25**: 605–615 (1946).
55. Saylor, Linda, and Clement A. Finch: Determination of Iron Absorption Using Two Isotopes of Iron, *Am. J. Physiol.*, **172**: 372–376 (1953).
56. Connally, R. E., and M. B. LeBoeuf: Analysis of Radionuclide Mixtures, *Anal. Chem.*, **25**: 1095 (1953).
57. Ennor, A. H., and H. Rosenberg: The Separation and Determination of ^{24}Na and ^{32}P in Animal Tissues, *Biochem. J. London*, **52**: 591–593 (1952).
58. Strajman, Enrique, and Nello Pace: In Vivo Studies with Radioisotopes, *Advances in Biol. and Med. Phys.*, **2**: 193–241 (1951).
59. MacIntyre, William J.: A Scintillation Counter for Measurement of I^{131} Uptake in the Thyroid Gland, *Proc. Soc. Exptl. Biol. Med.*, **75**: 561–565 (1950).
60. Allen, Herbert C., Jr., and William E. Goodwin: The Scintillation Counter as an Instrument for In Vivo Determination of Thyroid Weight, *Radiology*, **58**: 68–79 (1952).
61. Freedberg, A. Stone, David L. Chamovitz, and George S. Kurland: Thyroid Function in Normal and Pathological States as Revealed by Radioactive Iodine Studies. I. Thyroid I^{131} Uptake and Turnover in Euthyroid, Hyperthyroid and Hypothyroid Subjects, *Metabolism Clin. and Exptl.*, **1**: 26–35 (1952).
62. Fields, Theodore, and George V. LeRoy: An Accurate Method for the Measurement of Radioiodine in the Thyroid Gland by an External Counter, *Radiology*, **58**: 57–67 (1952).
63. Cassen, Benedict, Lawrence Curtis, Clifton Reed, and Raymond Libby: Instrumentation for I^{131} Use in Medical Studies, *Nucleonics*, **9**: 46–50 (1951).
64. Bauer, K. F., W. E. Goodwin, R. L. Libby, and B. Cassen: Visual Delineation of Thyroid Glands In Vivo, *J. Lab. Clin. Med.*, **39**: 153–158 (1952).
65. Goodwin, William E., Benedict Cassen, and Frank K. Bauer: Thyroid Gland Weight Determination from Thyroid Scintigrams with Postmortem Verification, *Radiology*, **61**: 88–92 (1953).
66. Anger, H. O.: A Multiple Scintillation Counter In Vivo Scanner, *Am. J. Roentgenol. Radium Therapy Nuclear Med.*, **70**: 605–612 (1953).
67. Blincoe, Clifton: In Vivo Determination of Thyroid I^{131} of Dairy Cows, *Nucleonics*, **11**: 70–71 (1953).
68. MacIntyre, William J., and Jack R. Leonards: A Continuous Recording Determination of Radioactive Tracers from Circulating Blood, NYO-4029, Apr. 21, 1953.
69. Kohl, Douglas: Scintillation-counter Brain Needle, *Nucleonics*, **8**: 79–83 (1951).
70. Jonas, H.: Some Effects of the Concentration of Potassium Bicarbonate on the Uptake of K^{42} by Sunflowers as Determined by a Localizing Scintillation Countrate Meter (Personal communication).
71. Schulman, John, Jr., and Marlene Falkenheim: Review of Conventions in Radiotracer Studies, *Nucleonics*, **3**: 13–23 (1948).

CHAPTER 6

PROPERTIES AND PROCEDURES FOR INDIVIDUAL RADIOISOTOPES

It is the intention in this chapter to present in concise form information that will enable the reader (*a*) to determine whether or not a given radioisotope can be used for a particular study, and (*b*) to get an idea of the procedures, equipment, and analytical precautions that will be required. Although the numerical values have been compiled with reasonable care, they should not be looked upon as standards, since the primary purpose is only to present data to allow decisions as to levels and methods that can be used. For brevity, complete documentation is not given, and unsupported statements in regard to naturally occurring levels of the element and pharmacological data will usually have been derived from the general references that are credited in this introductory statement. Consideration is given almost entirely to preparations available from the U.S. Atomic Energy Commission, and the listing is alphabetical, with the properties as described in the "Catalog and Price List" of the Oak Ridge National Laboratory. However, much of the general information will be applicable for radioisotopes produced in other countries.

The half-life is given in parentheses following the designation of the radioisotope. The beta and gamma energies are listed in millions of electron volts (Mev), and only the lowest- and highest-energy gamma rays are given; *IT* represents *isomeric transition,* and *K* denotes *electron capture* from the *K* shell. The current Catalog number is given and when followed by an I designates an *irradiated unit* which is an unprocessed irradiated target; the letter P designates a *processed* radioisotope which has usually been purified. The specific activity is given for the day of shipment in terms of activity per unit mass, usually millicuries per gram of element (mc/g). The term *carrier-free* (CF) is used to indicate that no carrier has been added and that all or nearly all the atoms of the element are atoms of the particular radioisotope. The cost is given in terms of, and therefore serves to indicate, the amount of activity present in an irradiated unit. For the processed unit the cost is given in terms of millicuries (mc) or microcuries (μc). Costs may change in time, but they have been included to give some idea of the scale of experiments that are feasible. For example, at $.75 per mc one could plan to use a considerable amount of I^{131}, whereas experimental work will be limited with Cl^{36} at $5 per μc. Chemical contaminants are listed where known or suspected, and radiochemical contaminants are given in terms of the amount present in the irradiated unit. The half-lives of the radiocontaminants are listed as well as an indication of daughter relationships. (Note added in proof: A revised summary will be found at the end of the book.)

Next are listed the minimal detectable activities for a thin-mica-end-window counter, an internal counter, and a scintillation counter as determined experimentally in this laboratory and in terms of the microcuries of activity required to give a count equivalent to the background of the instrument (see Chap. 5). These are arbitrary values for ordinary laboratory operating conditions as described below but should be helpful in estimating the amounts of activity required for adequate measurement of a sample. For these measurements all samples were prepared with essentially zero mass in a stainless-steel cup of 4.75-cm² area, with the cup edges 6 mm in height. The end-window tube was halogen-filled, with a 28-mm-diameter mica window of 1.4 mg/cm². It was operated at 750 volts in a standard lead shield and had a background of 20 counts/-min. The sample was placed 20 mm from the surface of the window. The internal counter was a commercial, windowless restricted-atmosphere proportional counter employing a gas mixture of 90 per cent argon and 10 per cent methane. It was operated at about 1750 volts. The counting chamber, which was 55 mm in diameter, was not shielded. The background averaged 100 counts/min. It should be pointed out that internal counters with a smaller counting chamber or a shielded chamber would have a lower background which might give sensitivities two- to threefold better than those reported here. The scintillation counter utilized a commercial NaI(Tl) crystal of 1-in. diameter which was encased in metal as furnished. A piece of thin aluminum foil was placed over it to prevent contamination, and for measurement the bottom of the metal cup was centered over the crystal. The unit was shielded with 2 in. of steel and had a background of 100 counts/min. In comparing sensitivities it should always be remembered that the beta counts will be reduced by self-absorption, whereas the gamma counts will be relatively unaffected.

The R_f/mc value represents the milliroentgens per hour at 1 ft from 1 mc of the radioisotope, which can be used for estimation of shielding requirements, as explained in Chap. 3. These were calculated from the published disintegration schemes and are therefore subject to any uncertainties therein. To give an idea of the magnitude of self-absorption, values are listed for the sample mass in mg per cm², which gives a 50 per cent reduction in counts, as measured with a thin-mica-end-window counter. As indicated, some of the values were actually determined (detn.), whereas others were derived from the relationship between measured aluminum absorption data and self-absorption values (calc.).

Data on the critical organ, body burden, air concentration, and water concentration were taken from *National Bureau of Standards Handbook* 52 (2). The maximum permissible body burden is given in microcuries (μc), and the maximum permissible concentrations in air and water for continuous exposure are given in microcuries per milliliter (μc/ml) of air and water. The effective half-life (*Effect.* $T_{1/2}$) takes into account both the physical and biological half-lives.

Under Intake Levels there is first given an indication of the normal intake for the animal and plant so that the investigator can estimate from the specific activities available, the sensitivities of measurement, and probable uptake whether it will be possible to use physiological dosages. Much of this information was taken from standard texts, particularly Monier-Williams (3), Maynard (4), and Farris and Griffith (5). Nutrient-solution data were calculated from Hoagland's recommendations, as given in Curtis and Clark (6), and the composition of crop plants taken from Beeson (7). It is also useful to know the amounts of the element which will cause injury, and such data were, in general, available from Sollmann (8), Fairhall (9), and Farris and Griffith (5). Toxic levels are usually given in terms of milligrams per kilogram of body weight (mg/kg).

The discussion under Radioassay is concerned first with the advantages or disadvantages of various preparations when more than one are available. An indication is given as to suitable methods of counting and especially any difficulties when these are known to occur.

Methods for chemical estimation are outlined because very often they give information as to techniques that are useful even when only radioassay is required. With biologically important elements, both chemical and radioactivity estimation is frequently required to permit turnover calculations. Where the information is available, the suitability of the various ashing methods has been mentioned.

Under the heading Typical Methods an attempt has been made to outline procedures that have actually been used in experimentation. The amount of radioactivity used in the system is listed to give an idea of dosage requirements. The procedures are described for handling the samples and making the counts, especially where variations or convenient techniques have been used. Where possible, examples have been given from both plant and animal studies. Although animal experimentation appears to predominate, it should be pointed out that sample-handling procedures are usually quite similar for both animal and plant tissue. No attempt has been made to give results obtained, since the emphasis is upon procedures.

It has been possible to refer to relatively few papers from among many, especially on the more widely used isotopes. The choice of references was often difficult and primarily based upon the suitability of the paper for illustration of certain points of technique. Thus it was not feasible to give due recognition to numerous contributions of outstanding scientific merit, both in the early days of isotope usage and in recent years.

GENERAL REFERENCES

1. Hollander, J. M., I. Perlman, and G. T. Seaborg: Table of Isotopes, *Revs. Med. Phys.*, **25**: 469–651 (1953).
2. Maximum Permissible Amounts of Radioisotopes in the Human Body and Maximum Permissible Concentrations in Air and Water, *Natl. Bur. Standards Handbook* 52, Mar. 20, 1953.
3. Monier-Williams, G. W.: "Trace Elements in Food," John Wiley & Sons, Inc., New York, 1950.
4. Maynard, Leonard A.: "Animal Nutrition," McGraw-Hill Book Company, Inc., New York, 1951.
5. Farris, Edmond J., and John Q. Griffith, Jr., eds.: "The Rat in Laboratory Investigation," 2d ed., J. B. Lippincott Company, Philadelphia, 1949.
6. Curtis, Otis F., and Daniel G. Clark: "An Introduction to Plant Physiology," McGraw-Hill Book Company, Inc., New York, 1950.
7. Beeson, K. C.: The Mineral Composition of Crops with Particular Reference to the Soils in Which They Were Grown, *U.S. Dept. Agr. Misc. Pub. No.* 369, March, 1941.
8. Sollmann, Torald: "A Manual of Pharmacology," W. B. Saunders Company, Philadelphia, 1949.
9. Fairhall, Lawrence T.: "Industrial Toxicology," The Williams & Wilkins Company, Baltimore, 1949.

Antimony 122 (2.8 days)   *Beta* 1.36, 1.94   *Gamma* 0.57

Cat. No.	*Sp. Act.*	*Form*	*Cost*	*Chem. Cont.*	*Radiochem. Cont.*
Sb-122-I	250 mc/g	Metal	$12/50 mc	—	1.4 mc Sb^{124} (60 days)

R_f/mc
3.4

Antimony 124 (60 days)   *Beta* 0.5–2.37   *Gamma* 0.121–2.3

Cat. No.	*Sp. Act.*	*Form*	*Cost*	*Chem. Cont.*	*Radiochem. Cont.*
Sb-124-I	12 mc/g	Metal	$33/2.4 mc	—	26 mc Sb^{122} (2.8 days)
Sb-124-P	500–1500 mc/g	Chloride	$3/mc	—	—

Mica W.	*Int. C.*	*Scint. C.*	R_f/mc	50% *Self-abs.*
1.3×10^{-4}	1.3×10^{-4}	1.1×10^{-3}	13	93 (calc.)

Antimony 125 ($\sim$2.7 yr)   *Beta* 0.128–0.616   *Gamma* 0.035–0.637

Cat. No.	*Sp. Act.*	*Form*	*Cost*	*Chem. Cont.*	*Radiochem. Cont.*
Sb-125-I	CF	From Sn	$33/0.4 mc	Sn	30 mc Sn^{121} (27.5 hr)
					3.7 mc Sn^{125} (9.4 days)
					0.7 mc Sn^{113} (112 days)
					Te^{125m} daughter (58 days)
Sb-125-P	CF	Chloride	$100/mc	Sn	Te^{125m} daughter (58 days)

Mica W.	*Int. C.*	*Scint. C.*	R_f/mc
3.3×10^{-4}	3.3×10^{-4}	2.6×10^{-3}	2.4

Intake Levels. Antimony is not an important naturally occurring constituent of biological materials and has been of interest primarily on account of its use as a chemotherapeutic agent against animal parasites. It appears that absorption from the tract primarily depends on the solubility of the compound, but the toxicity of absorbed material depends upon the oxidation state. It is considered that 1 to 5 ppm in food is undesirable; 3 to 8 mg of tartar emetic (antimony potassium tartrate) in man increases perspiration, 10 to 60 mg depresses the heart, 60 mg causes vomiting, and 150 mg may cause death. Four milligrams of tartar emetic has caused vomiting in dogs, and 50 mg/kg injected intravenously into rats was fatal.

Radioassay. Preparation Sb-124-P appears to be the one of choice, presenting a compromise of relatively high specific activity, medium half-life, and low radiocontamination. Sb^{122} offers a shorter half-life, but the longer-lived Sb^{124} makes an increasing contribution with increasing age of the sample. A mixture of Sb^{122} and Sb^{124} can be used, provided that a standard from the preparation administered to the organism is available for decay corrections. However, it must be remembered that the self-absorption characteristics may change as the composition of the mixture changes with time. If a very high specific activity or a longer-lived isotope is required, then preparation Sb-125-P may offer advantages. In this case, the 58-day Te^{125m} daughter will have to be taken into account by such means as resolution by measurement of different radiations, which will probably be most practical, since Te^{125m} is a weak gamma emitter and its contribution can be minimized by efficient beta counting; chemical separation of Sb^{125} and Te^{125m}; use and measurement of Sb^{125} before appreciable growth of Te^{125m} has occurred; or use in a system known to handle the two radioisotopes in the same way. With Sb^{124}, gamma counting is less sensitive but offers the advantage that no sample preparation or self-absorption corrections will be necessary.

Chemistry. It is suspected that routine dry-ashing of biological samples may cause losses on account of the volatility of antimony trichloride. A method for estimation of antimony in tissues has been described in which the sample is ashed with sulfuric-nitric-perchloric acid, iron removed by extraction with isopropyl ether from a HCl solution, and a complex formed with rhodamine B to give a color which is measured photometrically (Sb-1).

Typical Methods. Cyclotron-produced Sb^{122} and Sb^{124} were converted to tartar emetic and administered to dogs intravenously at a level of 0.8 mg antimony per kilogram body weight and to dogs and rats intraperitoneally at 1.6 mg/kg (Sb-2). Tissue samples were dried in vacuo over phosphoric acid anhydride at room temperature and after determination of dry weights were ground to a uniform powder in a mortar. An aliquot of the powder, usually 500 mg, was spread evenly in a Lucite cup for measurement with a Geiger counter. Standards were prepared by addition of a known amount of labeled tartar emetic to a weighed amount of nonradioactive tissue, which was then carried through the same procedures as were the samples. The antimonial drug Fuadin, which is a catechol disulfate complex of antimony, has been labeled with Sb^{122}-Sb^{124} (Sb-3). In a typical experiment the compound was synthesized from 75 mg Sb_2O_3 which had been in the pile more than a week, and about one-third of the yield was injected into a dog. Tissues samples were wet-ashed in concentrated HNO_3, and aliquots counted directly in a petri dish with an end-window tube.

Sb-1. Sandell, E. B.: "Colorimetric Determination of Traces of Metals," 2d ed., Interscience Publishers, Inc., New York, 1950.

Sb-2. Ness, A. T., Frederick J. Brady, D. B. Cowie, and Alfred H. Lawton: Anomalous Distribution of Antimony in White Rats Following the Administration of Tartar Emetic, *J. Pharmacol. Exptl. Therap.*, **90**: 174–180 (1947).

Sb-3. Bahner, Carl T.: Localization of Antimony in Blood, *Proc. Soc. Exptl. Biol. Med.*, **86**: 371–373 (1954).

Arsenic 73 (76 days)			*Beta*		*Gamma* 0.052	K
Arsenic 74 (17.5 days)			*Beta* 0.95, 0.72, 1.40		*Gamma* 0.59	K
Cat. No.	*Sp. Act.*	*Form*	*Cost*	*Chem. Cont.*	*Radiochem. Cont.*	
As-73-74-P	CF	Chloride	$75/mc	Ge	—	
Mica W.	*Int. C.*	*Scint. C.*	R_f/mc			
1.7×10^{-2}	7.1×10^{-4}	2.3×10^{-1}	As^{73}, 0.3			
			As^{74}, 3.9			

Arsenic 76 (26.8 hr)			*Beta* 0.4, 1.4, 2.56, 3.12		*Gamma* 0.567–2.1	
Cat. No.	*Sp. Act.*	*Form*	*Cost*	*Chem. Cont.*	*Radiochem. Cont.*	
As-76-I	550 mc/g	As$_2$O$_3$	$12/25 mc	—	—	
Mica W.	*Int. C.*	*Scint. C.*	R_f/mc	50% *Self-abs.*		
1.2×10^{-4}	1.3×10^{-4}	1.7×10^{-4}	3	328 (calc.)		
Critical Org.	*Body*	*Air*	*Water*	*Effect. T$_{1/2}$*		
Kidney	10 μc	2×10^{-6}	0.2	1.09 days		

Arsenic 77 (38 hr)				*Beta* 0.7	*Gamma*	
Cat. No.	*Sp. Act.*	*Form*	*Cost*	*Chem. Cont.*	*Radiochem. Cont.*	
As-77-I	CF	From GeO$_2$	$25/2.5 mc	Ge	2.5 mc Ge^{77} (12 hr)	
					2 mc Ge^{71} (11.4 days)	

Intake Levels. Arsenic is of biological interest primarily because of its high toxicity and its use as an insecticide and drug. Food levels of arsenious oxide are usually less than 1.4 ppm, although fish, especially shellfish, may contain up to 170 ppm. The minimum fatal dose for man is about 0.8 to 2.4 mg/kg and for the lower warm-blooded animals, about 15 mg/kg; there are considerable species differences. Crop plants range from about 0.1 to 4 ppm on a dry-matter basis.

Radioassay. As^{73,74} has perhaps been most widely used and has the advantages of high specific activity and low radiocontamination; however, it is somewhat more expensive. As^{76} has the lower specific activity but a shorter half-life, which may be of advantage for some purposes. As^{77} has both a high specific activity and a short half-life, but will require chemical processing to eliminate the germanium radiocontamination. Suitable methods for separation of arsenic and germanium have been described which are based on the fact that arsenic trichloride and germanium tetrachloride are volatile, whereas arsenic pentachloride is not (As-1). Beta counting may be used for all three isotopes, and also gamma counting for As^{73,74} and As^{76}.

Chemistry. The estimation of arsenic in biological materials has received considerable attention. The destruction of organic matter must be done carefully to avoid losses. Poor recoveries have been reported when dry-ashing was used. Wet-ashing with a mixture of HNO_3 and H_2SO_4 has been employed, with care taken to avoid charring (As-2). As a precaution, the liquid driven off at first can be condensed for recovery of any volatilized arsenic. Estimation of arsenic in the acid digest can be accomplished by distillation of pentavalent arsenic after addition of bromide, followed by colorimetric evaluation of a molybdenum blue reaction. The general literature should be consulted for methods of handling biological samples that are difficult to oxidize.

Typical Methods. Potassium arsenite was prepared to contain As^{74} from a germanium target and was made isotonic with NaCl for subcutaneous injection as a 0.1 per cent solution (As-1). Five daily doses were given at about the following levels, expressed in milligrams per kilogram of arsenic: rats, 0.6; guinea pigs, 1.6; rabbits, 0.9; apes, 0.14; and some human beings were given up to 4 mg/day. Fluid samples were evaporated onto filter paper, tissue samples were mashed into a thin layer and dried, and bone marrow samples were digested and then placed on paper. The filter paper was wrapped around the counter tube for measurement.

In another study (As-3) carrier-free cyclotron-produced As^{74} was prepared in an isotonic solution of pH 6 to 7 for intramuscular administration of about 7 μc to rats. The tissues were dried at 60 to 70°C for 48 hr, then ground to a powder and transferred to a dish of 10-cm^2 area for counting with an end-window tube. Mass corrections were made from an experimentally determined self-absorption curve. In a study with As^{76}, sodium arsenite was administered in buffered isotonic solution at the following levels: rat, 47 μc; rabbit, 235 μc; man, 3 mc (As-4). Tissue samples were wet-ashed in fuming HNO_3, and the solution evaporated to dryness for counting with an end-window tube. Stool samples were measured directly with a high-pressure gamma ionization chamber.

In a study with the silkworm, As^{74}-labeled solutions of sodium arsenate, calcium arsenate, and lead arsenate were prepared (As-5). The solution was injected directly into the fore-gut of the insect with a hypodermic syringe with a calibrated micrometer. Some groups received 0.01 to 0.02 mg arsenic per gram of insect, and others received 0.06 mg/g. The insect samples were digested for a short time in concentrated HNO_3, and measurements made on 1-ml aliquots with a dipping counter. The distribution of arsenic trioxide labeled with As^{76} was studied in insect larvae (As-6). Using a dipping counter on an acid tissue digest, it was possible to detect 10^{-11} g arsenic.

As-1. Hunter, F. T., A. K. Kip, and J. W. Irvine, Jr.: Radioactive Tracer Studies on Arsenic Injected as Potassium Arsenite. I. Excretion and Localization in Tissues, *J. Pharmacol. Exptl. Therap.*, **76**: 207–220 (1942).

As-2. Sandell, E. B.: "Colorimetric Determination of Traces of Metals," 2d ed., Interscience Publishers, Inc., New York, 1950.

As-3. Lanz, Henry, Jr., and Joseph G. Hamilton: The Comparative Metabolism and Distribution of Carrier-free Radioarsenic (As[74]), MDDC-1596, Jan. 8, 1948.

As-4. Ducoff, Howard S., William B. Neal, Robert L. Straube, Leon O. Jacobson, and Austin M. Brues: Biological Studies with Arsenic[76], *Proc. Soc. Exptl. Biol. Med.*, **69**: 548–554 (1948).

As-5. Norton, L. B., and Roy Hansberry: Radioactive Tracer Methods for Determination of the Disposition of Arsenic in the Silkworm, *J. Econ. Entomol.*, **34**: 431–437 (1941).

As-6. Morrison, F. O., and W. F. Oliver: The Distribution of Radioactive Arsenic in the Organs of Poisoned Insect Larvae, *Can. J. Research*, **D27**: 265–269 (1949).

| Barium **131** (12.0 days) | | | | | *Beta* | *Gamma* 0.26–1.2 | *K* |

Cat. No.	*Sp. Act.*	*Form*	*Cost*	*Chem. Cont.*	*Radiochem. Cont.*
Ba-131-I	0.25 mc/g	$Ba(NO_3)_2$	$33/6 mc	—	Cs^{131} daughter (9.6 days)
					C^{14} trace (5568 yr)

Mica W.	*Int. C.*	*Scint. C.*	R_f/mc	50 % *Self-abs.*
1.3×10^{-4}	8.4×10^{-5}	3.7×10^{-4}	3.2	11 (calc.)

Barium **140** (12.8 days)				*Beta* 0.48, 1.022	*Gamma* 0.306–0.540
Lanthanum 140 (40 hr)				*Beta* 1.32, 1.67, 2.26	*Gamma* 0.093–2.9

Cat. No.	*Sp. Act.*	*Form*	*Cost*	*Chem. Cont.*	*Radiochem. Cont.*
BaLa-140-P	CF	Chloride	$1/mc	—	La^{140} daughter (40 hr)

Mica W.	*Int. C.*	*Scint. C.*	50 % *Self-abs.*
2.3×10^{-3}	1.7×10^{-4}	3.8×10^{-2}	100 (calc.)

Critical Org.	*Body*	*Air*	*Water*	*Effect.* $T_{1/2}$
Bone	5 μc	6×10^{-8}	2×10^{-3}	12 days

Intake Levels. Barium occurs naturally in foods at levels usually less than 0.1 per cent. Crop plants may contain 3 to 1000 ppm. About 200 mg of soluble barium is toxic for man. About 335 mg/kg of ingested barium chloride is fatal for rats.

Radioassay. Preparation BaLa-140-P will probably be most useful because of its high specific activity and because the daughter activity will not interfere if the samples are allowed to stand for about 400 hr after being taken, to allow attainment of equilibrium between Ba^{140} and La^{140}. Either hard-beta or gamma counting is satisfactory.

Chemistry. Barium is usually isolated by use of the insoluble sulfate or chromate. Biological tissues may be either wet- or dry-ashed.

Typical Methods. An adult rat was fed 150 g of ration containing 3.3 per cent barium sulfate, the latter being labeled with 4 mc Ba^{140} (Ba-1); the entire amount was consumed in 5 days. The skinned and eviscerated body was dried at 110°C and ashed at 600°C. Two and one-half grams of ash was weighed into a shallow 3.7-cm-diameter aluminum tray which had been placed in a steel die. The powder was evenly distributed by hand, and a piece of glassined paper placed over the die. With a punch and laboratory press, the powder in the tray was compressed at 1000 lb/in.², and the tray then forced out of the die. The waxed paper could be removed without disturbing the ash, and the sample was then counted with an end-window tube. Standards were prepared using the same amount of ash and known amounts of activity.

In another study, goldfish were placed in solutions containing 0.1 to 5 μc/ml (Ba-2). The tissues were dried at 100°C and ashed at 800°C. In some cases, the ash was dissolved in HCl and transferred to capsules for measurement after evaporation; in others, the tissues were ashed directly in the capsules (probably porcelain) in which the counts were made. In a study with hornets the distribution of ingested Ba^{140} was followed by routine counting of dissected organs and autoradiography (Ba-3). The autoradiograms were prepared by mounting histological sections on the photographic emulsions and, after exposure and development, by mounting under a cover slip with 75 per cent glycerin. Similar techniques were employed to follow the uptake and distribution of Ba^{140} and La^{140} in larvae of *Drosophila repleta* (Ba-4). The larvae were grown on food enriched with the radioisotope; the shape of the decay curves was used to ascertain selective utilization by the organism. The plant uptake of Ba^{140} was studied, using applications of 18 μc in 3 to 4 kg of soil in a No. 10 can (Ba-5).

Ba-1. Crandall, Lathan A., Jr.: The Absorption of Barium Sulfate and Non-absorption of Zirconium Dioxide from the Gastrointestinal Tract, *Gastroenterology,* **13**: 513–526 (1949).
Ba-2. Prosser, C. Ladd, W. Pervinsek, Jane Arnold, George Svihla, and P. C. Tompkins: Accumulation and Distribution of Radioactive Strontium, Barium-Lanthanum, Fission Mixture and Sodium in Goldfish, MDDC-496, Oct. 13, 1945.
Ba-3. Bowen, V. T.: Barium Metabolism in Hornets Studied by Means of Radioisotopes, *Trans. N.Y. Acad. Sci.,* **2**: 68–72 (1949).
Ba-4. Bowen, V. T.: The Uptake and Distribution of Barium[140] and Lanthanum[140] in Larvae of *Drosophila repleta, J. Exptl. Zool.,* **118**: 509–529 (1951).
Ba-5. Menzel, R. G.: Competitive Uptake by Plants of Potassium, Rubidium, Cesium, and Calcium, Strontium, Barium from Soils, *Soil Science,* **77**: 419–425 (1954).

Beryllium 7 (52.93 days)				*Beta*	*Gamma* 0.48	*K*
Cat. No.	*Sp. Act.*	*Form*	*Cost*	*Chem. Cont.*	*Radiochem. Cont.*	
Be-7-P	CF	BeCl₂	$75/mc	Li	—	
Mica W.	*Int. C.*	*Scint. C.*				
0.038	0.032	0.0022				
Critical Org.	*Body*	*Air*		*Water*	*Effect. T½*	
Bone	670 μc	4 × 10⁻⁶		1	48 days	

Intake Levels. Beryllium has become of interest biologically on account of its high toxicity and the industrial hazard that it may produce (Be-1). Fatal doses for the rat are 0.4 mg/kg, intravenous, and 5 to 10 mg/kg, intraperitoneal (Be-2). Since the isotope preparation is carrier-free, it may be used for evaluation of normal metabolism of the element. Be⁷ was found to be metabolized differently when administered to rats with and without carrier (Be-3).

Radioassay. Since Be⁷ emits only gamma rays, absorbers and gamma counting can be used to eliminate any beta contaminants. However, if autoradiograms are to be made, the original preparation should be freed of such contaminants (Be-2).

Chemistry. No volatilization losses have occurred with wet- or dry-ashing (Be-4). Methods have been described which permit separations from biological material and estimation of 0.05 μg (Be-4, Be-5).

Typical Methods. About 20 μc Be⁷ was injected intramuscularly in the rat. Tissues and excreta were dried at 150°C for 2 days, ashed at 550°C for 24 hr, and measured with a Geiger counter through a lead filter of 0.99 g/cm² (Be-2). In another study various solutions and routes of administration were used. Doses were 33 to 300 μc per rat and 0.9 mc per dog. Small tissues were placed in 10-ml porcelain capsules, covered with concentrated HNO₃, dissolved, and dried. Larger samples were wet-ashed with HNO₃ and then diluted to 25 or 500 ml, aliquots of which were deposited in the porcelain capsules and dried. Radioactivity was measured with a mica-end-window counter through a 0.5-g/cm² absorber (Be-6).

Autoradiographic studies with Be⁷ have been described making use of an intensifying screen of 0.5-mil gold or platinum foil placed between the histological section and the emulsion (Be-7). Effects of chemical form and pH on the distribution have been reported (Be-8).

Be-1. Sachs, Frances L., and Kathryn D. Ballentine: Beryllium Toxicology, Carbide and Carbon Chemicals Company, Y-975, July 17, 1953.
Be-2. Crowley, Joseph F., Joseph G. Hamilton, and Kenneth G. Scott: The Metabolism of Carrier-free Radioberyllium in the Rat, *J. Biol. Chem.*, **177**: 975–984 (1949).

Be-3. Scott, J. K., W. F. Neuman, and Roberta Allen: The Effect of Added Carrier on the Distribution and Excretion of Soluble Be, *J. Biol. Chem.*, **182**: 291–298 (1950).
Be-4. Toribara, T. Y., and P. S. Chen, Jr.: Separation of Beryllium from Biological Material, *Anal. Chem.*, **24**: 539–542 (1952).
Be-5. Klemperer, F. W., and A. P. Martin: Determination of Traces of Beryllium in Biological Material, *Anal. Chem.*, **22**: 828–831 (1950).
Be-6. Schubert, Jack, and Marcia R. White: Effect of Citrate Salts and Other Chemical Factors on the Distribution and Excretion of Beryllium, *J. Lab. Clin. Med.*, **35**: 854–864 (1950).
Be-7. Kaylor, C. T., and C. D. Van Cleave: Radiographic Visualization of the Deposition of Radioberyllium in the Rat, *Anat. Record*, **117**: 467–482 (1953).
Be-8. Van Cleave, C. D., and C. T. Kaylor: Distribution and Retention of Carrier-free Radioberyllium in the Rat, *Arch. Ind. Hyg. and Occupational Med.*, **7**: 367–375 (1953).

Bismuth 210 (5.02 days)					*Beta* 1.17 *Gamma*
Cat. No.	*Sp. Act.*	*Form*	*Cost*	*Chem. Cont.*	*Radiochem. Cont.*
Bi-210-I	0.4 mc/g	Metal	$14/10 mc	—	Po^{210} daughter (138.3 days)
Mica W.	*Int. C.*		*Scint. C.*		50% *Self-abs.*
1.0 × 10^{-4}	7.6 × 10^{-5}		4.8 × 10^{-2}		72 (calc.)

Intake Levels. Bismuth does not occur naturally to any significant extent in biological materials; it is used as a drug. Bi^{210} was employed in early work for studies of blood flow. However, other radioisotopes, particularly of sodium, are now preferred for this purpose. Bismuth is relatively nontoxic. Continued dosage of 5 to 10 mg/kg daily produced kidney lesions in rabbits, and 40 to 50 mg/kg was tolerated when injected intramuscularly, although larger doses may cause kidney damage (Bi-1). About 20 mg/kg of sodium bismuthate injected intravenously was fatal for rats.

Radioassay. The contribution of Po^{210} daughter, which emits 5.3-Mev alpha particles and 0.77-Mev gamma rays, can be minimized by measurement so that the alpha particles are absorbed and the bismuth beta particles are efficiently counted.

Chemistry. A method for estimation of bismuth in biological materials consists in wet oxidation; addition of a small amount of copper and precipitation of bismuth, lead, and copper as the sulfides, which are then dissolved in HNO$_3$, brought to pH 9.5, and extracted with dithizone in chloroform in the presence of enough cyanide to retain the copper. The lead and bismuth are liberated from the dithizone, and their nitrates brought to pH 2 for another extraction with dithizone; this extracts the bismuth, which can be determined colorimetrically (Bi-1).

Typical Methods. References (Bi-2, Bi-3) describe, for historical interest, the use of this radioisotope for determination of blood-flow characteristics in human beings.

Bi-1. Monier-Williams, G. W.: "Trace Elements in Food," John Wiley & Sons, Inc., New York, 1950.
Bi-2. Blumgart, Herrmann, and Otto C. Yens: Studies on the Velocity of Blood Flow. I. The Method Utilized, *J. Clin. Invest.*, **4**: 1–13 (1927).
Bi-3. Blumgart, Herrmann L., and Soma Weiss: Studies on the Velocity of Blood Flow. II. The Velocity of Blood Flow in Normal Resting Individuals and a Critique of the Method Used, *J. Clin. Invest.*, **4**: 15–31 (1927).

Bromine 82 (35.87 hr)   *Beta* 0.465   *Gamma* 0.55–1.31

Cat. No.	*Sp. Act.*	*Form*	*Cost*	*Chem. Cont.*	*Radiochem. Cont.*
Br-82-I	120 mc/g	KBr	$12/70 mc	—	5 mc K^{42} (12.44 hr)

Mica W.	*Int. C.*	*Scint. C.*	R_f/mc
4×10^{-4}	2.6×10^{-4}	8.8×10^{-4}	16

Intake Levels. Bromine has been of interest biologically in regard to the movement and distribution of bromide ion in living systems, and particularly on account of the ease of labeling organic compounds and dyes with radiobromine. Foods may contain up to 9 ppm, and about 0.5 ppm in the diet of rats is known to be adequate, although Br is not considered essential. A recommended nutrient solution for plants contains 0.02 ppm, and crop plants range from 1 to 100 ppm on a dry basis. About 875 mg/kg of sodium bromide ingested daily by rats produced death in 20 days. For rabbits the LD$_{50}$ was 60 to 65 mg/kg of methyl bromide administered in oil.

Radioassay. The contribution of the K^{42} impurity can be eliminated by delay in counting samples until the K^{42} has decayed to an acceptable level. Routine beta or gamma counting can be used.

Chemistry. Biological samples may be dry-ashed in the presence of excess KOH or may be wet-ashed in KOH. Bromine may be estimated chemically by oxidation with chromic acid in sulfuric acid and collection of the bromine in potassium iodide solution, after which the liberated iodine can be titrated with thiosulfate.

Typical Methods. About 1 to 5 mg of Br^{82}-labeled dibromotrypan blue or dibrom-Evans blue containing 0.07 to 1.2 μc was injected into mice (Br-1). Approximately 0.5-g tissue samples were treated with 0.5 ml concentrated HNO$_3$ and 0.5 ml of 0.015 M AgNO$_3$ in a porcelain ashing capsule; the AgNO$_3$ served to reduce volatization of bromine. The residue was measured in the capsule with a Geiger counter. In another study, mice were injected with 0.3 to 0.5 mg of a synthetic estrogen containing 700 to 2500 counts/min of Br^{82} (Br-2); the tissues were dissolved in 20 per cent KOH, and the solution made to 5 ml and counted directly. In an experiment with eggs about 5 ml of the white was mixed with a Br^{82} solution and injected back into the egg, and at the end of the experimental period the egg was frozen in a mixture of ether and dry ice (Br-3). The yolk and white were then separated with a sharp blow and were diluted for solution measurement. Total body chloride in young infants was determined by intravenous administration of 2 μc Br^{82} per kilogram body weight and measurement of the serum Br^{82} and Cl after a 24-hr equilibration period (Br-4). Labeled methyl bromide was used to study its behavior as a fumigant (Br-5). The counting of AgBr precipitates was fifteen times more sensitive than solution counting.   The absorption and translocation of electrolytes in plants has been studied with radiobromine (Br-6).

Br-1. Moore, Francis D., Lester H. Tobin, and Joseph C. Aub: Studies with Radioactive Di-azo dyes.   III. The Distribution of Radioactive Dyes in Tumorbearing Mice, *J. Clin. Invest.*, **22**: 161–168 (1943).
Br-2. Twombly, Gray H., Erwin F. Schoenewaldt, and Doris Meisel: The Distribution of Radioactivity in the Tissues of Mice Receiving Triphenylbromoethylene-Br[82], *Cancer Research*, **11**: 780–782 (1951).
Br-3. Maurice, D. M., and A. Fridanza: Permeability of Yolk of the Hen's Egg to Bromine-82, *Nature*, **170**: 546 (1952).
Br-4. Forbes, Gilbert, Allen Reid, June Bondurant, and John Etheridge: Estimation of Total Body Chloride in Young Infants by Radiobromide Dilution, *Proc. Soc. Exptl. Biol. Med.*, **83**: 871–872 (1953).
Br-5. Winteringham, F. P. W.: Some Chemical Problems in the Use, as a Fumigant, of Methyl Bromide Labelled with [82]Br, *J. Chem. Soc.*, **1949**: 416–420.
Br-6. Broyer, T. C.: Further Observations on the Absorption and Translocation of Inorganic Solutes Using Radioactive Isotopes with Plants, *Plant Physiol.*, **25**: 367–376 (1950).

Cadmium 115 (53 hr)   *Beta* 0.46, 1.1   *Gamma* 0.52, 0.34

Cat. No.	*Sp. Act.*	*Form*	*Cost*	*Chem. Cont.*	*Radiochem. Cont.*
Cd-115-I-1	20 mc/g	Metal	$12/20 mc	—	0.3 mc Cd^{115m} (43 days)
					20 mc In^{115m} (4.5 hr)

Mica W.	*Int. C.*	*Scint. C.*	R_f/mc	50% *Self-abs.*
1.9×10^{-4}	1.4×10^{-4}	3.2×10^{-3}	4	100 (calc.)

Cadmium 115m (43 days)   *Beta* 1.67   *Gamma* 0.5

Cat. No.	*Sp. Act.*	*Form*	*Cost*	*Chem. Cont.*	*Radiochem. Cont.*
Cd-115-I-2	1 mc/g	Metal	$33/mc	—	22 mc Cd^{115} (53 hr)
					Cd^{109}
Cd-115-P	5–20 mc/g	Nitrate	$33/mc	—	—

Mica W.	*Int. C.*	*Scint. C.*	R_f/mc	50% *Self-abs.*
2.5×10^{-4}	3.8×10^{-4}	4.5×10^{-2}	3	156 (calc.)

Intake Levels. Foods contain about 1 ppm; crop plants range from 0.02 to 2 ppm. About 15 ppm in food produces mild poisoning, and about 135 ppm in the diet was toxic for rats.

Radioassay. Preparation Cd-115-P is probably the best for general use, since the others contain appreciable radiocontaminants. Routine beta or gamma counting is satisfactory.

Chemistry. Methods have been described for determination of as little as 0.4 μg cadmium in biological material (Cd-1, Cd-2). In general, the element is separated from the wet-ash matrix by extraction with dithizone in chloroform in preparation for spectrographic, polarographic, or colorimetric evaluation.

Typical Methods. Following is a method for ashing used in the chemical determination (Cd-1): The sample, up to 20 g of tissue, is wet-ashed with a H_2SO_4-HNO_3 mixture, and the digest evaporated to fumes of SO_3; any char is destroyed by repeated additions of nitric and perchloric acids. The ash solution is mixed with ammonium citrate and extracted with dithizone in chloroform.

Cd-1. Cholak, Jacob, and Donald M. Hubbard: Determination of Cadmium in Biological Material, *Ind. Eng. Chem. Anal. Ed.*, **16**: 333–336 (1944).
Cd-2. Shirley, Ray L., Erwin J. Benne, and E. J. Miller: Cadmium in Biological Materials and Foods, *Anal. Chem.*, **21**: 300–303 (1949).

Calcium 45 (152 days)				Beta 0.254	Gamma
Cat. No.	Sp. Act.	Form	Cost	Chem. Cont.	Radiochem. Cont.
Ca-45-I	0.4 mc/g	$CaCO_3$	$33/2.5 mc	—	0.2 mc A^{37} (35 days)
Ca-45-P-1	0.2–0.4 mc/g	$CaCl_2$	$2/mc	—	—
Ca-45-P-2	5–60 mc/g	$CaCl_2$	$5/mc	—	—
Ca-45-P-3	1000 mc/g	$CaCl_2$	$45/mc	—	—
Ca-45-P-4	CF	$CaCl_2$	$4000/mc	—	—

Mica W.	Int. C.	Scint. C.	50% Self-abs.
2.5×10^{-4}	1.5×10^{-4}	1.8×10^{-2}	14.6 (detn.)

Critical Org.	Body	Air	Water	Effect. $T_{1/2}$
Bone	65 μc	3×10^{-8}	5×10^{-4}	151 days

Intake Levels. The approximate daily intake of calcium for the various species is as follows: man, 0.9 g; rat, 40 mg; laying hen, 3 g; sheep, 4 g; 100-lb pig, 12 g; and cattle, 17 g. These values are lower, of course, for younger animals and increased under conditions of pregnancy or lactation. In studies of oral administration there is usually no problem in regard to the administration of too much mass because of the normal high intake. The plasma level of calcium in most species ranges from 9 to 11 mg/100 ml, and toxicity symptoms may be produced if the concentration gets above 15 mg/100 ml. For injection studies, therefore, the specific activity of the preparation may be an important factor. It has been reported that 60 to 90 mg/kg of the chloride or acetate injected into cats or dogs will produce toxicity symptoms (Ca-1). Soft tissues of animals contain 0.05 to 0.12 mg calcium per gram fresh weight, and bones range from about 80 to 250 mg/g. A recommended nutrient solution for plants contains about 160 ppm, and crop plants usually have from 0.1 to 3 per cent on a dry-matter basis.

Radioassay. Preparations Ca-45-P-1 and Ca-45-P-2 are most commonly used, and the choice between them is governed by the need for increased specific activity vs. the increased cost. Likewise the use of the other high-specific-activity preparations would have to be justified in terms of cost. Ca^{45} should be counted with a thin-mica-window tube (<4 mg/cm^2) or an internal counter. Self-absorption considerations are critical, so that a favorable Ca^{45}/mass ratio must be used to avoid undue loss of sensitivity.

Chemistry. The chemical estimation of calcium in biological tissues has been the subject of extensive investigation, and details are readily available in the standard literature. In general, the sample is ashed, and calcium oxalate precipitated from the ash solution and then measured gravimetrically or by titration. No particular precautions are required in the ashing process. Calcium oxalate represents an ideal compound for radioassay, and therefore the standard procedure with but slight modification can be utilized for both chemical and radioactivity measurements. Details are given in the next section.

Typical Methods. *Dosage Levels.* The following dosages have been used in general metabolism studies with animals and have allowed tissue analyses and bone autoradiograms (higher dosages should be used if there is a particular interest in long-term studies or in tissues of lower accumulation, and smaller amounts could be used if there is an interest only in bone): rats, 1 to 10 μc in about 1 to 10 mg Ca orally or parenterally (Ca-2, Ca-3); chicks, 580,000 counts/min in 0.8 mg Ca orally (Ca-4); laying hens, 15 μc in 1 mg Ca orally (Ca-5); young pigs, 0.75 mc/100 lb intravenously (Ca-6); cattle, 2 to 3 mc intravenously and 4 to 6 mc orally in not more than 200 mg Ca for 500- to 1000-lb animals (Ca-7); dairy cows, 2 to 15 mc in 40 to 210 mg Ca intravenously and orally (Ca-8); cattle, 150 to 300 μc intravenously daily for 10 to 15 days for determination of endogenous fecal calcium by isotope dilution (Ca-9).

Some levels that have been used in soil and plant work are as follows: For a 1-yr study of leaching and plant uptake, 5.4 μc Ca^{45} per gram $CaCO_3$ was used in treatments of soil up to an equivalent of 5000 lb $CaCO_3$ per acre (Ca-10). In a study of uptake by alfalfa from a Sassafras sandy loam, 43 μc Ca^{45} in various salts was used per pot containing 18 lb of soil (Ca-11). In a study of uptake of Ca^{45} by tobacco from band applications of $CaCO_3$, $CaSO_4$, and $CaH_4(PO_4)_2$ applied at rates of 21 to 31 lb Ca per acre, the tagged materials contained 90 μc Ca^{45} per gram Ca (Ca-12).

Analysis. Procedures for combined chemical analysis and radioassay have been described (Ca-13, Ca-14), from which the following is taken, not as representing the best or only methods, but ones that have been satisfactory.

SOFT TISSUES, BLOOD, AND URINE. It is usually desirable to use a large sample for a yield of as high a content of Ca^{45} as possible. However, experience has shown that it is difficult, on account of interfering substances, to precipitate calcium as the oxalate quantitatively from more than 200 mg of tissue ash with the amounts of reagents and the volumes used. In general, the sample is ashed, and calcium oxalate precipitated from the ash solution for titration to give the total calcium content. After titration the solution is neutralized, a standard amount of carrier calcium added, and the calcium oxalate reprecipitated for the counting procedure. This reprecipitation with carrier is necessary because the original sample does not contain enough calcium to yield an amount of precipitate large enough for counting.

If there is sufficient material available, an alternative to the reprecipitation is the use of two samples, one for chemical analysis and one for radioassay. Details are as follows: The sample is treated with fuming nitric acid and evaporated to dryness. Small quantities of 30 per cent H_2O_2 may be added during evaporation, and the process is repeated until the resultant ash is white and free of organic residues. The ash is dissolved in 2 N HCl, and an aliquot, equivalent to less than 200 mg of ash, is transferred to a 50-ml centrifuge tube. One milliliter of saturated $(NH_4)_2C_2O_4$ is added to the solution in the centrifuge tube, then 2 drops of 0.05 per cent methyl red, and 4 ml acetic acid $(1 + 4)$ with thorough mixing. With constant stirring, NH_4OH $(1 + 4)$ is added until the solution is faintly alkaline, and then a few drops of acetic acid is added until the color is adjusted to a faint pink (pH 5.0). The solution is allowed to stand overnight for complete precipitation of the calcium oxalate. The solution is then centrifuged, and the supernatant can be used for phosphorus determination if desired. The precipitate is dispersed in about 10 ml NH_4OH $(1 + 49)$ and recentrifuged. The precipitate is then treated with 2 ml H_2SO_4 $(1 + 4)$, heated to 80 to 90°C, and titrated with 0.02 N $KMnO_4$ according to the usual practice. A standard amount of carrier calcium, usually 8 mg, is added, and the solution neutralized with NH_4OH $(1 + 4)$. Three milliliters of saturated $(NH_4)_2C_2O_4$ is added, and the calcium reprecipitated as described above. A better precipitate is obtained if the NH_4OH is added until the calcium oxalate just begins to appear and the solution is then heated at about 80°C for a few minutes; the neutralization is carried on as above and the precipitate is collected in the plastic-tube-and-cup assembly by centrifugation, as described in Chap. 5. If chemical analysis is not required on a particular sample, there is no need to reprecipitate. In this case the ash solution aliquot is treated with 8 mg carrier calcium, 3 ml of saturated $(NH_4)_2C_2O_4$, and the precipitation is carried out as already described, with collection of the precipitated calcium oxalate for radioassay.

BONES AND TEETH. When large amounts of material are available, a representative fresh sample of at least 2 g is weighed into a tared porcelain crucible and ashed in the muffle furnace; it is seldom necessary to re-ash these samples. The ashed bone is ground directly in the crucible with a pestle, and after redrying, exactly 500 mg is weighed out and made to 50 ml with dilute HCl. Aliquots of 5 ml are used for the precipitation of the calcium oxalate, and the precipitate is collected in the plastic-tube-and-cup assembly as described. The weight of the carefully dried oxalate collected in the metal cup is used to calculate the total calcium and the self-absorption correction. This procedure of ashing a large amount of bone and selecting an aliquot of the ground ash has been found quite helpful in permitting representative sampling of large bones and sections thereof. With small samples of bone, as from rats, the total ash is made to a given volume with dilute acid, and an aliquot employed which will represent approximately 50 mg of bone ash.

FECES AND PLANT MATERIAL. Approximately 20 g of fresh feces from cattle and a 24-hr collection from rats are used for analysis. The sample is dried and ashed in the muffle furnace. The ash is dissolved in a few milliliters of 2 N HCl and made to 50 ml with distilled water. Any insoluble residue is allowed to settle, and 10-ml aliquots are taken and treated exactly as described under Bones and Teeth. Here again there will be sufficient calcium in the original sample so that the calcium oxalate collected in the metal cup can be used for gravimetric analysis as well as for radioassay.

BLOOD PLASMA. Chemical calcium may be determined by direct precipitation from plasma according to standard methods (Ca-15), and then carrier calcium is added for reprecipitation, as already described, and collection of the calcium oxalate for counting. Colorimetric and flame methods for estimation of calcium in small samples of biological fluids have been reported (Ca-16, Ca-17).

Ca-1. Sollmann, Torald: "A Manual of Pharmacology," 7th ed., W. B. Saunders Company, Philadelphia, 1949.
Ca-2. Harrison, Harold E., and Helen C. Harrison: Studies with Radiocalcium: The Intestinal Absorption of Calcium, J. Biol. Chem., 188: 83–90 (1951).
Ca-3. Hansard, Sam L., C. L. Comar, and M. P. Plumlee: Effect of Calcium Status, Mass of Calcium Administered and Age on Ca45 Metabolism in the Rat, Proc. Soc. Exptl. Biol. Med., 78: 455–460 (1951).
Ca-4. Migicovsky, B. B., and A. R. G. Emslie: Deposition of Radioactive Calcium in Rachitic and Nonrachitic Chick Tibia from Oral and Intramuscular Doses of Ca45, Arch. Biochem., 28: 324–328 (1950).
Ca-5. Comar, C. L., and J. Clyde Driggers: Secretion of Radioactive Calcium in the Hen's Egg, Science, 109: 282 (1949).
Ca-6. Comar, C. L., W. E. Lotz, and G. A. Boyd: Autoradiographic Studies of Calcium, Phosphorus and Strontium Distribution in the Bones of the Growing Pig, Am. J. Anat., 90: 113–125 (1952).
Ca-7. Hansard, Sam L., C. L. Comar, and M. P. Plumlee: Absorption and Tissue Distribution of Radiocalcium in Cattle, J. Animal Sci., 11: 524–535 (1952).
Ca-8. Visek, W. J., R. A. Monroe, E. W. Swanson, and C. L. Comar: Calcium Metabolism in Dairy Cows as Studied with Ca45, J. Dairy Sci., 36: 373–384 (1953).
Ca-9. Visek, W. J., R. A. Monroe, E. W. Swanson, and C. L. Comar: Determination of Endogenous Fecal Calcium in Cattle by a Simple Isotope Dilution Method, J. Nutrition, 50: 23–33 (1953).
Ca-10. Harris, Henry C., W. H. MacIntire, C. L. Comar, W. M. Shaw, S. H. Winterberg, and S. L. Hood: Use of Ca45 Labeled Calcium Carbonate in Determining Proportions of Native and Additive Calcium in Lysimeter Leachings and in Plant Uptake, Soil Sci., 73: 289–298 (1952).
Ca-11. Ririe, David, and Stephen J. Toth: Plant Studies with Radioactive Calcium, Soil Sci., 73: 1–10 (1952).
Ca-12. Blume, James M., and N. S. Hall: Calcium Uptake by Tobacco from Band Applications of Fertilizer Materials, Soil Sci., 75: 299–306 (1953).
Ca-13. Norris, William P., and Blanche J. Lawrence: Determination of Calcium in Biological Materials, Anal. Chem., 25: 956–960 (1953).

Ca-14. Comar, C. L., Sam L. Hansard, S. L. Hood, M. P. Plumlee, and B. F. Barrentine: Use of Calcium-45 in Biological Studies, *Nucleonics*, **8**: 19–31 (1951).

Ca-15. Kolmer, John A., and Fred Boerner: "Approved Laboratory Technic," 4th ed., Appleton-Century-Crofts, Inc., New York, 1945.

Ca-16. Severinghaus, J. W., and J. W. Ferrebee: Calcium Determination by Flame Photometry Methods for Serum, Urine, and Other Fluids: *J. Biol. Chem.*, **187**: 621–630 (1950).

Ca-17. Kibrick, Andre C., Dorris Palmer, and Sol Skupp: A Method for the Colorimetric Determination of Calcium in 0.5 Ml of Serum, *Proc. Soc. Exptl. Biol. Med.*, **76**: 115–116 (1951).

Carbon 14 (5568 yr)   *Beta* 0.155   *Gamma*

Cat. No.	*Sp. Act.*	*Form*	*Cost*	*Chem. Cont.*	*Radiochem. Cont.*
C-14-P-1	0.25–1.5 mc/mg	$BaCO_3$	$36/mc	—	—

Mica W.	*Int. C.*			50 % *Self-abs.*	
5×10^{-4}	0.9×10^{-4}			6 (calc.)	

Critical Org.	*Body*	*Air*	*Water*	*Effect. $T_{1/2}$*
Fat and bone	250 μc	10^{-6}	3×10^{-3}	180 days

Dosage Levels. Carbon 14 has been widely used as a label for so many organic compounds in biological experiments that it is virtually impossible to enumerate them individually and difficult to generalize. The amount of activity required will depend upon the purpose of the study (e.g., biosynthesis or tracer), the metabolic behavior of the labeled compound, and the sensitivity of the measurement. Following are some levels that have been used: With rats, mice, and guinea pigs, for routes of administration such as oral, intraperitoneal, intravenous, and skin and for such compounds as carbonate, bicarbonate, acetate, amino acids, ascorbic acid, adrenalin, codeine, digitoxin, and ergosterol, the dosage has ranged from 1 to 50 μc. With rabbits, 50 μc of labeled acetate has been employed to follow fatty acid metabolism (C-1). With pigeons, 0.4 to 20 μc has been used to study biosynthesis of uric acid (C-2); goats, 5 mc of labeled acetate to study lactose and glycerol formation (C-3); dairy cows, 7 mc sodium carbonate and 5 mc sodium propionate (C-4, C-5); and 1 to 6 mc of carbon-labeled substances has been used in perfused-udder studies (C-6). About 2.7×10^4 counts/min of C^{14} was injected into the silkworm for synthesis of radioactive silk (C-7). Cockroaches have been injected with 20 μg of C^{14}-labeled DDT with a specific activity of 1.5 mc/-mmole (C-8).

C^{14}-labeled acids were infiltrated into tobacco by cutting the leaves underwater and submerging them in a solution of pH 5.5 containing 5000 to 20,000 counts/min/ml (C-9). The container was paraffin-coated, and after the leaf was submerged, it was evacuated for 30 to 60 sec in a vacuum desiccator, and the vacuum then released slowly. For studies on rubber formation, guayule plants were grown in quartz sand with nutrient solution, and 0.231 mc of C^{14}-labeled acetate per plant was introduced and allowed to remain in contact with the plant for 55 hr (C-10). In a tracer study of C^{14} movement in the geranium, the attached leaf was enclosed in a glass photosynthetic chamber, and CO_2 supplied at a concentration of 1.5 per cent by volume containing about 0.25 mc C^{14} (C-11). Radioactive asparagine was prepared by placing 8- to 9-day-old seedlings in an 8-liter desiccator filled with air containing 5 per cent CO_2 and 0.25 mc $C^{14}O_2$ for 24 hr under continuous illumination (C-12). The yields were increased by using up to 3 mc and a 6-day exposure period (C-13). Labeled cotton cellulose was prepared by introducing 12.5 μc glucose-1-C^{14} through the sliced stem just below the 21-day boll (C-14). Plant pathogenic fungi have been grown satisfactorily on a medium containing 30 $\mu c/ml$ of C^{14}-labeled sucrose (C-15); fungal spores, tagged by a 5- to 7-day growth period on this medium, showed no radiation effects. Levels up to 100 $\mu c/ml$ were used, and although growth was retarded, there was no loss of pathogenicity in the surviving organisms. Callus cultures of *Sequoia sempervirens* were grown for 2, 16, 40, and 85 days on a medium containing 1 to 1.5 $\mu c/ml$ of C^{14}-labeled sucrose (C-16).

Preparation of Sample. Reference (C-17) may be consulted as a standard text for many of the procedural details in connection with C^{14} analysis. Perhaps the most general method involves the wet combustion of the biological materials, followed by collection of $BaCO_3$, details of which have been described in Chap. 5. However, many workers obtain adequate measurements by direct plating of the samples, and following are a few examples of some techniques employed: It was shown that C^{14}-nicotinic acid in urine, plasma, or laked erythrocytes could be directly plated over a given area to give results reproducible within 2 per cent (C-18). It was emphasized that calibration curves must be prepared under the same conditions as for sample measurement using the particular biological material. A procedure is described for direct mounting of C^{14}-labeled fatty acids which was less tedious and gave more sensitive measurements than conversion to $BaCO_3$ on account of a more favorable C^{14}/sample mass ratio (C-19). An aluminum disk, 1.75 in. in diameter, was lined with a piece of lens paper, weighed, and placed about 6 in. below an infrared lamp. An aliquot of the fatty acid solution (usually 1 ml) was added dropwise to the warmed lens paper so as to keep the surface constantly wet but without permitting the fat solution to creep over the edge. The disk and contents were reweighed for mass self-absorption corrections. Up to 40 mg was safely mounted in this way. If an ether solution and evaporation by an air stream were employed, it was practicable to deposit up to 150 mg of fatty acids. After administration of C^{14}-labeled adrenalin to rats, the tissues were ground with four portions of 1 per cent trichloroacetic acid with the aid of sand, and the combined extracts were centrifuged, washed, evaporated on aluminum plates, and counted (C-20). Combustion of macerated tissues indicated that more than 90 per cent of the radioactivity was consistently extracted by this procedure. Urine, plasma, and blood cells were plated directly.

Counting Techniques. The choice as to method of counting lies primarily among the thin-mica-window tube, the internal counter, and the ionization chamber plus the vibrating reed. The decision will be based in large part upon the required sensitivity, the self-absorption characteristics, the C^{14}/mass ratio in the sample to be measured, and the amount of sample available. In general, the ordinary thin-mica-window tube for counting $BaCO_3$ or solid samples is preferred if sufficiently sensitive, on account of simplicity and trouble-free operation and because the same equipment can be used for various measurements. If additional sensitivity is required, the internal counter can be used at the cost of slightly increased operating difficulties. The ionization chamber gives greatest sensitivity but requires specialized equipment and experience in handling the gas phase.

Table 6-1 illustrates the role of self-absorption and shows how the ratio of activity to total mass of the sample to be measured may govern the

TABLE 6-1. EFFECT OF SELF-ABSORPTION AND SIZE OF SAMPLE AVAILABLE ON RELATIVE SENSITIVITIES OF COUNTING TECHNIQUES FOR C^{14} [a]

	Mica window	Internal counter	Ion chamber
Background...................................	20 cpm	100 cpm	5×10^{-16} amp
Case 1: 10^{-3} μc C^{14} in zero mass.............	2	11	10
Case 2: $10^{-3}\mu c$ C^{14} in 1 mg C; equivalent to 16.4 mg $BaCO_3$ or 3.5 mg/cm² in 1-in. cup.......	1.25	5	10
Case 3: 10^{-3} μc C^{14} in 5 mg C; equivalent to 82 mg $BaCO_3$ or 17 mg/cm² in 1-in. cup.....	0.41	1.54	10
Case 4: 10^{-3} μc C^{14} in 120 mg C; 5-mg aliquot equivalent to 82 mg $BaCO_3$ or 17 mg/cm² used for solid counting in 1-in. cup; entire sample used in ion chamber.....................	0.017	0.064	10

[a] Values are given as ratio of counting rate observed to background of instrument.

choice of counting procedure. In case 1, assume that a sample contains 10^{-3} μc C^{14} in essentially zero mass. The internal counter and the ion chamber will be about five times as sensitive as the thin-mica-window tube. However, there would be no advantage in going to the ion-chamber measurement. Since C^{14} in a biological system becomes diluted with stable carbon, one would seldom encounter a situation as in case 1. In case 2, assume that the 10^{-3} μc C^{14} is contained in 1 mg carbon, which would be converted to about 16.4 mg $BaCO_3$. The self-absorption now causes a decrease in the sensitivity of the solid measurements, but the ion chamber still offers an advantage of only 2 over the internal counter. If the activity were contained in 5 mg carbon, as in case 3, this would give a solid sample approaching infinite thickness, and the advantage of the ion chamber over the internal counter becomes a factor of 6.5. If there were large amounts of a sample available, such as 10^{-3} μc C^{14} in 120 mg carbon, as in case 4, there would be no advantage in using more than 5 mg carbon for the solid counts, since this would approach infinite thickness. However, this entire sample could be converted to CO_2 for measurement in a 250-ml ionization chamber. Under these conditions the ion-chamber method has an actual effectiveness of about 150 times that of the solid-counting methods.

In summary, then, the gas measurement should be seriously considered for situations where considerable numbers of relatively large samples of very low activity are anticipated. Under other conditions, solid counting appears to be the more convenient.

Following is a list of commercially available C^{14}-labeled compounds (C-21). It is expected that any compound for which there is a demand will eventually be obtainable. See reference (C-21) for addresses of suppliers. (See page 71 regarding radiation decomposition.)

Acetic acid-1-C^{14}
Acetone-1,3-C^{14}
Acetone-2-C^{14}
Acetonitrile-2-C^{14}
Acetophenone-α-C^{14}
Acetophenone-7-C^{14}
Acetyl chloride-1-C^{14}
Acetylcholine bromide (trimethyl-2-acetoxyethyl-1,2-C^{14}–ammonium bromide)
Acetylcholine methyl-C^{14} chloride
Acetylene-C^{14}
Adenine-C^{14} (uniformly labeled)
Adenine-8-C^{14}
Adenosine diphosphate–C^{14} (uniformly labeled)
Adenosine-5-phosphoric acid–C^{14} (uniformly labeled)
Adenosine triphosphate–C^{14} (uniformly labeled)
Adenylic acid–C^{14} (uniformly labeled)
Adenylic acid A–C^{14} (uniformly labeled)
Adenylic acid B–C^{14} (uniformly labeled)
Adipic acid-1-C^{14}
Adipic acid-1,6-C^{14}
DL-Alanine-1-C^{14}
DL-Alanine-2-C^{14}
Algae-C^{14} (*C. pyrenoidosa*, dried)
Alkanes (C_5–C_{21})-C^{14}
Alloxan-2-C^{14}
p-Aminobenzoic acid–carboxyl-C^{14}
DL-Aminobutyric acid-1-C^{14}
DL-Aminobutyric acid-2-C^{14}
DL-Aminobutyric acid-3-C^{14}
DL-α-Aminobutyric acid-1-C^{14}
γ-Aminobutyric acid-1-C^{14}

n-Amyl alcohol-1-C^{14}
Amyl bromide-1-C^{14}
Aniline-1-C^{14}
Anthranilic acid–carboxylic-C^{14}
D-Arabinose-1-C^{14}
D-Arabinose-5-C^{14}
L-Arginine-C^{14} (uniformly labeled)
DL-Aspartic acid-4-C^{14}
L-Aspartic acid-C^{14} (uniformly labeled)
8-Azaguanine-2-C^{14}
Barbituric acid-2-C^{14}
Barbituric acid-4,6-C^{14}
Barium carbide-C^{14}
Barium carbonate–C^{14} (up to 1 μc in each vial)
Barium D-gluconate-1-C^{14}
Benzanthracene-5,6-C^{14}
Benzene-C^{14}
Benzene-1-C^{14}
Benzoic acid–C^{14}
Benzoic acid-1-C^{14}
Benzoic acid-7-C^{14} (up to 1 μc in each vial)
Benzoic acid–carboxyl-C^{14}
Benzyl alcohol-7-C^{14}
Bromoacetic acid-1-C^{14}
Bromoacetic acid-2-C^{14}
Butane-1-C^{14}
di-n-Butyl-1-C^{14} adiapate
n-Butyl alcohol-1-C^{14}
n-Butyl aldehyde-1-C^{14}
n-Butyl amine-1-C^{14}
n-Butyl halide-1-C^{14}
di-n-Butyl-1-C^{14} phthalate
di-n-Butyl sebacate-1-C^{14}

n-Butyl-1-C^{14} stearate
Butyric acid-1-C^{14}
n-Butyryl chloride-1-C^{14}
Cadmium D-ribonate-1-C^{14}
Cadmium D-talonate-1-C^{14}
Caffeine-1-methyl-C^{14}
Calcium D-galactonate-1-C^{14}
Calcium L-gluconate-1-C^{14}
Calcium glycolate-1-C^{14}
Calcium oxalate-C^{14}
Capric acid-1-C^{14}
Caproic acid-1-C^{14}
Caprylic acid-1-C^{14}
Carbon (amorphous)
Carbon black–C^{14}
Carbon monoxide–C^{14}
Chloroacetic acid-2-C^{14}
Chlorobenzene-1-C^{14}
Cholestenone-4-C^{14} (ring A)
Cholesterol-4-C^{14} (ring A)
Choline bromide-1,2-C^{14}
Choline methyl-C^{14} chloride
Chrysene-5,6-C^{14}
Citric acid-1,5-C^{14}
Citric acid-1,6-C^{14}
Codeine-3-methoxy-C^{14}
Cuprous cyanide–C^{14}
Cyanide-C^{14}
Cyclohexanone-2-C^{14}
Cyclopentanecarboxylic acid–carboxyl-C^{14}
Cytidylic acid–C^{14} (uniformly labeled)
2,6-Diaminopurine-2-C^{14}
p,p'-Dichlorodiphenyl-4-C^{14}-trichloro-ethane
2,4-Dichlorophenoxyacetic acid-1-C^{14}
2,4-Dichlorophenoxyacetic acid-2-C^{14}
Diethyl malonate-1,3-C^{14}
Diethyl malonate-2-C^{14}
Digitalis purpurea–C^{14} leaf tissue
Digitalis purpurea–C^{14} root tissue
DL-2,5-Dihydroxyphenylalanine-2-C^{14}
DL-3,4-Dihydroxyphenylalanine-2-C^{14}
Enanthylic acid-1-C^{14}
dl-Epinephrine-7-C^{14}-d-bitartrate
Ethane-C^{14}
Ethanol-1-C^{14}
Ethanol-2-C^{14}
DL-Ethionine-s-ethyl–C^{14}
Ethyl acetamino-cyanoacetate-2-C^{14}
Ethyl acetate-1-C^{14}

Ethylbenzene-C^{14} (labeled in side chain or ring)
Ethyl bromoacetate-1-C^{14}
Ethyl bromoacetate-2-C^{14}
2-Ethyl butanol-1-C^{14}
2-Ethyl butyric acid-1-C^{14}
Ethyl cyanoacetate-1-C^{14}
Ethyl cyanoacetate-2-C^{14}
Ethylene-C^{14}
Ethylene bromohydrin-1,2-C^{14}
Ethylene dibromide-1-C^{14}
Ethylene oxide-1,2-C^{14}
2-Ethyl hexanol-1-C^{14}
di-2-Ethyl hexyl-1-C^{14} adipate
di-2-Ethyl hexyl-1-C^{14} phthalate
di-2-Ethyl hexyl sebacate-1-C^{14}
Ethyl iodide–C^{14}
Ethyl iodide-1-C^{14}
Ethyl iodide-2-C^{14}
Fatty acids–C^{14}
Formaldehyde-C^{14}
Formic acid–C^{14}
Fructose-C^{14} (uniformly labeled)
D-Fructose-C^{14} (totally labeled)
D-Fructose-1,6-C^{14}
Fructose-1,6-diphosphate–C^{14}
Fumaric acid-2-C^{14}
Fumaric acid-2,3-C^{14}
D-Galactose-1-C^{14}
D-Galactose-2-C^{14}
Girard's Reagent T–C^{14}
D-Glucitol-1-C^{14}
Glucose-C^{14} (uniformly labeled)
Glucose-1-C^{14}
Glucose-6-C^{14}
d-Glucose-C^{14} (uniformly labeled)
D-Glucose-1-C^{14}
D-Glucose-2-C^{14}
D-Glucose-6-C^{14}
L-Glucose-1-C^{14}
Glucurone-6-C^{14}
L-Glutamic acid–C^{14} (uniformly labeled)
DL-Glutamic acid-1-C^{14}
DL-Glutamic acid-2-C^{14}
Glutaric acid-1,5-C^{14}
Glutathione-C^{14} (uniformly labeled)
Glycerol-1-C^{14}
Glycerol-1,3-C^{14}
Glycine-1-C^{14}
Glycine-2-C^{14}
Guanidine-C^{14}

Guanine-2-C^{14}
Guanine-4-C^{14}
Guanine-8-C^{14}
Guanine sulfate-2-C^{14}
Guanylic acid–C^{14} (uniformly labeled)
Guanylic acid–C^{14} (uniformly labeled, mixed isomers)
Guanylic acid A–C^{14} (uniformly labeled)
Guanylic acid B–C^{14} (uniformly labeled)
Hippuric acid-1-C^{14}
Hippuric acid-2-C^{14}
dl-Histidine-2-C^{14}
L-Histidine-C^{14} (uniformly labeled)
DL-Homoserine-2-C^{14}
Hydantoins-5-C^{14} (various)
Indoleacetic acid-1-C^{14}
Isonicotinic hydrazid–C^{14}
Isopropyl alcohol-1,3-C^{14}
Isopropyl iodide-1,3-C^{14}
Lactic acid–C^{14}
Lactic acid-1-C^{14}
Lactic acid-2-C^{14}
D-Lactose-1-C^{14}
Lauric acid-1-C^{14}
Lead formate–C^{14}
Lead D-xylonate-1-C^{14}
DL-Leucine-1-C^{14}
DL-Leucine-2-C^{14}
Linoleic acid-1-C^{14}
Lithium maltobionate-1-C^{14}
dl-Lysine-2-C^{14} monohydrochloride
L-Lysine-C^{14} (uniformly labeled)
D-Lyxono-lactone-1-C^{14}
D-Lyxose-1-C^{14}
Maleic anhydride-2-C^{14}
Maleic anhydride-2,3-C^{14}
Malonic acid-2-C^{14}
D-Maltose-1-C^{14}
D-Mannitol-1-C^{14}
Mannono-γ-lactone-1-C^{14}
D-Mannose-1-C^{14}
Methane-C^{14}
Methanol-C^{14}
DL-Methionine-2-C^{14}
DL-Methionine-s-methyl-C^{14}
L-Methionine-methyl-C^{14}
3-p-Methoxyphenyl-n-butyric acid–C^{14}
Methyl alcohol–C^{14}
Methyl amine hydrochloride–C^{14}
Methyl benzoate-1-C^{14}
Methyl bromoacetate-1-C^{14}

Methyl bromoacetate-2-C^{14}
Methyl chloride–C^{14}
Methyl cyanoacetate-2-C^{14}
Methyl iodide–C^{14}
1-Methylphenanthrene-9,10-C^{14}
Methyl stearate-1-C^{14}
Myristic acid-1-C^{14}
Naphthalene-1-C^{14}
α-Naphthaleneacetic acid-1-C^{14}
1-Naphthol-8-C^{14}
2-Naphthol-8-C^{14}
2-Naphthylamine-8-C^{14}
Nicotinic acid–carboxyl–C^{14}
Nitrogen mustard–C^{14}
n-Nitrosomethyl urea–C^{14}
DL-Norleucine-1-C^{14}
DL-Norleucine-2-C^{14}
DL-Norvaline-1-C^{14}
DL-Norvaline-2-C^{14}
Norvaline hydrochloride-3-C^{14}
Oleic acid-1-C^{14}
dl-Ornithine monohydrochloride-2-C^{14}
Oxalic acid-1,2-C^{14}
Palmitic acid-1-C^{14}
Pelargonic acid-1-C^{14}
Pentadecanoic acid-1-C^{14}
Phenanthrene-9-C^{14}
Phenol-1-C^{14}
Phenylacetate-2-C^{14}
Phenylacetic acid-1-C^{14}
DL-Phenylalanine-2-C^{14}
DL-3-Phenylalanine-2-C^{14}
DL-Phenylalanine-3-C^{14}
L-Phenylalanine-C^{14} (uniformly labeled)
dl-Phenylalanine hydrochloride-2-C^{14}
dl-Phenylalanine hydrochloride-3-C^{14}
4-Phenylbutyric acid-1-C^{14}
Phthalic acid-7-C^{14}
Pimelic acid-1,7-C^{14}
Polymethyl methacrylate–C^{14}
Polystyrene-C^{14}
Potassium D-arabonate-1-C^{14}
Potassium carbonate–C^{14}
Potassium cyanide–C^{14} (up to 1 μc in each vial)
Progesterone-4-C^{14} (ring A)
Propane-2-C^{14}
Propionaldehyde-1-C^{14}
Propionic acid-1-C^{14}
Propiophenone-α-C^{14}
Propyl iodide-1-C^{14}

Chlorine 36 ($\sim$4.4 $\times$ 10^5 yr)   *Beta* 0.713   *Gamma*

Cat. No.	*Sp. Act.*	*Form*	*Cost*	*Chem. Cont.*	*Radiochem. Cont.*
Cl-36-I	0.6 μc/g	KCl	$33/6 μc	—	145 mc K^{42} (12.44 hr)
					100 mc S^{35} (87.1 days)
					0.01 mc P^{32} (14.3 days)
Cl-36-P	10–20 μc/g	HCl	$5/$\mu$c	—	—

Mica W.	*Int. C.*	*Scint. C.*		
1.7 $\times$ 10^{-4}	1.8 $\times$ 10^{-5}	8.3 $\times$ 10^{-2}	50% *Self-abs.*	
			91 (calc.)	

Critical Org.	*Body*	*Air*	*Water*	*Effect. T$_{1/2}$*
Total body	200 μc	4 $\times$ 10^{-7}	2 $\times$ 10^{-3}	29 days

Intake Levels.   Animal intakes vary widely and usually exceed the needs.   About 5 mg/day is adequate for rats.   A recommended nutrient solution for plants contains 0.177 ppm.   Crop plants contain about 0.2 to 2 per cent.   Human beings and dogs have been reported to have about 1 g chlorine per kilogram body weight.   Serum contains about 6 mg/ml of chloride expressed as sodium chloride.

Radioassay.   Preparation Cl-36-P is probably the best to use, since most if not all of the radiocontaminants have been removed.   The K^{42} and P^{32} contamination is eliminated by decay.   However, time will not permit removal of S^{35} in this way.   If there is any possibility of S^{35} being present, the samples should be counted with an absorber of about 10 mg/cm^2 to eliminate the S^{35} contribution.   Solution counting is satisfactory, although the higher sensitivity of internal or end-window counter measurements employing solid samples may be required.   Attention is called to Cl^{38}, which may be used by workers near cyclotron production.   Cl^{38} has a half-life of 38 min, which restricts its use, but it emits very energetic beta particles and gamma rays, so that the radioassay can be made simple and rapid.

Chemistry.   Tissues can be ashed by treating up to a 5-g sample with 20 ml of a 5 per cent Na$_2$CO$_3$ solution in a Pt dish, evaporating to dryness, and igniting at dull-red heat.   The ash is extracted with hot H$_2$O, filtered, and washed, and the residue is reignited and extracted with acid.   This solution is added to the first H$_2$O extract.   Simple methods that do not require ashing have been described for determination of chlorides in serum and spinal fluid (Cl-1, Cl-2).   This allows determination of turnover by convenient procedures, since both the chemical and radioactivity measurements can be made directly on these samples.

Typical Methods.   In a study with dogs (Cl-3), about 5 μc Cl^{36} in 18 mg NaCl per 10 lb body weight was injected into the hind-leg vein. Aliquots of urine, blood serum, and Formalin suspensions of feces were dried on filter-paper disks, mounted on a metal backing, and counted with an end-window tube through an absorber of 10.335 mg/cm^2.   In a similar study (Cl-4, Cl-5) about 50 μc in 10 to 15 ml of normal saline was injected per patient.

Cl^{36} studies have been undertaken with plants grown in sand culture with a nutrient solution consisting of 0.003 M Ca(NO$_2$)$_2$·4H$_2$O, 0.007 M KNO$_3$, 0.001 M MgSO$_4$·7H$_2$O, 0.001 M KH$_2$PO$_4$, 1 ppm Fe, 0.5 ppm B, 0.025 ppm Mn, and 0.25 ppm Zn (Cl-6).   The applications of radioactivity were as follows: One microcurie Cl^{36} was poured on the surface of a sand culture containing a mature tomato plant and flushed in with 1 liter of nutrient solution; 1 μc Cl^{36} was added as above to a sand culture containing four alfalfa plants at 10 days before harvest; lima-bean plants were treated with 0.05 μc Cl^{36} added daily to the nutrient solution for 20 days before harvest; a mature corn plant was treated with 2 μc Cl^{36} at 10 days before harvest; and a solution containing 0.005 μc/ml of Cl^{36} and a wetting agent was painted daily for 14 to 21 days on the leaves of various plant species.   The plant tissue was measured for Cl^{36} by grinding the oven-dried material to 60 mesh and spreading 50 mg over the bottom of a metal planchet.   Counting was done with a 1.82-mg/cm^2 mica-end-window tube.   Losses of activity were noted when ashing temperatures above 300°C were employed, and the direct measurement of the dried material appeared to be the one of choice.

Cl-1. Franco, Vincent, and Bernard Klein: The Microdetermination of Chlorides in Serum and Spinal Fluid, *J. Lab. Clin. Med.*, **37**: 950–954 (1951).

Cl-2. Schales, O., and S. S. Schales: A Simple and Accurate Method for the Determination of Chloride in Biological Fluids, *J. Biol. Chem.*, **140**: 879 (1941).

Cl-3. Burch, G. E., S. A. Threefoot, and C. T. Ray: Rates of Turnover and Biologic Decay of Chloride and Chloride Space in the Dog Determined with the Long-life Isotope, Cl^{36}, *J. Lab. Clin. Med.*, **35**: 331–347 (1950).

Cl-4. Ray, C. T., G. E. Burch, and S. A. Threefoot: Biologic Decay Rates of Chloride in Normal and Diseased Man, Determined with Long-lived Radiochloride, Cl^{36}, *J. Lab. Clin. Med.*, **39**: 673–696 (1952).

Cl-5. Threefoot, S. A., G. E. Burch, and C. T. Ray: Chloride "Space" and Total Exchanging Chloride in Man Measured with Long-life Radiochloride, Cl^{36}, *J. Lab. Clin. Med.*, **42**: 16–33 (1953).

Cl-6. Toth, S. J., and A. E. Kretschmer: Plant Studies with Radioactive Chlorine, *Soil Sci.*, **77**: 293–302 (1954).

Chromium **51** (27.8 days)				*Beta*	*Gamma* 0.32	*K*
Cat. No.	*Sp. Act.*	*Form*	*Cost*	*Chem. Cont.*	*Radiochem. Cont.*	
Cr-51-I	50 mc/g	Metal	$34/50 mc	—	—	
Cr-51-P	100–400 mc/g	CrCl$_3$	$1/mc	—	—	

Mica W.	*Int. C.*	*Scint. C.*	R_f/*mc*	50% *Self-abs.*
1.9×10^{-2}	6.9×10^{-4}	4.2×10^{-3}	0.2	11 (detn.)

Critical Org.	*Body*	*Air*	*Water*	*Effect.* $T_{1/2}$
Kidney	390 μc	8×10^{-6}	0.5	22 days

Intake Levels. Chromium is not an important naturally occurring constituent of biological materials, although traces do occur in soils. A primary interest has been in the use of Cr^{51} for the determination of red-cell volume (Cr-1). The main advantage over other labels is that the Cr^{51}-labeled cells retain their activity for as long as a day or more. Human blood has been reported to contain about 14 to 20 μg/100 g (Cr-2). About 340 ppm chromium as potassium dichromate in food was about the limit of tolerance for rats, and a daily intake of 10 mg was fatal for dogs in 3 months. CrCl$_3$ was about as toxic as chromate.

Radioassay. For most animal work the high-specific-activity material will be needed to reduce the mass administered. Even higher specific activities than that listed can be obtained commercially from the bombardment of samples that have been enriched in Cr^{50}. However, these may not be necessary if sensitive measurements are made. Although the internal counter gives the highest sensitivity, the self-absorption considerations with such a soft-gamma radiation become of extreme importance, and therefore scintillation counting may often be the method of choice.

Chemistry. Dry-ashing yields low recoveries presumably on account of the sublimation of CrCl$_3$·6H$_2$O at 83°C, whereas wet digestion is satisfactory. Chromium has been estimated chemically in tissue by acid digestion, separation from extraneous ions by virtue of differential solubility properties in different valence states, and photometric evaluation of the color produced with diphenylcarbazide (Cr-2, Cr-3).

Typical Methods. Red cells from 50 ml of human blood were incubated with a solution containing 40 to 200 μc Cr^{51} in 336 to 2800 μg Cr as Na$_2$CrO$_4$ (Cr-4). The red cells were washed, reconstituted, and injected into the patient, from whom blood samples were taken 10 min thereafter. The whole blood was centrifuged, and the packed red cells diluted to four times their initial volume and inverted ten times to ensure complete hemolysis. A 0.2-ml aliquot was pipetted onto a planchet, 0.8 ml H$_2$O added, and the hemolysates dried for counting with either a gamma tube or an internal proportional counter. In this procedure the self-absorption was found to be uniform between samples, and therefore this method was preferred to an earlier one in which the red cells were dried and ground. In a study of Cr^{51} distribution, various preparations of chromic chloride, sodium chromite, sodium chromate, and sodium dichromate were administered to rats in amounts of 50 μc in 4 to 250 μg (Cr-5); 1 mc $Cr^{51}Cl_3$ per 100 lb body weight was intravenously injected into sheep. Tissue samples were placed in small metal cups and kept in a frozen state until measured directly with a scintillation counter. The bottom of the metal cup was placed in contact with the metal-enclosed crystal, and under these conditions the measurements were apparently independent of the mass of the sample. In another study, rabbits were given 200 μc Cr^{51} in 2 mg chromium; tissues were digested in 10 per cent NaOH, and bones in concentrated HNO_3 for measurement in a specialized cup-type toroidal gamma counter (Cr-6). Details of red-cell-labeling techniques for red-cell survival studies have been reported (Cr-7).

Cr-1. Gray, Seymour J., and Kenneth Sterling: Determination of Circulating Red Cell Volume by Radioactive Chromium, *Science*, **112**: 179–180 (1950).

Cr-2. Mitchell, Avard M., and Seymour J. Gray: The Colorimetric Determination of Trace Amounts of Chromium in Tissue, Document AECU-779, Harvard Medical School, Peter Bent Brigham Hospital, no date.

Cr-3. Urone, Paul F., and Hanns K. Anders: Determination of Small Amounts of Chromium in Human Blood, Tissues, and Urine, *Anal. Chem.*, **22**: 1317–1321 (1950).

Cr-4. Sterling, Kenneth, and Seymour J. Gray: Determination of the Circulating Red Cell Volume in Man by Radioactive Chromium, *J. Clin. Invest.*, **29**: 1614–1619 (1950).

Cr-5. Visek, W. J., I. B. Whitney, U. S. G. Kuhn III, and C. L. Comar: Metabolism of Cr^{51} by Animals as Influenced by Chemical State, *Proc. Soc. Exptl. Biol. Med.*, **84**: 610–615 (1953).

Cr-6. Kraintz, Leon, and Roy V. Talmage: Distribution of Radioactivity Following Intravenous Administration of Trivalent Chromium 51 in the Rat and Rabbit, *Proc. Soc. Exptl. Biol. Med.*, **81**: 490–492 (1952).

Cr-7. Necheles, T. F., Irwin M. Weinstein, and George V. LeRoy: Radioactive Sodium Chromate for the Study of Survival of Red Blood Cells. I. The Effect of Radioactive Sodium Chromate on Red Cells. II. The Rate of Hemolysis in Certain Hematologic Disorders, *J. Lab. Clin. Med.*, **42**: 358–367, 368–376 (1953).

| Cobalt 57 (270 days) | | | | Beta 0.26 | Gamma 0.014–0.131 |
| Cobalt 58 (72 days) | | | | Beta 0.47 | Gamma 0.81   K |

Cat. No.	Sp. Act.	Form	Cost	Chem. Cont.	Radiochem. Cont.
Co-5758-P	CF	$CoCl_2$	$75/mc	—	—

Mica W.	Int. C.	Scint. C.	R_f/mc	50% Self-abs.
3.3×10^{-4}	1.2×10^{-4}	6.1×10^{-4}	Co^{57}, 7	35 (calc.)
			Co^{58}, 2	

| Cobalt 60 (5.27 yr) | | | | Beta 0.31 | Gamma 1.17, 1.33 |

Cat. No.	Sp. Act.	Form	Cost	Chem. Cont.	Radiochem. Cont.
Co-60-I	34 mc/g	Co_2O_3	$33/24 mc	—	—
Co-60-P	0.5–5 mc/mg	$CoCl_2$	$2/mc	—	—

Mica W.	Int. C.	Scint. C.	R_f/mc	50% Self-abs.
1.8×10^{-4}	1×10^{-4}	3.6×10^{-4}	15	23 (calc.)

Critical Org.	Body	Air	Water	Effect. $T_{1/2}$
Liver	3 μc	10^{-6}	2×10^{-2}	9 days

Intake Levels. Ruminants require about 0.1 mg/day of cobalt per 100 lb body weight, or about 0.1 ppm in the dry matter of herbage. The requirements for nonruminants are not established, although cobalt must be required to satisfy vitamin B_{12} needs. For rats, 0.4 μg/day is adequate, and in rabbits deficiency symptoms were not produced on as little as 0.0024 ppm. Crop plants range from 0.03 to 0.4 ppm on a dry-weight basis. The glandular organs of animals usually show the highest concentrations ranging from 0.2 to 3 ppm on a dry basis. The lethal dose when injected into dogs is greater than 30 mg/kg. Fifty milligrams cobalt injected intravenously into young calves produced temporary distress but no deaths (Co-1), and growing dairy animals were able to consume up to 50 mg/100 lb body weight with no harmful effects (Co-2). Under certain conditions, cobalt given to animals in amounts greater than requirements, but by no means excessive, may produce polycythemia.

Radioassay. Preparation Co-5758-P, which is cyclotron-produced by bombardment of iron, is the one of choice provided the need for high specific activity can justify the cost. Inert or radioactive iron contamination will usually not be a problem. Preparation Co-60-P is satisfactory for general tracer work. Both of these radioisotopes can be counted efficiently by soft-beta methods. However, in most cases the simplicity of sample preparation for gamma counting will make it the procedure of choice.

Chemistry. The low concentrations of cobalt in plant and animal tissues have stimulated considerable research on analytical methods. Wet-ashing may be accomplished by the use of nitric and sulfuric acids or the usual treatment with nitric, sulfuric, and perchloric acids. A method for estimation of cobalt in biological material, including a description of dry-ashing procedures, has been reported as follows (Co-3): Samples were ashed overnight in silica dishes at 450 to 600°C. If ashing was not complete, HNO_3 and KNO_3 were added and taken to dryness, and the sample ashed again at 600 to 650°C. The nitric acid treatment was repeated if necessary. With samples high in silica, platinum dishes were used, and treatment with hydrofluoric and perchloric acids was employed. The ash solution was extracted with dithizone to eliminate iron interference, the complex oxidized, and the cobalt treated with o-nitrosocresol, which was extracted from the aqueous phase by ligroin for colorimetric evaluation. The following procedure has been described for the electroplating of radio-cobalt (Co-4): The ash solution was prepared so as to contain a minimum of acid, and an aliquot was added to the electroplating cell containing the plating solution (100 g ammonium sulfate, 180 ml concentrated ammonium hydroxide, and 5 g ammonium hypophosphite per liter). If necessary, carrier cobalt was added to provide about 10 mg of the element to be plated out. The cobalt was plated onto copper at 27 ma/cm² for several hours. If the sample contained salts that precipitated out under alkaline conditions, it was necessary to make a preliminary separation of the cobalt; this was done by reaction with α-nitroso-β-naphthol.

Typical Methods. In studies with normal and diabetic rats, about 1 μc Co^{60} in 52 μg of the element was injected intraperitoneally (Co-5); tissues were ashed and made to volume, and aliquots dried for counting with a Geiger tube. In work with cyclotron-produced $Co^{57,58}$, the following approximate dosages were used: rats, 20 μg, 25 μc; rabbits, intravenous, 2.4 μg, 20 μc; rabbits, oral, 60 μg, 600 μc; swine, 60 μg, 600 μc; calves, 60 μg, 600 μc; cattle, 2 mg, 500 μc (Co-6, Co-7). In these studies the electroplating procedure as described above was used for the preparation of samples. In a study with swine, the radioisotope was incorporated in the ration at a level of 13 μc Co^{60} per kilogram of feed. The animals were on experiment for 43 days, each pig consuming about 61 kg. Tissues were digested in a mixture of HNO_3 and H_2SO_4 plus cobalt carrier, and aliquots were liquid-counted (Co-8). In a study of vitamin B_{12} biosynthesis, 2 mc Co^{60} containing about 1.6 mg cobalt was administered orally and intravenously to sheep (Co-9). Samples of high activity were counted directly with an end-window counter using an 89.5-mg/cm² absorber, so that only gamma activity was measured; with lower activities, the samples were wet-ashed in concentrated HNO_3 and made to volume, and the liquid counted directly; with still smaller amounts, the samples were dry-ashed at 550°C in porcelain dishes, and the ash was spread with HNO_3, dried, and counted directly with a thin-window tube or an internal counter. All samples were separated into a vitamin-B_{12}-like fraction, an inorganic fraction, and a bound residue.

COBALT 241

Labeled vitamin B_{12} was produced by incorporation of 2 ppm Co with a specific activity of 1.94×10^5 counts/min/mg of Co^{60} into the fermentation broth in which *Streptomyces griseus* was grown. The activity of this vitamin B_{12} was about 0.25 μc/mg. However, much higher activities have since been produced (Co-10). In a study with pregnant rats, 0.2 μg of labeled vitamin B_{12} containing 60 μc/mg was administered subcutaneously daily for 2 to 4 days (Co-11). Tissues and carcass residues were digested with H_2SO_4 and HNO_3 plus cobalt carrier in a Kjeldahl flask, and the inorganic residues were transferred to planchets for counting with a Geiger tube.

The behavior of cobalt in soils was studied by adding labeled cobalt to a 5-g sample of soil and then following its removal in extracting solutions of ammonium acetate, 2.5 per cent acetic acid, and 0.1 N HCl. Radioactivity was measured on 100-ml samples using the Marinelli beaker arrangement; an amount of activity measuring 5200 counts/min was employed per 5-g soil sample (Co-12).

Co-1. Ely, Ray E., K. M. Dunn, C. F. Huffman, C. L. Comar, and George K. Davis: The Effect of Methionine on the Tissue Distribution of Radioactive Cobalt Injected Intravenously into Dairy Calves, *J. Animal Sci.*, **12**: 394–401 (1953).
Co-2. Keener, H. A., G. P. Percival, K. S. Morrow, and H. E. Ellis: Cobalt Tolerance in Young Dairy Cattle, *J. Dairy Sci.*, **32**: 527–533 (1949).
Co-3. Ellis, G. H., and J. F. Thompson: Determination of Cobalt in Biological Materials with Nitrosocresol, *Ind. Eng. Chem. Anal. Ed.*, **17**: 254–257 (1945).
Co-4. Comar, C. L., George K. Davis, and Ruth F. Taylor: Cobalt Metabolism Studies: Radioactive Cobalt Procedures with Rats and Cattle, *Arch. Biochem.*, **9**: 149–158 (1946).
Co-5. Ulrich, Frank, and D. Harold Copp: The Metabolism of Radioactive Cobalt (Co^{60}) in Normal and Alloxan Diabetic Rats, *Arch. Biochem. and Biophys.*, **31**: 148–153 (1951).
Co-6. Comar, C. L., and George K. Davis: Cobalt Metabolism Studies. III. Excretion and Tissue Distribution of Radioactive Cobalt Administered to Cattle, *Arch. Biochem.*, **12**: 257–266 (1947).
Co-7. Comar, C. L., and George K. Davis: Cobalt Metabolism Studies. IV. Tissue Distribution of Radioactive Cobalt Administered to Rabbits, Swine, and Young Calves, *J. Biol. Chem.*, **170**: 379–389 (1947).
Co-8. Braude, R.: The Distribution of Radioactive Cobalt in Pigs, *Brit. J. Nutrition*, **3**: 289 (1949).
Co-9. Monroe, R. A., H. E. Sauberlich, C. L. Comar, and S. L. Hood: Vitamin B_{12} Biosynthesis after Oral and Intravenous Administration of Inorganic Co^{60} to Sheep, *Proc. Soc. Exptl. Biol. Med.*, **80**: 250–257 (1952).
Co-10. Chaiet, Louis, Charles Rosenblum, and David T. Woodbury: Biosynthesis of Radioactive Vitamin B_{12} Containing Cobalt^{60}, *Science*, **111**: 601–602 (1950).
Co-11. Chow, Bacon F., Lois Barrows, and C. T. Ling: The Distribution of Radioactivity in the Organs of the Fetus or of Young Rats Born by Mothers Injected with Vitamin B_{12} Containing Co^{60}, *Arch. Biochem. and Biophys.*, **34**: 151–157 (1951).
Co-12. Banerjee, Dilip K., Roger H. Bray, and S. W. Melsted: Some Aspects of the Chemistry of Cobalt in Soils, *Soil Sci.*, **75**: 421–431 (1953).

Copper 64 (12.80 hr)				Beta 0.57, 0.65	Gamma 1.34	K
Cat. No.	Sp. Act.	Form	Cost	Chem. Cont.	Radiochem. Cont.	
Cu-64-I	300 mc/g	Metal	$12/100 mc	Possibly Zn, Ag, As	Possibly Zn⁶⁵, Zn⁶⁹, Ag¹¹⁰	

Mica W.	Int. C.	Scint. C.	R_f/mc
2.3×10^{-4}	7.8×10^{-5}	5.4×10^{-3}	1

Critical Org.	Body	Air	Water	Effect. $T_{1/2}$
Liver	150 μc	6×10^{-6}	8×10^{-2}	12.7 hr

Intake Levels. Daily food intake for man is about 2 mg. Sheep, cattle, and swine consume about 5 mg/day/100 lb body weight, which is equivalent to about 6 ppm in the dry matter of herbage. About 0.1 mg/day is optimum for rats. About 12 mg copper sulfate fed daily to rats is deleterious. One gram copper sulfate fed daily to sheep for 1 to 2 months was fatal. Cattle are not injured by 2 g copper sulfate daily. Copper mixed with feed is generally much less toxic, because of poor absorption, than is soluble copper administered as a solution. A recommended nutrient solution for plants contains 0.0127 ppm. Crop plants range from 3 to 75 ppm on a dry basis.

Radioassay. Routine solution counting or gamma counting can be used. Perhaps most useful, on account of the short half-life, is scintillation counting of the tissues themselves. The radiocontaminants may become of importance if the measurements are made after considerable decay has occurred or if there is a selective biological accumulation of the contaminants (Cu-1). If necessary, these impurities can be eliminated by electrolytic purification of the original preparation. On account of the relatively low levels of copper tolerated by most biological systems, it is often necessary to measure the Cu⁶⁴ as soon as possible with a high sensitivity, so that the dose can be made as small as possible.

Chemistry. Biological samples can be either dry-ashed or wet-ashed according to the methods described in Chap. 5. Recoveries are usually more certain with the wet-ashing procedures. A method for estimation of copper in small plant or animal samples is as follows (Cu-2): Five milliliters of blood, 1 to 5 g of wet tissue, or 1 g of dry tissue is oxidized with a mixture of sulfuric, perchloric, and nitric acids. Any iron present is deionized with ammonium citrate or pyrophosphate in strongly alkaline solution. A color is formed by addition of diethyldithiocarbamate, and the solution extracted with amyl alcohol for colorimetric evaluation.

Typical Methods. For a study with cattle (Cu-3), the irradiation unit of 0.32 g of copper wire was dissolved in 8 N HNO₃ and neutralized with 2 N NaOH to the point of incipient precipitation. An amount of solution containing about 250 mg Cu was used for oral dosage of 350-lb calves, and

100 mg was used for intravenous injection. The tissues were digested in HNO_3, and the fat extracted with isoamyl alcohol as described in Chap. 5 for direct solution counting. With a similar preparation, 1 to 8 mg copper was used for rats, and 7 to 25 mg for rabbits (Cu-4). The following levels have been employed, mainly using cyclotron-produced Cu^{64} (Cu-4): dogs, 523 to 870 μc in 39.5 to 62 mg $CuSO_4$ intravenously; human beings, 225 μc in 0.71 mg Cu intravenously; human beings, 75 μc in 1.22 mg Cu subcutaneously; human beings, 380 μc in 3.79 mg Cu orally; rats and guinea pigs, 5 to 250 μc.

In a study with chick embryos, cyclotron-produced Cu^{64} was prepared in 0.9 per cent saline containing 150 $\mu g/ml$ of copper (Cu-5). One milliliter of solution was injected into the albumen of each egg, since this was found to be the maximum amount that would not cause injury. At no longer than 48 hr after injection, the embryos were removed under warm 0.9 per cent saline, a drop of Bouin's picro-acetic-formaldehyde solution was placed in the live embryo, and then it was dried. Thin cellophane was placed between the embryo and Eastman no-screen X-ray safety film, and a glass-slide sandwich made and held together with spring clips for the exposure. After photographic processing, the autoradiogram was observed in comparison with the dried mounted embryo from which it was taken.

The metabolism of Cu^{64} in *Drosophila* was studied by incorporation of the isotope solution into hot fly food. The larvae were washed in Ringer solution before being processed. For whole counts and sectioning, larvae were fixed in hot Formalin-alcohol. For contact autoradiography, larvae were dissected without fixation on dry slides on which the organs were spread and subsequently oven-dried (Cu-6).

Cu-1. Frierson, W. Joe, Sam L. Hood, Ira B. Whitney, and C. L. Comar: Radiocontaminants in Biological Studies with Copper-64, *Arch. Biochem. and Biophys.*, **38**: 397–404 (1952).

Cu-2. Eden, Alfred, and Henry Hamilton Green: Micro-determination of Copper in Biological Material, *Biochem. J. London*, **34**: 1202–1208 (1940).

Cu-3. Comar, C. L., George K. Davis, and Leon Singer: The Fate of Radioactive Copper Administered to the Bovine, *J. Biol. Chem.*, **174**: 905–914 (1948).

Cu-4. Copper Metabolism, *McCollum-Pratt Inst. Contrib.* **5**, pp. 191–215 (1950).

Cu-5. Smith, Ellen E., and Peter Gray: The Distribution of Copper[64] in Early Embryo Chicks, *J. Exptl. Zool.*, **107**: 183–216 (1948).

Cu-6. Poulson, D. F., V. T. Bowen, R. M. Hilse, and A. C. Rubinson: The Copper Metabolism of *Drosophila*, *Proc. Natl. Acad. Sci. U.S.*, **38**: 912–921 (1952).

| Europium 152 (13 yr) | | | *Beta* 0.9, 1.7 | *Gamma* 0.3, 1.2 | *K* |
| Europium 154 (16 yr) | | | *Beta* 0.3, 0.7, 1.9 | *Gamma* 1.2 | |

Cat. No.	*Sp. Act.*	*Form*	*Cost*	*Chem. Cont.*	*Radiochem. Cont.*
Eu-152154-I	72 mc/g	Oxalate	$781/440 mc	—	—

Mica W.	*Int. C.*	*Scint. C.*	R_f/mc	*50% Self-abs.*
9.1×10^{-4}	6.6×10^{-4}	6.7×10^{-3}	6	25 (calc.)

Critical Org.	*Body*	*Air*	*Water*	*Effect.* $T_{1/2}$
Bone	22 μc	6×10^{-9}	3×10^{-2}	820 days

Intake Levels.   Europium, one of the rare-earth elements, has not been of interest biologically, and little or no information is available regarding its occurrence in plant and animal tissues.

Radioassay.   From the listed energies it would appear that routine beta or gamma counting would be satisfactory.

Chemistry.   From comparison with radioisotopes of other rare-earth elements, it would seem that wet- or dry-ashing could be employed without danger of losses.   However, this should be checked by the investigator.   One might also expect radiocolloid formation in the dosing solution to be a problem.   An iodometric method for chemical estimation has been reported (Eu-1).

Typical Methods.   Rats were given 50 μc either intravenously or intramuscularly, and autoradiographs made of the tissues (Eu-2).

Eu-1. Scott, W. W.: "Standard Methods of Chemical Analyses," 5th ed., vols. I and II, D. Van Nostrand Company, Inc., New York, 1939.

Eu-2. Van Cleave, C. D.: A Radioautographic Study of the Localization of Radioactive Europium in Certain Soft Tissues of the Rat, *Anat. Record*, **103**: 514–515 (1949).

Fission products (unseparated)

Cat. No.
FP-P-1

Description. The significant fission products include the following: Sr^{89}, Sr^{90}-Y^{90}, Y^{91}, Zr^{95}-Nb^{95}, Tc^{99}, Ru^{103}, Ru^{106}-Rh^{106}, Cs^{137}, Ce^{144}-Pr^{144}, and Pm^{147}. The preparation is a mixture of the mixed fission products as nitrates in strong HNO_3 and is separated from heavy metals that have been exposed for 40 to 60 days in the reactor and cooled only a short time. The concentration is 1 to 25 mc of gross beta activity per milliliter, and the cost is $1 per mc. The total solids run less than 10 mg/ml.

It is difficult to interpret measurements of such an uncertain mixture of activities, and ordinarily information is developed using the specific radioisotope of interest.

Gallium 72 (14.3 hr)			*Beta* 0.56–3.17		*Gamma* 0.631–2.50
Cat. No.	*Sp. Act.*	*Form*	*Cost*	*Chem. Cont.*	*Radiochem. Cont.*
Ga-72-I	235 mc/g	Ga$_2$O$_3$	$13/35 mc	—	—
Mica W.	*Int. C.*		*Scint. C.*	R_f/*mc*	50% *Self-abs.*
1.7 × 10^{-4}	1.5 × 10^{-4}		8.8 × 10^{-4}	15	61 (calc.)
Critical Org.	*Body*		*Air*	*Water*	*Effect.* $T_{1/2}$
Bone	8 μc		3 × 10^{-6}	9	0.59 day

Intake Levels. Gallium has been of interest biologically on account of its tendency to accumulate in bone and the possibilities of diagnostic and therapeutic use of Ga^{72} for bone malignancy in man. Since gallium chloride and nitrate precipitate at the pH of blood, attention was turned to the use of the citrate or lactate for injection purposes. The LD$_{50}$ of gallium lactate was as follows (Ga-1): Rats, intravenous, 46 mg Ga per kilogram; rats, subcutaneous, 121 mg Ga per kilogram; rabbits, intravenous, 43 mg Ga per kilogram; rabbits, subcutaneous, 97 mg Ga per kilogram. The intravenous toxicity of gallium citrate for the rabbit, given with calcium, was 30 mg Ga per kilogram (Ga-2). There was evidence that the toxicity was greater for large animals, such as dogs or goats, than for rabbits (Ga-3).

Radioassay. Routine beta or gamma counting presents no particular problem. In vivo measurements are practical. Since radiation effects are of primary interest, it becomes necessary to consider absolute measurements. Methods involving standardization against radium have been described (Ga-4).

Chemistry. An analytical method has been reported for estimation of 2 to 100 μg gallium in biological material (Ga-5) which is based on digestion in H$_2$SO$_4$, treatment with 8-hydroxyquinoline, and fluorescence measurement of the chloroform extract. Procedures have been described for preparation of gallium lactate and gallium citrate (Ga-6, Ga-7).

Typical Methods. About 0.2 to 0.4 mc Ga^{72} per kilogram body weight (6 mg/kg) as gallium lactate was injected subcutaneously into rats and rabbits (Ga-8). The animals were killed at 6 hr after dosage, and thin sections of bones and teeth prepared by grinding and then mounted on X-ray film for exposures of 3 to 48 hr to give autoradiograms. In another study, labeled gallium citrate (0.5 mc/kg) was injected subcutaneously into rabbits (Ga-9). Bone autoradiograms were made, and fresh tissues were gamma-counted using an end-window tube shielded with a 1700-mg/cm^2 absorber. Tissues have been assayed for Ga^{72} by dissolving in concentrated HNO$_3$ in 10-ml volumetric flasks, making to volume, and pouring into petri dishes for direct solution counting (Ga-10). Reference

(Ga-10) should be consulted for a most extensive summary of details in connection with metabolic and clinical use of Ga[72].

Ga-1. Dudley, Horace C., and Milton D. Levine: Studies on the Acute Toxicity of Gallium, Research Report No. 3, Project NM 011 013, Naval Medical Research Institute, National Naval Medical Center, Bethesda, Md., Jan. 13, 1949.
Ga-2. Dudley, H. C., L. J. Louviere, and J. C. Shaw: Effects of Injection of Radiogallium (Ga[72]), Research Report, Project NM 007 081.06.10, Naval Medical Research Institute, National Naval Medical Center, Bethesda, Md., Sept. 15, 1951.
Ga-3. Dudley, Horace C.: The Biological Significance of Radiogallium (Ga[72]), Research Report No. 6, Project NM 011 013, Naval Medical Research Institute, National Naval Medical Center, Bethesda, Md., May 12, 1949.
Ga-4. Brucer, Marshall, E. R. King, and H. D. Bruner: A Method for Standardization of Gallium[72], Document ORO-44, Oak Ridge Institute of Nuclear Studies, Oct. 4, 1951.
Ga-5. Dudley, Horace C.: Photofluorometric Determination of Gallium in Tissues, Research Report No. 1, Project NM 011 013, Naval Medical Research Institute, National Naval Medical Center, Bethesda, Md., Jan. 5, 1948.
Ga-6. Dudley, Horace C., and Ray F. Garzoli: Preparation and Properties of Gallium Lactate, Research Report No. 2, Project NM 011 013, Naval Medical Research Institute, National Naval Medical Center, Bethesda, Md., May 24, 1948.
Ga-7. Dudley, H. C.: Gallium Citrate and Radio-gallium (Ga[72]) Citrate, *J. Am. Chem. Soc.*, **72**: 3822 (1950).
Ga-8. English, James A., and H. C. Dudley: Distribution of Radioactive Gallium in the Teeth and Jaws of Experimental Animals, *J. Dental Research*, **29**: 93–100 (1950).
Ga-9. Dudley, H. C., G. W. Imirie, Jr., and J. T. Istock: Deposition of Radiogallium (Ga[72]) in Proliferating Tissues, *Radiology*, **55**: 571–578 (1950).
Ga-10. Brucer, Marshall: A Study of Gallium[72], *Radiology*, **61**: 534–613 (1953).

Gold 198 (2.69 days)   *Beta* 0.97   *Gamma* 0.411

Cat. No.	*Sp. Act.*	*Form*	*Cost*	*Chem. Cont.*	*Radiochem. Cont.*
Au-198-I	3 mc/mg	Metal	$12/50 mc	—	—

Mica W.	*Int. C.*	*Scint. C.*	R_f/mc	*50% Self-abs.*
6.7×10^{-5}	5.5×10^{-5}	5.9×10^{-4}	2.5	90 (calc.)

Critical Org.	*Body*	*Air*	*Water*	*Effect.* $T_{1/2}$
Kidney	10 μc	1×10^{-7}	3×10^{-3}	2.6 days

Gold 199 (3.15 days)   *Beta* 0.32   *Gamma* 0.051–0.207

Cat. No.	*Sp. Act.*	*Form*	*Cost*	*Chem. Cont.*	*Radiochem. Cont.*
Au-199-I	CF	From Pt	$12/9 mc	Pt	9 mc Pt^{197} (18 hr)
					0.3 mc Pt^{193m} (4.33 days)

Mica W.	*Int. C.*	*Scint. C.*	R_f/mc	*50% Self-abs.*
1.3×10^{-4}	8×10^{-5}	9.8×10^{-5}	0.9	17 (calc.)

Critical Org.	*Body*	*Air*	*Water*	*Effect.* $T_{1/2}$
Kidney	28 μc	2.5×10^{-7}	7×10^{-3}	3.1 days

Intake Levels.   Gold is primarily of biological interest on account of its use in the treatment of arthritis and the use of radioactive gold colloids for radiation therapy.   Toxic effects in rats have occurred from intraperitoneal administration of 23 to 50 mg/kg of gold as the chloride.

Radioassay. Au^{198} is apparently the isotope of choice except where material of very high specific activity is required.   This preparation has little if any radiocontamination and has been the most widely used. Either beta or gamma measurements are satisfactory. Au^{199} contains Pt^{197}, which could be eliminated by decay, and also Pt^{193m}, which would have to be removed chemically or could be prevented from contributing to the counts by using a high-efficiency beta counter.

Chemistry.   Biological materials can be wet- or dry-ashed.   A chemical method has been described which permits estimation of 0.2 μg (Au-1). Tissues were treated with concentrated H_2SO_4, dried, and ashed at 550°C for about 2 hr; urine was pretreated with tellurium tetrachloride, stannous chloride, and acid before dry-ashing.

Typical Methods.   Simplified devices have been described for dispensing conveniently the relatively high activities of Au^{198} used for intracavitary instillation or interstitial injection (Au-2).   In a study with dogs, radioactive gold solutions containing 1 to 2 mc Au^{198} were mixed with 4 to 5 ml of the animal's serum and then injected intravenously.   Blood samples were diluted with water, and 10-ml aliquots counted in a flat dish under an end-window tube.   Tissues were heated with HNO_3, and at the end of digestion 2 ml concentrated HCl was added to yield ionic gold, which tended to reduce adsorption of radioactivity on the glass walls.

Where large amounts of fat were present, acetone or dioxane was used to give a one-phase system suitable for liquid counting (Au-3). In studies with mice about 0.1 mc of a labeled solution was injected after the animal had been inoculated and had grown sarcoma 37 cells. About 0.05 ml of peritoneal fluid was withdrawn with a capillary glass pipette, diluted with 5 per cent sodium oxalate, and centrifuged to separate cellular content from serous exudate. Each fraction was dried in a tin cup and counted with a mica-end-window tube (Au-4). A method has been described for electrodeposition of gold from biological tissues (Au-5). The weighed tissues are digested with aqua regia or concentrated HNO_3 plus Superoxol, and 5 mg gold as the chloride is added. After digestion the HNO_3 is replaced by HCl, and the solution evaporated to 1 or 2 ml. This is treated with $NH_2OH \cdot HCl$ and 0.4 per cent $FeSO_4 \cdot 7H_2O$ to reduce the gold, which is then centrifuged. The precipitated gold is dissolved in aqua regia, is made alkaline with NaOH, and is ready for electrodeposition. Good recoveries of radiogold from biological tissue have been reported by a procedure based on treatment of an acid hydrolyzate with activated carbon (Au-6).

Au-1. Natelson, Samuel, and Joseph L. Zuckerman: Estimation of Gold in Biological Materials, *Anal. Chem.*, **23**: 653–655 (1951).

Au-2. Stapleton, J. E., and W. J. Wingo: Intracavity and Interstitial Administration Methods for Radioactive Colloidal Gold, *Nucleonics*, **11**: 60–62 (1953).

Au-3. Zilversmit, D. B., George A. Boyd, and Marshall Brucer: The Effect of Particle Size on Blood Clearance and Tissue Distribution of Radioactive Gold Colloids, *J. Lab. Clin. Med.*, **40**: 255–260 (1952).

Au-4. Goldie, Horace, Lincoln B. Calvin, Homer Nash, and Paul F. Hahn: Radioactive Colloidal Gold in Macrophages and Serous Exudate in Peritoneal Fluid of Sarcoma Bearing Mouse, *Proc. Soc. Exptl. Biol. Med.*, **76**: 480–484 (1951).

Au-5. Dunn, Rayburn: Recovery and Estimation of Radioactive Isotopes from Biologic Tissues, *J. Lab. Clin. Med.*, **33**: 1169–1176 (1948).

Au-6. Weiss, Louis C., Arthur W. Steers, and Howard M. Bollinger: Determination of Radioactive Gold in Biological Tissue, *Anal. Chem.*, **26**: 586–587 (1954).

Hafnium 181 (45 days)   *Beta* 0.405   *Gamma* 0.0807–0.480

Cat. No.	*Sp. Act.*	*Form*	*Cost*	*Chem. Cont.*	*Radiochem. Cont.*
Hf-181-I	60 mc/g	HfO$_2$	$64/48 mc	—	—

R_f/mc
4

Intake Levels. Little is known of the distribution or toxicity of hafnium compounds. The LD$_{50}$ for 10 days in rats for hafnium sodium mandelate administered intravenously was 75 to 100 mg/kg as Hf (Hf-1). When given intraperitoneally daily, the LD$_{50}$ was 2 to 3 g/kg. These values are similar to those for zirconium.

Radioassay. Hafnium 181 can be counted by routine beta or gamma methods, and there are no particular problems.

Chemistry. The chemistry of hafnium is similar to that of zirconium, and the difficulty of separating the two elements has hampered its study. Biological samples may be wet-ashed.

Typical Methods. Hf^{181}O$_2$ was used to prepare hafnium sodium mandelate (Hf-1). One-half milliliter of solution containing 3.06 mg of the metal (about 180 μc) was injected intravenously into the rat. Tissues were weighed and dissolved in concentrated HNO$_3$, and 10-ml samples counted with a thin-mica-window tube. Feces were homogenized by incubation with a concentrated papain solution to give an aliquot for counting. Filter paper on which urine was collected was digested with H$_2$SO$_4$ to give an aliquot for counting. It was found that erroneous results were obtained when fat was present in the counting solutions and that it was necessary to prepare a one-phase counting liquid by use of dioxane or acetone (Hf-2).

Hf-1. Kittle, C. Frederick, E. Richard King, Carl T. Bahner, and Marshall Brucer: Distribution and Excretion of Radioactive Hafnium[181] Sodium Mandelate in the Rat, *Proc. Soc. Exptl. Biol. Med.*, **76**: 278–282 (1951).
Hf-2. Bahner, Carl T., D. B. Zilversmit, and Etta McDonald: The Preparation of Wet Ashed Tissues for Liquid Counting, *Science*, **115**: 597–598 (1952).

Hydrogen **3**, tritium (12.46 yr)				*Beta* 0.0189	*Gamma*
Cat. No.	*Sp. Act.*	*Form*	*Cost*	*Chem. Cont.*	*Radiochem. Cont.*
H-3-P	CF	Gas	$.10/mc	He³ daughter	—
Critical Org.	*Body*		*Air*	*Water*	*Effect. T½*
Total body	$10^4 \mu c$		2×10^{-5}	0.2	19 days

Intake Levels. Tritium, H^3, occurs in natural water to the extent of about 10^{-18} g H^3 per gram H^1 (H-1). It has been of biological interest primarily on account of its use as a label for water and other metabolic compounds. The 30-day LD_{50} of H_2^3O for mice was determined as 1 mc/g body weight when given as a single injection (H-2).

Radioassay. On account of the unusually low beta energy, H^3 is quite difficult to count. In general, the measurements are accomplished by gas counting in ionization chambers or Geiger tubes or by solid counting with internal counters. Gas counting is highly efficient but requires complicated sample preparation and handling; solid counting is relatively inefficient. About 3×10^{-4} μc can be detected in an ionization chamber with the vibrating reed. Liquid-scintillation-counting procedures have been described (H-3, H-4) which offer possibilities of easier sample preparation than gas techniques and better sensitivity than solid techniques. However, there are many technical difficulties yet to be overcome.

Chemistry. The chemical behavior of H^3 is similar to that of H^1, and details of methods are presented below.

Typical Methods. A procedure has been described for combustion of a 10-mg biological sample for assay of H^3, C^{13}, and C^{14} (H-5). A micro-combustion train is used, and the H_2O produced is treated with *n*-butyl magnesium bromide to yield *n*-tritiobutane, which can be counted in the gas phase. The actual combustion takes only 5 to 6 min. A one-step method has been described for quantitative conversion of tritium in organic compounds to a mixture of methane and hydrogen by heating with zinc, nickelic oxide, and water in a sealed tube at 640°C (H-6). In a study with mice (H-7), tritium oxide was administered intraperitoneally daily for 13 days in 0.5 ml of physiological saline for a total of 1.2 mc. The entire carcass was ground with 100 ml benzene in a Waring Blendor, and the body water was obtained by distillation of the benzene suspension. To obtain the bound water, the benzene was removed from the carcass by distillation, and the dry residue mixed with copper oxide and burned in a combustion tube at 750°C. The water formed was collected in a dry-ice trap. Body water and combustion water were analyzed for tritium by treatment of the water with CaC_2 to produce acetylene, which was measured with an ionization chamber and vibrating-reed electrometer.

In a study of retention of tritium over periods of 4 to 8 months, rats were given 20 mc injected intraperitoneally weekly for 5 weeks; a sheep was given about 3 c intraperitoneally (H-8). To study the comparative metabolism of hydrogen, deuterium, and tritium, bean plants were grown from germination in water containing 100 $\mu c/ml$ of H^3 as the oxide and 0.99 per cent deuterium oxide (H-8). After harvest the plant water for each tissue was removed by azeotropic distillation with benzene. The benzene was removed from the residue, which was set aside for determination of ratios of tissue-bound isotopes. The incorporation of H_2^3O into algae was studied by growing the organisms in nutrient solution containing about 1 mc/ml (H-9). At termination the cells were washed twice in distilled water, which removed less than 6 per cent of the total tritium, then vacuum-dried and combusted over copper oxide in a conventional macro furnace. The combustion water was collected and analyzed for tritium.

Advantage was taken of the soft-beta energy to visualize the intracellular localization of H^3-labeled compounds by paramecia and yeast (H-10, H-11). The paramecia were grown in a medium containing sodium acetate labeled in the methyl groups with H^3. The acetate had an activity of 4×10^7 dis/min/mg, and the water of the medium, 2×10^7 dis/min/mg. After growth, the paramecia were fixed in 2 per cent aqueous osmic acid, centrifuged, washed, fixed in Formalin, washed, dehydrated in alcohol, embedded in paraffin, and cut in 1-μ sections. Nuclear-track types of emulsion were used. The sections were transferred to a water bath, floated onto photographic emulsions, deparaffinized, dried, and exposed for 1 to 4 weeks at about 5°C. After photographic development and processing, the specimens were viewed unstained. Yeast was grown also in labeled acetate, and a drop of distilled water containing the radioactive yeast was placed on the emulsion or placed on a glass slide, dried, and apposed to emulsion surfaces for exposure and subsequent processing. Control experiments to rule out pseudophotographic effects were run with nonradioactive organisms or with Formvar-coated emulsions to prevent contact of specimen and emulsion.

H-1. Johnston, W. H., R. L. Wolfgang, and W. F. Libby: Tritium in Nature, *Science*, **113**: 1–2 (1951).

H-2. Brues, Austin M., Agnes M. Stroud, and Leola Rietz: Toxicity of Tritium Oxide to Mice, *Proc. Soc. Exptl. Biol. Med.*, **79**: 174–176 (1952).

H-3. Farmer, Earl C., and Irving A. Berstein: Determination of Specific Activities of Tritium-labeled Compounds with Liquid Scintillators, *Science*, **117**: 279–280 (1953).

H-4. Hayes, F. N., and R. Gordon Gould: Liquid Scintillation Counting of Tritium-labeled Water and Organic Compounds, *Science*, **117**: 480–482 (1953).

H-5. Glascock, R. F.: A Combustion Technique for the Assay of Tritium, ^{13}C and ^{14}C in a Single 10 Mg Sample of Biological Material, *Biochem. J. London*, **52**: 699–704 (1952).

H-6. Wilzbach, K. E., Louis Kaplan, and W. G. Brown: The Preparation of Gas for Assay of Tritium in Organic Compounds, *Science,* **118**: 522–523 (1953).

H-7. Thompson, Roy C.: Studies of Metabolic Turnover with Tritium as a Tracer, *J. Biol. Chem.,* **197**: 81–87 (1952).

H-8. Thompson, R. C., and J. E. Ballou: Long-term Retention of Tritium in the Rat and Sheep, HW-28636, July 7, 1953.

H-9. Weinberger, D., and J. W. Porter: Incorporation of Tritium Oxide into Growing *Chlorella pyrenoidosa* Cells, *Science,* **117**: 636–638 (1953).

H-10. Fitzgerald, Patrick J., M. L. Eidinoff, J. E. Knoll, and E. B. Simmel: Tritium in Radioautography, *Science,* **114**: 494–498 (1951).

H-11. Eidinoff, M. L., P. J. Fitzgerald, E. B. Simmel, and J. E. Knoll: Intracellular Localization of Compounds Labeled with Tritium, H³, by Radioautography, *Proc. Soc. Exptl. Biol. Med.,* **77**: 225–229 (1951).

Indium 114 (49 days, 72 sec)		Beta 2.05, 0.65		Gamma 0.192–1.27	IT	K
Cat. No.	Sp. Act.	Form	Cost	Chem. Cont.	Radiochem. Cont.	
In-114-I	70 mc/g	Metal	$51/10 mc	—	—	
In-114-P	50–150 mc/g	Chloride	$5/mc	—	—	

Mica W.	Int. C.	Scint. C.	R_f/mc
7.3×10^{-5}	7.4×10^{-5}	3.5×10^{-3}	1.4

Intake Levels. Indium is a rare element and, so far as known, has not been of biological interest. With rats, 5 to 10 mg indium sulfate fed daily for 27 days had no ill effects. However, at 30 mg the animals lost weight. Indium is much more toxic when given parenterally.

Radioassay. No particular counting problems would be anticipated.

Chemistry. Indium resembles gallium and aluminum in its behavior. A colorimetric method has been reported for estimation of small amounts (In-1). The procedure is based upon formation of an 8-hydroxyquinoline derivative which is extracted into chloroform for colorimetric measurement.

In-1. Moeller, Therald: The Chemistry of Indium, *Ind. Eng. Chem. Anal. Ed.*, **15**: 270–272 (1943).

Iodine 131 (8.08 days)   *Beta* 0.33, 0.60, 0.15, 0.81   *Gamma* 0.080–0.720

Cat. No.	*Sp. Act.*	*Form*	*Cost*	*Chem. Cont.*	*Radiochem. Cont.*
I-131-I	CF	From Te	$33/250 mc	Te	12 mc Te^{127m} (115 days)
					10 mc Te^{129m} (33.5 days)
					Xe^{131m} daughter (12 days)
I-131-P	CF	NaI in basic Na_2SO_3	$.75/mc	—	Xe^{131m} daughter (12 days)

Mica W.	*Int. C.*	*Scint. C.*	R_f/mc	*50% Self-abs.*
1.4×10^{-4}	1.2×10^{-4}	1.6×10^{-4}	2.4	48 (calc.)

Critical Org.	*Body*	*Air*	*Water*	*Effect. $T_{1/2}$*
Thyroid	0.3 µc	3×10^{-9}	3×10^{-5}	7.7 days

Intake Levels. Iodine is widely distributed in nature in extremely small amounts. The daily requirement for man and animals is of the order of 2 to 4 µg/kg body weight. Some approximate levels of occurrence are as follows: sea water, 17 to 50 µg/liter; soils, 600 to 8000 µg/kg; crop plants, 2 to 500 µg/kg on a dry basis; meat, 30 µg/kg; milk and eggs, 10 to 400 µg/kg; sea fish, 400 to 900 µg/kg. These values serve only to indicate the order of magnitude, since considerable variations occur. The concentration in the thyroid is about 10,000 times that found in any other organ. The body of adult man contains roughly 20 mg iodine, 10 mg being in the thyroid gland and the other 10 mg in the rest of the body. Blood iodine ranges from 8 to 16 µg/100 ml.

The weight of the thyroid gland approximates 20 to 60 g for man, sheep, swine, horses, and cattle. Other species have values as follows: hen, 0.5 g; rats, 15 mg; chicks, 10 mg. The concentration of iodine in the gland ranges from 0.4 to 3 mg/g. Of particular importance is the fact that the thyroid under normal conditions has a mechanism that prevents the addition to its existing stores of more than 0.1 to 0.2 mg iodine per gram of thyroid weight (I-1). This means that the dosage should be limited to this mass of iodine in order to yield physiological results. Fortunately the specific activity of the radioisotope preparations allows compliance with this restriction (see Chap. 2 for possible physiological effects of I^{131}).

Radioassay. Radioiodine has been a most widely used isotope for the following reasons: (*a*) importance of iodine in the animal economy, (*b*) low concentrations of iodine in normal metabolism which have made chemical studies difficult in contrast to the ease of radiochemical procedures, (*c*) ideal radiation characteristics and short half-life of I^{131}, (*d*) possibilities of studying thyroid function in the live human being or animal by external measurement, (e) metabolic concentration of iodine which permits therapeutic applications.   Preparation I-131-P offers the advantage of freedom from radiocontamination which will usually offset the slightly higher cost.   Direct gamma counting of tissue samples is usually preferred, since this eliminates the necessity of ashing, handling procedures, and self-absorption corrections.   The amount of xenon daughter produced is very small and can be neglected for practical purposes.   A comparison has been presented of the relative effectiveness of nine methods of detection (I-2).   The values are in general agreement with those listed above.   In addition, it is pointed out that liquid samples can be counted with beta or gamma tubes usually with 0.1 to 0.01 of the effectiveness of other methods.   These procedures are useful for measurement of urines, etc., which may contain relatively high levels.

Chemistry.   It is usually desired to estimate total inorganic and protein-bound iodine in biological tissues, particularly thyroid gland and plasma.   The classical procedure (I-3) consists in digestion of the organic tissues, plasma, or protein precipitate with a mixture of chromic and sulfuric acids which oxidizes iodine to nonvolatile iodic acid.   The latter, plus the excess chromic acid, is reduced with phosphorus acid, and the volatile iodine formed is distilled and trapped in an alkaline solution. The iodine is then measured by its catalytic effect on the reduction of ceric sulfate by arsenious acid.   A simplifying modification has been described in which the oxidation and digestion are accomplished by chloric acid, thus avoiding the need for special distillation apparatus (I-4, I-5). The protein is precipitated with trichloroacetic acid, and the usual ceric-arsenious system is used for evaluation of iodine.   Another simplified method has been described which consists in ashing the thyroid glands with KOH, taking up the ash in water, acidifying, and then oxidizing with bromine to yield soluble iodate salts that are determined colorimetrically (I-6).   Thyroxine has been estimated by extraction with butyl alcohol from an alkaline hydrolysate, followed by conventional iodine determination (I-7).

In I^{131} studies, aliquots of the fractions separated in the above analytical procedures can be used for radioactivity measurements.   In a study of various tissue digestion procedures for radioassay, the following method appeared to give the best recoveries: Weighed portions of the tissue were placed in 50-ml centrifuge tubes, and a mixture of 2 N NaOH, 0.1 ml of 0.5 M NaI, and 0.1 ml of 0.5 M NaHSO$_3$ was added (I-8).   The tissue samples were incubated overnight at 70°C.   Obviously on account of the volatility of iodine, one must be sure that the ashing or digestion procedure employed does not cause losses.

Typical Methods.   In this laboratory the following dosages have been administered intraperitoneally or intravenously to permit external counting of the thyroid: cattle, 200 μc; burros, 10 μc; sheep, 25 μc; pigs, 35 μc. With mice, rats, and chicks a dosage of about 0.5 μc is adequate for assay of the dissected gland.   In man, dosages of 1 to 40 μc are used for diagnostic purposes (see Chap. 5).   In a study to determine the nature of plasma iodine, 150 μc I^{131} was injected into a rat that had been raised on a low iodine diet (I-9).   The plasma was extracted with butanol, and the extract added to filter-paper strips for preparation of a chromatogram with collidine-water-NH_3 solvent.   Autoradiograms were prepared by exposure of the dried chromatogram to no-screen X-ray film for 5 days. Most of the radioactivity was found in the same position occupied by added thyroxine, as determined by a color test with diazotized sulfanilic acid.

In a further study, l-thyroxine was labeled with I^{131} to give a specific activity of about 2 $\mu c/\mu g$ of the compound.   Donor rats were given 100 μg of the thyroxine, and bile samples collected for administration to recipient rats (I-10).   Filter-paper chromatograms were prepared, the tissues dissolved in strong alkali, and aliquots dried for counting with an end-window tube.   Distribution of I^{131} in mice was followed by administration of 3 to 20 $\mu c/g$ body weight (I-11).   The tissues were completely hydrolyzed in 20 per cent NaOH for solution counting of 5 ml.   To ascertain the age at which the thyroid of the embryo hamster becomes functional, 50 to 100 μc I^{131} was injected intraperitoneally into the gestating hamster at 8 to 15 days after copulation (I-12).   In addition to counting, the sectional embryos were exposed to dental X-ray films for 6 to 8 days, and after the autoradiograms were made, the sections were stained in Delafield's hematoxylin and eosin for histological study.   Blood, plasma, and "globulin" space of the guinea pig were determined by isotope dilution after intravenous injection of about 3.94 μc of I^{131}-labeled rabbit globulin (I-13).   Blood was obtained from the ear with a 20-mm^3 Sahli pipette and placed in an ointment tin lined with lens paper.   The pipette was washed with 1:10,000 heparin two or three times for quantitative transfer.   The samples were dried with an infrared lamp and counted with an end-window tube.   No self-absorption corrections were necessary.

The absorption characteristics of iodinated casein in mammals and the identification of some of the metabolites appearing in the blood were studied by use of I^{131}-labeled casein at the following levels: rats, 2×10^7 counts/min in 0.27 g iodocasein given orally; sheep, 2.8×10^7 to 5.5×10^8 counts/min in 0.96 to 3.2 g iodocasein administered intravenously, orally, in ventral sac of rumen, small intestine, and caecum (I-14). Standard chemical separations were used for estimation of thyroxine and diiodotyrosine–inorganic iodine fractions.   The distribution of I^{131} in sheep and the physiological manifestations of radiation injury were studied by daily feeding of a drilled food pellet containing 480 μc I^{131}

(I-15).   The thyroid uptake was followed by external counting, and the serum was analyzed for protein-bound iodine, protein-bound I^{131}, and inorganic I^{131}.   The chemical determinations were according to standard procedures, and the I^{131} was precipitated with carrier KI as silver iodide for counting.   The metabolism of iodine in the shark was studied by intraperitoneal injection of 20 to 50 μc into specimens of 141 to 1045 g (I-16).   A portion of the thyroid was wet-ashed in 5 per cent KOH for counting, another portion was fixed in Bouin's fluid, and the rest was held frozen for chemical analysis.   Histological sections of the fixed tissue were exposed on no-screen X-ray film, and the sections stained afterward for histological observations.   The frozen tissue was extracted overnight at 10°C with normal saline, the filtered extract hydrolyzed with trypsin, and the hydrolysate extracted with butyl alcohol for filter-paper chromatography using butanol–acetic acid or butanol ammonia as solvents. Frogs were given 10 μc I^{131} by injection into the ventral lymph sac via the thigh (I-17).   The thyroids were wet-ashed in 1 ml of hot 2 N KOH.   A disk of lens paper was placed on a copper planchet and wetted with a drop of 2 N KOH.   A 0.1-ml aliquot of the ash solution was added immediately, and the planchet placed on a rotating turntable under an infrared lamp.   Samples of gland were fixed in Bouin's fluid for 12 hr, washed in 70 per cent alcohol, dehydrated, and embedded in paraffin, and 10-μ sections were mounted on dental X-ray film for preparation of autoradiograms.

The absorption and disposition of neutral fat in man were studied by oral administration of 100 μc I^{131} in I^{131}-labeled commercial olive oil (I-18).   The thyroid uptake was followed by external counting at 35 cm from the neck with a directionally shielded gamma tube; 1-ml aliquots of urine in glass vials were also gamma-counted.   Serum was measured by pipetting 0.2-ml aliquots onto copper planchets covered with thin absorbent paper, and self-absorption was corrected for by use of standards prepared with identical amounts of nonradioactive serum.   The serum was also treated with zinc sulfate to precipitate the proteins and lipids and allow estimation of inorganic I^{131}, also lipid I^{131} by difference.

Some commercially available I^{131}-labeled compounds are listed as follows (I-19):

Alkyl iodides–I^{131}

Casein–I^{131}

2,4-Dichloro-5-iodophenoxyacetic acid–I^{131}
  (esters, salts, and amides)

3,5-Diiodo-4-aminobenzoic acid–I^{131}

3,5-Diiodoanthranilic acid–I^{131}

2,5-Diidobenzoic acid–I^{131}

3,4-Diiodobenzoic acid–I^{131}

Diiodofluorescein–I^{131}

3,5-Diiodosalicylic acid–I^{131}

Diiodotyrosine–I^{131}

Diodrast–I^{131}

Iodinated globulins and albumin–I^{131}

Iodinated human serum albumin–I^{131}

Iodinated oils and emulsions–I^{131}

3-Iodo-4-aminobenzoic acid–I^{131}

5-Iodoanthranilic acid–I^{131}

Iodobenzene-I^{131}

5-Iodosalicylic acid–I[131]
Pipsyl chloride–I[131]
Tetraiodophenolphthalein–I[131]
l-Thyroxine–I[131]

2,3,5-Triiodobenzoic acid–I[131]
3,4,5-Triiodobenzoic acid–I[131]
Triiodothyronine–I[131]
Urokon–I[131]

I-1. LeBlond, C. P.: Iodine Metabolism, *Advances in Biol. and Med. Phys.*, **1**: 353–386 (1948).

I-2. Bruner, H. D., and Jesse D. Perkinson, Jr.: A Comparison of Iodine–I[131] Counting Methods, *Nucleonics*, **10**: 57–61 (1952).

I-3. Taurog, Alvin, and I. L. Chaikoff: On the Determination of Plasma Iodine, *J. Biol. Chem.*, **163**: 313–322 (1946).

I-4. Zak, B., H. H. Willard, G. B. Myers, and A. J. Boyle: Chloric Acid Method for Determination of Protein-bound Iodine, *Anal. Chem.*, **24**: 1345–1348 (1952).

I-5. O'Neal, Lawrence W., and Ernest S. Simms: Determination of Protein-bound Iodine in Plasma or Serum, *Am. J. Clin. Pathol.*, **23**: 493–505 (1953).

I-6. Walaszek-Piotrowski, L. J., and F. C. Koch: A Simple Method for the Determination of Iodine in the Chick Thyroid, *J. Biol. Chem.*, **194**: 427–434 (1952).

I-7. Taurog, Alvin, and I. L. Chaikoff: The Determination of Thyroxine in the Thyroid Gland of the Rat, *J. Biol. Chem.*, **163**: 323–328 (1946).

I-8. Perkinson, Jesse D., Jr., and H. D. Bruner: Preparation of Tissues for Iodine-131 Counting, *Nucleonics*, **10**: 66–67 (1952).

I-9. Taurog, Alvin, I. L. Chaikoff, and W. Tong: The Nature of Plasma Iodine as Revealed by Filter Paper Partition Chromatography, *J. Biol. Chem.*, **184**: 99–104 (1950).

I-10. Briggs, F. N., Alvin Taurog, and I. L. Chaikoff: The Enterohepatic Circulation of Thyroxine in the Rat, *Endocrinology*, **52**: 559–567 (1953).

I-11. Rugh, Roberts: The Mouse Thyroid and Radioactive Iodine (I[131]), *J. Morphol.*, **89**: 323–365 (1951).

I-12. Hansborough, Louis A., and Hagalyn Seay: Accumulation of Radioiodine (I[131]) in Thyroid Gland of the Hamster Embryo, *Proc. Soc. Exptl. Biol. Med.*, **78**: 481–483 (1951).

I-13. Masouredis, S. P., and L. R. Melcher: Blood, Plasma and "Globulin" Space of Guinea Pigs Determined with I[131] Rabbit Globulin, *Proc. Soc. Exptl. Biol. Med.*, **78**: 264–266 (1951).

I-14. Campbell, D. J., F. N. Andrews, and J. E. Christian: A Study of the Absorption Characteristics of Iodine-131 Labeled Iodinated Casein in Some Mammals, *Endocrinology*, **47**: 242–250 (1950).

I-15. Weeks, M. H., J. Katz, and N. G. Farnham: Organic and Inorganic Iodine Levels in Serum of Sheep Receiving Daily Oral Doses of I[131], *Endocrinology*, **50**: 511–520 (1952).

I-16. Gorbman, Aubrey, Serge Lissitzky, Raymond Michel, and Jean Roche: Thyroidal Metabolism of Iodine in the Shark *Scyliorhinus (Scyllium) canicula*, *Endocrinology*, **51**: 311–321 (1952).

I-17. Matthews, Samuel A.: Effect of Thiouracil on Uptake of Radioactive Iodine by Thyroid Gland of Summer Frogs (*Rana pipiens*), *Am. J. Physiol.*, **162**: 590–597 (1950).

I-18. Stanley, Malcolm M., and Siegfried J. Thannhauser: The Absorption and Disposition of Orally Administered I[131]-labeled Neutral Fat in Man, *J. Lab. Clin. Med.*, **34**: 1634–1639 (1949).

I-19. *Isotopics*, **4**(1) (1954), U.S. Atomic Energy Commission, Oak Ridge, Tenn.

Iridium 192 (74.37 days)   *Beta* 0.67   *Gamma* 0.137–0.651

Cat. No.	*Sp. Act.*	*Form*	*Cost*	*Chem. Cont.*	*Radiochem. Cont.*
Ir-192-I	2.1 mc/mg	Metal	$35/400 mc	—	450 mc Ir^{194} (19 hr)
Ir-192-P	1–5 mc/mg	Chloroiridate	$1/mc	—	—

Mica W.	*Int. C.*	*Scint. C.*	*R_f/mc*	*50 % Self-abs.*
1.1×10^{-4}	9.5×10^{-5}	5.6×10^{-4}	10	50 (calc.)

Critical Org.	*Body*	*Air*	*Water*	*Effect. $T_{1/2}$*
Kidney	3.4 μc	5×10^{-8}	9×10^{-4}	17 days

Iridium 194 (19 hr)   *Beta* 2.18, 0.48   *Gamma* 0.38, 1.43

Cat. No.	*Sp. Act.*	*Form*	*Cost*	*Chem. Cont.*	*Radiochem. Cont.*
Ir-194-I	1.7 mc/mg	Metal	$12/75 mc	—	20 mc Ir^{192} (74.37 days)

R_f/mc
11

Intake Levels.   Iridium is found associated with platinum and has been of little or no biological interest.

Radioassay.   Preparation Ir-192-P will probably be most satisfactory for general use.   Ir^{194} offers a shorter half-life, but it should be noted that there is considerable radiocontamination with the longer-lived Ir^{192}. Routine beta or gamma counting, with the latter preferred, can be used for both isotopes.

Chemistry.   Chemical methods are available only for such materials as platinum scrap and ores that contain relatively large amounts of iridium. Presumably there would be no losses from biological materials upon conventional wet- or dry-ashing.   Iridium is apparently similar in chemical behavior to rhodium.

Iron **55** (2.94 yr)				*Beta*	*Gamma* K
Iron **59** (45.1 days)				Beta 0.26, 0.46	Gamma 1.3, 1.1
Cat. No.	*Sp. Act.*	*Form*	*Cost*	*Chem. Cont.*	*Radiochem. Cont.*
Fe-5559-I	Fe^{55}, 0.7 mc/g	Metal	\$33/12 mc Fe^{55}	—	—
	Fe^{59}, 0.4 mc/g		+ 6.5 mc Fe^{59}		
Fe-5559-P	Fe^{59}, 1–4 mc/g	$FeCl_3$	\$35/mc	—	—

Iron **55** (2.94 yr)				*Beta*	*Gamma* K
Cat. No.	*Sp. Act.*	*Form*	*Cost*	*Chem. Cont.*	*Radiochem. Cont.*
Fe-55-P	0.5–1.5 mc/mg	$FeCl_3$	\$50/mc	—	<10 % Fe^{59}

Mica W.	*Int. C.*				
8.3×10^{-3}	3.1×10^{-4}				
Critical Org.	*Body*	*Air*	*Water*	*Effect. $T_{1/2}$*	
Blood	1000 μc	6×10^{-7}	4×10^{-3}	61 days	

Iron **59** (45.1 days)				Beta 0.26, 0.46	*Gamma* 1.3, 1.1
Cat. No.	*Sp. Act.*	*Form*	*Cost*	*Chem. Cont.*	*Radiochem. Cont.*
Fe-59-P	0.5–1.5 mc/mg	$FeCl_3$	\$50/mc	—	<10 % Fe^{55}

Mica W.	*Int. C.*	*Scint. C.*	R_f/mc	*50 % Self-abs.*	
2.3×10^{-4}	4.2×10^{-5}	7×10^{-4}	7	30 (calc.)	
Critical Org.	*Body*	*Air*	*Water*	*Effect. $T_{1/2}$*	
Blood	11 μc	1.5×10^{-8}	1×10^{-4}	27 days	

Intake Levels. Adult man usually consumes about 12 mg iron per day. Livestock roughages provide 50 to 100 mg/lb, which is well above needs, estimated at about 9 mg/lb. Approximately 0.25 mg/day is adequate for rats. The body of man contains 3 to 3.5 g, of which 2.4 to 2.7 g is in the form of hemoglobin. Blood contains about 50 mg/100 ml, and plasma, about 0.5. A recommended nutrient solution for plants contains about 1.2 ppm, and crop plants range from 20 to 5000 ppm on a dry basis.

Radioassay. The mixture of Fe^{55} and Fe^{59} may be used in general tracer work, especially if the cost is an important factor. Usually the counting measurements will record only the Fe^{59}. Preparation Fe-59-P offers the advantage of a shorter half-life, which may be important in human studies, and more easily measured radiation. If beta counting is employed, self-absorption considerations will be important, whereas with gamma counting there will be no problems of sample preparation. Fe^{55} and Fe^{59} can be used as described in Chap. 5 for double-labeling experiments (Fe-1).

Chemistry. Tissues may be dry-ashed in a muffle furnace up to 550°C or may be wet-ashed with a mixture of nitric and sulfuric acids or with sulfuric and perchloric acids. Iron can be estimated chemically on an aliquot of the ash solution by the o-phenanthroline or α-α-dipyridil method (Fe-2, Fe-3).   An aliquot of the ash solution is titrated against methyl red with NH_4OH, and this same amount of NH_4OH added to another aliquot (about 0.1 mg iron) to be used for the determination.   A pinch of cevitamic acid is added and then 15 ml of a sodium acetate–acetic acid buffer solution (pH 5.4).   The α-α-dipyridil reagent is added to produce a color which is evaluated photometrically.

Methods have been described for estimation of iron in blood plasma or serum without the need of digestion (Fe-4, Fe-5).   It is often necessary to electroplate the iron to minimize self-absorption effects, and a satisfactory method has been described as follows (Fe-6): The samples are placed in a pyrex dish or beaker, and carrier iron as the nitrate is added, if necessary, to give 2 to 4 mg; 1 or 2 ml concentrated HNO_3 is added for each 5 g of sample.   The sample is evaporated to dryness at 100 to 110°C and placed in a cool muffle furnace, and the temperature raised to 500°C for overnight ashing.   If there is any residual carbon, the ash is moistened with concentrated HNO_3, dried, and returned to the muffle for about 30 min.   The ash is dissolved in concentrated HCl, and the free acid removed by evaporation, care being taken not to heat beyond the point of dryness.   The chloride residue is dissolved in saturated aqueous ammonium oxalate and transferred to the electrolysis cell.   If the ash is high in phosphorus and calcium, the chloride residue is dissolved in 8 N HCl and extracted with isopropyl ether, and the iron then extracted from the ether with saturated aqueous ammonium oxalate, which is filtered into the electrolysis cell.   The iron is plated onto a copper disk at a potential of 8 volts and a current density of 6 amp/100 cm² for about 3.5 hr.   The solution can be tested with o-phenanthroline to check the completeness of plating.

Typical Methods.   Ferric citrate or iron ammonium citrate labeled with Fe[55] was administered to rats in amounts of 0.05 mg Fe and 1 to 5 μc (Fe-7).   Because of the high concentration of iron in the blood, it was necessary to viviperfuse the animals to obtain reliable tissue analyses; this was done with a modified Tyrode's solution.   Individual tissues were wet-ashed in concentrated HNO_3 plus Superoxol, and whole carcasses were dry-ashed.   Aliquots of the ash solution were electroplated onto a metal ointment capsule in a simple apparatus from a citrate solution (Fe-3) for counting with a thin-mica-window tube.

In another study with rats (Fe-8) the irradiated metal unit containing Fe[55,59] was dissolved in HCl and diluted just before use so that a 0.5-ml dose contained about 2 mg iron and about 1.5×10^3 counts/min.   The animals were dosed orally every other day for 10 days.   Each carcass was placed in a 1000-ml beaker, and 100 ml concentrated HNO_3 plus 25 to 30 ml distilled H_2O was added.   The beaker was kept at 37°C until the rat had dissolved, the solution then evaporated to about 125 ml and cooled, and the fat skimmed off. The solution was made up to 200 ml with washings from the beaker and fat. Fifty-milliliter aliquots were dry-ashed and electroplated following the methods described above (Fe-6).

In a double-labeling experiment with rats (Fe-9), Fe^{55} containing 125,000 counts/min and 8 μg iron was given orally, whereas 10,000 counts/min of Fe^{59} in 0.1 μg iron was incubated for 1 hr with 1 ml of rat plasma and injected intravenously. Blood and tissues were wet-ashed with sulfuric and perchloric acids, whereas the carcass was dry-ashed. The iron was electroplated for the counting of Fe^{55} with an argon-filled Geiger tube plus a beryllium filter, and for the counting of Fe^{59} with a helium-filled tube. Doses of 200,000 to 1,000,000 counts/min of Fe^{59} containing 1.8 to 120 mg iron were administered orally to women patients (Fe-10). The red cells were dry-ashed at 620°C, and the ash solutions electroplated by the methods described in (Fe-3).

For histochemical studies, guinea pigs, rats, and a dog were given about 88, 4.4, and 380 μc, respectively, of $Fe^{55,59}$ orally (Fe-11). Tissues were fixed in Carnoy's fluid and Formalin or alcohol-Formalin and were stained for iron by Dry's modification of Perl's method or by Gomori's method. A paraffin section stained by Dry's method was used for a routine contact autoradiogram with Ansco nonscreen X-ray film. After exposure, the preparation was developed, fixed, dried, mounted in xylol-Clarite, and covered with a cover slip.

Labeled rat hemoglobin was prepared by use of a ferrous chloride–lactic acid solution in doses of 0.25 ml/100 g body weight containing 1 mg iron and 3300 counts/min (Fe-12). The optimum solution contained 400 mg % iron in 0.1 N lactic acid and was sterilized by filtration for storage. The rats were bled about 1.5 per cent of their body weight at 2- to 3-day intervals for 11 bleedings, and the injections were then begun daily for 7 days and then every other day for another seven doses. In another study, labeled cytochrome C was produced by administration of about 11 mg of high-specific-activity Fe^{55}-labeled iron to iron-depleted young rats (Fe-13). The cytochrome C was isolated to contain about 1235 counts/min/mg.

To study the effect of manganese on iron uptake, peanut plants were grown in nutrient solution containing varying amounts of manganese to which labeled iron was added. Each quart fruit jar, which contained the roots of two plants, received 14 μc Fe^{55} (Fe-14). Leaflets, which were taken 24 to 120 hr after addition of the Fe^{55}, were pressed between blotting paper, dried for 48 hr at 105°C, weighed, and then counted in an internal proportional counter. It was shown that the counts were essentially the same whether the leaflets were counted directly or digested in HNO_3, dried, and counted; the results were generally reproducible.

Fe-1. Peacock, Wendell C., Robley D. Evans, John W. Irvine, Jr., Wilfred M. Good, Arthur F. Kip, Soma Weiss, and John G. Gibson, 2d: The Use of Two Radioactive Isotopes of Iron in Tracer Studies of Erythrocytes, *J. Clin. Invest.*, **25**: 605–615 (1946).

Fe-2. Sandell, E. B.: "Colorimetric Determination of Traces of Metals," 2d ed., Interscience Publishers, Inc., New York, 1950.

Fe-3. Hahn, P. F.: Radioactive Iron Procedures, *Ind. Eng. Chem. Anal. Ed.*, **17**: 45–46 (1945).

Fe-4. Ramsay, W. N. M.: The Determination of Iron in Blood Plasma or Serum, *Biochem. J. London*, **53**: 227–231 (1953).

Fe-5. Jones, Frances: Colorimetric Determination of Serum Iron, *Anal. Chem.*, **21**: 1216–1217 (1949).

Fe-6. Vosburgh, Gilbert J., Louis B. Flexner, and Dean B. Cowie: The Determination of Radioactive Iron in Biological Material with Particular Reference to Purification and Separation of Iron with Isopropyl Ether, Ashing and Electroplating Technique, and Accuracy of the Method, *J. Biol. Chem.*, **175**: 391–404 (1948).

Fe-7. Copp, D. Harold, and David M. Greenberg: A Tracer Study of Iron Metabolism with Radioactive Iron. I. Methods: Absorption and Excretion of Iron, *J. Biol. Chem.*, **164**: 377–387 (1946).

Fe-8. Gubler, Clark J., George E. Cartwright, and Maxwell M. Wintrobe: The Anemia of Infection. X. The Effect of Infection on the Absorption and Storage of Iron by the Rat, *J. Biol. Chem.*, **184**: 563–574 (1950).

Fe-9. Saylor, Linda, and Clement A. Finch: Determination of Iron Absorption Using Two Isotopes of Iron, *Am. J. Physiol.*, **172**: 372–376 (1953).

Fe-10. Hahn, P. F., E. L. Carothers, W. J. Darby, M. Martin, C. W. Sheppard, R. O. Cannon, A. S. Beam, P. M. Densen, J. C. Peterson, and G. S. McClellan: Iron Metabolism in Human Pregnancy as Studied with the Radioactive Isotope, Fe[59], *Am. J. Obstet. Gynecol.*, **61**: 477–486 (1951).

Fe-11. Endicott, K. M., T. Gillman, G. Brecher, A. T. Ness, F. A. Clark, and E. R. Adamik: A Study of Histochemical Iron Using Tracer Methods, *J. Lab. Clin. Med.*, **34**: 414–421 (1949).

Fe-12. Wasserman, Karlman, and John K. Hampton, Jr.: Labeling of Rat Hemoglobin with Radioactive Iron, *Proc. Soc. Exptl. Biol. Med.*, **72**: 639–641 (1949).

Fe-13. Beinert, Helmut, and Heinz Maier-Leibnitz: Cytochrome C Labeled with Radioactive Iron, *Science*, **108**: 634 (1948).

Fe-14. Davis, Donald: Manganese Induced Chlorosis of the Peanut Plant as Correlated with the Uptake of Fe[55] (Unpublished).

Lanthanum 140 (40 hr)   *Beta* 1.32, 1.67, 2.26   *Gamma* 0.093–2.9

Cat. No.	Sp. Act.	Form	Cost	Chem. Cont.	Radiochem. Cont.
La-140-I	525 mc/g	La_2O_3	$12/40 mc	—	—

				R_f/mc	50% Self-abs.
				4	144 (calc.)

Critical Org.	Body	Air	Water	Effect. $T_{1/2}$
Bone	24 μc	10^{-6}	1	1.6 days

Intake Levels. Lanthanum is one of the rare-earth group, and little or no information is available as to the naturally occurring levels in biological material. Since La^{140} results from fission, there is an interest in its behavior in the animal. There have been reports that yeast tends to accumulate lanthanum, and this has been studied using the Ba^{140}-La^{140} isotopes (La-1) (see references under Barium).

Radioassay. Routine beta or gamma counting presents no particular problem.

Chemistry. Biological samples may be wet- or dry-ashed. It is sometimes necessary to separate the La^{140} daughter from Ba^{140}, and this can be done as follows (La-2): The $BaCl_2$ solution into which the lanthanum has grown is treated with $FeCl_3$ and made basic with NH_4OH, and the $Fe(OH)_3$ is separated out and dissolved in HCl and reprecipitated twice with NH_4OH, Ba being added as a holdback carrier each time. The iron in acid solution can finally be extracted with isopropyl ether to leave the lanthanum in the aqueous phase.

Typical Methods. About 5 μc of purified La^{140} obtained from Ba^{140} (La-2) was injected intraperitoneally or intramuscularly into a rat. The tissues were ashed at 500°C in porcelain, and the ash transferred to a porcelain dish 4 cm in diameter. One milliliter of H_2O was added and evaporated in hot air. Weak samples were measured with an 11-mg/cm² end-window tube, and stronger samples with an electroscope. Self-absorption curves using the La^{140} in NaCl were established and used for correction of samples.

In a study of the effects of chelating agents on the distribution and excretion of radioisotopes, a dose of 200 μc La^{140} as the EDTA complex was administered intravenously to a patient, and the urine collected by catheter for radioassay (La-3).

La-1. Bowen, V. T., and Ann C. Rubinson: Uptake of Lanthanum by a Yeast, *Nature*, **167**: 1032 (1951).
La-2. Hamilton, Joseph G.: Metabolism of Fission Products (Progress Report for Month Ending March 15, 1943), MDDC-1142, Mar. 15, 1943.
La-3. Hart, Hiram, and Daniel Laszlo: Modification of the Distribution and Excretion of Radioisotopes by Chelating Agents, *Science*, **118**: 24–25 (1953).

Manganese 52 (6.0 days)   *Beta* 0.582   *Gamma* 0.73–1.46   K
Manganese 54 (300 days)   *Beta* 1.0   *Gamma* 0.835   K

Cat. No.	*Sp. Act.*	*Form*	*Cost*	*Chem. Cont.*	*Radiochem. Cont.*
Mn-5254-P	CF	$MnCl_2$	$100/mc	Possibly Cr	—

Mica W.	*Int. C.*	*Scint. C.*	R_f/mc
6.4×10^{-3}	9.1×10^{-4}	1.7×10^{-3}	Mn^{52}, 20
			Mn^{54}, 5

Critical Org.
Kidney, liver

Intake Levels.   Normal intake is about 4 mg/day for man and about 0.8 mg/day for rats.   Dietary levels on a dry-matter basis approximate 50 ppm for sheep and cattle, 7 to 50 ppm for swine, and 50 ppm for poultry.   Animal tissues contain 0.2 to 4 ppm manganese.   In rabbits as much as 0.2 to 0.3 g daily for 3 weeks produced no toxic symptoms.   A recommended nutrient solution for plants contains about 0.11 ppm, and crop plants have been found to have from 25 to 1000 ppm.

Radioassay.   No problems are presented by routine beta or gamma counting.

Chemistry.   The general methods of Chap. 5 may be followed for dry- or wet-ashing.   Manganese is usually determined by oxidation to permanganate in acid solution with periodate or persulfate, followed by colorimetric evaluation.   These methods are not generally so sensitive as desired for biochemical studies.   A modified catalytic method has been described which requires about 0.005 μg manganese in the sample (Mn-1).   A microbiological method requiring 0.5 μg/ml of test solution has been reported (Mn-2).

Typical Methods.   In a study of pancreatic localization and secretion, mice and rats were injected intravenously with 50 to 60 μc Mn^{54}, whereas dogs received 333 to 541 μc in 7 mg Mn as $MnCl_2$ in saline (Mn-3). Radiomeasurements were made with a gamma-ray ionization chamber. Cyclotron-produced Mn^{54} was used for distribution studies in rats and in chicks on manganese-deficient diets (Mn-4, Mn-5).   For counting, the tissues were dry-ashed at 500°C, and carrier added to facilitate subsequent precipitation of MnO_2.   Direct beta or gamma counting would eliminate the necessity for the chemical operations and probably give comparable results.   The manganese metabolism of hornets has been studied using cyclotron-produced radioactivity (Mn-6).   In one experiment the 2.59-hr Mn^{56} was used, and in another, a mixture of Mn^{52} and Mn^{54}.   The radioisotopes were incorporated into a honey solution upon which the insects fed.   Routine chemical analyses, Geiger counting, and contact autoradiography were employed.

The uptake of Mn^{54} was studied in flax, peas, cabbage, and tomato plants grown in nutrient solution (Mn-7). About 35 μc Mn^{54} was used in each culture solution, and the level of manganese was varied from 0.5 to 50 ppm. For radioassay, the plant tissue was dried at 105°C, then finely ground, and spread evenly over an aluminum pan for measurement with a Geiger tube. Autoradiograms were made using Kodirex no-screen X-ray film. The tissue was first pressed flat and then placed on the film in the dark; with fresh material, the film and tissue were separated by cellophane. The film and sample were pressed between two glass plates and exposed for 6 to 12 days at refrigerator temperatures.

Mn^{54} was employed to study absorption and distribution in plants, the fate of manganese applied to the soil, and the effects of various trace elements on manganese behavior in the soil-plant system (Mn-8). Seedlings were grown for 3 weeks in standard nutrient solution in 4-gal solution jars, to which was added 5 μc Mn^{54} per week. In pot studies about 30 μc Mn^{54} was used per 7 lb of air-dry soil. Plant tissue was assayed by ashing 0.3-g samples in a metal planchet at 500°C and counting directly with an end-window tube. Soil was treated with HNO_3 and $HClO_4$ to destroy organic matter, and the sample concentrated to a definite volume. Aliquots were pipetted into a pyrex glass planchet, the inside walls and top edges of which were coated with silicone grease to prevent creeping. The solution was evaporated to dryness for counting. For autoradiograms, leaves were dried in a botanical press and placed in direct contact with no-screen X-ray film.

Mn-1. Fore, H., and R. A. Morton: Microdetermination of Manganese in Biological Material by a Modified Catalytic Method, *Biochem. J. London*, **51**: 594–598 (1952).

Mn-2. Charney, Jesse, and W. P. Fisher: A Microbiological Assay Method for Microgram Quantities of Manganese in Biological Material, *Science*, **114**: 687–688 (1951).

Mn-3. Burnett, William T., Jr., Robert R. Bigelow, Allyn W. Kimball, and Charles W. Sheppard: Radiomanganese Studies on the Mouse, Rat and Pancreatic Fistula Dog, *Am. J. Physiol.*, **168**: 620–625 (1952).

Mn-4. Greenberg, David M., and W. Wesley Campbell: Studies in Mineral Metabolism with the Aid of Induced Radioactive Isotopes. IV. Manganese, *Proc. Natl. Acad. Sci. U.S.*, **26**: 448–452 (1940).

Mn-5. Mohamed, Mustafa Safwat, and David M. Greenberg: A Tracer Study with Mn^{56} on Chicks with Perosis Produced by a Synthetic Manganese Deficient Diet, *Proc. Soc. Exptl. Biol. Med.*, **54**: 197–200 (1943).

Mn-6. Bowen, Vaughan T.: Manganese Metabolism of Social Vespidae, *J. Exptl. Zool.*, **115**: 175–205 (1950).

Mn-7. Millikan, C. R.: Radio-autographs of Manganese in Plants, *Australian J. Sci. Research*, **4**: 28–41 (1951).

Mn-8. Romney, Evan M., and Stephen J. Toth: Plant and Soil Studies with Radioactive Manganese, *Soil Sci.*, **77**: 107–117 (1954).

| **Mercury 197** (65 hr) | | | | *Beta* | *Gamma* 0.077 | | *K* |
| **Mercury 197**^{m_2} (24 hr) | | | | *Beta* | *Gamma* 0.135–0.273 | | *K* |

Cat. No.	*Sp. Act.*	*Form*	*Cost*	*Chem. Cont.*	*Radiochem. Cont.*
Hg-197-I	200 mc/g	HgO	$12/2600 mc	—	Au^{197m} (7.4 sec) daughter
					40 mc Hg^{203} (47.9 days)

R_f/mc
Hg^{197}, 2
Hg^{197m_2}, 0.5

Mercury 203 (47.9 days)					*Beta* 0.205	*Gamma* 0.286

Cat. No.	*Sp. Act.*	*Form*	*Cost*	*Chem. Cont.*	*Radiochem. Cont.*
Hg-203-I	72 mc/g	HgO	$33/160 mc	—	3000 mc Hg^{197}
					(65 hr, 24 hr)
Hg-203-P	50–100 mc/g	Hg(NO₃)₂		—	—

Mica W.	*Int. C.*	*Scint. C.*	R_f/mc	*50% Self-abs.*
2×10^{-4}	1.1×10^{-4}	1.9×10^{-3}	1.7	28 (calc.)

Intake Levels.　Nearly all foods contain about 0.005 to 0.05 ppm mercury. The daily intake by man is of the order of 0.02 mg. Human glandular tissues range from 0.01 to 0.13 ppm on the fresh basis, whereas others contain 0.001 to 0.01 ppm. About 50 mg/kg of mercuric chloride given orally is fatal to rats. A biologic interest in this element, besides its toxicity, is the use of organic mercurial drugs, particularly for diuresis.

Radioassay.　Hg^{197} exists in two isomeric states; thus the two half-lives. Preparation Hg-203-P appears to be the one of choice, and soft-beta counting or gamma counting will be required. An advantage of the latter will be the elimination of sample preparation and self-absorption problems.

Chemistry.　Routine wet-ashing, dry-ashing, or even heating of certain organic mercury compounds may lead to volatilization losses. A method described for estimation of mercury in biological material is as follows (Hg-1): The sample is digested in a special apparatus by boiling with H_2SO_4 and HNO_3, followed by addition of permanganate and a second boiling. Mercury is extracted from the digest with a chloroform solution of di-β-naphthylthiocarbazone which is then treated with a sulfuric acid–sodium thiosulfate mixture to separate the mercury from copper. The mercury is extracted from the copper-free aqueous phase with a chloroform solution of di-β-naphthylthiocarbazone which is used for colorimetric evaluation.

Typical Methods.　Measurements of Hg^{203} were made on water, plasma, and urine to which the radioisotope had been added and also on serum, plasma, urine, and ascitic fluid from subjects who had previously been injected (Hg-2). Either 0.25 or 0.30 ml of the fluid was delivered onto a filter-paper disk by means of a micropipette. The preparation was dried, and the filter-paper mounted to a metal disk with rubber cement for end-window counting. In another study (Hg-3) both Na^{22} and a Hg^{203}-labeled mercurial diuretic were added to the same filter-paper disk as above. It was shown that heating of the disk at 250°C for 80 min was sufficient to drive off almost all the Hg^{203} without change in the Na^{22} activity. This procedure was suggested for use in double-labeling studies with the two radioisotopes. In a study with rats (Hg-4), 1 mg Hg in $HgCl_2$ containing 50 μc Hg^{203} was injected intravenously. Kidney sections were fixed in 10 per cent Formalin in 0.85 per cent NaCl solution, embedded in paraffin, and cut at a thickness of 8 μ. Exposures were made on 10- and 25-μ emulsions with 8 to 15 million beta particles per square centimeter employing Eastman Kodak NTB nuclear-track plates. After development, the paraffin sections were stained with hematoxylin and eosin for microscopic examination.

Hg-1. Cholak, Jacob, and Donald M. Hubbard: Microdetermination of Mercury in Biological Material, *Ind. Eng. Chem. Anal. Ed.*, **18**: 149–151 (1946).
Hg-2. Burch, George, Paul Reaser, Thorpe Ray, and Sam Threefoot: A Method of Preparing Biologic Fluids for Counting of Radioelements, *J. Lab. Clin. Med.*, **35**: 626–633 (1950).
Hg-3. Reaser, P. B., G. E. Burch, S. A. Threefoot, and C. T. Ray: Thermal Separation of Radiomercury from Radiosodium, *Science*, **109**: 198 (1949).
Hg-4. Lippman, Richard W., Raymond D. Finkle, and Dale Gillette: Effect of Proteinuria on Localization of Radiomercury in Rat Kidney, *Proc. Soc. Exptl. Biol. Med.*, **77**: 68–70 (1951).

Molybdenum 99 (2.85 days)					*Beta* 0.5, 1.22	*Gamma* 0.141
Cat. No.	*Sp. Act.*	*Form*	*Cost*	*Chem. Cont.*	*Radiochem. Cont.*	
Mo-99-I	7 mc/g	MoO_3	\$12/46 mc	—	10^{-6} mc Tc^{99m} (6 hr) daughter	
Mica W.	*Int. C.*		*Scint. C.*		R_f/mc	*50% Self-abs.*
1.3×10^{-4}	1.4×10^{-4}		8.7×10^{-3}		1.8	156 (calc.)
Critical Org.	*Body*		*Air*		*Water*	*Effect. T$_{1/2}$*
Bone	50 μc		2×10^{-3}		14	2.8 days

Intake Levels. Molybdenum is almost universally found in plant and animal materials. There is suggestive evidence that it is essential for animals in trace amounts as a constituent of xanthine oxidase (Mo-1). The normal dietary level is probably less than 1 ppm, and most plants contain of the order of 0.5 ppm on a dry basis. In some areas from 5 to 200 ppm may be present in the plants, which are then usually toxic for ruminants, especially if the copper levels are low. Molybdenum is definitely essential for plants, and 0.1 ppm in the nutrient solution has been found to stimulate the growth of lettuce, whereas 0.01 ppm has been found essential for the growth of tomato seedlings (Mo-2). Soluble molybdenum compounds were fatal when fed to rats and guinea pigs at 1200 to 6000 mg/kg but much less so at 120 to 600 mg/kg. Levels of 400 to 800 mg/kg administered intraperitoneally to guinea pigs were highly toxic. Chronic toxicity largely depends on the amount of copper in the diet, and with low copper as little as 80 ppm has caused toxic symptoms in rats (Mo-3).

Radioassay. The technetium-99m daughter will usually not interfere, especially if hard-beta or gamma counting is used, or if about 60 hr is allowed to lapse between the taking of the sample and the measurement so as to allow attainment of equilibrium. Gamma counting, although somewhat less sensitive, offers the advantage that self-absorption corrections will not be necessary. Solution counting is also convenient. The specific activity available is not particularly high, and there may be some difficulties in reducing the dosage to physiological levels.

Chemistry. Biological samples may be dry-ashed, but the temperature should not exceed 450°C in order to avoid losses. However, wet-ashing is usually preferred, and a recent modification of a widely used procedure has been described (Mo-4). The dry, ground tissue is digested with sulfuric, nitric, and perchloric acids, and after boiling to remove the last traces of perchloric acid, it is diluted with distilled water and boiled again. The solution is neutralized to methyl orange with ammonia, acidified with HCl, and treated with sodium fluoride, an iron solution, and then potassium thiocyanate. After addition of stannous chloride the molybdenum complex is extracted into isoamyl alcohol for colorimetric evaluation.

Typical Methods. The 10 g MoO_3 in the irradiation unit was dissolved in 35 ml of 14.3 per cent NaOH and stirred until clear, after which it was diluted to a convenient volume with distilled water to give a pH near 7 (Mo-3). For tissue distribution studies about 7 g of the MoO_3 was administered orally to cattle, 1.9 g given intravenously to cattle, and about 40 mg given orally to rats. The tissues were wet-ashed in concentrated HNO_3 and extracted with isoamyl alcohol to give two solutions for each sample which were counted directly with a Geiger tube. In a study with plants, carrier-free Mo^{93} and Mo^{99} produced in the cyclotron were used (Mo-5). It was thus possible to study the uptake of as little as 1 μg molybdenum by tomato plants from nutrient solutions. To demonstrate that molybdenum is part of xanthine oxidase, about 15 mc Mo^{99} was injected into a dairy cow, and the Mo^{99}/xanthine oxidase ratio was followed through several purification steps (Mo-1). The radioactivity was measured by gamma counting.

Mo-1. Totter, John R., William T. Burnett, Jr., R. A. Monroe, Ira B. Whitney, and C. L. Comar: Evidence that Molybdenum Is a Non-dialyzable Component of Xanthine Oxidase, *Science*, **118**: 555 (1953).

Mo-2. Monier-Williams, G. W.: "Trace Elements in Food," John Wiley & Sons, Inc., New York, 1950.

Mo-3. Comar, C. L., Leon Singer, and George K. Davis: Molybdenum Metabolism and Interrelationships with Copper and Phosphorus, *J. Biol. Chem.*, **180**: 913–922 (1949).

Mo-4. Dick, A. T., and J. B. Bingley: Further Observations on the Determination of Molybdenum in Plant and Animal Tissue, *Australian J. Exptl. Biol. Med. Sci.*, **29**: 459–462 (1951).

Mo-5. Stout, P. R., and W. R. Meagher: Studies of the Molybdenum Nutrition of Plants with Radioactive Molybdenum, *Science*, **108**: 471–473 (1948).

Neodymium 147 (11.3 days)				Beta 0.17, 0.78	Gamma 0.035, 0.58
Promethium 147 (2.6 yr)				Beta 0.223	Gamma
Cat. No.	*Sp. Act.*	*Form*	*Cost*	*Chem. Cont.*	*Radiochem. Cont.*
NdPm-147-P	CF	NdCl$_3$	$50/mc	—	Pm^{147} daughter (2.6 yr)
Mica W.	*Int. C.*		*Scint. C.*	*R_f/mc*	*50 % Self-abs.*
5×10^{-6}	2×10^{-6}		2×10^{-3}	1.4	97 (detn.)

Intake Levels.   Neodymium is a rare-earth element and is not of biological interest.   Nd^{147} is produced in relatively small yields by the fission process and tends to deposit in the skeleton.

Radioassay.   The Pm^{147} will usually present no particular counting problem, because the growth is relatively slow and the contribution will be minimized by gamma or hard-beta counting.

Chemistry.   Neodymium is similar in chemical behavior to lanthanum and praseodymium.   Various separation procedures have been described in reference (Nd-1).   Presumably, conventional wet- or dry-ashing methods would cause no losses.

Nd-1. Coryell, Charles D., and Nathan Sugarman: "Radiochemical Studies: The Fission Products," Books 1–3, National Nuclear Energy Series, McGraw-Hill Book Company, Inc., New York, 1951.

Nickel 63 (85 yr) $\qquad$ *Beta* 0.063 $\qquad$ *Gamma*

Cat. No.	Sp. Act.	Form	Cost	Chem. Cont.	Radiochem. Cont.
Ni-63-I	0.35 mc/g	Metal	$33/3.5 mc	—	~1 μc Ni^{59} (8 × 10^4 yr)
Ni-63-P	5–50 mc/g	NiCl$_2$	$45/mc	—	~0.01 % Ni^{59}

Mica W.	Int. C.	Scint. C.
5 × 10^{-2}	2.6 × 10^{-4}	1.4

Critical Org.
Liver

Intake Levels. Nickel is found in almost all biological materials, although, so far as is known, it is not essential for plants or animals. A normal low intake for man has been reported as 0.3 to 0.5 mg daily (Ni-1). Some typical values for tissues on a fresh basis are as follows: human liver, 0.09 ppm; human pancreas, 0.04 ppm; ox liver, 0.125 ppm; ox pancreas, 0.135 ppm; cow's milk, 0.004 ppm; egg yolk, 0.02 ppm; and fish, 0.015 ppm (Ni-1). Crop plants range from about 0.15 to 4 ppm on a dry basis, with an average of about 0.9 ppm. A recommended nutrient solution for plants contains about 0.01 ppm. Oral doses of 10 to 20 mg/kg produced no symptoms in dogs, but 22 to 44 mg/kg caused vomiting and diarrhea. The toxicity is much higher when given intravenously; 7 to 8 mg/kg of nickel sodium citrate was fatal to rabbits and dogs (Ni-1). Rats will tolerate doses of 10 mg/kg of the nickel sodium citrate subcutaneously, whereas only 1 mg/kg appears to be tolerated intravenously with any degree of safety; this latter applies for the chloride also (Ni-2).

Radioassay. Preparation Ni-63-P will probably be the one of choice, although the high cost should be noted. The extremely low beta energy of Ni^{63} has made the counting measurement very difficult and has discouraged the use of this radioisotope. The Ni^{59} radiocontamination does not present any particular problem. For counting, it will be essential that the nickel be separated from as much extraneous material as possible in order to eliminate serious sensitivity losses from self-absorption. The removal of nickel from the sample may be accomplished either by chemical separation procedures employing dimethylglyoxime or by electroplating. The latter method has proved the more satisfactory, and a procedure has been developed in which the sample is ashed in the muffle furnace, the ash taken up in concentrated H$_2$SO$_4$, and the entire solution or an aliquot put into electroplating solution (100 g ammonium sulfate, 180 ml concentrated ammonium hydroxide, and 5 g ammonium hypophosphite per liter). The nickel is then electroplated in the presence of inert carrier, preferably with the use of a controlled-cathode electroplating device (Ni-2). For measurement, the internal counter will be the instrument of choice on account of the much higher sensitivity.

Chemistry. A typical analytical method employing dimethylglyoxime is described as follows (Ni-3, Ni-4): The organic material is destroyed by dry-ashing, provided the ash can be brought into HCl solution, or alternatively by acid digestion with HNO_3 and H_2SO_4. The acid ash solution is treated with sodium citrate, excess ammonia, and dimethylglyoxime and is then extracted with chloroform for treatment with bromine water and colorimetric evaluation. In another procedure (Ni-1) the sample is ashed in a muffle furnace, the ash is dissolved in HCl, and the solution is neutralized and then made slightly acid for separation of heavy metals by H_2S. The filtrate is treated with bromine water to oxidize iron, which is then removed as phosphate. The remaining solution is treated with potassium dithiooxalate for colorimetric evaluation.

Typical Methods. In a study with mice, $1\mu c$ $Ni^{63}Cl_2$ (102 μg) dissolved in physiological saline was administered intraperitoneally (Ni-5). The tissues were digested with HNO_3 and $HClO_4$, and the digests taken to dryness four to five times; the residues were further treated with $HClO_4$ until a pure white inorganic residue was obtained. The final residue was dissolved in dilute acid, and 0.5 mg of stable Ni (as $NiCl_2$) was added to an aliquot as a carrier. The solution was treated with 10 ml of 0.75 M $(NH_4)_2SO_4$ in 7.5 M NH_4OH, and the nickel electroplated onto a copper planchet at 5 volts and 40 ma current. The plated samples were assayed in a gas-flow detector.

Ni-1. Monier-Williams, G. W.: "Trace Elements in Food," John Wiley & Sons, Inc., New York, 1950.
Ni-2. Kuhn, U. S. G., III and H. Helms: Unpublished results.
Ni-3. Scott, W. W.: "Standard Methods of Chemical Analysis," 5th ed., vols. I and II, D. Van Nostrand Company, Inc., New York, 1939.
Ni-4. Sandell, E. B.: "Colorimetric Determination of Traces of Metals," 2d ed., Interscience Publishers, Inc., New York, 1950.
Ni-5. Wase, Arthur W., Donald M. Goss, and M. John Boyd: The Metabolism of Nickel. I. Spatial and Temporal Distribution of Ni^{63} in the Mouse, *Arch. Biochem. and Biophys.*, **51**: 1–4 (1954).

Niobium 95 (35 days) Beta 0.146 Gamma 0.758

Cat. No.	Sp. Act.	Form	Cost	Chem. Cont.	Radiochem. Cont.
Nb-95-P	CF	Complex in oxalic acid	$10/mc	—	—

Mica W.	Int. C.	Scint. C.	R_f/mc	50% Self-abs.
5.8×10^{-4}	1.6×10^{-4}	2.5×10^{-3}	4.6	8 (calc.)

Critical Org.	Body	Air	Water	Effect. $T_{1/2}$
Bone	90 μc	4×10^{-7}	4×10^{-3}	21 days

Intake Levels. In previous American usage, element 41 has been designated as *columbium*. However, the name *niobium* has been adopted by the International Union of Chemistry. This element is not an important naturally occurring constituent of biological materials and has been of interest primarily on account of the production of Nb^{95} in the fission process. Nb^{95} is a daughter of another fission product, Zr^{95}.

Radioassay. Although soft-beta counting is most sensitive, the problems of self-absorption will make gamma counting the method of choice.

Chemistry. Methods are not available for estimation of niobium in biological materials. Routine wet- or dry-ashing methods may be used.

Typical Methods. In a study with rats (Nb-1), 5 μc Nb^{95} in 0.25 ml of a 0.01 per cent sodium citrate solution (pH 6) was injected by way of the great saphenous vein. Tissue samples were dried, then ashed at 650°C for 10 hr, and the ash dissolved in 2 N HCl. Aliquots, up to 5 ml, were placed in $\frac{1}{2}$-oz metal ointment capsules for counting with a thin-mica-window tube. It would be important to check recoveries because of the possible adsorption of niobium on glass surfaces and insolubility in HCl.

Nb-1. Kawin, Bergene, D. H. Copp, and J. G. Hamilton: Studies of the Metabolism of Certain Fission Products and Plutonium, UCRL-812, Aug. 7, 1950.

Osmium 191 (16.0 days)   *Beta* 0.142   *Gamma* 0.039–0.127

Cat. No.	*Sp. Act.*	*Form*	*Cost*	*Chem. Cont.*	*Radiochem. Cont.*
Os-191-I	73 mc/g	Metal	$35/40 mc	—	Os[185] (97 days)
					18 mc Os[193] (30.6 hr)

$$R_f/mc$$
$$1$$

Intake Levels. Osmium occurs with platinum ores and has not been of biological interest. Osmium tetroxide has been recognized as dangerous on account of its volatility and production of ocular disturbances, asthmatic condition on inhalation, and dermatitis on skin contact (Os-1).

Radioassay. The contaminating Os[193] can be eliminated by decay. The presence of Os[185] should present no difficulties if a pilot sample of the material administered to the biological system is kept for the decay corrections. Also it must be remembered that in beta measurements the self-absorption characteristics of the mixture may change with time. Gamma counting will probably be preferred, provided the sensitivity is adequate for the particular samples.

Chemistry. Methods are not available for estimation of osmium in biological tissue. The volatility of osmium compounds must be taken into account before the use of any wet- or dry-ashing procedures. Separation of osmium from platinum metals has been accomplished by virtue of the volatility of osmium tetroxide, and procedures have been described for its colorimetric estimation by use of reaction with thiourea (Os-2).

Os-1. Fairhall, Lawrence T.: "Industrial Toxicology," The Williams & Wilkins Company, Baltimore, 1949.
Os-2. Sandell, E. B.: "Colorimetric Determination of Traces of Metals," 2d ed., Interscience Publishers, Inc., New York, 1950.

Palladium 109 (13.6 hr)   *Beta* 0.95   *Gamma*

Cat. No.	*Sp. Act.*	*Form*	*Cost*	*Chem. Cont.*	*Radiochem. Cont.*
Pd-109-I	220 mc/g	Metal	$15/220 mc	—	Pd^{103} (17 days)
					2 mc Ag^{111} (7.6 days)

Mica W.	*Int. C.*	*Scint. C.*	*50% Self-abs.*
5.5×10^{-5}	9.4×10^{-5}	7.2×10^{-2}	116 (calc.)

Critical Org.
Kidney

Intake Levels. Palladium is found associated with metals of the platinum group and has not been of biological interest. Palladium salts are not highly toxic; 16- to 21-mg dosages of palladium chloride, injection of 50 mg weekly into abdominal fat, and subcutaneous injection were tolerated. However, intravenous administration of buffered palladium chloride caused toxic symptoms (Pd-1).

Radioassay. Pd^{103}, which emits no beta particles, would not interfere with the use of preparation Pd-109-I, especially if efficient beta counting were employed. However, it will probably be necessary to separate the Ag^{111}, which could probably be done by modification of the following chemical procedure (Pd-2): A hot nitrate solution of the palladium and silver is treated with ammonia to produce a tetrammine salt. The solution is acidified with acetic acid and treated hot with a slight excess of dilute HCl to precipitate silver chloride.

Chemistry. Routine wet- or dry-ashing of biological material should be satisfactory. Chemical methods have usually been based upon separation from interfering metals and colorimetric evaluation after reaction with substances such as *P*-nitrosodimethylaniline, *P*-dimethylaminobenzylidine rhodanine and *p*-fuchsin (Pd-2).

Pd-1. Fairhall, Lawrence T.: "Industrial Toxicology," The Williams & Wilkins Company, Baltimore, 1949.
Pd-2. Sandell, E. B.: "Colorimetric Determination of Traces of Metals," 2d ed., Interscience Publishers, Inc., New York, 1950.

Phosphorus **32** (14.30 days)				*Beta* 1.712	*Gamma*	
Cat. No.	*Sp. Act.*	*Form*	*Cost*	*Chem. Cont.*	*Radiochem. Cont.*	
P-32-I	30 mc/g	KH$_2$PO$_4$	$33/215 mc	—	100 mc K^{42} (12.44 hr)	
					Possibly phosphite	
P-32-P-1	40 mc/mg	H$_3$PO$_4$	$1.10/mc	—	—	
P-32-P-2	CF	H$_3$PO$_4$	$3/mc	—	—	

Mica W.	*Int. C.*	*Scint. C.*	50% *Self-abs.*	
8.9 × 10^{-5}	8.6 × 10^{-5}	4 × 10^{-2}	310 (detn.)	

Critical Org.	*Body*	*Air*	*Water*	*Effect.* T$_{1/2}$
Bone	10 μc	1 × 10^{-7}	2 × 10^{-4}	14 days

Intake Levels. The approximate daily intake of phosphorus for the various species is as follows: man, 1.5 g; rat, 45 mg; laying hen, 1 g; sheep, 2.5 g; 100-lb pig, 8 g; and cattle, 15 g. In studies of oral administration there is usually no problem in regard to administration of excess mass because of the normal high intake and the high specific activities available. The whole blood in most species contains 35 to 45 mg/100 ml, whereas the inorganic phosphorus of the plasma ranges from 4 to 9 mg/100 ml. Mass is usually not a problem with injection studies, since it takes relatively large doses to produce toxic symptoms. Soft tissues of animals contain 2 to 3 mg phosphorus per gram fresh weight, and bones range from 40 to 130 mg/g. A recommended nutrient solution for plants contains about 32 ppm, and crop plants usually range from 0.1 to 2 per cent on a dry-matter basis.

Radioassay. P^{32} has been one of the most widely used radioisotopes on account of the biological importance of the element, the ease of production, a convenient half-life, and the energetic beta emission. Preparation P-32-I may have the advantage of low cost for large-scale fertilizer use, but one must be careful that there are no significant amounts of labeled phosphite in the particular preparation used. The K^{42} radiocontamination is eliminated by measurement of samples after a lapse of time sufficient to permit decay. Preparation P-32-P-1 appears to be most useful for general purposes and has a specific activity high enough to meet most biological requirements. When extremely high specific activities are required, preparation P-32-P-2 may be used, but care must be taken to avoid loss of activity from these solutions by adsorption to glass walls of beakers, pipettes, etc. It has been shown that such losses become especially significant at low levels of total phosphorus and high pH values (P-1). Under such conditions it may become necessary to coat all glassware with a material like silicone. Routine hard-beta counting, including direct liquid measurements, is entirely satisfactory for P^{32}, and self-absorption corrections are not usually important. It is seldom necessary to separate P^{32} from the extraneous mass of a biological sample merely for counting purposes.

Chemistry. Standard methods for estimation of phosphorus in various biological materials have been described in the literature (P-2 to P-4). Usually an aliquot of the ash solution can be used for radioassay, or the entire ash solution can be counted and then used for chemical estimation of phosphorus. Plant and animal samples can be dry-ashed at 500 to 600°C, usually with the addition of magnesium nitrate, and the ash dissolved in dilute HCl. Wet-ashing may be done with 30 per cent H_2O_2 in H_2SO_4 solution. The H_2O_2 must be phosphorus-free and must be completely removed from the final ash solution. The latter can be accomplished by adding distilled water and evaporating to white fumes in the final step. The phosphorus in an aliquot of the ash solution can be estimated colorimetrically by various modifications of the Fiske Subbarow method (P-3): An aliquot of the ash solution, usually containing of the order of 0.2 mg P, is mixed in order with a molybdate reagent and an aminonaphthol sulfonic acid reagent and is then diluted for colorimetric evaluation after a standard time interval. Plasma is treated with trichloroacetic acid, and the filtrate used directly for development of the molybdenum blue color as above.

Typical Methods. In studies with dairy cows (P-5), 40 mc P^{32} was injected intravenously, and casein containing 2 $\mu c/g$ was prepared from milk collected during the 3 days postinjection. For counting, 0.1-ml samples of milk were pipetted onto disks of lens paper, dried on an aluminum disk, and fixed with a spray of an alcoholic shellac dispersion. For ordinary distribution studies the dosage for cattle might range from 2 to 10 mc. Labeled casein was used to study the digestion of this compound by the calf and also to estimate the fecal phosphorus excretion of calves; 27 to 72 μc of P^{32}-labeled casein was fed to 55- to 140-lb animals, and radioactivity was determined on both fresh and dry-ashed samples (P-6, P-7). In tissue distribution studies with swine, 1.5 to 5 mc was injected intravenously into 25- to 180-lb animals (P-8). For the estimation of endogenous fecal phosphorus in dairy cattle (P-9), about 1.3 mc P^{32} was injected intravenously twice daily for 23 days. In work with poultry about 300 μc was given orally to laying hens (P-10), and about 20 μc to chicks (P-11). One to ten microcuries is adequate for most studies with mice and rats. In a study of P^{32} in the embryo and larva of frogs, fertilized eggs were maintained in solutions of 65 to 550 $\mu c/750$ ml (P-12). The utilization of P^{32} by developing chick embryos has been followed by injections of 0.2 to 5 μc per egg (P-13, P-14).

Labeled mosquitoes were produced by treatment of late third—and fourth—instar larvae with about 0.1 μc P^{32} per larva in 1 ml water (P-15). Adult mosquitoes were tagged by allowing them to feed on a rabbit that had been dosed with 10 mc or to feed on P^{32}-labeled raisins, flowers, or sugar solutions. Counting measurements were made directly on live mosquitoes, and no self-absorption corrections were necessary.

A typical fertilizer experiment, one of numerous similar studies that have been undertaken all over the country, may be described as follows (P-16): A factorial design including placement and source was employed with sugar beets, wheat, and barley. Placements were (a) phosphorus mixed in a band 4 in. wide and 4 in. deep (2 and 4 in. for wheat and barley) and (b) phosphorus placed in a single band 4 in. deep and 4 or 5 in. to one side of the row on beets. The materials studied were superphosphate, calcium metaphosphate, dicalcium phosphate, and alpha tricalcium phosphate applied at the rate of 40 lb P_2O_5 per acre and with an activity at planting time of about 0.1 mc/g P_2O_5. Each sugar beet plot was eight rows wide and 64 ft long, and three rows 32 ft long were treated with radioactive fertilizer. The wheat and barley plots were 41 ft long and six rows wide, and one row of each crop 17 ft long was treated with radioactive fertilizer. The dates of planting were Apr. 24 to May 3, and the last sampling dates were Sept. 13–14.

Much of the counting of plant material has been done by the briquet method (P-17), since little effort is required in preparation of the sample. A modification to increase the sensitivity has been suggested which involves preparation of a cylindrical briquet and counting with a cylindrical thin-wall tube (P-18). A solution-counting technique for plant materials has been described (P-19). Samples containing 1 to 30 mg P were heated in 50-ml pyrex beakers at 500°C for 6 hr, and HNO_3 was added, evaporated to dryness, and heated at 400°C for 15 min to destroy organic matter completely. Concentrated HCl was used to dehydrate the silica, and the residue taken up in 2 N HNO_3 and made to volume, an aliquot of which could be used for chemical determination. A convenient arrangement of dipping Geiger tube and solution holder was used which required 9 ml of sample. It was pointed out that the K^{40} contribution could be neglected unless the P^{32} sample count was only a few times background. The K^{40} was easily corrected for, if necessary, by counting a plant sample that had not received P^{32}.

P^{32}-labeled phytin for use in poultry-nutrition experiments was prepared from a crop of corn grown in gravel culture beds and nutrient solution (P-20). When the kernels were in early milk stage, the nutrient solutions were replaced with tap water containing 166.25 mc P^{32} per 42 liters, equivalent to 38 g KH_2PO_4. The crop was harvested 31 days after P^{32} administration, and calcium phytate was isolated containing about 470 counts/min/mg.

A typical study of plant uptake from nutrient solution may be described as follows (P-21): Maize plants were grown individually in 1-gal crocks containing a standard nutrient solution which was enriched to contain about 10 μc P^{32} per liter. When the plants were small, 200 ml of nutrient solution was used which was increased progressively up to 1000 ml as the plants grew. The total activity taken up by the plant was estimated from measurements on the nutrient solution at the beginning and end of the experiment. Since the interest was primarily in comparing given tissues between different plants, measurements were made directly on the tissues, which were prepared in the same way for each plant and which therefore had about the same self-absorption. Thin cross sections of the roots were cut by hand, and circular or rectangular pieces of leaf were used. Radioactivity was calculated on the basis of area.

In a study of uptake by bacteria (P-22), P^{32} as Na_2HPO_4 was used at concentrations of 10^5 dis/min/ml of culture medium. The P^{32} content of the bacteria was estimated by taking 8 ml of the culture, fixing by making the solution 2 per cent with respect to formaldehyde, centrifuging, washing in 0.8 per cent saline, and counting the pellets with an end-window tube. It was shown that the measured activity was not due to adsorption of P^{32} on the bacterial surfaces or to residues from the radioactive culture.

P-1. Rubin, B. A.: A Source of Error in Tracer Experiments with P^{32}, *Science*, **110**: 425 (1949).

P-2. Koch, Frederick C., and Martin E. Hanke: "Practical Methods in Biochemistry," 5th ed., The Williams & Wilkins Company, Baltimore, 1948.

P-3. Fister, Harold J.: "Manual of Standardized Procedures for Spectrophotometric Chemistry," Standard Scientific Supply Corporation, New York, 1950.

P-4. "Methods of Analysis of the Association of Official Agricultural Chemists," 6th ed., Association of Official Agricultural Chemists, Washington, D.C., 1945.

P-5. Kleiber, Max, Arthur H. Smith, and N. P. Ralston: Secretion in Cow's Milk of Intravenously Injected Radioactive Phosphorus P^{32}, *Proc. Soc. Exptl. Biol. Med.*, **69**: 354–356 (1948).

P-6. Lofgreen, G. P., Max Kleiber, and J. R. Luick: The Metabolic Fecal Phosphorus Excretion of the Young Calf, *J. Nutrition*, **47**: 571–582 (1952).

P-7. Lofgreen, G. P., Max Kleiber, and A. H. Smith: The Digestion and Absorption of P^{32} Labeled Casein by the Young Calf, *J. Nutrition*, **43**: 401–412 (1951).

P-8. Smith, Arthur H., Max Kleiber, Arthur L. Black, Melvin Edick, Robert R. Robinson, and Hubert Heitman, Jr.: Distribution of Intravenously Injected Radioactive Phosphorus (P^{32}) among Swine Tissues, *J. Animal Sci.*, **10**: 893–901 (1951).

P-9. Kleiber, Max, Arthur H. Smith, N. P. Ralston, and Arthur L. Black: Radiophosphorus (P^{32}) as Tracer for Measuring Endogenous Phosphorus in Cow's Feces, *J. Nutrition*, **45**: 253–263 (1951).

P-10. Shirley, R. L., J. C. Driggers, J. McCall, G. K. Davis, and N. R. Mehrhof: Excretion and Retention of P^{32} and Ca^{45} by Laying Hens, *Poultry Sci.*, **30**: 730–734 (1951).

P-11. Patrick, H., and G. K. Schweitzer: Absorption and Retention of Radioactive Phosphorus by Chicks, *Poultry Sci.*, **31**: 888–892 (1952).

P-12. Hansborough, Louis A., and David Denny: Distribution of Phosphorus^{32} in the Embryo and Larva of the Frog, *Proc. Soc. Exptl. Biol. Med.*, **78**: 437–441 (1951).

P-13. Branson, Herman, Martin Brooks, and Pauline F. Piper: The Order of Utilization of Phosphorus Compounds in the Egg by the Chick Embryo, *Science*, **112**: 357–358 (1950).

P-14. Stevens, Kingsley M.: Relation of Uptake of Radiophosphorus into Nucleic Acids to Age of Developing Chick Embryos, *Cancer Research*, **12**: 62–64 (1952).

P-15. Hassett, C. C., and D. W. Jenkins: The Uptake and Effect of Radiophosphorus in Mosquitoes, *Physiol. Zoöl.*, **24**: 257–266 (1951).

P-16. Olsen, Sterling R., and Robert Gardner: Utilization of Phosphorus from Various Fertilizer Materials. IV. Sugar Beets, Wheat, and Barley in Colorado, *Soil Sci.*, **68**: 163–169 (1949).

P-17. MacKenzie, A. J., and L. A. Dean: Measurement of P^{32} in Plant Material by the Use of Briquets, *Anal. Chem.*, **22**: 489–490 (1950).

P-18. Kristjanson, A. M., H. G. Dion, and J. W. T. Spinks: Hollow Cylinder Method of Measurement of P^{32} in Plants, *Can. J. Technol.*, **29**: 496–501 (1951).

P-19. McAuliffe, Clayton: Determination of Radiophosphorus in Plant Material by Solution Counting, *Anal. Chem.*, **21**: 1059–1061 (1949).

P-20. Singsen, E. P., L. D. Matterson, and Anna Kozeff: Phosphorus in Poultry Nutrition. IV. Radioactive Phosphorus as a Tracer in Studying the Metabolism of Phytin by the Turkey Poult, *Poultry Sci.*, **29**: 635–639 (1950).

P-21. Rabideau, Glenn S., W. Gordon Whaley, and Charles Heimsch: The Absorption and Distribution of Radioactive Phosphorus in Two Maize Inbreds and Their Hybrid, *Am. J. Botany*, **37**: 93–99 (1950).

P-22. Labaw, Louis W., Vernon M. Mosley, and Ralph W. G. Wyckoff: Radioactive Studies of the Phosphorus Metabolism of *Escherichia coli*, *J. Bacteriol.*, **59**: 251–262 (1950).

Potassium 42 (12.44 hr)   *Beta* 3.58, 2.04   *Gamma* 1.51

Cat. No.	Sp. Act.	Form	Cost	Chem. Cont.	Radiochem. Cont.
K-42-I	20 mc/g	K_2CO_3	$12/130 mc	—	Possibly Na^{24}, Rb^{86}, Cs^{134}

Mica W.	Int. C.	Scint. C.	R_f/mc	50 % Self-abs.
1×10^{-4}	8.8×10^{-5}	1.2×10^{-3}	2.3	510 (calc.)

Critical Org.	Body	Air	Water	Effect. $T_{\frac{1}{2}}$
Muscle	20 μc	2×10^{-6}	1×10^{-2}	12.24 hr

Intake Levels. The daily intake of potassium by the human adult averages 2 to 3 g. Rats require 8 to 15 mg/day, and 0.5 per cent in the diet is normally adequate. Chicks and swine require 0.15 to 0.24 per cent. A recommended nutrient solution for plants contains about 236 ppm, and crop plants may have 1 to 5 per cent K on the dry-weight basis. Animal tissues have about 3 mg K per gram fresh weight; plasma, about 0.2; and urine, about 2 mg/ml.

Radioassay. Routine hard-beta or gamma counting of K^{42} is entirely satisfactory on account of the energetic radiations emitted. If the target material is of low Na assay, there will usually be no significant contaminating Na^{24}. Otherwise the K^{42} can be purified by reprecipitation as perchlorate in the presence of carrier Na (K-1). There is always the question of the contribution of naturally occurring K^{40} (beta, 1.35; K) to the radioactivity measurement. It has been calculated that 1 mg of natural potassium contains about 0.75×10^{-6} μc K^{40} (K-2). If the amount of total potassium in the sample is known, then the amount of K^{40} can be calculated and its contribution estimated from sensitivity values. For example, a 10-ml sample of urine might contain 20 mg K and therefore 1.5×10^{-5} μc K^{40}. Even if the sensitivity for K^{40} were as high as for K^{42}, it can be seen that this sample would probably have a net count less than the background of the instrument.

Chemistry. Wet-ashing, and dry-ashing with H_2SO_4 are satisfactory. The flame photometer may be conveniently used to determine potassium in ash solutions. A method for ashing plant samples is as follows (K-3): The sample was weighed into a porcelain crucible, wetted down with 1:1 H_2SO_4 plus distilled water, dried on a steam bath and then in an oven, and ashed at 500 to 550°C overnight. The ash was digested in 3 ml concentrated HCl, made to volume, filtered, and used for direct flame-photometer measurement. Animal tissues have been prepared for flame photometry by digestion in HNO_3, use of mild heat to avoid charring, and removal of excess nitrates with formic acid (K-1). Plasma was diluted 1:25 and compared with standard solutions containing 1 ml of 0.145 *M* NaCl to correct for the sodium effects in the plasma.

Typical Methods. About 60×10^6 counts/min of K^{42} in 0.15 milli-equivalent KCl was injected into rabbits. Untreated plasma was measured directly into counting planchets, mixed with 2 to 4 drops of 5 per cent trichloroacetic acid, dried under a heat lamp, and counted with a 2-mg/cm^2 end-window Geiger tube. The trichloroacetic acid reduces production of dry protein flakes. Tissues were digested in HNO_3, and dilutions thereof dried for counting (K-1). In another study with rabbits, 5 ml solution containing 30 μc in 0.5 milliequivalent potassium was injected intravenously (K-4). Tissue samples (1 to 3 g) were digested in concentrated H_2SO_4 and made up to 20 ml, and an aliquot counted with a dipping tube. The potassium concentration in the urine was determined by flame photometry. In a study with dogs, 150 to 1000 μc was injected, and plasma and spinal fluid carefully evaporated for measurement with a Lauritsen electroscope (K-5).

Methods used for study of exchange between plasma and red cells may be described as follows (K-6): Venous blood was heparinized with 10 mg of heparin in 1 ml of 0.15 M NaCl per 50 ml of blood. Fifty milliliters of blood was placed in a 200-ml round-bottom paraffin-coated flask fitted with a top, allowing gas flow and sample removal. About 2×10^5 counts/min of K^{42} and about 1×10^5 counts/min of Rb^{86} were incorporated in 1 to 2 ml of plasma and mixed with the whole blood at zero time. Glucose was also added to raise the initial blood glucose by 250 mg %. There was some indication that the original K^{42} preparation contained a trace of radiocontamination, probably Rb^{86}. The flasks were rotated mechanically, and small aliquots taken for measurement at given time intervals. Potassium was estimated chemically using the flame photometer with diluted plasma and hemolyzed red cells. Radioactivity was determined by the pipetting of solutions onto filter-paper disks. Whole blood was hemolyzed by freezing before pipetting, and a detergent solution (1.7 per cent Hemosol) was used to facilitate even distribution of the red cells. K^{42} and Rb^{86} were determined in the same sample by measurement initially, and again after the K^{42} had decayed away.

In a study of relationships of electrolyte accumulation and tissue metabolism, about 300 mg of rabbit kidney slices were suspended in 2.5 ml of medium in a Warburg vessel (K-7). About 0.2 μc K^{42} in 0.2 ml of medium was placed in the side compartment. At termination of the incubation and gas measurements, the tissues were digested in HNO_3, and aliquots of the ash solution as well as of the medium were counted. Total Na and K were estimated by flame photometry. Similar methods have been described for estimation of the exchange rate of K in brain and retina tissue (K-8).

Potassium absorption has been studied using barley roots from seedlings grown in the dark at a uniform temperature to give reproducible biological material (K-9).   The pattern of K^{42} uptake by sunflower plants has been followed with a scintillation counter which permitted localization of the activity in an area of 6.8-mm radius (K-10).   The plants were grown in vermiculite with No. 2 Hoagland's solution, to which the $K^{42}HCO_3$ was added at the start of the experiment.   For measurement, the scintillation crystal was placed 1.6 mm above the leaf surface.

K-1. Walker, W. Gordon, and Walter S. Wilde: Kinetics of Radiopotassium in the Circulation, *Am. J. Physiol.*, **170**: 401–413 (1952).

K-2. Hurst, W. M.: K^{40} Measurements in Body Fluids, ORNL-1165, Jan. 16, 1952.

K-3. Johnston, Betty R., C. W. Duncan, Kirk Lawton, and E. J. Benne: Determination of Potassium in Plant Materials with a Flame Photometer, *J. Assoc. Offic. Agr. Chemists*, **35**: 813–816 (1952).

K-4. Aikawa, Jerry K.: Effect of Starvation on Exchangeable Potassium and Tissue K^{42} Content in Rabbits, *Proc. Soc. Exptl. Biol. Med.*, **78**: 524–528 (1951).

K-5. Greenberg, David M., Robert B. Aird, Muriel D. D. Boelter, W. Wesley Campbell, Waldo E. Cohn, and Makio M. Murayama: A Study with Radioactive Isotopes of the Permeability of the Blood-Cerebrospinal Fluid Barrier to Ions, *Am. J. Physiol.*, **140**: 47–64 (1943).

K-6. Love, William D., and George E. Burch: A Comparison of Potassium, Rubidium, and Cesium as Tracers of Potassium in the Study of Cation Metabolism of Human Erythrocytes In Vitro, *J. Lab. Clin. Med.*, **41**: 351–362 (1953).

K-7. Mudge, Gilbert H.: Electrolyte Metabolism of Rabbit-kidney Slices: Studies with Radioactive Potassium and Sodium, *Am. J. Physiol.*, **173**: 511–522 (1953).

K-8. Krebs, H. A., L. V. Eggleston, and C. Terner: In Vitro Measurements of the Turnover Rate of Potassium in Brain and Retina, *Biochem. J. London*, **48**: 530–537 (1951).

K-9. Jacobson, Louis, Roy Overstreet, H. M. King, and Raymond Handley: A Study of Potassium Absorption by Barley Roots, *Plant Physiol.*, **25**: 639–647 (1950).

K-10. Jonas, H.: The Time Course of K^{42} Uptake by Sunflowers as Observed with a Localizing Scintillation Count-rate Meter (In press).

Praseodymium 142 (19.2 hr)   *Beta* 0.66, 2.23   *Gamma* 0.134–1.59

Cat. No.	*Sp. Act.*	*Form*	*Cost*	*Chem. Cont.*	*Radiochem. Cont.*
Pr-142-I	550 mc/g	Pr_2O_3	$13/40 mc	—	—
Mica W.	*Int. C.*	*Scint. C.*	*R_f/mc*	50% *Self-abs.*
7×10^{-5}	5×10^{-5}	1×10^{-3}	0.4	210 (calc.)

Praseodymium 143 (13.7 days)   *Beta* 0.92   *Gamma*

Cat. No.	*Sp. Act.*	*Form*	*Cost*	*Chem. Cont.*	*Radiochem. Cont.*
Pr-143-P	CF	$PrCl_3$	$50/mc	—	—
Mica W.	*Int. C.*		50% *Self-abs.*		
6×10^{-4}	7×10^{-4}		88 (detn.)		

Critical Org.	*Body*	*Air*	*Water*	*Effect. $T_{1/2}$*
Bone	29 μc	7.5×10^{-7}	0.4	11 days

Intake Levels. Praseodymium is a rare earth and has not been of biological importance except that Pr^{143} is produced in the fission process and its metabolism in living systems is therefore of interest.

Radioassay. Preparation Pr-142-I has the advantage of lower cost and more energetic and easily measured radiation, but the disadvantage of a lower specific activity and, for some studies, too short a half-life. Routine beta or gamma counting can be employed for Pr^{142}, but only beta methods for Pr^{143}.

Chemistry. Methods are not available for chemical estimation of this element in biological material. Presumably, wet- or dry-ashing methods may be used. Separation from other rare earths may be accomplished by dry oxidation with $NaNO_3$ and extraction with buffered acetic acid which leaves the praseodymium behind as an insoluble residue (Pr-1).

Pr-1. Coryell, Charles D., and Nathan Sugarman: "Radiochemical Studies: The Fission Products," Books 1–3, National Nuclear Energy Series, McGraw-Hill Book Company, Inc., New York, 1951.

Promethium 147 (2.6 yr)   *Beta* 0.223   *Gamma*

Cat. No.	*Sp. Act.*	*Form*	*Cost*	*Chem. Cont.*	*Radiochem. Cont.*
Pm-147-I	CF	From Nd_2O_3	\$31/μc	—	0.06 mc Nd^{147} (11.3 days)
					0.05 mc Pm^{149} (54 hr)
Pm-147-P	CF	$PmCl_3$	\$5/mc	—	Traces Am^{241}, Cm^{242}

Mica W.	*Int. C.*	*Scint. C.*	*50% Self-abs.*	
3.7×10^{-4}	1.4×10^{-4}	3.9×10^{-2}	11.3 (calc.)	

Critical Org.	*Body*	*Air*	*Water*	*Effect. $T_{1/2}$*
Bone	120 μc	2×10^{-7}	1	140 days

Intake Levels. Pm^{147} (element 61) was discovered during studies of the rare-earth activities produced by uranium fission and was shown to be a member of the lanthanum group of rare earths (Pm-1). Biological interest has centered about its behavior in the animal and its property of accumulation in bone and liver.

Radioassay. Preparation Pm-147-P appears to offer advantages of both low cost and freedom from radiocontamination. On account of the soft-beta energy, which is about that of Ca^{45}, self-absorption considerations will be quite important in the counting of samples.

Chemistry. Presumably, routine wet- and dry-ashing methods can be employed with biological samples. Methods for chemical estimation are not available. However, ion-exchange resins have been employed most effectively in the separation and identification of the radioisotope.

Typical Methods. Although few details of methods are given, reference (Pm-2) presents results of the distribution in rats of Pm^{147} as well as other fission products.

Pm-1. Coryell, Charles D., and Nathan Sugarman: "Radiochemical Studies: The Fission Products," Books 1–3, National Nuclear Energy Series, McGraw-Hill Book Company, Inc., New York, 1951.
Pm-2. Hamilton, J. G.: The Metabolism of the Fission Products and the Heaviest Elements, The Plutonium Project, *Radiology*, **49**: 325–343 (1947).

Rhenium 186 (3.87 days)   *Beta* 0.64, 0.95, 1.09   *Gamma* 0.132–1.7

Cat. No.	*Sp. Act.*	*Form*	*Cost*	*Chem. Cont.*	*Radiochem. Cont.*
Re-186-I	1.23 mc/mg	Metal	$12/65 mc	—	150 mc Re^{188} (16.9 hr)

R_f/mc
0.2

Critical Org.
Thyroid, skin

Intake Levels.   Rhenium is a rare element, and little is known of naturally occurring levels in biological material.   In rats, 900 to 1000 mg/kg of rhenium as $NaRe_2O_4$ administered intraperitoneally is fatal.

Radioassay.   Routine beta- or gamma-counting methods can be used. If desired, the Re^{188} can be allowed to decay out.   However, this is usually not necessary, since standards can be measured along with the samples to give the decay corrections for the particular preparation. However, if both isotopes are measured, it must be remembered that the self-absorption characteristics will change with time.

Chemistry.   Tissues can be dry-ashed; wet-ashing may cause losses under certain conditions.   Chemical methods have been described for rhenium, but these are applicable only for samples with relatively high concentrations, and procedures have yet to be developed for biological materials.

Typical Methods.   A study has been described on the thyroid accumulation of this element (Re-1).   The rhenium metal irradiation unit was dissolved in 2 ml concentrated HNO_3 and diluted for dosage to the animal. The Re^{188} was allowed to decay out before the time of experiment.   Rats were injected intraperitoneally with about 300,000 counts/min of activity in 3 to 100 μg Re in 1 ml solution.   One- to two-gram samples of blood, lung, liver, and muscle and the entire thyroid were placed in 15-mm metal planchets, moistened with 1 per cent NaOH, and dried at 105°C and then at 120 to 130°C.   The samples were ashed at 450 to 500°C for 18 hr, the ash coated with about 1 ml of 1 per cent celloidin, and the activity counted with a thin-mica-window tube.   No self-absorption corrections were necessary.

Re-1. Baumann, Emil, N. Zizmer, Eleanor Oshry, and S. M. Seidlin: Behavior of Thyroid toward Elements of the Seventh Periodic Group.   II. Rhenium, *Proc. Soc. Exptl. Biol. Med.*, **72**: 502–506 (1949).

Rubidium 86 (19.5 days)

				Beta 1.822, 0.72	Gamma 1.1
Cat. No.	*Sp. Act.*	*Form*	*Cost*	*Chem. Cont.*	*Radiochem. Cont.*
Rb-86-I	45 mc/g	Rb_2CO_3	$42/220 mc	—	—
Mica W.	*Int. C.*		*Scint. C.*	R_f/mc	*50 % Self-abs.*
1.1×10^{-4}	1.9×10^{-4}		2×10^{-2}	1.3	215 (calc.)
Critical Org.	*Body*		*Air*	*Water*	*Eff. $T_{1/2}$*
Muscle	60 μc		4×10^{-7}	3×10^{-3}	7.8 days

Intake Levels. Rubidium is widespread in nature. It is taken up rapidly by plants and has been found at levels of 3.4 and 5.7 ppm in beans and barley, respectively. It has been found in most human tissues examined except bone. Human livers have been reported to contain as much as 14 ppm fresh weight. Rubidium is of interest in relation to its similarity to potassium.

Radioassay. Routine hard-beta or gamma counting is satisfactory on account of the energetic radiations.

Chemistry. Little information is available in regard to ashing or analytical procedures. However, it would be expected that methods for potassium would also be satisfactory for rubidium. Ashing will usually not be required when only radioassays are needed. Chemical estimation in biological material will require development of procedures.

Typical Methods. One millicurie of labeled Rb_2CO_3 in 1 liter of 5 per cent KCl was introduced into a watertight trough constructed around part of a tree trunk (yellow birch and white pine) (Rb-1). The KCl was used to facilitate the entrance and movement of the rubidium in the translocation stream. The incision was made underwater to a depth of 1 in. using a 3/4-in. chisel with its face parallel to the vertical axis. A portable scintillation counter was used for detection of the radioactivity in various parts of the tree. In another study, carrier-free Rb^{86} from cyclotron production was used to study the uptake by barley roots from a solution of the order of 10^{-9} mole Rb per liter (Rb-2). The solution contained about 12 mc Rb^{86} per liter and was adjusted to pH 5.5. A 2-cm apical segment from a 3-week-old plant was placed in the stirred solution for a measured time, removed, washed thoroughly with distilled H_2O, counted with a Geiger tube, and then replaced in the solution for continuation of the uptake study by repetition of the process. The uptake of Rb^{86} by disks of rutabaga tissue as affected by auxins was studied using a wet-ashing technique (Rb-3). In a study with dogs, using cyclotron-produced activity, about 300 μc in 10 to 15 ml of isotonic $Rb^{86}Cl$ (2 per cent) was injected intravenously. Samples of spinal fluid and plasma were measured into 10-ml Coors ashing capsules and evaporated without boiling (Rb-4). The radioactivity was measured with a Lauritsen electroscope.

Rb-1. Fraser, D. A., and C. A. Mawson: Movement of Radioactive Isotopes in Yellow Birch and White Pine as Detected with a Portable Scintillation Counter, *Can. J. Botany*, **31**: 324–333 (1953).

Rb-2. Overstreet, Roy, and Louis Jacobson: The Absorption by Roots of Rubidium and Phosphate Ions at Extremely Small Concentrations as Revealed by Experiments with Rb[86] and P[32] Prepared without Inert Carrier, *Am. J. Botany*, **33**: 107–112 (1946).

Rb-3. Higinbotham, N., H. Latimer, and R. Eppley: Stimulation of Rubidium Absorption by Auxins, *Science*, **118**: 243–245 (1953).

Rb-4. Greenberg, David, Robert B. Aird, Muriel D. D. Boelter, W. Wesley Campbell, Waldo E. Cohn, and Makio M. Murayama: A Study with Radioactive Isotopes of the Permeability of the Blood-Cerebrospinal Fluid Barrier to Ions, *Am. J. Physiol.*, **140**: 47–64 (1943).

Ruthenium 97 (2.8 days)   *Beta*   *Gamma* 0.22   *K*

Cat. No.	*Sp. Act.*	*Form*	*Cost*	*Chem. Cont.*	*Radiochem. Cont.*
Ru-97-I	0.03 mc/g	RuO$_3$	$44/0.1 mc	—	0.003 mc Tc^{97m} (90 days)
					7 mc Ru^{103} (39.8 days)
					26 mc Rh^{105} (36.5 hr)

R_f/mc
1.4

Critical Org.
  Kidney

Ruthenium 103 (39.8 days)   *Beta* 0.222, 0.684   *Gamma* 0.494

Cat. No.	*Sp. Act.*	*Form*	*Cost*	*Chem. Cont.*	*Radiochem. Cont.*
Ru-103-P	CF	Chloride	$5/mc	—	< 10% Ru^{106}-Rh^{106}

Mica W.	*Int. C.*	*Scint. C.*	R_f/mc	*50% Self-abs.*
4 × 10^{-4}	2.1 × 10^{-5}	7.5 × 10^{-4}	3	13

Critical Org.
  Kidney

Ruthenium 106 (1.0 yr)   *Beta* 0.041   *Gamma*
Rhodium 106 (30 sec)   *Beta* 3.55, 2.30   *Gamma* 0.51–2.23

Cat. No.	*Sp. Act.*	*Form*	*Cost*	*Chem. Cont.*	*Radiochem. Cont.*
RuRh-106-P	> 2c/g	Chloride	$10/mc	—	< 10% Ru^{103} (39.8 days)
					Rh^{106} daughter (30 sec)

Mica W.	*Int. C.*	*Scint. C.*	R_f/mc	*50% Self-abs.*
9.8 × 10^{-5}	7.3 × 10^{-5}	1.4 × 10^{-3}	1.3	670 (calc.)

Critical Org.	*Body*	*Air*	Water	*Effect. T$_{1/2}$*
Kidney	4 μc	3 × 10^{-8}	0.1	19 days

Intake Levels. Little is known of the naturally occurring levels of ruthenium in biological material. The metabolism of this element has been of interest primarily because it is a fission product. Survey experiments indicated that mice should receive less than 3 mg/kg, injected into the heart, to avoid chemical toxic effects (Ru-1).

Radioassay. The Ru^{106}-Rh^{106} preparation is perhaps the best, although the Ru^{103} does not present too many difficulties from radio-contamination. The Rh^{106} daughter is so short-lived that the samples will have to stand for only about 5 min for equilibrium to be reached. Thus the energetic Rh^{106} radiations may be readily measured by either hard-beta or gamma methods and will indicate the amount of Ru^{106} present in the sample.

Chemistry. Ruthenium may exist in nine valence states from 0 to 8, and although the melting point of the metal is high, many of its compounds are quite volatile. Losses occurred when tissue samples were dry-ashed at temperatures over 300°C, and recoveries were also poor when wet-ashing methods were used (Ru-1). This volatility may represent a health hazard and cause contamination of the environment with radio-ruthenium. Ruthenium can be determined colorimetrically by reaction with rubeanic acid (Ru-1) or thiourea or as potassium ruthenate (Ru-2).

Typical Methods. Carrier-free radioruthenium in an isotonic solution of NaCl at pH 2.6 was injected into rats (Ru-3). Tissue samples were ashed at 250 to 300°C in small metal capsules. The excreta, carcass, skeleton, skin, and gastrointestinal tract were dissolved in 15 per cent NaOH at 100°C, which made it possible to separate out the bones. The solutions were counted. The skeleton was dried and ground, and a weighed portion counted. However, it was found that alkali digestion had caused some losses. Mass absorption corrections were estimated from measurements made with the activity present in known amounts of water.

In an inhalation study the rat organs were handled as follows (Ru-1): The smaller tissues—lung, trachea, kidney, and spleen—were minced in capsules and dried for 24 hr at 110°C. The liver was divided among three capsules and dried in the same way. These were then counted without further treatment. The larger tissues—gastrointestinal tract, skin, carcass, and femurs—were dried at 110°C and then muffled at 550°C for 5 days. (A 35 per cent correction was made for loss in this step.) After muffling, the gastrointestinal tract, skin, and the balance of the carcass (ash remaining after removing the skeleton) were dissolved in 6 N HCl plus H_2O_2 and transferred to capsules for counting. Femurs were spread uniformly in the capsules by dissolving in HCl and reevap-orating. After the skeletons were dissolved in concentrated HCl, 6 to 10 mg of Ru carrier was added, and the Ru precipitated with H_2S in 50-ml centrifuge tubes. The precipitate was slurried into counting cap-sules after centrifugation.

Ru^{106} was incorporated into soil at a rate of 100 dis/sec/g of soil. Plant samples were dried at 70°C and ground, and 500 mg counted directly with an end-window tube (Ru-4).

Ru-1. Daily, Mary, Irving Wender, and Richard Abrams: Tracer Studies with Inhaled 1.0 Year Ruthenium, University of Chicago, MDDC-420, Aug. 30, 1945.

Ru-2. Marshall, E. D., and R. R. Rickard: Spectrophotometric Determination of Ruthenium, *Anal. Chem.*, **22**: 795–797 (1950).

Ru-3. Overstreet, Roy, Louis Jacobson, Harvey Fisher, Kenneth Scott, and Dorothy Axelrod, Progress Report on Metabolism of Fission Products for Period Ending October 15, 1943, Argonne National Laboratory, MDDC-1011.

Ru-4. Romney, Evan M., William A. Rhoads, and Kermit Larson: Plant Uptake of Sr^{90}, Ru^{106}, Cs^{137}, and Ce^{144} from Three Different Types of Soils, UCLA-294, June 10, 1954.

Samarium 153 (47 hr)   *Beta* 0.68, 0.80   *Gamma* 0.0695–0.61

Cat. No.	*Sp. Act.*	*Form*	*Cost*	*Chem. Cont.*	*Radiochem. Cont.*
Sm-153-I	1 mc/mg	Sm_2O_3	\$9/8.6 mc	—	0.002 mc Eu^{155} (1.7 yr)

$$R_f/mc$$
$$1$$

Critical Org.
  Bone

Intake Levels. Samarium is one of the rare-earth elements and has not been of biological interest.

Radioassay. In order to obtain preparation Sm-153-I, the target material must be supplied by the investigator. The Eu^{155} radiocontamination becomes of increasing importance with the age of the sample. The contribution of the Eu^{155} in a sample could be corrected for by making the original count, then making another count about 470 hr later, at which time the Sm^{153} would have decayed to about 0.1 per cent of its original count. This latter value would be subtracted from the original (see Chap. 5 for a general treatment of the assay of mixed radioisotopes). As an alternative, the europium could be separated by chemical procedures.

Scandium 46 (85 days)   *Beta* 0.36, 1.49   *Gamma* 1.12, 0.89

Cat. No.	*Sp. Act.*	*Form*	*Cost*	*Chem. Cont.*	*Radiochem. Cont.*
Sc-46-I	750 mc/g	Sc_2O_3	$33/15 mc	—	0.1 μc Ca^{45} (152 days)
Sc-46-P	>5 c/g	$ScCl_3$	$3/mc	—	—

Mica W.	*Int. C.*	*Scint. C.*	*R_f/mc*	*50% Self-abs.*
1.6 × 10⁻⁴	1.6 × 10⁻⁴	1.1 × 10⁻³	12	28 (calc.)

Critical Org.	*Body*	*Air*	*Water*	*Effect. $T_{1/2}$*
Spleen	6 μc	7 × 10⁻⁸	0.4	13 days

Intake Levels.   Traces of scandium are widely distributed in rocks, but there is little or no information in regard to its occurrence in biological material.

Radioassay.   Preparation Sc-46-P appears to be the one of choice from the standpoint of specific activity and lack of radiocontamination. Actually the Ca^{45} contamination in the irradiation unit would offer little difficulty, especially if all measurements were made with about 60-mg/cm² absorber to eliminate any Ca^{45} beta contribution.   Gamma counting will probably be preferred, provided the loss of sensitivity can be accepted.

Chemistry.   Methods are not available for estimation of scandium in biological materials.   Presumably, wet- or dry-ashing methods can be employed.   Reference (Sc-1) may be consulted for details of various separation and analytical procedures.   A gravimetric method has been described based on separation of other ions that react with 8-quinolinol and then precipitation of the scandium with this compound (Sc-2).

Sc-1. Sandell, E. B.: "Colorimetric Determination of Traces of Metals," 2d ed., Interscience Publishers, Inc., New York, 1950.
Sc-2. Pokras, Lewis, and Peter M. Bernays: Determination of Scandium with 8-Quinolinol, *Anal. Chem.*, **23**: 757–759 (1951).

Selenium 75 (127 days)   *Beta*   *Gamma* 0.067–0.405   *K*

Cat. No.	*Sp. Act.*	*Form*	*Cost*	*Chem. Cont.*	*Radiochem. Cont.*
Se-75-I	3.3 mc/g	Metal	$33/65 mc	—	—
Se-75-P	50–100 mc/g	Chloride	$1/mc	—	—

Mica W.	*Int. C.*	*Scint. C.*
2×10^{-3}	4.1×10^{-4}	5×10^{-4}

Intake Levels. Selenium is of agricultural importance due to its occurrence in crops in certain regions and its toxic effect on animals. Under ordinary conditions the limit of toxicity to animals is about 3 to 4 ppm in the diet. Grain from seleniferous areas may exceed this value, but the mixed diet of humans usually does not. In small animals, daily ingestion of 0.2 mg/kg body weight may cause disorders. The minimum lethal dose, in milligrams per kilogram body weight, is about 3 for horses, 9 for cattle, and 12 for pigs. About 10 ppm in the food of rats was fatal.

Radioassay. Preparation Se-75-P will usually be the one of choice, and gamma counting presents no particular problems. It has been reported that animal tissues lost appreciable amounts of Se^{75} merely as a result of drying (Se-1).

Chemistry. Tissue samples may be wet-ashed. However, unless oxidizing conditions are maintained, the selenium may be reduced to form volatile compounds. Even with excess HNO_3, it has been reported that losses occur if the digestion is carried out too quickly or at too high a temperature. For chemical determination it is recommended that mercuric oxide be used together with H_2SO_4 and HNO_3, followed by distillation as the bromide. The selenium in the distillate can be determined volumetrically with hydriodic acid or colorimetrically with codeine. If only radioassays are required, it would perhaps be best to make gamma counts on the undigested tissue.

Typical Methods. Sodium selenate was synthesized from the metal irradiation unit and by analysis was found to contain 263 counts/min/μg of selenium (Se-2). Dogs were injected three times subcutaneously at 24-hr intervals, and samples of whole blood, plasma, and packed red blood cells were measured with a Geiger tube. Various blood fractions were prepared and wet-ashed with concentrated HNO_3 and H_2O_2. Digests were diluted to 10 ml, and 1-ml aliquots taken for counting. Recovery studies were performed by carrying known amounts of radioselenium through all the experimental steps. In another study, radioselenium was used as follows to determine the life span of the duck red blood cell (Se-3): Ducks weighing about 2 kg were injected intraperitoneally with 2.5×10^6 counts/min in 8 mg selenium in three doses. Red blood cells from these animals were washed, reconstituted with isotonic saline, and reinjected into other ducks, each recipient getting about 1.74×10^3 counts/min. These ducks were bled at various intervals up to 10 days, and the amount of red-blood-cell activity determined as described in (Se-2).

Se-1. Heinrich, Max, Jr., and F. E. Kelsey: Selenium Metabolism: Loss of Selenium from Mouse Tissues on Heating, *Federation Proc.*, **13**: 364 (1954).

Se-2. McConnell, Kenneth P., and Betty J. Cooper: Distribution of Selenium in Serum Proteins and Red Blood Cells after Subcutaneous Injection of Sodium Selenate Containing Radioselenium, *J. Biol. Chem.*, **183**: 459–466 (1950).

Se-3. McConnell, Kenneth P., O. W. Portman, and R. H. Rigdon: Intravascular Life Span of the Duck Red Blood Cell as Determined by Radioactive Selenium, *Proc. Soc. Exptl. Biol. Med.*, **83**: 140–143 (1953).

Silver 110^m (270 days)   *Beta* 0.087, 0.53, 2.12, 2.86   *Gamma* 0.116–1.51€

Cat. No.	*Sp. Act.*	*Form*	*Cost*	*Chem. Cont.*	*Radiochem. Cont.*
Ag-110-I	5 mc/g	AgNO$_3$	$33/22 mc	—	Trace C^{14}
Ag-110-P	100–300 mc/g	AgNO$_3$	$1/mc	—	—

Mica W.	*Int. C.*	*Scint. C.*	*R$_f$/mc*	*50% Self-abs.*
2.2 × 10^{-4}	8 × 10^{-5}	4 × 10^{-4}	16	41 (calc.)

Critical Org.
Liver

Silver 111 (7.6 days)   *Beta* 1.06   *Gamma*

Cat. No.	*Sp. Act.*	*Form*	*Cost*	*Chem. Cont.*	*Radiochem. Cont.*
Ag-111-I	CF	From Pd	$15/3 mc	Pd	330 mc Pd^{109} (13.6 hr)
					Pd^{103}

Critical Org.	*Body*	*Air*	*Water*	*Effect. T$_{\frac{1}{2}}$*
Liver	36 μc	3 × 10^{-5}	4	2.1 days

Intake Levels. It has been estimated that the daily intake of silver in foods amounts to 0.06 to 0.08 mg, and as much as 0.3 and 0.9 ppm have been found in wheat flour and bran, respectively. The biological interest is primarily in the therapeutic use of radioactive silver colloids and the possibilities of detection of abscesses and tumors (Ag-1).

Radioassay. Preparation Ag-110-P will probably be preferred when there are no objections to the long half-life. The energies are such that routine beta or gamma counting presents no difficulties. Ag^{111} has the advantages of higher specific activity and a shorter half-life. However, there are the disadvantages of radiocontaminants and the fact that pure beta emitters are not usually satisfactory for therapeutic purposes. The Pd^{109} contribution can be eliminated by decay before the counting of the samples.

Chemistry. Biological samples may be either wet- or dry-ashed without any particular precautions. Silver may be estimated chemically by various colorimetric methods including the use of dithizone.

Typical Methods. Silver colloids were prepared with Ag^{111} and parenterally administered to mice in amounts of 10^4 to 10^6 counts/min (Ag-2). Tissues were dry-ashed at 625 to 650°C, and the ash dissolved in concentrated HNO$_3$. With samples of low activity and salt content, the HNO$_3$ solution was decanted into a seamless tin counting cup, the bottom of which had been layered with concentrated NH$_4$OH to prevent corrosion. With other tissues such as liver and bone, the decantations were made into volumetric flasks, care being taken to keep the solution acid. After mixing, 1- to 3-ml aliquots were taken and transferred to counting cups layered with NH$_4$OH. Transfers from the ashing vessel were made quantitative by allowing NH_4OH to stand therein for several hours to dissolve silver precipitated by the tissue chlorides.　Samples in the cups were dried under infrared and counted with an end-window Geiger tube.

In a study with carrier-free Ag^{106} (half-life, 8.2 days; gamma, 1.63, 0.69; K) from cyclotron production, the tissues were ashed at 500°C, and the ash spread evenly on porcelain dishes for Geiger counting (Ag-3). The self-absorption curve for correction of sample counts was prepared as follows: A solution (0.1 ml) containing about 3000 counts/min was added to a dish which had been previously treated with a few milligrams of an aerosol to promote spreading.　The activity was measured in the same way as the samples.　Dilute HNO_3 was stirred into the dish to give additional mass, and the sample recounted.　This was repeated, and the sample was counted after every addition of mass.　After the last portion of dilute acid was added, the activity at zero mass was determined by evaporating the solution to dryness and recounting the activity in the dish.

In a study with Ag^{110}, the tissues were digested in Kjeldahl flasks with H_2SO_4 plus several crystals of $CuSO_4$.　After cooling and dilution, $AgNO_3$ was added as a carrier, and the silver precipitated in small beakers with NaCl.　The precipitates were collected and dried for Geiger counting (Ag-4).

Ag-1. West, Harold D., Alfonso P. Johnson, and Charles W. Johnson: The Use of Radioactive Silver for the Detection of Abscesses and Tumors.　I. The Concentration of Ag^{111} in Spontaneous and Experimentally Induced Abscesses, *J. Lab. Clin. Med.*, **34**: 1376–1379 (1949).

Ag-2. Gammill, James C., Brownell Wheeler, E. L. Carothers, and P. F. Hahn: Distribution of Radioactive Silver Colloids in Tissues of Rodents Following Injection by Various Routes, *Proc. Soc. Exptl. Biol. Med.*, **74**: 691–695 (1950).

Ag-3. Scott, Kenneth G., and Joseph G. Hamilton: The Metabolism of Silver in the Rat with Radio-silver Used as an Indicator, *Univ. Calif. Berkeley Publs. Pharmacol. E*211, **2**: 241–262 (1950).

Ag-4. West, Harold D., Raven Rivera Elliott, Alphonso P. Johnson, and Charles W. Johnson: In Vivo Localization of Radioactive Silver at Predetermined Sites in Tissues, *Am. J. Roentgenol. Radium Therapy*, **64**: 831–834 (1950).

Sodium 22 (2.6 yr)				Beta 0.58	Gamma 1.28
Cat. No.	Sp. Act.	Form	Cost	Chem. Cont.	Radiochem. Cont.
Na-22-P	CF	NaCl	$100/mc	—	—
Mica W.	Int. C.	Scint. C.	R_f/mc	50% Self-abs.	
1.1×10^{-4}	1.1×10^{-4}	4.1×10^{-4}	11	52 (calc.)	

Sodium 24 (15.06 hr)				Beta 1.39	Gamma 2.758, 1.380
Cat. No.	Sp. Act.	Form	Cost	Chem. Cont.	Radiochem. Cont.
Na-24-I	90 mc/g	Na_2CO_3	$12/12 mc	—	—
Na-24-P	1 mc/mg	NaCl	$2/mc	—	—
Mica W.	Int. C.	Scint. C.	R_f/mc	50% Self-abs.	
1.1×10^{-4}	1.1×10^{-4}	8.8×10^{-4}	25	170 (calc.)	
Critical Org.	Body	Air	Water	Effect. $T_{1/2}$	
Total body	15 μc	2×10^{-6}	8×10^{-3}	14. 6 hr	

Intake Levels. Approximate daily intakes of sodium for the various species are as follows: man, 4 g; rats, 50 mg; poultry, 0.5 g; sheep, 5 g; swine, 3 g; cattle, 8 g. The sodium content of the adult man is 60 to 65 g, and it is present mainly in the plasma and interstitial fluids. Blood serum contains about 330 mg/100 ml, and the red cells, about 23. Crop plants range from 0.1 to 3 per cent on the dry-matter basis. A recommended nutrient solution for plants contains about 0.5 ppm.

Radioassay. The choice as to isotope will depend primarily on the half-life requirements and secondarily on cost. For short-term experiments, especially with human beings or where repeated studies are necessary on the same subject, preparation Na-24-P will be of advantage. For long-time studies, Na^{22} will have to be used. On account of the high normal Na intake and the high specific activities available, there will usually be no difficulties in the use of a physiological dosage. Gamma counting appears to be the most convenient, since sample preparation can thereby be avoided. The energetic radiation facilitates sample measurement, and the isotopes are also ideal for in vivo studies. Double-labeling experiments can easily be carried out by use of differential decay methods.

Chemistry. Standard wet- or dry-ashing techniques may be employed. The flame photometer is widely used for chemical estimation of sodium in biological material (Na-1 to Na-3). Rapid methods for estimation of sodium in biological fluids have been based on use of the uranyl zinc acetate reagent (Na-4, Na-5).

Typical Methods. In a study of mobilization of Na^{24} from the muscle of dogs, about 5 to 20 μc in physiological saline was injected into the muscle, and the removal of activity with time measured externally with a Geiger tube (Na-6). In a similar study it was possible to measure the comparative removal by the lymph and blood (Na-7). To investigate sodium turnover rates in the dog, about 1 mc Na^{24} was injected into the jugular vein (Na-8). Food and feces were homogenized in distilled H_2O and 2 N HNO_3, and the calcium removed by oxalate precipitation. Bone was heated in concentrated HNO_3 until dissolved, the solution diluted and chilled, the fat removed, and the calcium removed by precipitation with oxalate. Aliquots of these solutions were counted with a dipping Geiger tube, and sodium estimated chemically by use of a flame photometer with an internal standard. Plasma and cells were diluted and measured directly.

In studies of circulation in human beings, about 200 μc Na^{24} has been injected, and external counts made with conventional Geiger tubes (Na-9). For determination of sodium space in adults and infants, a dosage of 1 to 1.5 μc Na^{24} per kilogram body weight in 1 to 2 ml of a sterile isotonic solution was intravenously injected (Na-10, Na-11). One-milliliter samples of serum, urine, and cerebrospinal fluid plus 1 drop of a detergent (Acidolate) were dried at 70°C in metal planchets for counting with an end-window tube. Tissue samples were digested in HNO_3 for solution counting. For chemical analyses, dry-ashing at 540°C was employed, followed by removal of the greater part of calcium and phosphorus and then reaction with zinc uranyl acetate. The circulation of damaged skin and the circulatory efficiency of tubed pedicles and flaps have been measured by intradermal injection of 0.1 to 3 μc Na^{24} and estimation of its removal by a Geiger tube placed over the injection site (Na-12, Na-13). In a long-term study of Na removal in man, 50 to 90 μc Na^{22} as NaCl in 2 ml H_2O was injected intravenously (Na-14). Sixteen free-falling drops of serum or urine from a calibrated micropipette was placed on filter-paper disks attached with rubber cement to metal disks for counting with an end-window tube. For measurements of exchangeable Na in man, 50 to 70 μc Na^{24} was injected intravenously, and fluids assayed directly by liquid counting (Na-15).

Na-1. Wallace, William M., Malcolm Holliday, Margaret Cushman, and J. Russell Elkinton: The Application of the Internal Standard Flame Photometer to the Analysis of Biologic Material, *J. Lab. Clin. Med.*, **37**: 621–629 (1951).

Na-2. Zak, Bennie, Robert E. Mosher, and Albert J. Boyle: A Review on Flame Analysis in the Clinical Laboratory, *Am. J. Clin. Pathol.*, **23**: 60–77 (1953).

Na-3. Mosher, Robert E., A. J. Boyle, Edward J. Bird, S. D. Jacobson, Thomas M. Batchelor, Lloyd T. Iseri, and Gordon B. Myers: The Use of Flame Photometry for the Quantitative Determination of Sodium and Potassium in Plasma and Urine, *Am. J. Clin. Pathol.*, **19**: 461–470 (1949).

Na-4. O'Sullivan, Michael: Rapid Determination of Urinary Sodium, *J. Lab. Clin. Med.*, **41**: 959–962 (1953).

Na-5. Stone, Gilbert C. H., and Joseph W. Goldzieher: A Rapid Colorimetric Method for the Determination of Sodium in Biological Fluids and Particularly in Serum, *J. Biol. Chem.*, **181**: 511–521 (1949).

Na-6. Franke, Frederick R., Joseph B. Boatman, Robert S. George, and Campbell Moses: Effect of Physical Factors on Radiosodium Clearance from Subcutaneous and Intramuscular Sites in Animals, *Proc. Soc. Exptl. Biol. Med.*, **74**: 417–421 (1950).

Na-7. Stone, Peter W., and William B. Miller, Jr.: Mobilization of Radioactive Sodium from the Gastrocnemius Muscle of the Dog, *Proc. Soc. Exptl. Biol. Med.*, **71**: 529–534 (1949).

Na-8. Stern, Thomas N., Vinton V. Cole, Anne C. Bass, and R. R. Overman: Dynamic Aspects of Sodium Metabolism in Experimental Adrenal Insufficiency Using Radioactive Sodium, *Am. J. Physiol.*, **164**: 437–449 (1951).

Na-9. Quimby, Edith H.: Radioactive Isotopes in Clinical Diagnosis, *Advances in Biol. and Med. Phys.*, **2**: 243–268 (1951).

Na-10. Forbes, Gilbert B., and Anne Perley: Estimation of Total Body Sodium by Isotopic Dilution. I. Studies on Young Adults, *J. Clin. Invest.*, **30**: 558–565 (1951).

Na-11. Perley, Anne, Gilbert B. Forbes, and Miriam M. Pennoyer: Determination of Sodium[24] "Space" in Infants, Children, and Adults, *J. Pediatrics*, **38**: 299–305 (1951).

Na-12. Roswit, Bernard, Lawrence H. Wisham, and Joseph Sorrentino: The Circulation of Radiation Damaged Skin; Radiosodium Clearance Studies, *Am. J. Roentgenol. Radium Therapy Nuclear Med.*, **69**: 980–990 (1953).

Na-13. Conway, Herbert, Bernard Roswit, Richard B. Stark, and Rosalyn Yalow: Radioactive Sodium Clearance as a Test of Circulatory Efficiency of Tubed Pedicles and Flaps, *Proc. Soc. Exptl. Biol. Med.*, **77**: 348–351 (1951).

Na-14. Threefoot, Sam, George Burch, and Paul Reaser: The Biological Decay Periods of Sodium in Normal Man, in Patients with Congestive Heart Failure, and in Patients with the Nephrotic Syndrome as Determined by Na[22] as the Tracer, *J. Lab. Clin. Med.*, **34**: 1–13 (1949).

Na-15. Miller, H., and G. M. Wilson: The Measurement of Exchangeable Sodium in Man Using the Isotope [24]Na, *Clin. Sci.*, **12**: 97–111 (1953).

Strontium 89 (53 days)   *Beta* 1.50   *Gamma*

Cat. No.	*Sp. Act.*	*Form*	*Cost*	*Chem. Cont.*	*Radiochem. Cont.*
Sr-89-I	0.11 mc/g	$Sr(NO_3)_2$	$33/1.5 mc	—	Possibly C^{14}
Sr-89-P	CF	$SrCl_2$	$1/mc	—	$<10\%$ Sr^{90}-Y^{90}

Mica W.	*Int. C.*	*Scint. C.*	*50% Self-abs.*
0.8×10^{-4}	1×10^{-4}	1.2×10^{-2}	300 (calc.)

Critical Org.	*Body*	*Air*	*Water*	*Effect. $T_{\frac{1}{2}}$*
Bone	$2\mu c$	2×10^{-8}	7×10^{-5}	52 days

Strontium 90 (19.9 yr)   *Beta* 0.537   *Gamma*
Yttrium 90 (2.54 days)   *Beta* 2.18   *Gamma*

Cat. No.	*Sp. Act.*	*Form*	*Cost*	*Chem. Cont.*	*Radiochem. Cont.*
SrY-90-P	CF	Chlorides	$1/mc Sr^{90}	—	Y^{90} daughter 20% Sr^{89} (53 days)

Mica W.	*Int. C.*	*Scint. C.*	*50% Self-abs.*
6.6×10^{-5}	5.0×10^{-5}	7.3×10^{-3}	68 (calc.)

Critical Org.	*Body*	*Air*	*Water*	*Effect. $T_{\frac{1}{2}}$*
Bone	$1 \mu c$	2×10^{-10}	8×10^{-7}	7.4 yr

Intake Levels. Strontium occurs in traces in most biological material but is not considered an essential element for plants and animals. It is similar to calcium in chemical and physiological behavior. On account of the low naturally occurring levels and the difficulties of analysis, there are no comprehensive survey values available. Early workers reported 0.01 to 0.1 μg/g of Sr in fresh animal tissue, 0.1 to 0.3 ppm in human livers, and about 10 ppm in sea water. In a recent study (Sr-1) the Sr content of human bones was found to average 0.016 per cent of the ash for fetal specimens and 0.024 for adult. The metabolism of the radioisotopes of strontium has been widely investigated because these activities are perhaps the most hazardous of the fission products. This is due to the fact that radiostrontium is usually well absorbed by the biological system, is deposited in the bones of animals by the growth and/or exchange processes, is transmitted in relatively large amounts to milk and to the developing fetus, and is known to cause bone tumors. The LD_{50} in rats for intravenously injected strontium acetate was about 260 mg/kg.

Since strontium and calcium have similar biological behavior, it is of interest to gain information on their relative utilization from the Sr/Ca ratio in various materials. In terms of number of strontium atoms per 1,000 calcium atoms, a value of 9.23 has been reported for sea water (Sr-1a) and 2.7 to 3 for fossils (Sr-2). Also, evidence is now available from tracer studies that plants and animals selectively utilize calcium by about a factor of 3 over strontium (Sr-9; see also Ba-5). The above

Sr/Ca ratios, considered in terms of calcium-intake levels, give an indication of limitations of strontium mass in tracer studies.

Radioassay. Preparation Sr-89-P is probably the preparation of choice for general tracer studies. The Sr^{90}, which is present in less than 10 per cent amount at the time of processing, may become of importance if an old preparation is used. Interference from the Sr^{90}-Y^{90} in the Sr^{89} preparation can be eliminated by the following procedure: (a) use of an aliquot of the preparation administered to the organism for a standard against which the samples are compared; (b) allowance of about 25 days between taking of sample and measurement to permit attainment of equilibrium between Sr^{90} and Y^{90}; (c) recognition of the fact that the self-absorption characteristics will change with the composition of the mixture. Actually the beta energies are sufficiently high so that self-absorption will not be an important factor unless relatively large sample masses are used. Preparation SrY-90-P is equally useful for tracer studies, provided a long half-life is acceptable. Routine hard-beta measurements after the 20- to 25-day waiting period are quite satisfactory (see Chap. 2). Attention is called to the hazard of these radioisotopes, and special emphasis should be placed on the avoidance of conditions under which they might be taken into the body of personnel.

Chemistry. Routine wet- or dry-ashing methods are satisfactory. Chemical estimation is perhaps best accomplished by spectrographic methods (Sr-1). Chemical procedures developed for the separation of radiostrontium from the fission mixture (Sr-3) may be useful in isolating activity from low-level samples. These methods are usually based on precipitation of the nitrate by the fuming nitric acid procedure. An alternative procedure has been proposed which consists in adding strontium carrier to the sample, removing three ferric hydroxide scavenging precipitates, and isolating the strontium as the carbonate (Sr-4). Identification of Sr^{90} in a sample containing an unknown activity may be easily obtained by carrying out such a separation and observing the growth of the yttrium daughter. For low-level counting of Sr^{90} there may be some advantage in separating the Y^{90} daughter; this can be done by precipitation with yttrium or lanthanum carrier (see page 63 for a listing of the advantages of this procedure).

Typical Methods. In a study of the transmission of Sr^{89} from mother to offspring in mice, levels of 0.01 to 5 $\mu c/g$ body weight were administered (Sr-5). Mothers were measured for activity with a Geiger tube by caging the living animal in a cellulose acetate container (thickness, 0.18 mm) which prohibited movement. Factors for conversion of counts to Sr^{89} content were derived from experiments in which numerous animals were measured in this way and then sacrificed for actual tissue determinations. By standardization of conditions, reasonably reliable estimates were obtained. The higher doses produced injuries, and a level of about 0.1 $\mu c/g$ body weight could be generally satisfactory for tracer work.

In a study of $Sr^{89,90}$ and Th^{230} distribution, 1.4 ml of the following solution was injected intraperitoneally into rats: pH 4, 1 per cent citric acid, 0.15 M Na^+, 15 $\mu c/ml$ of $Sr^{89,90}$, 0.64 $\mu c/ml$ of Th^{230} (Sr-6). Excreta and tissue samples were covered with concentrated HNO_3 and evaporated to near dryness, fresh acid added and evaporated, and this process repeated three to eight times until a light-colored ash was obtained. The residue was made to volume, and aliquots dried for counting with a mica-window tube plus a 110-mg/cm² absorber for strontium, and with an alpha counter unresponsive to beta particles for thorium.

In another study, weanling pigs, about 30 lb, were injected intravenously with about 507 μc Sr^{90}-Y^{90} at pH 6 (Sr-7). Tissue samples were wet-ashed in concentrated HNO_3, and aliquots counted directly with an end-window tube after a period of 24 days. Bone autoradiograms were prepared as described in Chap. 7. From 0.5 to 5 mc Sr^{89} and Sr^{90}-Y^{90} have been administered to dairy cows for estimation of the transfer to milk (Sr-8, Sr-9). Five to ten millicuries Sr^{90}-Y^{90} was orally administered to yearling steers for long-term studies of retention and possible pathologic responses (Sr-9). Studies have been reported with rabbits and monkeys receiving relatively high dosages, 25 to 1000 μc Sr^{90} per kilogram body weight (Sr-10, Sr-11).

A series of soils was prepared to contain about 100 dis/sec/g of oven-dry soil as follows (Sr-12): Each soil consisted of material that had been passed through a 2-mm screen and then mixed. An aliquot of the soil consisting of particles less than 150 μ was suspended in water (1:1), and the radioactivity added. The samples were well agitated, dried for at least 5 days at 70°C, and then reconstituted by thorough mixing. The test soils were placed in plastic-painted 6-in. clay pots on the basis of 1600 g of oven-dry soil per pot. Barley, bean, carrot, lettuce, and radish were grown therein to marketable maturity. Soil was prepared for counting by gentle pulverizing and spreading uniformly over the surface of a stainless-steel cup. An end-window tube was used, and self-absorption corrections were made. Plant material was dried and ground to pass a 40-mesh screen, and 0.5-g samples counted as above except that no self-absorption corrections were necessary. The radioactive plant material from this experiment containing about 7000 dis/sec/g of dried material was used for feeding experiments with rats (Sr-13). For stomach-tube feeding, the dry material was mixed into a paste with water to contain about 500 dis/sec/ml. For pellet feeding, the plant material was added to pulverized commercial rat pellets, mixed to dough consistency with water, cut into sections, and baked until hard.

Mosquitoes were labeled by the use of 10 to 20 m$\mu c/ml$ of $Sr^{89}Cl_2$ in the larval bath with a density of about five larvae per milliliter. The larvae were placed in the radioactive solution contained in photographic trays during the fourth stage (Sr-14).

Sr-1. Hodges, Robert M., Norman S. MacDonald, Ralph Nusbaum, Richard Stearns, Florita Ezmirlian, Patricia Spain, and Clare McArthur: The Strontium Content of Human Bones, *J. Biol. Chem.*, **185**: 519–524 (1950).

Sr-1a. Odum, Howard T.: Notes on the Strontium Content of Sea Water, Celestite Radiolaria, and Strontianite Snail Shells, *Science*, **114**: 211–213 (1951).

Sr-2. Odum, Howard T.: The Stability of the World Strontium Cycle, *Science*, **114**: 407–411 (1951).

Sr-3. Coryell, Charles D., and Nathan Sugarman: "Radiochemical Studies: The Fission Products," Books 1–3, National Nuclear Energy Series, McGraw-Hill Book Company, Inc., New York, 1951.

Sr-4. Turk, Elton: A Modified Radiochemical Strontium Procedure, ANL-5184, December, 1953.

Sr-5. Finkel, Miriam P.: The Transmission of Radio-strontium and Plutonium from Mother to Offspring in Laboratory Animals, *Physiol. Zoöl.*, **20**: 405–421 (1947).

Sr-6. Schubert, Jack, and Herschel Wallace, Jr.: The Effect of Zirconium and Sodium Citrate on the Distribution and Excretion of Simultaneously Injected Thorium and Radiostrontium, *J. Biol. Chem.*, **183**: 157–166 (1950).

Sr-7. Comar, C. L., W. E. Lotz, and G. A. Boyd: Autoradiographic Studies of Calcium, Phosphorus and Strontium Distribution in the Bones of the Growing Pig, *Am. J. Anat.*, **90**: 113–129 (1952).

Sr-8. Erf, L. A., and Charles Pecher: Secretion of Radio-strontium in Milk of Two Cows Following Intravenous Administration, *Proc. Soc. Exptl. Biol. Med.*, **45**: 762–764 (1940).

Sr-9. Comar, C. L., Ira B. Whitney, R. A. Monroe, and S. L. Hood: Unpublished results.

Sr-10. Jowsey, Jenifer, Barbara Rayner, Margaret Tutt, and Janet Vaughan: The Deposition of ^{90}Sr in Rabbit Bones Following Intravenous Injection, *Brit. J. Exptl. Pathol.*, **34**: 384–391 (1953).

Sr-11. Jowsey, Jenifer, Maureen Owen, and Janet Vaughan: Microradiographs and Autoradiographs of Cortical Bone from Monkeys Injected with ^{90}Sr, *Brit. J. Exptl. Pathol.*, **34**: 661–667 (1953).

Sr-12. Neel, James W., Jon H. Olafson, Allen J. Steen, Barbara E. Gillooly, Hideo Nishita, and Kermit H. Larson: Soil-Plant Interrelationships with Respect to the Uptake of Fission Products. I. The Uptake of Sr^{90}, Cs^{137}, Ru^{106}, Ce^{144}, and Y^{91}, UCLA-247, Mar. 18, 1953.

Sr-13. Gross, Warren J., Janice F. Taylor, Joshua A. Lee, and James C. Watson, The Availability of Radio-strontium to Mammals by Way of the Food Chain, UCLA-259, June 18, 1953.

Sr-14. Bugher, John C., and Marjorie Taylor: Radiophosphorus and Radiostrontium in Mosquitoes, Preliminary Report, *Science*, **110**: 146–147 (1949).

Sulfur 35 (87.1 days) Beta 0.166 *Gamma*

Cat. No.	*Sp. Act.*	*Form*	*Cost*	*Chem. Cont.*	*Radiochem. Cont.*
S-35-I	0.3 mc/g	Elemental	$33/7.5 mc	SO_4^-, NO_3^-	Possibly P^{32} (14.3 days)
S-35-P-1	CF	H_2SO_4	$2/mc	—	<0.01% P^{32} (14.3 days)
S-35-P-2	>10 mc/mg	BaS	$4/mc	$Ba(OH)_2$, SO_4^-	—
S-35-P-3	>1 mc/mg	Elemental S in benzene	$5/mc	—	—

Mica W.	*Int. C.*	50% *Self-abs.*		
4.8×10^{-4}	1.4×10^{-4}	8.2 (detn.)		

Critical Org.	*Body*	*Air*	*Water*	*Effect. $T_{1/2}$*
Skin	100 μc	10^{-6}	5×10^{-3}	18 days

Intake Levels. The body contains about 0.15 per cent sulfur, which is present mainly in proteins, and the daily intake for man is approximately 1.3 g, which, however, must be supplied as particular organic compounds. A recommended nutrient solution for plants contains about 64 ppm, and crop plants range from about 0.1 to 1.5 per cent on a dry-matter basis. As a result of the high-specific-activity preparations available, there will usually be no problem in keeping the mass of sulfur administered at or below physiological levels.

Radioassay. Any of the processed units is satisfactory. The main difficulty in counting procedures arises from the soft-beta particles, which are similar in energy to those of C^{14}. This means that thin-window (<4 mg/cm²) or internal counters must be used and that the ratio of activity to the mass of sample must be high to avoid undue loss of sensitivity. An interesting method has been reported for counting liquid samples containing S^{35} in an internal counter using a stainless-steel cup with an airtight cover of aluminum 1.5 mg/cm² thick (S-1). The minimal detectable activity was about 1.5×10^{-2} μc; this means that the sensitivity was about 0.01 of that of conventional methods. This procedure would be convenient if the loss of sensitivity could be afforded.

Chemistry. Sulfur cannot be determined by routine methods of ashing, because the organic sulfur may be oxidized and lost. Some of the methods that have been employed for oxidation of biological samples are illustrated in the next section. After conversion of the sulfur in the sample to sulfate, the latter can be estimated chemically and/or prepared for counting by precipitation as barium or benzidine sulfate. Benzidine sulfate has better physical characteristics, but its precipitation requires careful control and cannot be carried out after sodium peroxide fusion (S-2).

Typical Methods. *Direct Counting.* About 1 μg sulfate as S^{35}-labeled sodium sulfate containing 15×10^4 counts/min was intravenously injected into rats (S-3). Aqueous homogenates of organs and feces were prepared by grinding a 1-g sample in a ground-glass blender and diluting to 15 ml. One-milliliter aliquots were added to cupped planchets and dried under infrared for counting with a 1.7-mg/cm^2 end-window tube. Standards were prepared by addition of known amounts of activity to corresponding amounts of nonradioactive tissue samples. In a study with rats, 2-p-toluenesulfonamidofluorene-S^{35}, a carcinogen, was orally administered (S-4). The tissues, feces, and intestinal contents were dried, ground in a mortar, and then suspended in 1 per cent NaOH plus a wetting agent by mixing in a Waring Blendor. A few drops of capryl alcohol was used to prevent foaming. After standing for 24 hr at 5°C, the mixture was brought to room temperature and agitated in the Blendor, and a 1-ml aliquot dried on an aluminum planchet for measurement with an internal counter. One-milliliter portions of urine, plasma, and blood-cell samples were placed directly in the planchet. Standards were prepared to contain the same mass as the sample.

Alkaline Peroxide Digestion. Methionine labeled with 91 μc/g of S^{35} was fed to rats and dogs in amounts of 1 and 3.7 g, respectively (S-5). Some of the tissues were refluxed for 24 hr with concentrated HNO$_3$ and made to volume, and 0.5-ml aliquots dried on watch crystals under infrared for counting. It was claimed that there were some losses within the expected limits of error. Other workers, however, have claimed quantitative results by this method (S-2). Other samples were treated by alkaline digestion as follows: The tissue was dried at 105°C, and 500 mg weighed into an iron crucible for a 6- to 8-hr hydrolysis with 10 ml of 10 per cent NaOH on a steam bath. The hydrolysate was concentrated to about 1 ml, 4g anhydrous Na$_2$CO$_3$ added, the mixture dried at 105°C, 4 g Na$_2$O$_2$ added, and the mixture slowly fused to a cherry-red color. The melt was made to a known volume with HCl to give pH 3, and an aliquot transferred to a centrifuge tube with a removable bottom. Carrier sulfate was added, the solution warmed, and 10 ml of 10 per cent BaCl$_2$ added dropwise. The sample was centrifuged, washed twice with distilled water, collected, and dried for counting with a 2.6-mg/cm^2 end-window tube.

Magnesium Nitrate Digestion. Laying hens were given orally or intramuscularly about 3×10^6 counts/min of carrier-free S^{35} in the form of H$_2$S^{35}O$_4$ (S-6). Egg samples were digested according to the standard magnesium nitrate procedure (S-7), except that to the ashing mixture was added 5 ml of a 50 per cent solution of copper nitrate per 100 ml magnesium nitrate solution (150 g MgO dissolved in 1:1 HNO$_3$ and made to 1 liter). At least 12 ml of ashing mixture was used per gram of dried sample. The general method is to use a porcelain crucible and heat the sample plus ashing mixture at 180°C on a hot plate and then to muffle at a temperature below red heat until the charge is oxidized. The mixture can then be taken up in HCl solution, made to volume, and filtered. $BaSO_4$ is precipitated by standard methods; collected, washed, and weighed for estimation of sulfur; and plated out for radioassay. In the egg studies the S^{35} in the albumen and yolk was characterized as dialyzable sulfate S, dialyzable organic S, nondialyzable sulfate S, and nondialyzable organic S. Also cystine and methionine were isolated from albumen hydrolysates by ion-exchange chromatography on Dowex 50 to determine the extent of incorporation of the administered sulfate S^{35}.

Carius Procedure. Reference (S-8) may be consulted for a detailed description of the Carius benzidine sulfate procedure for estimation of S^{35} in various biological materials. In general, the sample is placed in the pyrex glass bomb together with NaBr and red fuming HNO_3, and the bomb sealed and heated at 300°C in a Carius furnace for not less than 4 hr. The contents of the bomb are washed into an evaporation tube and taken to dryness. The residue is dissolved, 95 per cent ethanol added, and then the benzidine hydrochloride reagent. The precipitate of benzidine sulfate is centrifuged and resuspended in 95 per cent alcohol and can be collected for counting by one of the methods outlined in Chap. 5.

Autoradiographic Procedure. Two milligrams of sodium sulfate containing 8.24×10^5 counts/min was injected intraperitoneally into a suckling rat (S-9). The bones were trimmed of soft tissue and fixed for 24 hr in 3.7 per cent Formalin. The bones were embedded in paraffin and cut at 7 μ, and sections transferred to slides coated with egg albumin. The paraffin was removed with xylol, and the mounted sections covered with Kodak Process Ortho film. The top surface of the section was kept about 20 μ from the emulsion surface by a narrow strip of glassine paper placed at each end of the slide. A clean slide was used as backing for the film, and the assembly was held together by rubber bands and wrapped in black paper for the 3- to 7-week exposure. The film was developed, and the sections subsequently stained with hematoxylin eosin or with toluidine blue.

Bean leaves infected with rust or powdery mildew or sunflower leaves infected with rust were detached from greenhouse plants and exposed to vapors from 50 ml of 0.01 per cent Na_2S containing 5 to 8 μc S^{35} at pH 8 in sealed pint jars for 8 hr at about 22°C (S-10). The greater absorption of S^{35} by the infected leaves was demonstrated by autoradiograms made with X-ray film using an exposure of 48 hr. Localized areas of the leaves, 0.2 to 13 mm^2, were measured by use of a Geiger counter and a perforated lead shield. References (S-11, S-12) may be consulted for techniques in the use of S^{35} with crop plants.

A study has been reported on the preservation of silage with S^{35}-labeled SO_2 and the fate of the S^{35} when the silage was subsequently fed to the lactating cow (S-13). About 30 mc was oxidized to SO_2 and stored in standard 550-ml SO_2-gas tanks. The silage was preserved in gastight 55-gal steel drums. The $S^{35}O_2$ was allowed to flow into the drum to give the desired treatment level. After storage, it was determined that no free $S^{35}O_2$ was present, and the silage was fed to dairy cows, with subsequent analysis of urine, feces, milk, and blood samples by standard methods.

Some commercially available S^{35}-labeled compounds are listed as follows (S-14):

Benzyl cysteine–S^{35}	l-Methionine-S^{35}
Cell hydrolysates–S^{35} (*E. coli* and *S. cerevisiae*)	dl-Methionine-S^{35}
Cells-S^{35} (*E. coli* and *S. cerevisiae*)	Mustard gas–S^{35}
Cells-S^{35} (*S. cerevisiae* and *T. utilis*)	Penicillin G–S^{35}
L-Cystine-S^{35}	Pentothal–S^{35}
2,4-Dinitrobenzene sulfenyl chloride–S^{35}	Phenothiazine-S^{35}
Ethionine-S^{35}	Pipsyl chloride–S^{35}
Glutathione-S^{35}	Potassium ethyl xanthate–S^{35}
Glutathione-S^{35} (oxidized)	Potassium thiocyanate–S^{35}
Heparin-S^{35}	Sucaryl-S^{35}
Homocystine-S^{35}	Sulfanilic acid–S^{35}
Insulin-S^{35}	Thiourea-S^{35}

S-1. Walser, M., A. F. Reid, and D. W. Seldin: A Method of Counting Radiosulfur in Liquid Samples, and Its Application to the Determination of S^{35} Excretion Following Injection of $S^{35}O_4$, *Arch. Biochem. and Biophys.*, **45**: 91–96 (1953).

S-2. Tarver, Harold: Radioactive Sulfur and Its Applications in Biology, *Advances in Biol. and Med. Phys.*, **2**: 281–311 (1951).

S-3. Everett, Newton B., and Barbara S. Simmons: The Distribution and Excretion of S^{35} Sodium Sulfate in the Albino Rat, *Arch. Biochem. and Biophys.*, **35**: 152–156 (1952).

S-4. Ray, Francis E., and Mary F. Argus: Studies on the Metabolism, Distribution, and Excretion of 2-p-Toluenesulfonamidofluorene–S^{35} in the Rat, *Cancer Research*, **11**: 783–787 (1951).

S-5. Maass, Alfred, Franc C. Larson, and Edgar S. Gordon: The Distribution in Normal Tissues of Radioactive Sulfur Fed as Labeled Methionine, *J. Biol. Chem.*, **177**: 209–216 (1949).

S-6. Machlin, L. J., P. B. Pearson, C. A. Denton, and H. R. Bird: The Utilization of Sulfate Sulfur by the Laying Hen and Its Incorporation into Cystine, *J. Biol. Chem.*, **205**: 213–219 (1953).

S-7. "Methods of Analysis of the Association of Official Agricultural Chemists," 6th ed., Association of Official Agricultural Chemists, Washington, D.C., 1945.

S-8. Young, L., M. Edson, and J. A. McCarter: The Measurement of Radioactive Sulphur (^{35}S) in Biological Material, *Biochem. J. London*, **44**: 179–185 (1949).

S-9. Dziewiatkowski, Dominic D.: Radioautographic Visualization of Sulfur-35 Disposition in the Articular Cartilage and Bone of Suckling Rats Following Injection of Labeled Sodium Sulfate, *J. Exptl. Med.*, **93**: 451–458 (1951).

S-10. Yarwood, C. E., and Louis Jacobson: Selective Absorption of Sulphur-35 by Fungus-infected Leaves, *Nature*, **165**: 973 (1950).

S-11. Thomas, Moyer D., Russell H. Hendricks, Loren C. Bryner, and G. R. Hill: A Study of the Sulphur Metabolism of Wheat, Barley and Corn Using Radio-Active Sulphur, *Plant Physiol.*, **19**: 227–244 (1944).

S-12. Harrison, Bertrand F., Moyer D. Thomas, and G. R. Hill: Radioautographs Showing the Distribution of Sulphur in Wheat, *Plant Physiol.*, **19**: 245–257 (1944).

S-13. Keener, H. A., A. E. Teeri, R. V. Harrington, and R. R. Baldwin: Metabolic Fate of S^{35} in the Lactating Cow When Fed $S^{35}O_2$ Preserved Silage, *J. Dairy Sci.*, **36**: 1205–1211 (1953).

S-14. *Isotopics*, **4**(1) (1954), U.S. Atomic Energy Commission, Oak Ridge, Tenn.

Tantalum 182 (115 days).   *Beta* 0.5, 1.1   *Gamma* 0.046–1.237

Cat. No.	Sp. Act.	Form	Cost	Chem. Cont.	Radiochem. Cont.
Ta-182-I	105 mc/g	Metal	$33/20 mc	—	—
Ta-182-P	0.5–1.5 mc/mg	Tantalate in KOH	$2/mc	—	—

Mica W.	Int. C.	Scint. C.	50% Self-abs.
1.6×10^{-4}	7.4×10^{-5}	1.8×10^{-3}	15 (calc.)

Intake Levels. Tantalum is not of importance in regard to its natural occurrence in biological materials. The LD_{50} for tantalum chloride in rats was 958 mg/kg of the metal for ingestion and 38 for intraperitoneal administration. Tantalum oxide, which is highly insoluble, was considered nontoxic, since oral doses of 8 g/kg produced no symptoms in rats (Ta-1). Tantalum has been used as a source of gamma radiation.

Radioassay. Gamma counting is preferred when possible, since self-absorption corrections are thus eliminated and tissues can be measured directly.

Chemistry. Conventional wet- or dry-ashing is satisfactory. Methods for chemical estimation of tantalum in biological materials are not available.

Typical Methods. Sheep were given orally about 5 mc Ta^{182} as potassium tantalate. Tissue samples were dry-ashed at about 550°C, and the ash spread uniformly on porcelain dishes for counting with a thin-mica-window counter (Ta-2).

Ta-1. Cochran, Kenneth W., John Doull, Marcella Mazur, and Kenneth P. DuBois: Acute Toxicity of Zirconium, Columbium, Strontium, Lanthanum, Cesium, Tantalum and Yttrium, *Arch. Ind. Hyg. and Occupational Med.*, **1**: 637–650 (1950).
Ta-2. Comar, C. L., and I. B. Whitney: Unpublished results.

Technetium 99 (2.12 × 10⁵ yr)   *Beta* 0.30   *Gamma*

Cat. No.	*Sp. Act.*	*Form*	*Cost*	*Chem. Cont.*	*Radiochem. Cont.*
Tc-99-I	CF	From MoO_3	\$33/0.005 μc	Mo	33 mc Mo^{99} (2.85 days)
Tc-99-P	CF	NH_4TcO_4	\$20/20 μc	—	—

Critical Org.
  Kidney

Intake Levels. Technetium is the name proposed for element 43, radioisotopes of which were identified in fission material. The natural occurrence of this element is questionable, and it has been of little or no biological interest.

Radioassay. Preparation Tc-99-P appears to be the one of choice on the basis of cost and freedom from radiocontamination. The Mo^{99} contamination of Tc-99-I can be eliminated by decay. Soft-beta-counting techniques will be required, and self-absorption will be an important factor.

Chemistry. Technetium, being chemically similar to rhenium, may be distilled from H_2SO_4 solution, and therefore wet-ashing must be employed with caution. Presumably dry-ashing may be satisfactory. Reference (Tc-1) presents details in regard to separation of technetium from the fission-product mixture.

Tc-1. Coryell, Charles D., and Nathan Sugarman: "Radiochemical Studies: The Fission Products," Books 1–3, National Nuclear Energy Series, McGraw-Hill Book Company, Inc., New York, 1951.

Thallium 204 (3.5 yr)				Beta 0.783	Gamma
Cat. No.	Sp. Act.	Form	Cost	Chem. Cont.	Radiochem. Cont.
Tl-204-I	1.3 mc/g	TlNO₃	$33/8 mc	—	Possibly C¹⁴
Tl-204-P	50–300 mc/g	TlNO₃	$5/mc	—	—
Mica W.	Int. C.	Scint. C.		50% Self-abs.	
1 × 10⁻⁴	0.8 × 10⁻⁴	0.13		66 (calc.)	

Intake Levels. Thallium does not occur naturally in biological materials, but animals and humans may be exposed to it on account of its use as a vermin poison. The lethal oral dose for mammals is about 25 mg/kg body weight, which amounts to 3 to 6 mg per rat. The LD_{50} of Tl_2SO_4 given intravenously was 12 mg/kg for the adult male rat (Tl-1). About 0.12 mg per rat causes loss of hair. Thallium is poisonous to plant life at about 5 ppm in the soil.

Radioassay. The higher-specific-activity preparation appears to be the one of choice. Reliance is placed on beta counting, with correction for or elimination of self-absorption.

Chemistry. The method for the handling of tissues described in the next section is the same as used for chemical estimation, except that for the latter no carrier is added and the chloroform solution is evaporated, the organic matter destroyed, and the thallium oxidized to thallic chloride with bromine in the presence of NH_4Cl. Excess bromine is removed, and KI added; this reacts with the thallic chloride to liberate iodine, which is determined colorimetrically (Tl-2). Methods of analysis for thallium from a toxicological standpoint have been reviewed (Tl-3), and an analytical procedure described which is based on activation analysis (Tl-4).

Typical Methods. Following is a description of methods used for studies of distribution in the chick embryo, rat, and man (Tl-1): Labeled $TlNO_3$ with a specific activity of 0.218 mc/mg was used. Rats were injected with 5 μc, fertile eggs were injected with 25 μc, and a patient received 500 μc orally. The tissues were digested with concentrated HNO_3 and concentrated H_2SO_4, the digest cooled, and a pinch of sodium bisulfite added to reduce thallic to thallous ion. The solution was neutralized with 50 per cent KOH, and 0.15 ml of a 10^{-3} M Tl_2SO_4 solution added as carrier, followed by 2 ml of a solution of 12.5 g KCN and 12.5 g ammonium citrate per liter. The mixture was extracted four times with 1-ml portions of a 0.1 per cent solution of dithizone in chloroform, and the chloroform extracts placed on planchets and evaporated under infrared. The planchets were counted with a Geiger tube with a 2.2-mg/cm² window. The assays showed an average loss of 10 per cent which was applied as a correction factor.

Tl-1. Barclay, Ralph K., Wendell C. Peacock, and David A. Karnofsky: Distribution and Excretion of Radioactive Thallium in the Chick Embryo, Rat, and Man, *J. Pharmacol. Exptl. Therap.*, **107**: 178–187 (1953).

Tl-2. Sandell, E. B.: "Colorimetric Determination of Traces of Metals," 2d ed., Interscience Publishers, Inc., New York, 1950.

Tl-3. Emara, M., and M. A. Soliman: On the Application of the Methods of Assay of Thallium, *J. Roy. Egypt. Med. Assoc.*, **32**: 895–905 (1949).

Tl-4. Delbecq, C. J., L. E. Glendenin, and P. H. Yuster: Determination of Thallium by Radioactivation, *Anal. Chem.*, **25**: 350 (1953).

Tin 113 (112 days)   *Beta*   *Gamma* 0.09   *K*

Cat. No.	*Sp. Act.*	*Form*	*Cost*	*Chem. Cont.*	*Radiochem. Cont.*
Sn-113-P	0.1–1 mc/g	Chloride	$35/mc	—	Sb^{125} (2.7 yr)
					Te^{125m} (58 days)
					In^{113} daughter (17 hr)

Mica W.	*Int. C.*	*Scint. C.*	50% *Self-abs.*
1.8×10^{-4}	9×10^{-5}	2×10^{-3}	110 (calc.)

Critical Org.	*Body*	*Air*	*Water*	*Effect. T½*
Bone	80 μc	6×10^{-7}	0.2	44 days

Intake Levels. Only traces of tin occur naturally in biological material. It is not considered an essential element and is of interest on account of possible entrance into foods from tin plate. Up to 4 ppm on a dry basis has been reported in grain, and levels of about 286 ppm in food are considered dangerous. The fatal dose of tin chloride for the dog has been given as 4 to 6 g, and 1 g of tin salts fed every 6 or 10 days killed rabbits in 1 or 2 months (Sn-1).

Radioassay. Samples should be allowed to stand about 170 hr after being taken from the biological system in order to permit the attainment of equilibrium between Sn^{113} and the In^{113} daughter. Information should be obtained from the supplier as to how much Sn^{125} is present, since this will determine the amount of interference to result from the Sb^{125} and Te^{125m} daughters.

Chemistry. Several methods are available in the literature for estimation of tin in foods. Dry-ashing is not recommended, since an insoluble oxide may be formed. Although nitric acid may tend to produce insoluble metastannic acid, most procedures do call for oxidation with a mixture of sulfuric and nitric acids. In one method the acid digest is extracted with dithizone to remove copper, the tin reduced with thioglycolic acid, and a dithiol reagent added to produce a color for photometric evaluation (Sn-2).

Sn-1. Monier-Williams, G. W., "Trace Elements in Food," John Wiley & Sons, Inc., New York, 1950.

Sn-2. Sandell, E. B., "Colorimetric Determination of Traces of Metals," 2d ed., Interscience Publishers, Inc., New York, 1950.

Tungsten 185 (73.2 days)   *Beta* 0.428   *Gamma* 0.134

Cat. No.	*Sp. Act.*	*Form*	*Cost*	*Chem. Cont.*	*Radiochem. Cont.*
W-185-I	7 mc/g	WO$_3$	$33/mc	—	780 mc W^{187} (24.1 hr)
W-185-P	100–400 mc/g	Tungstate in KOH	$4/mc	—	

Mica W.	*Int. C.*	*Scint. C.*
9.3 × 10^{-5}	8 × 10^{-5}	5 × 10^{-2}

Tungsten 187 (24.1 hr)   *Beta* 1.318, 0.627   *Gamma* 0.0708–0.680

Cat. No.	*Sp. Act.*	*Form*	*Cost*	*Chem. Cont.*	*Radiochem. Cont.*
W-187-I	350 mc/g	WO$_3$	$12/35 mc	—	0.15 mc W^{185} (73.2 days)

Mica W.	*Int. C.*	*Scint. C.*	*R$_f$/mc*
1.3 × 10^{-4}	1 × 10^{-4}	3.8 × 10^{-3}	3

Intake Levels. Tungsten does not usually occur in biological materials. With rats, 0.1 per cent tungsten as the oxide or tungstate in the food produced slight weight losses in 70 days; 0.5 per cent as the tungstate caused death.

Radioassay. For tracer work, either preparation W-185-P or W-187-I would be satisfactory. For W^{185}, gamma counting is considerably less sensitive than beta counting. However, if the samples contain sufficient activity, gamma methods would eliminate problems of sample preparation and self-absorption.

Chemistry. Wet-ashing has been shown to be satisfactory. A method for estimation of tungsten in biological material is as follows (W-1): About 2 ml of blood, 10 ml of urine, or 2 g of tissue is used. The sample is heated in a Kjeldahl flask with glass beads, 4 ml concentrated H$_2$SO$_4$, and 10 ml HNO$_3$-HClO$_4$ mixture. Heating is continued until all dense white fumes are driven off. Bones and feces may require more H$_2$SO$_4$, and if charring occurs, additional HNO$_3$-HClO$_4$ is required. The acid residue is made alkaline with NaOH and then diluted to contain about 0.1 mg W per 5 ml. The solution is filtered, and an aliquot treated with potassium thiocyanate, concentrated HCl, and titanium trichloride reagent for development and measurement of color.

W-1. Aull, J. C., and Frederick W. Kinard: The Determination of Tungsten in Biological Materials, *J. Biol. Chem.*, **135**: 119–121 (1940).

Yttrium 90 (2.54 days)   *Beta* 2.18   *Gamma*

Cat. No.	*Sp. Act.*	*Form*	*Cost*	*Chem. Cont.*	*Radiochem. Cont.*
Y-90-I	115 mc/g	Y_2O_3	$33/95 mc	—	—

Critic l Org.
  Bone

Yttrium 91 (61 days)   *Beta* 1.537   *Gamma* 0.2, 1.22 (very weak)

Cat. No.	*Sp. Act.*	*Form*	*Cost*	*Chem. Cont.*	*Radiochem. Cont.*
Y-91-P	CF	YCl_3	$1/mc	—	—

Mica W.	*Int. C.*	*Scint. C.*	50% *Self-abs.*
2.1×10^{-5}	3.7×10^{-5}	2.1×10^{-2}	250 (calc.)

Critical Org.	*Body*	*Air*	*Water*	*Effect.* $T_{1/2}$
Bone	15 μc	4×10^{-8}	0.2	51 days

Intake Levels. Yttrium is not an important naturally occurring constituent of biological materials. A primary interest is concerned with the radioisotopes of this element, produced by fission, and their tendency to deposit in the bones of animals. The metabolism of Y^{90}, which is a radioactive daughter of Sr^{90}, may well be governed by the metabolism of the parent strontium. There has been some interest in the use of Y^{90} colloids for therapeutic purposes. The LD_{50} values for three yttrium compounds ranged from 117 to 395 mg/kg administered intraperitoneally to rats (Y-1). Intravenous dosage of 20 to 30 mg/kg of yttrium nitrate was fatal to rats.

Radioassay. Yttrium 91 appears to be the preparation of choice, primarily on account of the high specific activity, unless a shorter-lived activity is required. Routine beta or gamma counting can be used. With an end-window counter, the measurements on solid samples were about four times as sensitive as on 10 ml solution in a 5-cm petri dish.

Chemistry. No losses have been observed upon routine wet- or dry-ashing. Stable yttrium has been determined spectrographically in bone ash (Y-2). As noted below, care must be taken in the preparation of solutions for administration to the biological system on account of tendencies for colloid formation and adsorption onto glass.

Typical Methods. Immediately before use, the yttrium solution was neutralized with NaOH to about 0.1 N HCl (Y-3). Rats were given about 30 μc per animal, and livestock were dosed with 1.4 mc/100 lb body weight. With cattle, the isotope was mixed with the animal's own heparinized plasma, which was then reinjected. Blood, urine, and milk samples were counted directly or, if low in activity, were dried in Coors No. 1 capsules and dry-ashed. Feces and tissue samples were either wet- or dry-ashed.

In another study using Pu and Y simultaneously, colloid formation was prevented by diluting the acid solution of the isotopes with an excess of 2 per cent citric acid and then carefully adjusting the pH to 6.5 with NaOH (Y-4).   The tissue samples were digested with concentrated HNO_3 and evaporated to near dryness.   This was repeated three or four times until only a white ash remained.   The ash was dissolved in HNO_3, and aliquots deposited in a porcelain dish, slowly dried under infrared, and counted through a 13.5-mg/cm^2 absorber with an end-window Geiger tube.   The absorber eliminated any contribution from the plutonium.

The chemical form of Y as excreted in the urine was studied by intravenous administration of 2 μc $Y^{91}Cl_3$ to rats and subsequent fractionation of the urine by paper chromatography (Y-5).   The coincidence of radioactivity and ninhydrin coloration demonstrated the existence of yttrium–amino acid complexes.   A detailed study of the deposition of Y^{91} in rabbit bones as a function of time after injection has been reported (Y-6). Single intravenous injections of 12 to 500 μc $Y^{91}Cl_3$ were given.   The effect of carrier was emphasized by extensive animal studies which showed that with increased carrier Y (1 mg/0.1 mc) there was a marked increase in localization of Y^{90} at the site of intrapleural, intraperitoneal, intramuscular, intratumoral, and subcutaneous injection (Y-7).

Uptake in plants has been studied using nutrient solutions containing about 10^{-3} μc/ml and also the Neubauer technique (Y-8).

Y-1. Cochran, Kenneth W., John Doull, Marcella Mazur, and Kenneth P. DuBois: Acute Toxicity of Zirconium, Columbium, Strontium, Lanthanum, Cesium Tantalum and Yttrium, *Arch. Ind. Hyg. and Occupational Med.*, **1**: 637–650 (1950).

Y-2. MacDonald, Norman S., Ralph E. Nusbaum, George V. Alexander, Florita Ezmirlian, Patricia Spain, and Donald E. Rounds: The Skeletal Deposition of Yttrium, *J. Biol. Chem.*, **195**: 837–841 (1952).

Y-3. Hood, S. L., and C. L. Comar: Tissue Distribution and Placental Transfer of Yttrium-91 in Rats and Cattle (In press).

Y-4. Schubert, Jack, Miriam P. Finkel, Marcia R. White, and Gertrude M. Hirsch: Plutonium and Yttrium Content of the Blood, Liver, and Skeleton of the Rat at Different Times after Intravenous Administration, *J. Biol. Chem.*, **182**: 635–642 (1950).

Y-5. Kawin, Bergene: Metabolism of Radioyttrium, *Arch. Biochem. and Biophys.*, **45**: 230–231 (1953).

Y-6. Rayner, Barbara, Margaret Tutt, and Janet Vaughan: The Deposition of ^{91}Y in Rabbit Bones, *Brit. J. Exptl. Pathol.*, **34**: 138–145 (1953).

Y-7. Kyker, Granvil C., Edgar A. Cress, and G. I. Gleason: Distribution of Yttrium Administered by Various Routes, *Fed. Proc.*, **13**: 245–246 (1954).

Y-8. Rediske, J. H., and A. A. Selders: The Uptake and Translocation of Yttrium by Higher Plants, *Am. J. Botany*, **41**: 238–242 (1954).

Zinc 65 (250 days)				Beta 0.32	Gamma 1.11 K
Cat. No.	*Sp. Act.*	*Form*	*Cost*	*Chem. Cont.*	*Radiochem. Cont.*
Zn-65-I	1.9 mc/g	Metal	$33/15 mc	—	130 mc Zn^{69m} (13.8 hr)
Zn-65-P-1	75–300 mc/g	$ZnCl_2$	$2/mc	—	—
Zn-65-P-2	5 c/g	$ZnCl_2$	$100/mc	Possibly Cu	—

Mica W.	*Int. C.*	*Scint. C.*	R_f/mc	50% *Self-abs.*
4×10^{-3}	4×10^{-4}	2.7×10^{-3}	3	56.5 (detn.)

Critical Org.	*Body*	*Air*	*Water*	*Effect.* $T_{1/2}$
Bone	430 μc	2×10^{-6}	6×10^{-2}	21 days

Intake Levels. The normal intake for human beings is 12 to 20 mg/day, and rats require at least 0.04 mg/day. Some values for zinc content are: liver, 40 to 140 ppm; blood, 6 to 9 ppm; milk, 3 to 5 ppm; crop plants, 10 to 200 ppm on a dry basis. A recommended nutrient solution for plants contains 0.02 ppm, whereas 60 ppm is toxic. The health of rats was impaired by 1 per cent zinc carbonate in the diet, and a fatal dose for rabbits was 34 mg/kg daily for 11 days.

Radioassay. Preparation Zn-65-P-1 appears to be the one of choice unless very high specific activity is required and the cost of cyclotron-produced Zn-65-P-2 can be justified. Gamma counting is preferred, since complicated separations may be avoided and the tissues counted directly or in solution.

Chemistry. Routine dry- or wet-ashing may be used. Zinc may be estimated by dithizone methods. A method has been described for blood and tissues (Zn-1, Zn-2) which consists in ashing at 660°C, dissolving in HCl, and, after buffering to pH 5.5, extracting with dithizone in CCl_4 and measuring the color photometrically. In order to measure Zn^{65} on the same sample as used for total zinc, the zinc dithizonate is returned to a clean separatory funnel, a drop of concentrated H_2SO_4 added, followed by 10 ml H_2O, and the mixture shaken until all the zinc has gone into the aqueous phase, as shown by the return of green color in the CCl_4 phase. A method for plant material (Zn-3) has been described which is similar but involves a "mixed-color" dithizone method that eliminates interference from other elements.

Typical Methods. A preparation of cyclotron-produced Zn^{65} was tested for the presence of radiocontaminants of cobalt, nickel, lead, and cadmium by adding a small quantity of these elements to aliquots of the preparation, separating the added metal from the zinc, and testing the recovered metal for radioactivity (Zn-4). If there had been any of the radiocontaminant in the original Zn^{65} preparation, it would have shown up in the separated sample. Mice were injected intravenously with about 0.33 μg of labeled zinc, and dogs with about 6 μg. Mice excreta were ashed at 450°C, the ash transferred to squares of blotting paper which were wrapped in cellophane, and the gamma rays measured with a Geiger counter.   Fairly large samples of dog excreta were ashed at 450°C, the ash dissolved in HCl, and the insoluble portion re-ashed and redissolved.   Any HCl-insoluble material was measured directly.   Aliquots of the HCl solution were treated with $ZnCl_2$ and K_2CO_3 to precipitate $ZnCO_3$, which was collected, dried, and counted as above.

In another study, a cow was given orally 3 mc Zn^{65} in 7 mg $ZnCl_2$, and solution counts made on milk and urine (Zn-5).   The distribution in rabbits of the following Zn^{65}-labeled compounds was studied: zinc carbonate, zinc phosphate, and zinc dithizone complex.   Tissues were prepared for counting by a modification of the dithizone method for chemical analysis (Zn-6).   The investigator should establish the necessity for such a complicated procedure before using it.

The uptake by tomato plants of Zn^{65} adsorbed onto bentonite was studied (Zn-7).   The oven-dry plant material was ashed at 550°C, and the ash spread uniformly on the bottom of seamless tin boxes for counting with an Al absorber of 0.13 g/cm^2.   Greenhouse studies on the plant uptake of Zn^{65} from soils and fertilizers have been described (Zn-8).   As an example of the general procedure, 30 ml of a solution containing 1 g zinc and 0.3 mc Zn^{65}, both as the chloride, was incorporated into 1 kg of dry sand, which was then stored in a closed glass jar and weighed out as needed at the rate of 10 mg zinc and 3 μc Zn^{65} per kilogram of soil.   The sand and soil for each pot were thoroughly mixed.   For analysis, plant material was dried and ground, and 1- to 2-g samples wet-ashed with HNO_3, $HClO_4$, and H_2SO_4.   The zinc-sand-fertilizer mixture was extracted with 0.1 N HCl.   The zinc from both types of samples was determined by dithizone methods on aliquots containing 5 to 40 mg zinc. Radioassays were made by pipetting 1 ml of the CCl_4 remaining from the chemical determination into an aluminum pan, evaporating at room temperature, muffling at 400°C for an hour to oxidize the dithizone, and counting with an internal counter.

Zn-1. Vallee, Bert L., and John G. Gibson, 2d: An Improved Dithizone Method for the Determination of Small Quantities of Zinc in Blood and Tissue Samples, *J. Biol. Chem.*, **176**: 435–443 (1948).

Zn-2. Vallee, Bert L., and John G. Gibson, 2d: The Zinc Content of Normal Human Whole Blood, Plasma, Leucocytes, and Erythrocytes, *J. Biol. Chem.*, **176**: 445–457 (1948).

Zn-3. Cowling, Hale, and E. J. Miller: Determination of Small Amounts of Zinc in Plant Materials, *Ind. Eng. Chem. Anal. Ed.*, **13**: 145–149 (1941).

Zn-4. Sheline, G. E., I. L. Chaikoff, H. B. Jones, and M. Laurence Montgomery: Studies on the Metabolism of Zinc with the Aid of Its Radioactive Isotope, *J. Biol. Chem.*, **147**: 409–414 (1943).

Zn-5. Bergh, Helge: Studies on the Metabolism of Zinc Using Radiozinc Zn-65, *Kgl. Norske Videnskab. Selskabs. Forh.*, **23B**(5): 49–51 (1950).

Zn-6. Banks, T. E., R. L. F. Tupper, and A. Wormall: The Fate of Some Intravenously Injected Zinc Compounds, *Biochem. J. London*, **47**: 466–472 (1950).

Zn-7. Epstein, Emanuel, and Perry R. Stout: The Micronutrient Cations Iron, Manganese, Zinc, and Copper: Their Uptake by Plants from the Adsorbed State, *Soil Sci.*, **72**: 47–65 (1951).

Zn-8. Shaw, Ellsworth, Ronald G. Menzel, and L. A. Dean: Plant Uptake of Zinc[65] from Soils and Fertilizers in the Greenhouse, *Soil Sci.*, **77**: 205–214 (1954).

Zirconium 95 (65 days)   *Beta* 0.4, 0.887   *Gamma* 0.708

Cat. No.	*Sp. Act.*	*Form*	*Cost*	*Chem. Cont.*	*Radiochem. Cont.*
Zr-95-I	0.05 mc/g	Zr(OH)$_4$	$12/0.06 mc	—	0.1 mc Zr^{97} (17 hr)
					Nb^{95} daughter (35 days)

R_f/mc
4

Zirconium 95 (65 days)   *Beta* 0.4, 0.887   *Gamma* 0.708
Niobium 95 (35 days)   *Beta* 0.146   *Gamma* 0.758

Cat. No.	*Sp. Act.*	*Form*	*Cost*	*Chem. Cont.*	*Radiochem. Cont.*
ZrNb-95-P	CF	Oxalate	$1/mc	—	Nb^{95} daughter (35 days)
		complex			

Intake Levels. Zirconium is not an important naturally occurring constituent of biological materials. Of interest has been its use to increase the removal of bone-seeking radioisotopes from the body, as well as the possibilities of using radiocolloids of zirconium for therapeutic irradiation. The acute oral LD$_{50}$ values for rats for five zirconium salts ranged from 990 to 2290 mg/kg, indicating a relatively low toxicity (Zr-1). The intraperitoneal LD$_{50}$ values were 63 to 939 mg/kg, zirconyl sulfate being the least toxic and zirconium sulfate the most toxic.

Radioassay. The primary difficulty in the use of Zr^{95} as a tracer results from the relatively long-lived Nb^{95} daughter. At equilibrium the Zr^{95}/Nb^{95} ratio is 0.465. It requires a waiting period of 6 months to 1 yr after the sample has been taken from the biological system to permit the attainment of equilibrium between Zr^{95} and Nb^{95}. For short-term experiments, preparation Zr-95-I containing small amounts of Nb^{95} might be used before appreciable growth of Nb^{95} has occurred. Other methods might involve the double assay of the two activities in the samples by differential beta-absorption measurements or by separations such as ion exchange or filter-paper chromatography. In a distribution study of Zr colloids in the rabbit, it was shown that the Nb^{95} had the same metabolic behavior as did the Zr^{95} (Zr-2). Routine beta or gamma counting is satisfactory.

Chemistry. Biological material may be wet- or dry-ashed. Methods are not available for chemical estimation of traces of zirconium in plant or animal tissues. For separation of zirconium, the insoluble zirconium phosphate or barium fluozirconate is used (Zr-3). Attention is called to the possibility of aggregate formation in dosing solutions, since precipitation of a hydroxide or basic salt will take place from a dilute solution of a simple salt at pH 2. The colloidal properties may be minimized by the use of a little oxalic or hydrofluoric acid or by citric acid at pH 4.

Typical Methods. Procedures have been described for preparation of the following labeled colloids for use in biological studies: zirconium oxide in dilute HNO_3, zirconium phosphate, zirconium oxide in sodium lactate solution, and various anionic colloids (Zr-2). In studies with rats, the usual dosages employed were about 1.6 ml, administered intraperitoneally, of a 10 per cent sodium citrate solution containing 5 μc Zr^{95} freshly separated from the Nb^{95} daughter, with 0 to 40 mg zirconium added as carrier. Two microcuries Zr^{95} was used for intravenous injection (Zr-4). Tissues and excreta were dried, then ashed at 650°C for 10 hr, the ash dissolved in 2 N HCl, and aliquots placed in $\frac{1}{2}$-oz metal ointment capsules and dried for counting with an end-window tube. Self-absorption corrections were applied when necessary.

In a study of uptake by plants (Zr-5), the preparation, received as the oxalate, was treated with H_2O_2 in strong H_2SO_4 to destroy the complex. The radioactivity was adsorbed onto clay and soil in amounts of 780 counts/min/5 g of soil for leaching studies. Plant uptake from soil treated with Zr^{95}-Nb^{95} was also studied. In another study, about 10 μc/liter was added to a bentonite suspension in which barley plants were grown (Zr-6). The uptake in various plant parts, as well as the fixation on clay, was measured by the counting of mechanically separated samples.

Zr-1. Cochran, Kenneth W., John Doull, Marcella Mazur, and Kenneth P. DuBois: Acute Toxicity of Zirconium, Columbium, Strontium, Lanthanum, Cesium, Tantalum and Yttrium, *Arch. Ind. Hyg. and Occupational Med.*, **1**: 637–650 (1950).

Zr-2. Gofman, John W.: Studies with Colloids Containing Radioisotopes of Yttrium, Zirconium, Columbium, and Lanthanum. I. The Chemical Principles and Methods Involved in Preparation of Colloids of Yttrium, Zirconium, Columbium, and Lanthanum, *J. Lab. Clin. Med.*, **34**: 297–304 (1949).

Zr-3. Coryell, Charles D., and Nathan Sugarman: "Radiochemical Studies: The Fission Products," Books 1–3, National Nuclear Energy Series, McGraw-Hill Book Company, Inc., New York, 1951.

Zr-4. Kawin, Bergene, D. H. Copp, and J. G. Hamilton: Studies of the Metabolism of Certain Fission Products and Plutonium, UCRL-812, Aug. 7, 1950.

Zr-5. Vlamis, J., and G. A. Pearson: Absorption of Radioactive Zirconium and Niobium by Plant Roots from Soils and Its Theoretical Significance, *Science*, **111**: 112–113 (1950).

Zr-6. Jacobson, L., and R. Overstreet: Progress Report on Plant Studies: The Fixation and Absorption of Fission Products by Plants, MDDC-571, Dec. 18, 1944.

CHAPTER 7

AUTORADIOGRAPHY

GENERAL CONSIDERATIONS—Laboratory Requirements; Photographic Emulsions; Properties of the Radioisotope; Dosage of Isotope and Exposure Time; Handling of Tissues. SPECIFIC TECHNIQUES—Simple Apposition; Mounting Method; Coating Method; Stripping-film Method. APPLICATIONS—Chemical; Anatomical Relationships; Metabolic: *Translocation; Bone growth and development; Cellular biosynthesis; Embryonic development; Dysfunction;* Quantitative Aspects; *Track and grain counting.* INTERPRETATION.

Ionizing radiations act upon the photographic emulsion in the same manner as light does. If a piece of film is exposed to an object containing radioactive material, a photographic image is produced upon development which provides visualization of the location of the radioactivity in the sample. This image is known by such terms as *autoradiogram, autoradiograph, autogram,* and *radioautogram.* General references (4, 9, 10) may be consulted for historical aspects which date back to the observations of Becquerel in 1895 on the fogging of a photographic plate by uranium ore.

On the gross scale, autoradiography is of particular advantage with heterogeneous samples in providing information that is unobtainable by counting methods. But perhaps of greatest import from the biological standpoint is the fact that the autoradiographic technique permits study of cellular function at the cell level. It becomes possible to develop correlations between cytological structure, cellular physiology and pathology, physicochemical properties of the cells, and the location pattern of specific chemical elements introduced into the system.

The same requirements for interpretation as discussed in Chap. 2 for general radioisotope usage must be taken into account, namely, chemical effects, radiochemical contamination, radiation effects, exchange reactions, and isotope effects. In addition, there is always the possibility of artifacts, which must be guarded against by careful technique, control experiments, and reserve in the interpretation of the autoradiogram. There seems little question, however, that the tedium of precautionary measures, which decreases with experience and use of standardized procedures, is far overbalanced by the information made available.

The autoradiographic technique has one appeal to the biologist: electronic equipment is not required. From this point of view the methods may be regarded as relatively simple and inexpensive. However, much the same art and science will be required for meaningful results as are needed for conventional histochemical technique.

GENERAL CONSIDERATIONS

Laboratory Requirements. The laboratory facilities should be reasonably close to the source of the fresh tissue, at least in the same building. It is essential that the facilities not be located in the vicinity of high background levels from radioisotopes or X-ray machines which may produce background fog in the film. Space is required, as determined by the volume and variety of work, for dissection of specimens, routine histological processing, storage of specimens during and after exposure, photographic processing, examination of autoradiograms, and recording of data. When possible, the space should be divided into individual work areas. The usual laboratory and darkroom service utilities are needed, and it is particularly desirable that room temperatures be controlled. The darkroom should be arranged for convenient operation, with appropriate light locks, constant-temperature water, and adequate ventilation, since noxious solvents are often employed. In addition to chemical glassware, typical histological equipment is needed such as dissecting instruments, microscope slides, cover glasses, slide boxes, diamond or glass-marking pencils, water baths, staining jars, paraffin oven, microtome, microscope, and refrigerator for storage of films. If large numbers of tissues are to be fixed, it may be wise to invest in an automatic processing unit. As indicated later, equipment such as freeze-drying apparatus and special bone saws may be useful for particular purposes.

A radiation survey meter is helpful for checking possible contamination and also for measurement of tissue sections in order to estimate exposure times. A line-operated count-rate meter with a thin-mica-end-window Geiger tube has been found satisfactory for this purpose. The amount of radioactivity contained in a thin tissue section will usually be small, so that contamination of the microtome knife or staining equipment is not a serious matter. However, the original tissue samples may contain considerable activity, and appropriate health-physics measures should be taken.

Photographic Emulsions. Extensive discussions of the properties of films, photographic processing, resolving power, and tissue dosage are beyond the scope of this text and have been adequately covered in general references (4, 11). However, resolution is so important that it is necessary to consider this matter, at least qualitatively. If there are two point sources of radiation in a sample, each one will produce a circular area of darkening in the emulsion.   If these areas overlap, then it becomes impossible to interpret from the autoradiogram that there were two distinct sources.   The greater the resolution, the closer together are the areas of darkening that can still be distinguished from each other.   Since the primary objective is the correlation of areas of darkening with localization of radioactivity in the sample, it is clear that increased resolution is always a major goal, especially for studies on the cellular level.   In general, the following conditions promote increased resolution: radiation of low energy; thin specimens; thin emulsions; minimum of scattering from film backing and slide; fine-grained emulsion; and close contact between specimen and emulsion, which is perhaps the most important variable. These factors form the basis for many of the techniques that have been devised and are discussed subsequently from a practical point of view.

The emulsion to be employed should be fast enough so that long exposure times or high tissue levels of radioactivity will not be required; on the other hand, the grain size must not be so large that the resolution is inadequate.   There should be a low background fog, especially when individual grains or tracks are to be observed.   Commercial films are available for autoradiographic studies which offer a balance between these factors and permit a choice dependent upon experimental requirements. Some of these films are described subjectively in Table 7-1, and recommendations are given for their use.

TABLE 7-1. FILM FOR AUTORADIOGRAPHY

Type	Sensitivity	Resolution	Background	Recommendation
No-screen X-ray.......	High	Poor	High	Gross localization or minimal concentrations
Medium lantern slide..	Medium	Good	Medium	Histological sections of moderate concentrations
NTB................	Medium	Very good	Low	Histological sections that are mounted
NTB₃................	High for β tracks	Very good	Increases rapidly	When β tracks are to be observed
NTA................	High for α tracks	Very good	Low	When α tracks are to be observed
Liquid emulsion.......	High	Very good	Increases rapidly	When tracks are to be observed
Stripping film.........	Low	Very good	Low	Cellular localization

[From Patrick J. Fitzgerald, Eva Simmel, Jerry Weinstein, and Cynthia Martin, Radioautography: Theory, Technic, and Applications, *Lab. Invest.*, **2**: 181–222 (1953), (Paul B. Hoeber, Inc., publisher).]

Film should be used as fresh as practicable, since background fog and graininess increase with time and may become a real problem, especially in work with small amounts of radioactivity. Also the film should be stored at refrigerator temperatures in a place where it is not exposed to extraneous radiation or high humidity. The safelight to be employed during handling should be known to produce no fogging and/or should be tested under actual working conditions. The film should be handled carefully at all times to avoid scratching or fingerprints. Photographic processing is carried out according to the manufacturer's directions with such modifications as are developed by experience for particular circumstances. A general procedure is as follows: The film is developed in the dark for 2 to 5 min at 18 to 20°C using Eastman D-19 solution. The film is then rinsed for about 15 sec in two changes of water, fixed in the usual hypo for twice the time it takes to clear, and then washed in running water for 20 to 30 min. All solutions should be maintained at a constant temperature to minimize background fog and softening of the emulsion which may occur at higher temperatures.

Properties of the Radioisotope. Alpha particles allow very high resolution on account of their short range. However, the biological interest in alpha emitters stems primarily from their toxicity in the body. Most of the autoradiograms in biological experimentation are produced from beta particles. Elements with low beta energies such as H^3 (0.0189 Mev), C^{14} (0.155 Mev), S^{35} (0.166 Mev), and Ca^{45} (0.254 Mev) give very good resolution. As the beta energy increases, the autogram becomes more and more diffuse. Radioisotopes such as Fe^{55} which emit soft K and L X rays give good resolution. Gamma rays, with their great range and low ionization, are relatively inefficient and normally contribute little to the autoradiogram when the isotope also emits beta particles.

Radioisotopes with half-lives shorter than several hours offer some disadvantage since, after the experimental period and the time required for histological processing, the tissue sections may be low in activity. In such cases, longer-lived radiocontaminants may present a problem.

Dosage of Isotope and Exposure Time. There is no simple way to determine the amount of radioactivity that must be put into a biological system in order to ensure an autoradiographic image within a reasonable exposure period. A balance must be struck between high doses, which may produce radiation effects, and low doses, which will require unduly long exposure periods. As a rule of thumb, it has been stated that approximately 5 to 10 million beta particles per square centimeter must strike an X-ray emulsion during exposure to produce adequate blackening; with alpha particles, 1 to 2 million particles per square centimeter are required (7). For example, with gross autoradiograms, if a section monitored with an end-window counter gives a measurement of 100 counts/-

min at a collection efficiency of about 10 per cent, this would indicate that a 10- to 15-day exposure period would be required.   This type of measurement may be misleading in the prediction of inadequate exposure, should the radioactivity be limited to a small area.   Fitzgerald et al. (10) have calculated that the following approximate tissue concentrations are required for histological sections of 10 μ to give an image on X-ray film with a 15-day exposure: C^{14}, 0.05 $\mu c/g$; Ca^{45}, 0.05 $\mu c/g$; I^{131}, 0.2 $\mu c/g$; P^{32}, 0.4 $\mu c/g$; Zn^{65}, 2.0 $\mu c/g$.   If the percentage of uptake in a given tissue can be estimated from tracer experiments, then the above values will permit an estimation of the order of magnitude of the dose required.

In practice, with plants and animals it is usually feasible to run some preliminary experiments with graded levels of activity.   This permits a more accurate estimation of the dose required, as well as an indication of the optimum exposure time.   It is important to avoid overexposure, since this causes a loss of resolution.   Under standard experimental conditions the optimum exposure time may be estimated from tissue counts by previous determination of the relationship between tissue counts and image densities.   However, it is often practicable to expose several sections; after one or two have been developed at different times, usually being underexposed, it is then possible to estimate fairly closely the best exposure time.

Handling of Tissues.   For gross autoradiograms, thin sections offer no advantage, and the problem is primarily that of presenting a smooth surface to the emulsion and maintaining a close contact by pressure.   For studies at the cellular level it is necessary to employ thin sections of the order of 5 to 10 μ or less, and the conventional histological procedures are heavily drawn upon for the preparation of such sections.   The reader unfamiliar with the basic methods of fixation, dehydration, embedding, and sectioning should consult references (1 to 3) for background information.

In addition to the histological requirements of the fixatives and other agents, it is most important that these materials do not inhibit or increase photographic action and do not leach the radioisotopes from the tissue. Boyd and Board (12) demonstrated the production of artifacts by chemical action of various soft tissues on the photographic emulsion, and Everett and Simmons (13) have emphasized that even the protective coatings such as Formvar or silicone do not provide absolute elimination of chemical reduction of the emulsion.   The leaching problem is a serious one, as may be noted from the papers of Williams (14), Holt and Warren (15), and Blank et al. (16).   It is generally agreed that mercury-containing fixatives such as Zenker's cannot be used.   There seems to be some question as to whether neutral Formalin is satisfactory (10, 17).   Alcohol has been used satisfactorily from the leaching standpoint but was not entirely satisfactory for cytoplasmic fixation (18).   Bouin's solution has been reported as satisfactory by Fitzgerald et al. (10), but it produced some uncertainties in the hands of Doniach and Pelc (18).

The extent of leaching depends upon the radioisotope and its combination in the tissue.   For example, inorganic P^{32} in a tissue is easily leached, whereas organically bound P^{32} is tenaciously retained.   There are two approaches to the leaching problem: the careful use of fixatives known to be satisfactory for the specific samples, and the use of various freezing methods in which there is no opportunity for leaching losses.   Holt et al. (19) found that loss of inorganic P^{32} from tissues was minimized by a fixing procedure that called for 2 hr in alcohol-Formalin (9:1) and three changes of dioxane (2 hr, 1 hr, 1 hr), followed by the usual paraffin infiltration and embedding.   The dioxane was shown to be preferable to the use of alcohols for dehydration.   It is emphasized that Formalin should always be neutralized, since acid fixatives tend to increase the leaching loss.   Formalin is usually neutralized by allowing it to stand over an excess of magnesium carbonate.   Blank et al. (16) have described a procedure in which losses were minimized by using cold propylene glycol as a fixative and Carbowax as the embedding medium.   Although paraffin is most widely used as an embedding material, Carbowax may offer some advantage in that it can be removed by aqueous solvents as well as fat solvents; when aqueous solvents are used, it is possible to retain fats in the tissue.

Witten and Holmstrom (20) have described a freezing method that avoids the use of liquids.   The tissue specimen is frozen by means of CO_2 gas on the object disk of the freezing microtome and is then sectioned with a microtome blade kept cold by dry ice held in place on its upper surface. The section in the frozen state is transported directly from the blade to the photographic emulsion.   Holt and Warren (21) have described simplified freeze-drying procedures for autoradiographic studies.   Two embedding media are compared—paraffin (Tissuemat, melting point 50 to 52°C) and Carbowax (three parts Carbowax 4000, three parts Carbowax 1000, and one part Carbowax 1500; melting point about 56°C). The embedding material is placed at the bottom of the tissue tube, which is attached to a commercial freeze-drying apparatus.   The fresh tissue is frozen at about −170°C by immersion in isopentane cooled with liquid nitrogen and quickly transferred to the tissue tubes.   The tissue tubes are held in Dewar flasks surrounded by dry ice and attached to the apparatus for 48 to 82 hr at a pressure of about 10^{-4} mm Hg.   The dry ice is allowed to evaporate, permitting a gradual warming to room temperature, and at the end of the 48- to 72-hr period the tubes are warmed to melt the embedding material and facilitate infiltration.   The desired handling techniques are then employed.

If the autoradiographic preparation is such that the film and section

TABLE 7-2. DIRECTIONS FOR STAINING AFTER PHOTOGRAPHIC PROCESSING AND CHARACTERISTICS OF AUTORADIOGRAMS OF MOUNTED TISSUE SECTIONS

Stain	Visibility of tracks	Color contrast for photographic reproduction	Histologic detail	Remarks
Basic fuchsin (dry slide; 0.1% aqueous fuchsin for 4 min; differentiate in distilled H_2O; dehydrate in 95% alcohol, absolute alcohol, toluol; mount in balsam)	Good	Fair	Fair	Monochromatic. Simple procedure
Hematoxylin and eosin (dry slide; overstain in Harris's hematoxylin; differentiate in acid H_2O, alkaline H_2O; stain in aqueous eosin; dehydrate, clear, mount in balsam)	Poor	Good	Very good	Dichromatic. Much absorption of stain by emulsion and tissue; nuclei too dark to permit visualization of tracks in emulsion
Weigert's acid–iron hematoxylin (Weigert's stain for 2 min; tap H_2O for 5 min; dehydrate in 3 changes of acetone; clear in 1:1 acetone-xylene and 3 changes of xylene; mount in xylene-Clarite)	Fair	Fair	Fair	Monochromatic. At times emulsion becomes very tacky and soft in solution of iron hematoxylin
Hematoxylin (immediately after photographic processing, stain in dilute hematoxylin at 1 to 2°C overnight; dehydrate in 95% alcohol, absolute alcohol, alcohol-xylol, 3 changes of xylol; dilute balsam solution for 5 min, mount in balsam)	Poor	Fair	Fair	Monochromatic. Nuclei stain quite deeply; therefore tracks are not easy to visualize

TABLE 7-2. DIRECTIONS FOR STAINING AFTER PHOTOGRAPHIC PROCESSING AND
CHARACTERISTICS OF AUTORADIOGRAMS OF MOUNTED TISSUE SECTIONS
(*Continued*)

Stain	Visibility of tracks	Color contrast for photographic reproduction	Histologic detail	Remarks
Metanil yellow and iron hematoxylin (dry slide; 0.25% metanil yellow for 5 to 15 sec; tap H_2O for about 15 sec; iron hematoxylin for 1 to 3 min; dehydrate in 70% alcohol, 95% alcohol, acetone, acetone and xylene, xylene; mount in synthetic resin)	Excellent	Fair	Fair	Dichromatic. At times emulsion becomes tacky and soft in solution of iron hematoxylin
Lithium carmine (dry slide; lithium carmine reagent for 2 min; acid alcohol about 2 min; rinse in 70% alcohol, then 95% alcohol; counterstain in picric acid alcohol; rinse in absolute alcohol; clear in xylol; mount in gum dammar)	Excellent	Very good	Very good	Dichromatic

[Courtesy of Victor H. Witten and Vera Holmstrom, New Histologic Technics for Autoradiography, *Lab. Invest.*, **2**: 368–375 (1953), Paul B. Hoeber, Inc., publisher.]

are separated after exposure, then the section can be stained in the usual way at that time, since any removal of radioactivity would have no effect. The section can be stained before contact with the emulsion, but in this case one must be sure that leaching does not occur. Therefore, with preparations that consist of combined section and emulsion, staining is usually done after development, and special attention must be paid to the problem of absorption of the stain by the emulsion. The thinner the emulsion, the less difficulty from this cause.

Directions and characteristics of some of the stains used for autoradiograms of mounted tissue sections are presented in Table 7-2, as compiled by Witten and Holmstrom (20).

SPECIFIC TECHNIQUES

There are four commonly used procedures which differ primarily in the method of contact between tissue section and emulsion. These methods have been reviewed by Heller (7), Fitzgerald et al. (10), Leblond and Gross (6), and Bourne (8). A brief statement of advantages, disadvantages, and representative procedural details is presented for each. The original literature should be consulted for application to specific problems, since individual workers develop modifications and refinements that lead to improvement in results. Also it is not feasible to include the numerous details, many of which can be appreciated only as a result of actual experience. Illustrative autoradiograms prepared by the various methods will be found in the section on Applications.

Simple Apposition. *Principle.* The specimen to be studied is placed in contact with the photographic emulsion and kept in contact by pressure, and at the end of the exposure period the specimen is removed, and the film developed.

Advantages. The method is rapid and simple, and pretreatment of the sample is minimal, so that radioisotope losses are avoided. Since poor resolution is inevitable, it is possible to make advantageous use of a sensitive film to decrease the exposure time and/or the amount of radioactivity required in the sample. The autoradiogram can be used for densitometric measurement, since there will be no interference from the specimen. The sections can be stained after preparation of the autoradiogram, and there is no interference from the emulsion.

Disadvantages. Poor contact is responsible for loss of resolution, and cellular localization is usually not possible. It is difficult to superimpose accurately the object and autoradiogram.

Recommended Usage. This method is satisfactory for gross autoradiograms, especially for samples in which the radioisotope localizations are widely separated. It has been particularly useful in studies with plant material, bones, frozen tissue, and paper chromatograms.

GROSS SOFT TISSUES. Soft tissues may be frozen, sectioned with a chilled blade or fine electric saw, and then applied to the photographic emulsion in a frozen state (5).

BONE. It is not feasible to use a decalcification procedure for studies of most elements that deposit in the crystal or organic matrix of bone. Bone and teeth sections may be cut with various types of saws or may be ground to a smooth surface (21a to 24). Gross et al. (5) have described a procedure in which the sample is glued to a microtome mount and then polished with a motor-driven fine emery stone cooled by a stream of water. A simple miter box and Zona saw have been used satisfactorily for gross sectioning of rat bones.   An embedding procedure has been described by Arnold (21b).

The following is a procedure described by Lotz, Gallimore, and Boyd (23) for the preparation of large autoradiograms from undecalcified bones:

1. The freshly excised bone is cleaned of excess tissue and is mounted on a soft board using Duco cement, care being taken to align the longitudinal axis of the bone parallel with the straight edge of the board.

Fig. 7-1. Glove box housing band saw for sectioning bones.   A viewing window above the glove ports is provided and a vacuum cleaner is used to maintain slight negative pressure.   [*From W. E. Lotz, J. C. Gallimore, and George A. Boyd, How to Get Good Gross Autoradiographs, Nucleonics, 10: 28–31 (1952).*]

2. To avoid contamination by bone dust, a band saw is housed in a glove box (see Fig. 7-1).   Metal cutting blades, ¼ in. wide with 15 teeth to the inch, have been found suitable.   The guide is adjusted for the desired thickness of section (about 2 mm), and the bone is fed to the blade with a slow uniform motion.

3. The sections are cleaned of bone particles.   Under safelight conditions a thin piece of cardboard is placed in a Kodak X-ray exposure cassette.   On this is placed the bone section, then an 0.8-mil sheet of Pliofilm to prevent chemical fogging, and then the film.   The cassette is closed and held in a plywood press with a piece of sponge rubber inserted

between the cassette and wood to ensure uniform contact between film and bone.   The assembly is kept at refrigerator temperatures for the duration of the exposure.

4. Upon completion of exposure, the film is processed.

PLANT MATERIAL.   With fresh material, the plant may be blotted, pressed flat, and then placed on the film under safelight conditions with a thin piece of cellophane or Pliofilm between the emulsion and plant to avoid chemical effects.   The film and sample can be held in contact for exposure by means of an X-ray cassette with glass plates or any convenient press.   When desired, the whole plant or parts thereof can be dried between blotting paper under pressure to produce a sample that allows uniform contact with the film.   Roots tend to stick to blotting paper, and the use of glass cloth has therefore been suggested (25).   Overheating should be avoided, since this tends to make the plant material brittle. After drying, the sample should be removed from the original blotting surfaces so as to avoid contamination from any radioactive material exuded during the drying-pressing operation.   The material may be taped down on the fresh blotting paper to minimize movement and covered with Pliofilm or cellophane to protect the emulsion.   Exposure and photographic processing are done as already described.

HISTOLOGICAL SECTIONS [after Fitzgerald et al. (10)]:

1. The tissue is fixed, dehydrated, embedded, sectioned, and mounted on a glass slide "subbed" with albumin-glycerin or gelatin to ensure good adhesion.

2. To prevent chemical effects of tissue on film, the section or emulsion is dipped in 1 per cent Parlodion in amyl acetate, drained, and dried.

3. The section on the glass slide is placed against the emulsion surface of a 1- by 3-in. glass slide.

4. The slides are aligned and held together with a clamp for exposure in a lighttight box at refrigerator temperatures.

5. After exposure, the emulsion is dipped in amyl acetate for 5 min, followed successively by 95 per cent alcohol, 70 per cent alcohol, 50 per cent alcohol, and water in order to remove the Parlodion layer.

6. The film is processed.

7. Embedded tissue is deparaffinized, and the tissue stained.

8. The autogram and section can be examined separately or together under the necessary magnification.

Buie et al. (26) have described a method that permits separation of the tissue and emulsion during photographic processing or staining but still allows alignment of the autogram and section at will for simultaneous observation.   This is accomplished by mounting the tissue section at one end of a plastic, flexible cover slip.   The opposite end is cemented with beeswax and rosin to the emulsion side of a photographic plate.   The plate and section are held together tightly during exposure. Afterward the cover slip can be bent, and the plate then processed without the section coming in contact with the developing and fixing solutions. When the cover slip is released, the section returns to its original position superimposed upon the autoradiogram.

Mounting Method. *Principle.* The sections are mounted on the emulsion and remain permanently bonded thereto throughout the subsequent photographic and staining processes.

Advantages. The methods are relatively simple. The contact, registry, and resolution are good, thus permitting studies on the cellular level. The autoradiogram and section are always in alignment and are observed simultaneously; this allows correlation between structure and photographic image.

Disadvantages. There are possibilities of radioisotope loss during the fixation and processing of the tissue. There may be spotty development on account of nonuniform penetration of the tissue by the developer. The emulsion gelatin tends to absorb the tissue stain, and also the photographic darkening may be masked by the opacity of the tissue. There is the possibility of chemical effects on the emulsion due to direct contact with the tissue. This technique is difficult to use with plastic or celloidin-embedded material.

Recommended Usage. The mounting method has been widely used for I^{131} localization in thyroid tissue. Also, blood smears and bone marrow smears have been studied by applying such samples directly to the surface of the emulsion.

Typical Method. Details of this method were described by Evans (27), Bourne (8), and Heller (7). The following procedure is essentially that used by Gross et al. (5) and is illustrated in Fig. 7-2 [from Fitzgerald et al. (10)]:

1. Unstained paraffin sections are floated on water at 40°C to remove wrinkles. They are then transferred to a bath of distilled water at 18 to 20°C. Under safelight conditions, the photographic film or plate is dipped into the water under the tissue section, a corner of which is held against the plate, and then removed. After drainage of excess water the section adheres to the emulsion. With blood smears or similar specimens, the sample is spread over the surface of the emulsion, and the preparation rapidly dried in air.

2. For exposure, the film is stored at refrigerator temperatures in light-tight boxes containing a drying agent.

3. Prior to development, paraffin is removed by a 1-min treatment in each of two changes of absolute xylol, which is then allowed to evaporate completely since traces may cause photographic darkening; this takes about 15 min. This step is omitted for smears.

4. The film is developed and stained according to one of the procedures outlined in Table 7-2. It is important that heavy staining be avoided on account of uptake by the emulsion.

Evans and McGinn (28) have recently described a modification that gives three images on the same slide: the tissue alone, the composite tissue-autoradiogram, and the autoradiogram alone. This is accomplished by use of two adjacent sections, one of which is inverted on the cover slip and is also used to produce an autoradiogram by apposition, whereas the other is mounted permanently on the emulsion.

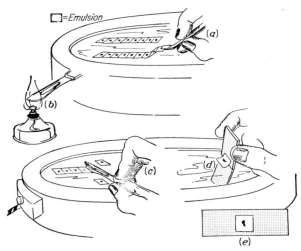

FIG. 7.2. Mounting method. Cut tissue sections are floated on warm water to remove the wrinkles (a), a knife blade heated (b), the sections separated from the ribbon (c), and the sections picked up by placing the plate in the water beneath them (d) to obtain the permanently mounted section shown at (e). [*Courtesy of Patrick J. Fitzgerald, Eva Simmel, Jerry Weinstein, and Cynthia Martin, Radioautography: Theory, Technic, and Applications, Lab. Invest.,* **2:** 181–222 (1953), Paul B. Hoeber, Inc., publisher.]

Coating Method. *Principle.* The section is covered with a fluid emulsion which is allowed to harden and forms a permanent bond for subsequent exposure and processing.

Advantages. Good contact and constant registry are obtained which lead to good resolution and allow good correlation of radioactivity with histological structure, since the photographic image and section are observed simultaneously. A celloidin layer protects the tissue from photographic processing fluids, and in the inversion method the photographic image is protected from staining fluids. The thickness of the fluid emulsion can be somewhat controlled.

Disadvantages. The handling of the emulsion tends to increase the background fog, and the preparation of an emulsion of uniform thickness

is difficult.   There are possibilities of radioisotope loss during any preliminary histological processing and also by solution into the liquid
emulsion.

   Recommended Usage.   Coating autoradiograms have proved satisfactory for cytological studies with bones, teeth, and soft tissues.

   Typical Method.   This procedure was first described by Belanger and
Leblond (29) and represents perhaps the first successful method in which

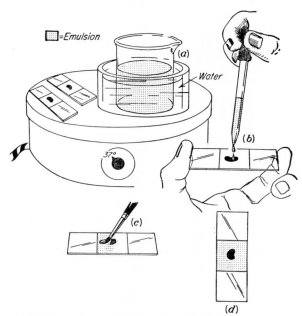

Fɪɢ. 7-3. Coating method.   The gel is maintained at 37°C in a beaker, and the slides
are warmed (*a*); drops of the fluid emulsion are applied to specimen on marked slide
(*b*); the drops are spread evenly (*c*); and the slide is tilted to give even distribution (*d*).
[*Courtesy of Patrick J. Fitzgerald, Eva Simmel, Jerry Weinstein, and Cynthia Martin,
Radioautography: Theory, Technic, and Applications, Lab. Invest.,* **2**: 181–222 (1953),
Paul B. Hoeber, Inc., publisher.]

intimate contact was accomplished between specimen and emulsion.
The following procedure was presented by Gross et al. (5) and is illustrated in Fig. 7-3 [from Fitzgerald et al. (10)]:

   1. Stained or unstained histological sections are coated with celloidin
by dipping twice in a 1 per cent ether alcohol solution.

   2. Ansco autoradiographic emulsion *A* is used, or Eastman Kodak
medium lantern-slide emulsion, which is obtained by soaking the glass
plates for 10 min in distilled water at 19°C and scraping.

   3. The emulsion is placed in a beaker and maintained at 37°C for
15 min.   Improved resolution is obtained by diluting 1 ml of lantern-

slide emulsion with 6 ml of distilled water and 1 ml of a wetting agent (Duponol *C*).

4. The stained slides are warmed to 37°C, and 2 drops of fluid emulsion applied per square inch. The drops are spread evenly and quickly with a camel's-hair brush, and even distribution is accomplished by tilting the slide.

5. The slide is maintained at 37°C for 30 to 60 sec on a level surface and then allowed to cool for 30 min on a level surface.

6. The slides are stored for exposure at refrigerator temperature in a horizontal position in lighttight boxes, which, in turn, are placed in jars containing a drying agent.

7. The preparation is developed in Kodak *D*-72 at 18 to 20°C for $1\frac{1}{2}$ min, fixed in acid fixer for 3 to 6 min, washed for 15 min in water below 20°C, and dehydrated in 95 per cent alcohol, absolute alcohol, alcohol-xylol, and three changes of xylol.

8. The slides are immersed in 1 per cent balsam and mounted in balsam under a cover slip.

Modifications. Belanger (30) has described an inversion procedure that permits staining of the tissue without any interference from the emulsion. In principle, the unstained celloidin-covered section is coated with fluid emulsion in the usual way. After exposure and photographic processing, the preparation is removed from the slide and sealed to a clean slide, with the processed emulsion next to the glass and the tissue surface now available. The tissue can then be stained, and the celloidin protects the emulsion from the staining reagents.

A "wet-process" technique has been proposed by Gomberg (31) which is based on application to the specimen of a celloidin layer containing bromide ions. The specimen is then transferred to a silver nitrate bath, which forms a sensitive layer. The potential of this method arises from the resolution theoretically possible, since the photographic layer is only about 1 μ thick.

Stripping-film Method. *Principle.* An emulsion is stripped from its base and flattened over the histological section or smear on a glass slide. The specimen can be stained either before contact with the film or through the film base after exposure. Unstained sections can be studied by phase microscopy.

Advantages. The procedure is somewhat less tedious than the coating method; offers the advantages of even emulsion thickness, good contact, constant registry, and excellent resolution; and permits good correlation of radioactivity with histological structure. Depending upon the method used, the impervious base emulsion may protect the emulsion from the tissue.

Disadvantages. There are possibilities of radioisotope loss during the wet processing. The sensitivity is relatively low, and the base emulsion may interfere with staining and tend to reduce the resolution.

Recommended Usage. The stripping-film method has proved satisfactory for cytological studies with both plant and animal tissues. Quantitative results at low levels of activity have been made possible by the counting of grains.

Typical Method. The stripping-film technique was described by Pelc (32), and the following is the procedure, as later described by Doniach

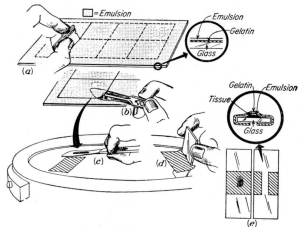

FIG. 7-4. Stripping-film method. The film is cut, as at (*a*); removed, as in (*b*); inverted and floated on water, as shown at (*c*); and picked up on the mounted specimen, as shown at (*d*). The film is draped around the slide to make a tight fit, as in (*e*). [*Courtesy of Patrick J. Fitzgerald, Eva Simmel, Jerry Weinstein, and Cynthia Martin, Radioautography: Theory, Technic, and Applications, Lab. Invest.,* **2**: 181–222 (1953), Paul B. Hoeber, Inc., publisher.]

and Pelc (18) [Fig. 7-4 is a schematic representation from Fitzgerald et al. (10)]:

1. The fresh tissue is placed in absolute alcohol for 8 to 15 hr, then consecutively in fresh absolute alcohol for 1 hr, in benzene for 15 min, and in warm benzene for 15 min; embedded in paraffin; sectioned; and floated on warm water.

2. The sections are picked up on slides that have been previously "subbed" (dipped in an aqueous solution of 1 per cent gelatin and 0.1 per cent chrome alum and dried). The slide and section are drained, blotted, and dried on a hot plate.

3. The preparation is dewaxed with xylene, followed by alcohol and thorough washing in water.

4. Under safelight conditions the emulsion, of appropriate size, is mechanically peeled from the glass plate and floated on water at 20°C, with the side that was formerly in contact with the glass now facing upward; that is, the emulsion side is face downward. After about 2 to 3 min, during which time the emulsion has swelled, the slide carrying the tissue section is slipped under the emulsion, so that the emulsion covers the section and drapes around the slide to make a tight fit. The preparation is dried and set aside for exposure. It has been emphasized that the stripping should be done carefully in a humid atmosphere or underwater to avoid static charges, which fog the film (8, 33). Lotz and Johnston (34) have discussed the advantages in using a strip of emulsion long enough to wrap completely around the breadth of the slide, enabling the ends to overlap at least $\frac{1}{2}$ in.

5. After exposure the preparation is photographically processed and can be stained if desired.

Other Methods. Boyd and Williams (33) and MacDonald et al. (35) have described various techniques for the stripping-film method. It is pointed out that commercial stripping films are available with a 5- to 10-μ emulsion supported by a 5- to 10-μ base, and that the stripping base can be used either to protect the emulsion while staining or to protect the tissue while developing.

APPLICATIONS

It is not feasible to review the numerous individual applications that have been made with autoradiograms in biological studies. Rather, an attempt will be made to indicate and illustrate the main fields of usefulness, with the expectation that the investigator will consider the principles involved in terms of his specific problems. The applications are classified as below in order to emphasize functional aspects. It is recognized that the terminology is arbitrary and that any given study often provides information in several of the categories.

Chemical. Consideration is given to a few chemical applications that are particularly important in biological studies. As discussed in Chap. 2, many radioisotopes under certain conditions tend to form aggregates or so-called *radiocolloids*. The existence of these aggregates in a solution to be administered to a biological system may have a profound effect on the results obtained. The presence of radiocolloids can be readily demonstrated by simple autoradiographs, as discussed by Yagoda (4). Similarly it is possible to study the appearance and disappearance of such aggregates in the blood. Figure 7-5, taken from Gallimore (36), shows the autoradiographic appearance of rat blood at 2 to 10 min and 2 to 24 hr, respectively, after intravenous injection of polonium chloride. This demonstrates that the polonium immediately after injection existed as aggregates, as shown by the sunbursts, and as dispersed atoms or molecules, as shown by the individual alpha tracks.   It is also obvious that the aggregated polonium was selectively and almost completely removed from the blood in about 2 hr.   The autoradiograms were made by apposition of a dried blood smear with alpha-track emulsion (NTA).

As discussed in Chap. 8, autoradiography has been of great value when used in conjunction with paper chromatography.   With these combined

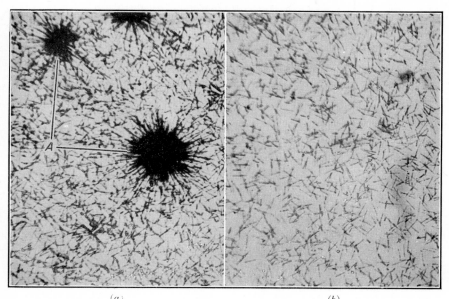

(a)   (b)

Fig. 7-5. (a) Autoradiogram of rat blood at 2 to 10 min after intravenous administration of polonium chloride.   Note sunbursts A, which indicate presence of aggregates. (b) Autoradiogram at 2 to 24 hr after administration.   Note presence of individual alpha tracks only.   (*From John C. Gallimore, Jr., A Radiochemical and Autoradiographic Study of the Distribution of Polonium in Rats after Intravenous Administration, University of Rochester Atomic Energy Project Report UR-220, 1952.*)

techniques it becomes a simple matter to identify various labeled compounds and also to establish the purity of a particular labeled compound before its use in an experiment.   This may be of particular importance in the testing of C^{14}-labeled organic compounds to determine whether or not significant radiation decomposition has occurred.   A classical example of the procedure is the work of Taurog, Chaikoff, and Tong (37), who identified the organic iodine of the plasma as thyroxine.   Figure 7-6a shows the position taken by thyroxine added to the butanol extract of plasma from rats given I^{131}, as determined by spraying with diazotized sulfanilic acid.   Figure 7-6b is the autoradiogram of the filter-paper strip, and the correspondence in position and shape leaves little question as to the identity of the I^{131}-labeled material with the added thyroxine.

The autoradiogram is also of considerable help in the sampling of heterogeneous samples for radioactivity measurements. An idea of the magnitude of this problem may be gained merely from inspection of a Ca^{45} bone autoradiogram (Fig. 7-7), as discussed in the next section.

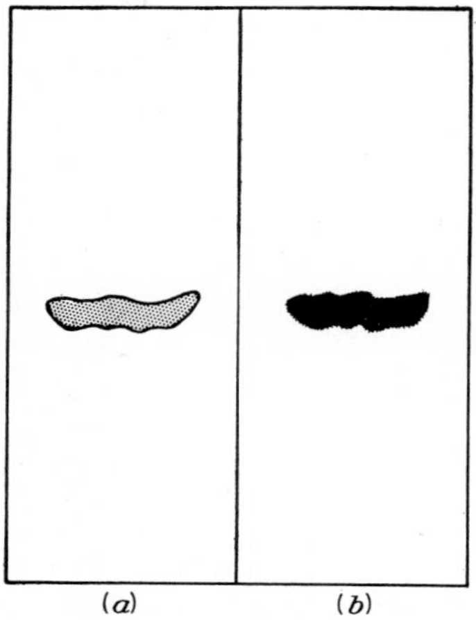

(a)   (b)

FIG. 7-6. (a) Filter-paper chromatogram of butanol extract of plasma containing added thyroxine, with color developed by diazotized sulfanilic acid. (b) Autoradiogram of same chromatogram resulting from I^{131}-labeled substance present in plasma. [*From Alvin Taurog, I. L. Chaikoff, and W. Tong, The Nature of Plasma Iodine as Revealed by Filter Paper Partition Chromatography, J. Biol. Chem.,* **184**: 99–104 (1950).]

Anatomical Relationships. An illustration is presented in Fig. 7-7 of the relationship between the deposition of Ca^{45} in bone and the anatomical structure. The autoradiogram is of a longitudinal section of the metatarsal bone of a 30-day-old calf that had been given orally about 0.5 mc Ca^{45} and sacrificed 7 days later. The autoradiogram was made by the apposition method of Lotz et al. (23), as described earlier. It is noted that the extent and nature of the Ca^{45} deposition is characteristic and is a reflection of the particular bone structure, as follows: *A*, heavy and relatively diffuse deposition occurs below the epiphyseal plate, probably as a result of vascularity and increased blood flow in this region which results in optimum conditions for the exchange of calcium ions between blood and bone crystals. Also, new bone mineral is formed in this region. Note the absence of this characteristic heavy deposition at the other end of this bone, where there is no epiphyseal plate.

B, the subperiosteal accumulation is characterized by a sharp line of deposition which is related to the narrow layer of growth cells and the limited blood circulation that occurs in this region. *C*, the area of endochondral bone growth shows a linear deposition, which, however, is readily distinguished from the periosteal lay-down by its spottiness. *D*, the region of trabecular bone shows a more generalized spotty distribution at a lower intensity than the areas already mentioned. *E*, the compact bone of the shaft shows little or no radioactivity, probably as a result of the poor circulation. It would be necessary to use longer exposure periods if a study of activity in this region were desired.

Figure 7-8 presents a similar autoradiogram except that it is from an older animal. However, the general features are the same. In addition, it is possible to observe the deposition corresponding to the Haversian sys-

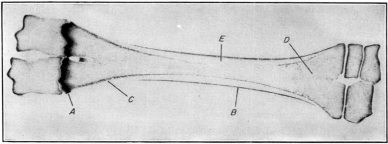

FIG. 7-7. Ca[45] autoradiogram of metatarsus of 1-month-old calf sacrificed 7 days after administration. *A*, heavy deposition below epiphyseal plate; *B*, sharp subperiosteal deposition; *C*, spotty deposition in area of endochondral bone growth; *D*, trabecular bone; *E*, compact bone of shaft.

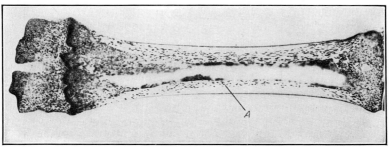

FIG. 7-8. Ca[45] autoradiogram of metatarsus of yearling heifer. Note same general features as in Fig. 7-7. In addition, however, there is deposition in compact bone corresponding to Haversian systems *A*.

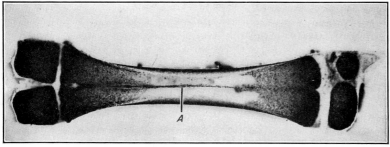

FIG. 7-9. Ca[45] autoradiogram of metatarsus of 8-month bovine fetus taken at 7 days after administration of radioactivity to dam. Note general distribution of radioactivity and indication of residual periosteal function *A*.

tems in the compact bone. Figure 7-9 is an autoradiogram of a metatarsal from an 8-month bovine fetus that was taken at 7 days after administration of Ca[45] to the dam. Of anatomical interest is the line of deposition down the center of the bone which represents residual periosteal function, since this particular bone is being fused from two bones. Also the radioactivity is more generally distributed than in the case of the older animals.

Figure 7-10 presents an autoradiogram of the pyloric region of a 10-day-old rat sacrificed 2 hr after a subcutaneous injection of S^{35} (courtesy of L. F. Belanger). There is considerable deposition of radioactivity all over the pyloric gland A. However, there is little or no deposition over Brunner's glands B. Individual spots over the duodenal villi coincide with the position of the mucous goblet cells C. This autoradiogram

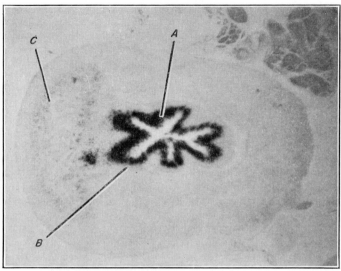

Fig. 7-10. S^{35} autoradiogram ($\times$32) of pyloric region of 10-day-old rat at 2 hr after injection. There was considerable deposition over the pyloric gland A, little or no deposition over Brunner's glands B, and slight deposition over mucous goblet cells C. *(Courtesy of L. F. Belanger. Inverted coating method.)*

($\times$32) was prepared by Belanger's inversion modification of the coating method (30).

Figure 7-11 shows the distribution of C^{14} in the roots of corn seedlings after exposure of the plant to an atmosphere of labeled CO_2 (38). The greatest amount of radioactivity was found in the terminal millimeter, and it can be seen from Fig. 7-11 that the C^{14} was concentrated in the inner cortex A, outer stele B, and the superficial cells C. The path of translocation of the C^{14}-labeled compounds is probably indicated by the dark areas of the more basipetal portions of the root apex D. In this experiment the plants were grown in a bell jar and, after introduction of about 100 μc C^{14}, illuminated for a 24-hr period. The root apices were embedded in paraffin and sectioned longitudinally at 8 to 10 μ using standard histological techniques. The sections were mounted onto NTB_2 plates and exposed for 5 to 8 days. After exposure the paraffin was

removed with xylene, and the slides hydrated, photographically processed, and stained with Delafield's hematoxylin.

Metabolic. *Translocation.* Figure 7-12 shows the translocation pattern of Fe⁵⁵ injected into the stem of the peanut plant (courtesy of
D. Davis). The site of injection is indicated by A. The stem above and
below the region of injection was cut so that as much plant material as

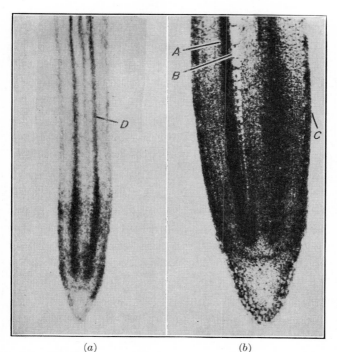

(a)   (b)

Fig. 7-11. Median longitudinal section of terminal millimeter of a root [(×50) (a),
(×80) (b)]. Note concentration of C¹⁴ in the inner cortex A, outer stele B, and
superficial cells C. Probable path of translocation is indicated by D. [*From G. S.
Rabideau and Leo W. Mericle, The Distribution of C¹⁴ in the Root and Shoot Apices of
Young Corn Plants, Plant Physiol.*, **28**: 329–333 (1953).]

possible could be placed on the film. As shown by B, the leaves, petioles,
and stem below the site of injection exhibited little darkening, thus indicating that there had been relatively slight downward movement of the
Fe⁵⁵. It will be noted from the stem above the site of injection (C, D)
that considerably more translocation occurred along the left-hand side of
the stem. This undoubtedly resulted from the mechanics of injection
and is also reflected in the fact that the leaves on the left showed higher
concentrations than those on the right. It was also noted that the petiole
bearing leaves E showed a higher concentration on the left; this was

reflected in the fact that one-half of the terminal leaf had a lower deposition of the radioisotope.

Figure 7-13 is a P^{32} autoradiogram of roots of the barley plant illustrating the different abilities of different parts of the root to absorb and translocate phosphate [courtesy of H. Wiebe (25)]. In the plant on the left the P^{32} was applied several centimeters back of the root tip, as indicated by A, and there was considerable translocation to other parts of the plant.

FIG. 7-12. Translocation pattern of Fe^{55} injected into stem of peanut plant. A, site of injection; B, little activity below site of injection; C, D, more translocation occurring on left-hand side of stem; E, one-half of terminal leaf and leaf on right-hand side of petiole showing lower concentrations than F.

Also note the tendency for selective accumulation at the root tip B. In the plant on the right the same amount of P^{32} was applied at the root tip C, and it is clear that much less of the radioisotope was transported to other parts of the plant than when the P^{32} was applied some distance back.

Bone Growth and Development. A clarification of the process of bone growth was made possible by the autoradiographic studies of Leblond et al. (39) using P^{32} in rats. Similar studies using Ca^{45} with swine were reported by Comar et al. (40, 41). Figure 7-14 illustrates some of the findings. It can be shown from these autoradiograms and from many

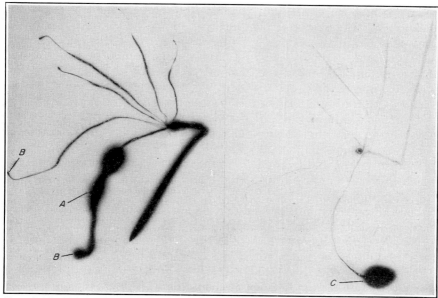

FIG. 7-13. P³² autoradiogram of barley roots. *A*, when P³² was applied several centimeters back of root tip, there was considerable translocation; *B*, note selective accumulation at root tip; *C*, when same amount of P³² was applied at root tip, less activity was transported to other parts of plant than when application was made at position *A*. (*Courtesy of H. Wiebe.*)

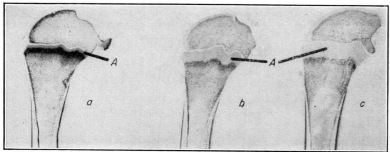

FIG. 7-14. Measurement of bone growth by Ca⁴⁵ autoradiograms. *A* represents low concentration of radioactivity in bone formed between time of Ca⁴⁵ dosage and sacrifice. (*a*) Distal end of femur of pig *A* grew 2.1 mm in 10 days. (*b*) In a comparative study, the corresponding growth of bone of pig *B*, on a low dietary intake, was 7.9 mm in 45 days, whereas (*c*) the growth for pig *C*, on a high dietary intake, was 10.0 mm in 45 days.

other similar studies that, once Ca⁴⁵ is deposited in bone, it tends to stay in its original location and that new bone formed has a much lower concentration of radioactivity (note region *A*). Thus it becomes easy to visualize the growth that has occurred between the time of administration of the radioactivity and the sacrifice of the animal. Quantitative estimates of bone growth are possible from measurement of the auto-radiogram. Thus, for example, the distal end of the femur of pig A on a controlled diet grew 2.1 mm in 10 days. That of animal B, on a low dietary intake, grew 7.9 mm in a 45-day experimental period, whereas the corresponding part of the bone of pig C, on a high dietary intake, grew 10.0 mm in the 45-day period. The growth of other regions of the bone can be readily measured in the same manner.

This type of information is also of practical importance from the health-physics standpoint in studying the removal of various bone seekers from bone (41). In general, it can be stated that the removal of isotopes such as radiostrontium and radiocalcium primarily depends upon the region in which they were originally deposited and upon the growth of the bone. Referring to the various regions as denoted in Fig. 7-7, numerous studies of bone autoradiograms have led to the following conclusions: (a) Activity deposited directly below the epiphyseal plate will not be removed until by bone growth it becomes located in the trabecular region where resorption is taking place and removal is relatively rapid. (b) Subperiosteal deposition will not be removed until by bone growth the activity becomes located in the endosteal portion of the shaft. (c) Activity deposited in the region of endochondral growth is apparently not significantly removed by the growth or resorption process. (d) Resorption is taking place continually in the trabecular regions, and activity deposited here is relatively rapidly removed.

Cellular Biosynthesis. Howard and Pelc (42) have described experiments that demonstrate the time of synthesis of desoxyribonucleic acid (DNA) in relation to the mitotic cycle. This procedure, in contrast to Geiger counting methods, allowed study of specific cells from among many. The method was based on resolution adequate to distinguish activity in single cells or cell parts, and on removal of all radioactivity from the cell except that which was in the compound of interest. Roots of *Vicia faba* seedlings were grown in water containing about 0.2 μc/ml of P^{32} and 16 mg/liter of carrier phosphate. After treatment of 2 to 48 hr the roots were fixed in alcohol–acetic acid and put on slides for the preparation of autoradiograms by the stripping-film method. Experiment showed that DNA was probably the only P^{32}-containing compound left by this treatment. Further evidence was the fact that no autoradiogram was obtained when the section was treated with a solution of desoxyribonuclease. It was shown that in the meristem of *Vicia faba* the synthesis of DNA occurs during interphase and that about 6 hr elapses between the end of synthesis and the beginning of visible prophase. Similar studies were carried out using S^{35}-labeled sodium sulfate at 1 μc/ml. Since the pretreatment of the section was expected to remove all inorganic and acid-soluble sulfur, it was reasoned that the autoradiograms were due to the S^{35} in the form of nucleoprotein which had been synthesized in the time between treatment with radioactivity and sampling. Figure 7-15 shows a phase-contrast photomicrograph and an autoradiogram of the same section which demonstrates the typical localization of S^{35} in the chromosomes.

Leblond et al. (43) have also studied in rats the histological localization of newly formed desoxyribonucleic acid that was found in tissues where cell divisions are numerous. P^{32} was used, and all the phosphorus com-

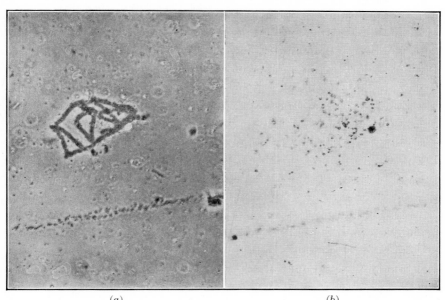

(a) (b)

FIG. 7-15. Autoradiographic appearance of S^{35} over a group of chromosomes from a root cell. (a) Phase-contrast microphotograph. (b) Autoradiogram of same field. [*Courtesy of S. R. Pelc and A. Howard, Brit. Med. Bull.*, **8**: 132–135 (1952).]

pounds except desoxyribonucleic acid were removed by the fixing and staining procedures plus treatment with ribonuclease. Taylor (44) has also detected the incorporation of P^{32} into individual nuclei. The data suggested that the period of P^{32} incorporation corresponded to the time of chromosome reproduction and that desoxyribonucleic acid constituted a permanent framework of the chromosome. Lily anthers and *Tradescantia* were used as experimental material, and perchloric acid was employed for differential extraction of the phosphorus compounds from the cell.

Figure 7-16 presents a phase photograph and autoradiogram of a cell of the gastric caecum of *Drosophila* fixed 1½ hr after feeding on food containing P^{32} (45). This autoradiogram was prepared by fixation of the

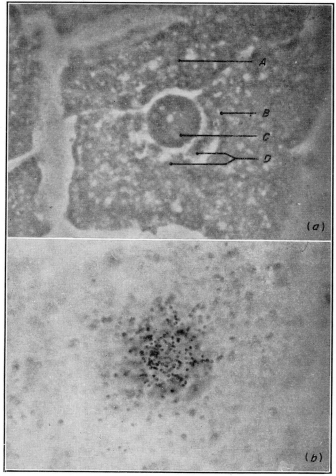

FIG. 7-16. Autoradiogram (×1220) of cell of gastric caecum fixed 1½ hr after feeding of *Drosophila* on P³². (a) Phase photograph of cell, indicating *A*, cytoplasm; *B*, nuclear membrane; *C*, nucleolus; *D*, chromatin. (b) Distribution of silver grains above same cell. [*From J. Herbert Taylor, Intracellular Localization of Labeled Nucleic Acid Determined with Autoradiographs, Science,* **118**: 555–557 (1953).]

larvae in Carnoy's fluid, embedding in paraffin, sectioning at 7 μ, and washing in hot ether alcohol, lower grades of alcohol, cold 5 per cent trichloroacetic acid, and water, followed by the usual stripping-film procedure. By study of similar sections that were treated with ribonuclease, it was possible to show the most of the P³² found within the nucleolus, cytoplasm, and chromatin of the cell was probably present in the ribonucleic acids. At early periods after exposure of the larvae to labeled food, the highest concentrations of P³² were observed in the nucleolus and chromatin. It was postulated that the nucleolus may be a center of RNA synthesis or a reservoir of RNA produced in other parts of the nucleus, possibly the chromatin. Similar studies have been described by Taylor and Taylor (46).

Embryonic Development. Autoradiography has been of especial advantage in the study of embryology, primarily on account of the difficulty of

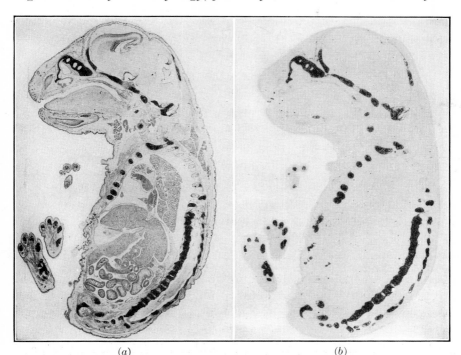

(a)   (b)

Fig. 7-17. Autoradiographic appearance of S³⁵ in the 20-day-old rat embryo. (a) Stained section. (b) Autoradiogram showing selective deposition in cartilage. [*From Dominic D. Dziewiatkowski, Sulfate-Sulfur Metabolism in the Rat Fetus as Indicated by Sulfur-35, J. Exptl. Med.,* **93**: 119–128 (1953).]

precise dissection of newly developed organs and their small mass. Figure 7-17 shows a stained section and S³⁵ autoradiogram of a 20-day-old rat embryo, as reported by Dziewiatkowski (47). It is clear from the autoradiogram that there was considerably more deposition in the skeleton than in other tissues and that the cartilage showed a higher concentration than did the calcified or calcifying regions. The embryo was fixed for 6 days at 25°C in 3.7 per cent formaldehyde, dehydrated in upgraded concentrations of ethanol, cleared in xylol, and embedded in paraffin, and sections were cut at 7 μ. The sections were mounted on microscopic slides with egg albumin, treated with xylol, and then placed in contact with the film for exposure.   After the photographic processing, the sections were stained with toluidine blue.   Other studies of embryonic development utilizing autoradiography include S^{35} in the rabbit fetus (48), I^{131} in the chick (49, 50), I^{131} in the hamster (51), P^{32} in the frog (52), and Cu^{64} in the chick (53).   Radioiodine studies have been particularly helpful in

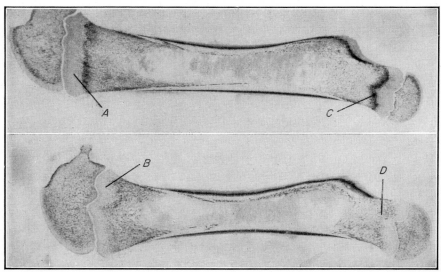

Fig. 7-18. Effect of fluorine on bone growth and Ca^{45} deposition.   *A*, growth of distal end of femur was 7.9 mm in control pig.   *B*, comparative value was 5.0 mm in fluorine-treated pig.   *C*, line of subepiphyseal deposition in control.   *D*, note absence of original line of subepiphyseal lay-down in bone of fluorine-treated pig.   [*From C. L. Comar, W. J. Visek, W. E. Lotz, and John H. Rust, Effects of Fluorine on Calcium Metabolism and Bone Growth in Pigs, Am. J. Anat.,* **92**: 361–389 (1953).]

determination of the beginning of thyroid function in the frog, rat, and mouse (7).

Dysfunction.   Figure 7-18 illustrates the use of Ca^{45} bone autoradiograms to show the effects in pigs of high dietary fluorine, as reported by Comar et al. (40).   The two animals, about 135 days of age, were pair-fed and thus consumed the same amount of feed except that the ration of the treated pig contained about 1000 ppm fluorine.   These animals were sacrificed 45 days after intravenous administration of 0.5 mc Ca^{45} per 100 lb body weight.   The autoradiograms are of the femur and were made by the method of Lotz et al. (23), as previously described.   It may first be noted that the new growth of the distal end in the 45-day period was 7.9 mm for the control as compared with 5.0 mm for the treated animal. It is also noted that the original line of epiphyseal deposition is not present in the bone of the treated pig.   Numerous similar autoradiograms confirmed these findings and, along with histological evidence, led to the hypothesis that the fluorine probably caused an increased rate of bone resorption in the primary and secondary *spongiosa*, in addition to causing a retardation of bone growth by an effect manifested in the region of hypertrophied cartilage cells.

There are numerous examples in the literature of the use of autoradiographic methods for the study of various pathologic conditions, particularly thyroid neoplasms (54). Some specific applications are as follows: P^{32}, S^{35}, and C^{14} in callus culture of *Sequoia sempervirens* (55); absorption of S^{35} by fungus-infected leaves (56); localization of C^{14}-labeled tobacco

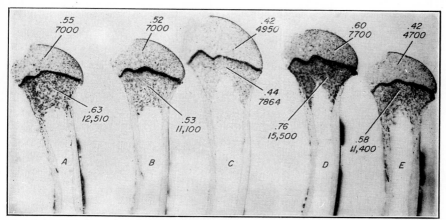

FIG. 7-19. Relation of optical densities (values less than 1) and concentrations of Ca^{45} (expressed as counts per minute), as determined by radioassay in comparable areas of sheep femurs. (*Courtesy of W. E. Lotz.*)

mosaic virus antigen (57); P^{32} in tooth cavities (58); P^{32} in cerebral tumors (59); S^{35} in chondrosarcomas (60).

Quantitative Aspects. In general, the greater the concentration of a radioisotope in a tissue, the greater will be the blackening of the emulsion exposed to it. However, the difficulties in obtaining accurate measurement of radioactivity from autoradiograms have been formidable indeed, primarily on account of the inherent variables. Lotz (61) has had reasonable success in correlating the optical densities of gross bone autograms, obtained by use of a densitometer, with radiochemical assays of the same region. It was necessary to expose the samples on the same piece of film and to compare only the same anatomical regions. Figure 7-19 presents a series of Ca^{45} autoradiograms from sheep that had received different hormone treatment. The values given in the illustration represent the optical density and the counts per minute of Ca^{45}, as measured with a Geiger counter on a sample taken from the region used for den-

sitometric measurement.   Statistical analysis of these data indicated that
there was a correlation between radioassay and densitometric measurement significant at the 1 per cent level.   The agreement between bones
is such as to give greater confidence in densitometric comparison than in
radioassay.   This results from the difficulty of sampling regions containing narrow lines of deposition.   Similar studies have been reported by
Dudley and Dobyns (62), particularly in connection with the estimation
of radiation dosage to tissue.

Track and Grain Counting.   At high magnifications it becomes necessary to count tracks or grains for estimation of photographic density.
This can be accomplished by the use of a micrometer placed in the ocular
to outline a given area.   Some of the photographic and technical considerations have been discussed in references (4 to 6, 8, 10, 11, 18).   In general, the stripping-film method is best for quantitative autoradiography,
since the emulsion thickness and the distance between specimen and emulsion are constant and reproducible.   The coating method, however, has
also been used satisfactorily.   Nuclear emulsions should be employed on
account of the regularity of the grains.   If the number of grains is sufficiently low to be counted, their number is proportional to the amount of
radioactivity in the specimen.   Also, since grain counting is tedious at
best, exposure and development should be controlled so as to produce low
grain concentrations.   Doniach and Pelc (18) have found a count of 10
grains/100 μ^2 above background to be statistically significant.   This provides a real advantage in reducing the amount of radioactivity and/or
exposure time required, as compared with methods based on densitometric
or photometric measurements.

Alpha particles give well-defined tracks in nuclear emulsions, in which
case each track may serve to identify a single disintegrating atom.
Miller and Hoecker (63) have described methods for quantitative estimation of alpha emitters in bone by observation of the numbers of tracks
produced.   Special emulsions are now available which can be used to show
tracks of beta particles, as illustrated by the studies of Boyd and Levi (64)
on C^{14} appearance in the liver of rats injected with C^{14}-labeled glycine.
By varying the focus of the microscope, it is possible to trace a track to
its origin at the surface of the emulsion.

Perhaps of more importance than absolute quantitation is the fact that
grain- or track-counting procedures provide excellent resolution and permit the objective estimation of fine differences in intensity between adjacent cells or parts of cells.   Johnston (65) has described grain-counting
procedures used for localization of P^{32} in the intracellular zones of the
columnar absorbing cell of the rat.   Histological and stripping-film techniques were employed, as described earlier, with every effort to obtain
maximum resolution.   Grain counts were made over a standard area of

100 μ^2 using an ocular micrometer calibrated to 4 μ^2.   Grain counts were made of the emulsion over the *muscularis*, the lumen of the gut, and the nuclear and supranuclear zones of selected epithelial cells.   Table 7-3 presents typical data.   It is clear that the grain density over both the nuclear and supranuclear regions was higher than over the lumen or muscle; the counts over the latter were little, if any, higher than the emulsion background.   Comparison of the autoradiograms and specially treated sections indicated that at least some of the activity in the supra-nuclear zone was probably incorporated in the Golgi apparatus.

TABLE 7-3. GRAIN COUNTS OVER 100-μ^2 AREAS OF EPITHELIAL CELLS FROM RAT GIVEN P^{32}

Slide No.	Mean ± standard deviation of 20 areas				
	Emulsion	Lumen	Muscle	Nuclear	Supranuclear
1	2.1 ± 1.6	2.1 ± 2.2	3.6 ± 2.2	15.0 ± 4.1	23.8 ± 3.8
2	2.4 ± 1.2	6.4 ± 3.0	7.3 ± 2.6	24.7 ± 7.9	37.3 ± 7.9

[From Perry Max Johnston, The Localization of P^{32} in the Supranuclear Zone of the Columnar Absorbing Cell of the White Rat, *J. Morphol.*, **95**: 77–93 (1954).]

INTERPRETATION

In recapitulation, a listing follows of possible sources of error in auto-radiograms, all of which should be kept in mind when one translates the black specks of the photographic image into meaningful information:

1. Removal or relocation of the radioactive atoms by biological or physical processes during the time between sampling and formation of the photographic image

2. Extraneous sources of image production, such as chemically active substances in the specimen; pressure on the emulsion; radioactivity in the films, chemicals, or glass used in processing; and stray light or ionizing radiation

3. Fading of the latent image or desensitization of the emulsion by the specimen

4. Nonuniform development

5. Scratches in the film, deposition of debris

6. Effects of staining solution on the emulsion

7. Movement of sample on film during exposure

An example of artifacts commonly encountered is presented in Fig. 7-20, which represents a stripping-film autoradiogram of cartilage of a 9-day chick embryo that received Ca^{45} at the start of hatching.   The straight lines *A* were probably caused by scratches on the emulsion; the fact that all these grains appear in the same plane of focus is suspicious. Darkening due to debris *B* or to bubbles or dust particles *C* can usually be recognized by the characteristic appearance. In this autoradiogram there seemed to be a greater concentration of grains over the intercellular

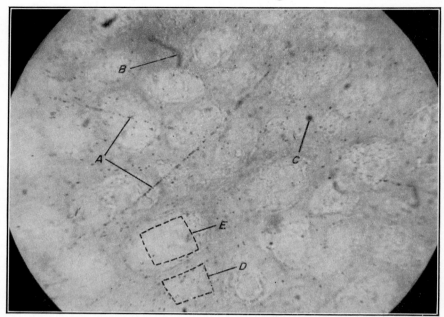

Fig. 7-20. Artifacts in Ca⁴⁵ autoradiogram of cartilage of 9-day chick embryo. *A*, straight lines probably caused by scratch on emulsion; *B*, darkening probably due to debris; *C*, dark spot probably due to bubble or dust particle. Note greater concentration of grains over intercellular matrix *D* than over chondriocytes *E*. (*Courtesy of P. M. Johnston.*)

matrix *D* than over the chondriocytes *E*. When the autoradiographic localization does not conform to some anatomical or physiological pattern, then one should strongly consider the possibility of artifacts.

Many of the uncertainties have been eliminated in the procedures that have been described. However, it is always wise in making a series of autoradiograms to include similar samples with no radioactivity as a control for errors that may tend to produce extraneous images. With gross samples, it is sometimes possible to dissect out regions corresponding to different areas of darkening and measure the radioactivity.

GENERAL REFERENCES

1. Guyer, Michael F.: "Animal Micrology," University of Chicago Press, Chicago, 1930.
2. Glick, David: "Techniques of Histo- and Cytochemistry," Interscience Publishers, Inc., New York, 1949.

3. McClung, Ruth Jones, ed.: "McClung's Handbook of Microscopical Technique," Paul B. Hoeber, Inc., New York, 1950.
4. Yagoda, Herman: "Radioactive Measurements with Nuclear Emulsions," John Wiley & Sons, Inc., New York, 1949.
5. Gross, J., R. Bogoroch, N. J. Nadler, and C. P. Leblond: The Theory and Methods of the Radioautographic Localization of Radioelements in Tissues, *Am. J. Roentgenol. Radium Therapy*, **65**: 420–458 (1951).
6. Leblond, C. P., and J. Gross: Autoradiography as a Tool in Medical Research, in Paul F. Hahn, ed., "A Manual of Artificial Radioisotope Therapy," pp. 250–273, Academic Press, Inc., New York, 1951.
7. Heller, Dorothy Axelrod: The Radioautographic Technique, *Advances in Biol. and Med. Phys.*, **2**: 133–170 (1951).
8. Bourne, Geoffrey H.: Autoradiography, *Biol. Rev. Cambridge Phil. Soc.*, **27**: 108–131 (1952).
9. Fitzgerald, Patrick J.: Radioautography in Cancer, *Cancer*, **5**: 165–194 (1952).
10. Fitzgerald, Patrick J., Eva Simmel, Jerry Weinstein, and Cynthia Martin: Radioautography: Theory, Technic, and Applications, *Lab. Invest.*, **2**: 181–222 (1953).
11. Herz, R. H.: Photographic Fundamentals of Autoradiography, *Nucleonics*, **9**: 24–39 (1951).
11a. Nadler, N. J.: Quantitative Estimation of Radioactive Isotopes by Radioautography, *Am. J. Roentgenol. Radium Therapy Nuclear Med.*, **70**: 814–823 (1953).

CITED REFERENCES

12. Boyd, George A., and Francis A. Board: A Preliminary Report on Histochemography, *Science*, **110**: 586–588 (1949).
13. Everett, Newton B., and Barbara S. Simmons: Observations on the Histochemical Reduction of Photographic Emulsion in Radioautography, *Anat. Record*, **117**: 25–36 (1953).
14. Williams, Agnes I.: Method for Prevention of Leaching and Fogging in Autoradiographs, *Nucleonics*, **8**: 10–14 (1951).
15. Holt, Margaret W., and Shields Warren: Radioautographic Solubility Studies of I^{131} and P^{32} in Frozen-Dehydrated Tissues, *Proc. Soc. Exptl. Biol. Med.*, **76**: 4–9 (1951).
16. Blank, Harvey, Philip L. McCarthy, and Edward D. DeLamater: A Non-vacuum Freezing-Dehydrating Technic for Histology, Autoradiography and Microbial Cytology, *Stain Technol.*, **26**: 193–197 (1951).
17. Howard, Alma, and S. R. Pelc: P^{32} Autoradiographs of Mouse Testis, *Brit. J. Radiol.*, **23**: 634–641 (1950).
18. Doniach, I., and S. R. Pelc: Autoradiograph Technique, *Brit. J. Radiol.*, **23**: 184–192 (1950).
19. Holt, Margaret W., Russell F. Cowing, and Shields Warren: Preparation of Radioautographs of Tissues without Loss of Water-soluble P^{32}, *Science*, **110**: 328–329 (1949).
20. Witten, Victor H., and Vera Holmstrom: New Histologic Technics for Autoradiography, *Lab. Invest.*, **2**: 368–375 (1953).
21. Holt, Margaret W., and Shields Warren: Freeze-drying Tissues for Autoradiographic Study, *Lab. Invest.*, **2**: 1–14 (1953).
21a. Arnold, James S., David H. Taysum, and Webster S. S. Jee: Apparatus for Bone Sectioning, *Stain Technol.*, **29**: 55–58 (1954).
21b. Arnold, James S.: A Method for Embedding Undecalcified Bone for Histologic Sectioning, and Its Application to Radioautography, *Science*, **114**: 178–180 (1951).

22. Roofe, Paul G., Frank E. Hoecker, and Carroll D. Voorhees: A Rapid Bone Sectioning Technic, *Proc. Soc. Exptl. Biol. Med.*, **72**: 619–622 (1949).

23. Lotz, W. E., J. C. Gallimore, and George A. Boyd: How to Get Good Gross Autoradiographs, *Nucleonics*, **10**: 28–31 (1952).

24. Myers, Howard M., Elizabeth Jennings, and Hermann Becks: A Rapid Radio-autographic Technique for Combined Calcified and Soft Tissues, *J. Dental Research*, **31**: 416–420 (1952).

25. Wiebe, Herman: Personal communication.

26. Buie, Dan H., Frank E. Hoecker, and Paul G. Roofe: A Constant Registry Autoradiographic Technic, *Proc. Soc. Exptl. Biol. Med.*, **75**: 747–749 (1950).

27. Evans, T. C.: Radioautographs in Which the Tissue Is Mounted Directly on the Photographic Plate, *Proc. Soc. Exptl. Biol. Med.*, **64**: 313–315 (1947).

28. Evans, Titus C., and Walter E. McGinn, Jr.: A Method of Preparing Radio-autographs with Adjacent Sections, *Cancer Research*, **13**: 661–665 (1953).

29. Belanger, L. F., and C. P. Leblond: A Method for Locating Radioactive Elements in Tissues by Covering Histological Sections with a Photographic Emulsion, *Endocrinology*, **39**: 8–13 (1946).

30. Belanger, Leonard F.: A Method for Routine Detection of Radiophosphates and Other Radioactive Compounds in Tissues. The Inverted Autograph, *Anat. Record*, **107**: 149–160 (1950).

31. Gomberg, Henry J.: A New High-resolution System of Autoradiography, *Nucleonics*, **9**: 28–43 (1951).

32. Pelc, S. R.: Autoradiographic Technique, *Nature*, **160**: 749–750 (1947).

33. Boyd, George A., and Agnes I. Williams: Stripping Film Technics for Histological Autoradiographs, *Proc. Soc. Exptl. Biol. Med.*, **69**: 225–232 (1948).

34. Lotz, W. E., and P. M. Johnston: Preparation of Microautoradiographs with the Use of Stripping Film, *Nucleonics*, **11**: 54 (1953).

35. MacDonald, A. M., J. Cobb, A. K. Solomon, and D. Steinberg: Stripping Film Technic for Radioautographs, *Proc. Soc. Exptl. Biol. Med.*, **72**: 117–121 (1949).

36. Gallimore, John C., Jr.: A Radiochemical and Autoradiographic Study of the Distribution of Polonium in Rats after Intravenous Administration, University of Rochester Atomic Energy Project Report UR-220, 1952.

37. Taurog, Alvin, I. L. Chaikoff, and W. Tong: The Nature of Plasma Iodine as Revealed by Filter Paper Partition Chromatography, *J. Biol. Chem.*, **184**: 99–104 (1950).

38. Rabideau, G. S., and Leo W. Mericle: The Distribution of C^{14} in the Root and Shoot Apices of Young Corn Plants, *Plant Physiol.*, **28**: 329–333 (1953).

39. Leblond, C. P., G. W. Wilkinson, L. F. Belanger, and J. Robichon: Radioauto-graphic Visualization of Bone Formation in the Rat, *Am. J. Anat.*, **86**: 289–341 (1950).

40. Comar, C. L., W. J. Visek, W. E. Lotz, and John H. Rust: Effects of Fluorine on Calcium Metabolism and Bone Growth in Pigs, *Am. J. Anat.*, **92**: 361–389 (1953).

41. Comar, C. L., W. E. Lotz, and G. A. Boyd: Autoradiographic Studies of Calcium, Phosphorus and Strontium Distribution in the Bones of the Growing Pig, *Am. J. Anat.*, **90**: 113–129 (1952).

42. Howard, Alma, and S. R. Pelc: Synthesis of Deoxyribose Nucleic Acid and Nuclear Incorporation of S^{35} as Shown by Autoradiographs, in G. E. W. Wolstenholme, ed., "Ciba Foundation Conference on Isotopes in Biochemistry," pp. 138–151, J. and A. Churchill, Ltd., London, 1951.

43. Leblond, C. P., C. E. Stevens, and R. Bogoroch: Histological Localization of Newly-formed Desoxyribonucleic Acid, *Science*, **108**: 531–533 (1948).

44. Taylor, J. H.: Autoradiographic Detection of Incorporation of P[32] into Chromosomes during Meiosis and Mitosis, *Exptl. Cell Research*, **4**: 164–173 (1953).
45. Taylor, J. Herbert: Intracellular Localization of Labeled Nucleic Acid Determined with Autoradiographs, *Science*, **118**: 555–557 (1953).
46. Taylor, J. Herbert, and Shirley H. Taylor: The Autoradiograph—A Tool for Cytogeneticists, *J. Heredity*, **44**: 128–132 (1953).
47. Dziewiatkowski, Dominic D.: Sulfate-Sulfur Metabolism in the Rat Fetus as Indicated by Sulfur-35, *J. Exptl. Med.*, **98**: 119–128 (1953).
48. Bostrom, Harry, and Erik Odeblad: Autoradiographic Observations on the Incorporation of S[35]-labeled Sodium Sulfate in the Rabbit Fetus, *Anat. Record*, **115**: 505–513 (1953).
49. Hansborough, Louis A., and Mustapha Khan: The Initial Function of the Chick Thyroid Gland with the Use of Radioiodine (I[131]), *J. Exptl. Zool.*, **116**: 447–454 (1951).
50. Wollman, Seymour H., and Edgar Zwilling: Radioiodine Metabolism in the Chick Embryo, *Endocrinology*, **52**: 526–535 (1953).
51. Hansborough, Louis A., and Hagalyn Seay: Accumulation of Radioiodine (I[131]) in Thyroid Gland of the Hamster Embryo, *Proc. Soc. Exptl. Biol. Med.*, **78**: 481–483 (1951).
52. Hansborough, Louis A., and David Denny: Distribution of Phosphorus[32] in the Embryo and Larva of the Frog, *Proc. Soc. Exptl. Biol. Med.*, **78**: 437–441 (1951).
53. Smith, Ellen E., and Peter Gray: The Distribution of Copper[64] in Early Embryo Chicks, *J. Exptl. Zool.*, **107**: 183–216 (1948).
54. Fitzgerald, Patrick, and Frank W. Foote: The Function of Various Types of Thyroid Carcinoma as Revealed by the Radioautographic Demonstration of Radioactive Iodine (I[131]), *J. Clin. Endocrinol.*, **9**: 1153–1170 (1949).
55. Ball, Ernest: Studies of the Accumulation of Certain Radioisotopes by a Callus Culture, *Am. J. Botany*, **40**: 306–316 (1953).
56. Yarwood, C. E., and Louis Jacobson: Selective Absorption of Sulphur-35 by Fungus-infected Leaves, *Nature*, **165**: 973 (1950).
57. Gavosto, F., and A. Ficq: Radioautographic Study of the Localization of Tobacco Mosaic Virus Antigen, *Nature*, **172**: 406–407 (1953).
58. Martin, Noel D., and E. S. Slater: Direct Tissue Radioautography Technique Applied to Teeth, *Science*, **113**: 721–722 (1951).
59. Steinberg, Daniel and Bertram Selverstone: Radioautography of Cerebral Tumors Employing P[32], *Proc. Soc. Exptl. Biol. Med.*, **74**: 304–308 (1950).
60. Gottschalk, Raymond G., and Herbert C. Allen, Jr.: Uptake of Radioactive Sulfur by Chondrosarcomas in Man, *Proc. Soc. Exptl. Biol. Med.*, **80**: 334–339 (1952).
61. Lotz, W. E.: Personal communication.
62. Dudley, Robert A., and Brown M. Dobyns: The Use of Autoradiographs in the Quantitative Determination of Radiation Dosages from Ca[45] in Bone, *Science*, **109**: 327–328 (1949).
63. Miller, Bruce L., and Frank E. Hoecker: Quantitation of Alpha Emitters in Bone, *Nucleonics*, **8**: 44–52 (1951).
64. Boyd, George A., and Hilde Levi: Carbon 14 Beta Track Autoradiography, *Science*, **111**: 58–59 (1950).
65. Johnston, Perry Max: The Localization of P[32] in the Supranuclear Zone of the Columnar Absorbing Cell of the White Rat, *J. Morphol.*, **95**: 77–93 (1954).

CHAPTER 8

PAPER CHROMATOGRAPHY

GENERAL METHODS—Chromatograph Chamber; Filter Paper; Application of Sample; Solvents; Detection of Spots; Quantitative Aspects: *Color comparison; Determination of spot area; Elution;* Use of an Electrical Field. ORGANIC SEPARATIONS. INORGANIC SEPARATIONS. APPLICATIONS.

The development of chromatography, a process destined to have wide application, is generally credited to the botanist M. S. Tswett, who used the method in 1906 for the separation of plant pigments. However, it has been pointed out that perhaps others in the field of petroleum chemistry had preceded him (1). The method is essentially a countercurrent distribution process in which the substances to be separated become distributed between a solvent and solid phase. The general procedure, which is exceedingly simple, consists in passing the solution to be analyzed through a column of adsorbent, thus bringing the substances into contact with the solid interface at which they concentrate. As the substances are moved down the column with the addition of solvent, the more weakly adsorbed ones will move faster, thereby effecting the separation. This method is variously called *chromatography, Tswett-column analysis, chromatographic adsorption analysis,* or *differential countercurrent adsorption analysis.* The general references may be consulted for details of technique and application (2 to 6, 10a). Also in the early 1900's, Goppelsroeder devised a separation procedure called *capillary analysis* which was based on the use of filter paper and was actually the forerunner of present-day paper partition chromatography.

The term *partition chromatography* is now used to designate methods of separation based upon the distribution of substances between two liquid phases, one of which is mobile and the other essentially fixed to a support by sorption. In an early application of this principle, Martin and Synge (11) separated acetylated amino acids by use of silica gel to hold the fixed liquid phase, water. A most important development was the modification of this procedure by Consden, Gordon, and Martin (12) in which the silica gel was replaced by filter paper as the inert support. Thus the process of paper partition chromatography, or, more simply, paper chromatography, became recognized as a practical and invaluable analytical tool for the biochemist.

In essence, the procedure is carried out by the application of a small drop of test solution a short distance from one end of a strip of filter paper. After the drop has dried, this end of the strip is placed in an appropriate solvent so that the latter moves past the spot by capillary action and along the paper. This results in a differential movement of the components of the test solution along the paper. The solvent usually consists of a stationary aqueous phase which has a strong affinity for the filter paper, and an organic or mobile phase which tends to move along the paper. As the mixed solvent flows through the section of paper containing the test substances, the latter are distributed between the organic phase, which is moving rapidly ahead, and the stationary aqueous phase. After completion of the separation, the individual zones or spots are identified by color reactions, radioactivity, or other methods.

The potentialities of paper chromatography, especially when used in conjunction with radioisotopes, are so vast that the worker in biochemistry can ill afford not to have these techniques at hand. It is first noted that, as a separation procedure, paper chromatography, on account of its countercurrent nature, is highly efficient as compared with batch procedures. The sensitivity is high, the detection of the spots usually being the limiting factor; this is precisely where radioisotope techniques may offer considerable advantage. Another important feature is that the procedure is simple and rapid, requiring no equipment except filter paper, chemicals, and glassware, all of which are to be found in the usual laboratory. This is in contrast to other chemical separation procedures such as fractional crystallization or distillation. Also the latter procedures can be used only with substances that can be crystallized or distilled, and they often require elevated temperatures, which may degrade the test substance. Large numbers of samples can be analyzed by paper chromatography even with limited facilities. Williams (9), for example, reports that his laboratory averaged about 700 analyses each working day for over a year, an output that would have been prohibitive by other methods.

The primary usefulness of paper chromatography lies in the following: (a) separation of mixtures into their constituents, (b) demonstration of homogeneity of chemical substances, (c) demonstration of identity of substances, and (d) quantitative or qualitative estimation of one or more substances present in a mixture. The method has become of particular value because a great many important biochemical compounds occur in nature as complex mixtures of substances of similar properties and structure and are therefore most difficult to resolve by other means.

The general references may be consulted for a discussion of the theory of chromatographic separations (4, 7, 8). At the present time, however, the practice is primarily based upon arbitrary experimental conditions. The resolution of substances, although chiefly dependent upon partition between solvents, may also be affected by surface adsorption and ion exchange. Attention is called to the widely used constant R_f, which is defined as follows:

$$R_f = \frac{\text{movement of band}}{\text{movement of advancing front of liquid}} \tag{8-1}$$

R_f is easily determined in paper chromatograms. Absolute values of R_f have little meaning, since they are dependent upon solvent composition, temperature, pH, presence of salts, and other factors. The primary use of a listing of R_f values, determined under similar conditions, is to indicate whether or not the separation of a given mixture is possible; or, if there are data for several solvents, the listing permits a choice of the most suitable solvent.

GENERAL METHODS

Chromatograph Chamber. The primary requirement is a mechanical arrangement that permits one end of a filter-paper strip or sheet to be immersed in the solvent. It is also necessary to keep the atmosphere saturated at all times with the solvent, since otherwise the capillary flow would cease because of evaporation. Apparently it makes little difference whether the solvent ascends, descends, or does both, as described by Block et al. (8). Commercial chambers are available, as well as auxiliary items such as solvent troughs and paper racks. However, homemade equipment may serve equally well. Figure 8-1 illustrates a simple assembly that has been found satisfactory for strips. An ordinary glass cylinder is placed within a cylindrical jar which can be covered with a glass plate to make a reasonable seal. A clear glass pipette washer or hydrometer jar with a flanged neck is satisfactory for the cylindrical jar. A histological staining dish is placed on top of the inner cylinder, as shown, to hold the solvent, and the paper strips are held in place, with an end submerged in the solvent, by means of microscope slides (13). This arrangement provides for a descending flow of solvent. However, the ascending technique can be employed with a simple modification in which the inner cylinder is not used and the strips are supported from a rack attached to the cover plate, with the bottom of the strip dipping into the solvent.

Figure 8-2 illustrates a simple cabinet in which sheets can be used. It is necessary only to have a box large enough to accommodate the size of paper to be used, with some device for holding the sheets. With this apparatus, solvent troughs about 30 in. long are supported on the cleats near the top of the box. The inside of the box is lined with glass plates, and the inside exposed wooden surfaces are paraffined to resist the action of solvents.   The box must be reasonably vaportight when closed.   Fish aquarium tanks can be readily adapted for this purpose (8).   Datta et al. (14) have described a convenient frame for processing up to 12 sheets

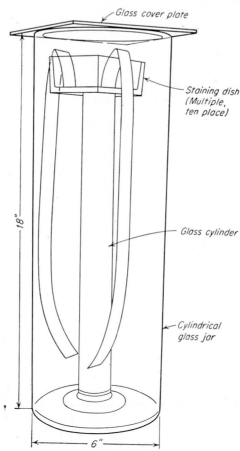

Glass cover plate

Staining dish
(Multiple,
ten place)

Glass cylinder

Cylindrical
glass jar

18"

6"

Fig. 8-1. Simple assembly for development of paper-strip chromatograms with descending solvent flow. [*From W. Joe Frierson and John W. Jones, Radioactive Tracers in Paper Partition Chromatography of Inorganic Ions, Anal. Chem.,* **23**: 1447–1452 (1951).]

simultaneously.   The frame consists of two duralumin plates which are connected by four removable rods, one at each corner; the plates are of the same dimensions as the sheets to be used.   The sheets of filter paper are threaded onto the rods, with a 2-cm collar placed on the rods between each sheet to keep the papers apart.   In this case, a tray containing the solvent is placed at the bottom of the box, and the frame plus filter paper stands

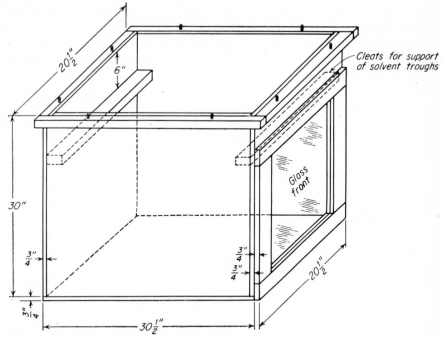

Fig. 8-2. Homemade plywood cabinet for development of filter-paper sheets in two-dimensional chromatography (cover is not shown).

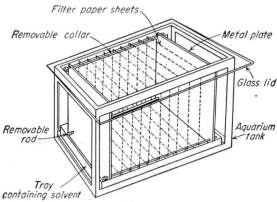

Fig. 8-3. Schematic diagram of assembly in which filter-paper sheets are supported on frame which stands in tray containing solvent. [*From S. P. Datta, C. E. Dent, and H. Harris, An Apparatus for the Simultaneous Production of Many Two-dimensional Paper Chromatograms, Science,* **112**: 621–623 (1950).]

in it without the need of any special support.   This arrangement is shown schematically in Fig. 8-3.

When sheets are used, *two-dimensional chromatograms* can be made. This is done by application of the sample at one corner of the sheet and development with solvent in the same way as in the strip or one-dimensional method.   After development, the sheet is turned at right angles so that the separated spots can be resolved further by use of a second solvent.   As a practical matter, it is most convenient to use two chambers for two-dimensional work, one for each solvent.   Winteringham (15) has

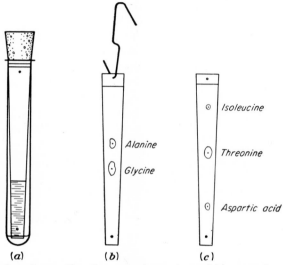

Fig. 8-4. Procedure for small-scale paper-chromatographic separations.   [*From Louis B. Rockland and Max S. Dunn, A Capillary-ascent Test Tube Method for Separating Amino Acids by Filter Paper Chromatography, Science,* **109**: 539–540 (1949).]

described a method by means of which the individual zones separated by the first solvent can be concentrated by controlled evaporation and transferred to a fresh strip of paper, which can then be treated for further separation with another solvent.   This procedure permits *multidimensional* chromatography provided the zones can be identified, as by radioisotopes, without degradation of the separated components.

A simple procedure for small-scale separations has been described by Rockland and Dunn (16) and is illustrated in Fig. 8-4.   About 0.4 ml of solvent is pipetted into the bottom of a 6-in. test tube.   A filter-paper strip is cut so as to be 13.6 cm long, 1.8 cm wide at one end, and 1.0 cm wide at the other.   The test substance is applied at about 6 mm from the narrow end, and the paper is dried and then placed in the test tube so that the strip does not touch the walls except at the upper end. The tube is then stoppered with a cork for development of the chromatogram.

Various procedures have been described for carrying out paper chromatography so as to permit isolation of larger quantities than by ordinary methods (17 to 20). Other modifications include the use of impregnated filter paper, which gives a "reversed-phase" chromatogram in which the less polar solvent is the stationary phase (8, 21). A *gradient-elution* analysis has also been reported in which a continuously changing solvent is employed (22).

Filter Paper. There are numerous commercial filter papers that are satisfactory for chromatographic separations. The best paper for any given experimental requirements and conditions would have to be determined by trial. The results of Rockland et al. (23), who rated 13 different papers as to suitability for the separation of amino acid mixtures, may be used as a guide in the initial selection. Table 8-1 presents a listing of the papers tested in approximate decreasing order of suitability. In addition, Kowkabany and Cassidy (24) have reported satisfactory results with the following: Whatman 3, Schleicher and Schuell 595, Whatman 4, Schleicher and Schuell 589 black, Whatman 2, and Schleicher and Schuell 589 white.

TABLE 8-1. FILTER-PAPER CHARACTERISTICS (IN APPROXIMATE DECREASING ORDER OF SUITABILITY)

Type	Texture	Uniformity[a]	Solvent speed[b]
Schleicher and Schuell 589	Medium rough	A	260
Schleicher and Schuell 507	Smooth	A	240
Schleicher and Schuell 589 red	Medium rough	A	180
Schleicher and Schuell 602 E and D	Medium rough	A	270
Whatman 1	Medium rough	B	190
Schleicher and Schuell 602	Medium rough	A	280
Schleicher and Schuell 576	Smooth	A	280
Munktells 0	Rough	B	60
Schleicher and Schuell 598 YD	Medium rough	A	100
Eaton and Dikeman 7	Medium rough	C	120
Munktells IF	Very rough	B	80
Eaton and Dikeman 248	Very rough	B	240
Eaton and Dikeman 613	Very rough	A	180

[a] Based on percentage of transmittance as determined photoelectrically. Mean deviation from mean values: A, less than 1 per cent; B, 1 to 2 per cent; C, more than 2 per cent.

[b] Minutes required at 26°C for water-saturated phenol to ascend 120 mm on trapezoidal filter-paper strips.

[From Louis B. Rockland, Jeremiah L. Blatt, and Max S. Dunn, Small Scale Filter Paper Chromatography, *Anal. Chem.*, **23**: 1142–1146 (1951).]

Application of Sample.   The application of the sample to the paper is quite simple and yet may be tedious when large numbers of chromatograms are involved.   Usually 5-μl pipettes are employed.   If it is necessary to use larger amounts of solution, the paper should be dried after each 5-μl application.   Larger pipettes may be used if the sample can be continuously dried in a current of warm air.   If the initial spot is too large (greater than about 1-cm diameter), the chromatogram tends to be diffuse and indefinite.   Williams (9) has described a method for the stacking of filter-paper sheets between supports in echelon which facilitates the application of the sample.

Solvents.   Numerous solvent mixtures have been employed for specific separations, and an indication of usage is presented later in the tabular summaries.   In most solvent mixtures the water is used to saturate the organic solvent, and only the saturated organic phase is used on the chromatogram.   The following is a description of some of the more widely used solvents, as reported by Williams (9):

Phenol solvent: 100 g phenol (Mallinckrodt, analytical grade) saturated with an aqueous solution containing 6.3 per cent sodium citrate and 3.7 per cent sodium (or potassium) dihydrogen phosphate.   About 20 ml of the aqueous solution is required to saturate the phenol.   The salts serve a dual purpose: they inhibit the diffusion of the spots on urine chromatograms, and they prevent the migration of a contaminant in the paper which otherwise obscures the lower half of the chromatogram.

Butanol–acetic acid solvent: 80 ml *n*-butanol, 20 ml glacial acetic acid, and 20 ml water.   This solvent must be freshly prepared for each determination.

Butanol-ethanol solvent: 80 ml *n*-butanol, 20 ml of 95 per cent ethanol, and 20 ml water.

Isobutyric acid solvent: 80 ml isobutyric acid and 20 ml water.

Lutidine solvent: 65 ml 2,6-lutidine and 35 ml water.   Lutidine is preferred to collidine because of the greater uniformity of the commercially available product.

Collidine-lutidine solvent: 33 ml of the fraction of mixed collidines boiling between 158 and 165°C, 50 ml 2,6-lutidine, and 17 ml water.

Pyridine-butanol solvent: 80 ml pyridine, 20 ml *n*-butanol, and 20 ml water.

Butanol-pyridine solvent: 50 ml *n*-butanol, 50 ml pyridine, and 20 ml water.

Butanol-ethanol-ammonia solvent: 80 ml *n*-butanol, 10 ml of 95 per cent ethanol, and 30 ml concentrated ammonium hydroxide.

Ethanol solvent: 100 ml of 95 per cent ethanol.

Methanol solvent: 95 ml absolute methanol and 5 ml water.

Pyridine solvent: 65 ml pyridine and 35 ml water.

Ethanol–acetic acid solvent: 95 ml of 95 per cent ethanol and 5 ml glacial acetic acid. This solvent must be freshly prepared before each determination.

Ethanol-ammonia solvent: 95 ml of 95 per cent ethanol and 5 ml concentrated ammonium hydroxide.

Butanol–ethylene glycol–hydrochloric acid solvent: 80 ml *n*-butanol, 20 ml ethylene glycol, and 20 ml of 0.1 *N* hydrochloric acid.

Phenol–acetic acid solvent: Same as phenol solvent except that glacial acetic acid is employed in a separate container within the chromatograph chamber to maintain an acid atmosphere.   This solvent is useful in separating acidic substances.

Phenol-ammonia solvent: Same as phenol solvent except that concentrated ammonium hydroxide is employed as above to maintain an alkaline atmosphere. After 24 hr a pink discoloration is detectable in the solvent mixture, and the solution must be discarded. This solvent is useful in separating basic substances.

Butanol–ethanol–hydrochloric acid solvent: 80 ml *n*-butanol, 20 ml of 95 per cent ethanol, and 40 ml of 2 *N* hydrochloric acid. This solvent is especially useful in the determination of cystine and histidine.

Ethanol–hydrochloric acid solvent: 80 ml of 95 per cent ethanol and 20 ml of 0.1 *N* hydrochloric acid. This solvent has been used exclusively in the determination of sodium and potassium.

Isobutyric acid–acetic acid solvent: 80 ml isobutyric acid, 20 ml glacial acetic acid, and 20 ml water. This solvent has been used for the resolution of certain unidentified urinary constituents.

Detection of Spots. If radioactive materials are being studied, then the spots may be readily detected by counting procedures or autoradiograms. Descriptions have been presented of various automatic scanning devices based on measurements of radioactivity (13, 25 to 27). These devices are based upon a method of moving the paper strip slowly past a Geiger tube, with the counts being automatically recorded on a chart which can be matched against the chromatogram. Figure 8-5 shows such an arrangement, as developed by Frierson and Jones (13); this type of assembly is also available commercially. Some substances may be detected by virtue of their color or fluorescence. However, in general, it is necessary to use a reagent that reacts with the substances being separated to produce a visible color. If possible, the reagent should be applied in alcoholic solution, since this permits rapid drying and minimizes the spreading of spots. Usually the reagent is applied by light spraying. Following is a description of some of the commonly used color-developing reagents, as employed by Williams (9), particularly in the analysis of urine:

FIG. 8-5. Assembly for scanning of paper strips. The strip is attached to the chart of a recording Brown potentiometer and is fed past a collimated Geiger tube. The pulses are fed to a count-rate meter which operates the recorder. [*From W. Joe Frierson and John W. Jones, Radioactive Tracers in Paper Partition Chromatography of Inorganic Ions, Anal. Chem., 23: 1447–1452 (1951).*]

Alizarin-ammonia reagent: Chromatograms are sprayed with a 0.1 per cent solution of alizarin in 95 per cent ethanol and then exposed to ammonia vapor. The reagent, tightly stoppered, is stable indefinitely. Calcium and sodium salts of weak acids appear as blue to purple spots against a lavender background. Acid areas appear as yellow immediately; the background fades to yellow on standing. All these substances can be detected in amounts as low as 5 μg.

Aniline acid phthalate reagent: To 100 ml of water-saturated *n*-butanol are added 1.66 g phthalic acid and 0.93 g aniline. The reagent is stable for 2 to 3 months at room temperature. On sheets sprayed with this reagent and heated 5 min at 100°C, aldopentoses appear as red spots and hexoses as green to brown spots.

Azide-iodine reagent: Fifty milliliters of a 0.1 *N* iodine solution (aqueous solution prepared using potassium iodide to effect solution) is added to 50 ml of 95 per cent ethanol, and 1.5 g sodium azide is dissolved in this solution. If kept tightly stoppered in brown bottles, this reagent is stable indefinitely. This reagent is particularly useful for the detection of sulfur-containing amino acids. Methionine, cystine, and cysteine decolorize the reagent immediately, appearing as white areas against a brown background. After an hour these spots show considerable fluorescence under ultraviolet light. These amino acids may be detected in concentrations of about 5 μg or more. Spots must be marked soon after development, because within a few hours the background fades to give a uniformly colored sheet. Rose and yellow spots due to unidentified constituents appear on urine chromatograms.

Bromine reagent: Liquid bromine (0.5 ml) is added to 50 ml glacial acetic acid and 50 ml water. This reagent is stable for 2 or 3 weeks if kept in the refrigerator. After the chromatograms are sprayed with this mixture, they are heated in an oven at 90°C for 3 to 5 min. Histidine may be detected by this procedure in amounts of 25 μg or more. On exposing the damp sheet to ammonia vapor, the brown histidine spot becomes purple, and the sensitivity is increased so that 10 μg becomes visible. The histidine spot does not fade. In addition to histidine, a number of unidentified urinary constituents show up with this reagent as pink, brown, and green spots. Some of these spots show a bright yellow fluorescence under ultraviolet light as well. Their ability to fluoresce decreases after several days.

Bromocresol green indicator reagent: This reagent is a typical acid-base indicator and, as such, can be used to detect acidic or basic substances on the chromatogram. A 0.04 per cent solution in 95 per cent ethanol is employed. Before using the solution, the color should be adjusted to blue-green with dilute sodium hydroxide solution. The indicator solution is stable indefinitely. Chromatograms developed in acidic or basic solvents must, of course, be thoroughly dried before spraying. Acids give yellow spots against a blue-green background, and bases show intensification of the blue basic color. Acidic areas on urine chromatograms correspond to chloride, sulfate, phosphate, citrate, lactate, and hippuric acid. Urea appears as a slightly basic spot, and the weak acid alkali gives a strong basic spot. Some metal ions, e.g., lead and copper, give a bright pink color with this indicator. The colors developed are affected by acidic or basic substances in the atmosphere but are otherwise quite stable.

2,6-Dichlorophenolindophenol reagent: A 0.4 per cent solution of 2,6-dichlorophenolindophenol in ethanol is sprayed on the chromatograms. The reagent is stable indefinitely. This reagent acts as an acid-base indicator as well as an oxidation-reduction indicator. Initially the background is blue, with acidic areas appearing as pink spots. The most conspicuous spot in urine is chloride (pink). The weak-acid alkali spot appears as a darker blue area. Although amino acids do not appear as acidic or basic substances, they become apparent as completely bleached areas in 1 hr to several days, depending on the concentration present. Ascorbic acid causes almost immediate bleaching. Creatinine and creatine appear as bleached areas in about 45 min. Lactic and hippuric acids, as well as chloride at fairly high concentrations, cause slow bleaching. Urea may appear as a blue area at high concentrations. The bleached areas remain unchanged indefinitely, although the background changes from blue to pink in 48 to 72 hr, necessitating the marking of the acid areas before this change occurs. Most of the substances mentioned above are detectable in amounts above about 5 μg.

2,6-*Dichloroquinonechloroimide reagent:* The reagent is prepared as a 1 per cent solution of 2,6-dichloroquinonechloroimide in 95 per cent ethanol. When stored in the refrigerator, the reagent is stable for 2 to 3 weeks. On sheets sprayed with this reagent, alkaline areas appear as blue spots, uric acid as a yellow spot, and creatinine as a brown spot. On standing several hours, certain unidentified substances in urine appear as brown, pink, and red spots on the chromatogram. Contact with phenolic substances must be strictly avoided, and sheets that have been sprayed with DCC should be kept apart from those developed with other reagents because of interaction between this reagent and others, especially sulfanilic acid, the ferricyanide-nitroprusside reagent, and p-dimethylaminobenzaldehyde.

p-Dimethylaminobenzaldehyde reagent: p-Dimethylaminobenzaldehyde (2.0 g) is dissolved in 100 ml of 1.2 N hydrochloric acid. Storage in a refrigerator will keep this reagent 3 to 5 days without deterioration. Urea and allantoin give bright yellow spots against a white background. The colors do not fade on drying or standing. The minimum concentration of urea that is detectable is 5 to 10 μg.

Ferric chloride reagent: A 1 per cent aqueous solution of ferric chloride is employed. The reagent may be kept for 7 to 10 days in a refrigerator. Sheets must be sprayed lightly to avoid streaking. Spots appear most clearly after the sheet has dried except in the case of tartaric acid, which is visible as a yellow spot only on the wet sheet. Phosphate and sulfate produce white areas against a light yellow background. Amounts of phosphate and sulfate greater than 10 to 20 μg can be detected. Urea appears as a pale area slightly lighter than the background and can be detected only in fairly high concentrations (30 μg). Basic areas are light brown, presumably on account of precipitation of ferric hydroxide. Phenol derivatives produce green to purple spots. Aspirin appears in urine chromatograms as an intense purple spot. As little as 0.5 μg salicylic acid or acetyl salicylic acid can be detected.

Ferricyanide-nitroprusside reagent (alkaline): Equal volumes of 10 per cent sodium hydroxide, 10 per cent sodium nitroprusside, and 10 per cent potassium ferricyanide solutions are mixed. The mixture is diluted with three volumes of water. After standing for about 20 min, the initial dark color changes to a pale yellow, and the reagent is ready for use. This reagent is quite unstable at room temperature but may be kept for 2 to 3 weeks in the refrigerator without deterioration. Creatinine, guanidine, glycocyamine, and arginine give rise to orange colors against a light yellow background. Creatinine gives a blue color. Certain other nitrogenous compounds also respond to the reagent. The colors are stable over long periods, provided precautions are taken to exclude phenol vapors during development and contact with phenolic substances afterward, since these cause marked color changes on the chromatograms.

Hydrolytic reagent: Following the procedure outlined for the picric acid reagent as described below but omitting the picric acid spray, a pink color is developed with indole and a gray color with tryptamine. In addition, several unknown urinary constituents give pink, blue, and green colors.

Lead cobaltinitrite reagent: Lead nitrate (11.5 g) and 15 g sodium nitrite are dissolved in a small amount of water. When these are completely dissolved, 10 g cobalt nitrate is added, and the solution diluted to 100 ml with water. This solution is allowed to stand for at least 1 hr before filtering to remove the orange-brown precipitate. A 1:2 dilution of the filtrate is prepared immediately before spraying. The reagent is stable for 1 to 2 days at room temperature. Contact with the vapor of the reagent while spraying should be avoided. Potassium and ammonium ions produce brown spots against a light yellow background.

Mercuric nitrate–ammonium sulfide reagent: Chromatograms are dipped into a 0.25 *M* solution of mercuric nitrate in 0.5 *N* nitric acid and then heated for 10 min at 80°C. They are next washed by dipping in 0.5 *N* nitric acid and then in water. After having dried at room temperature, the sheets are dipped in a solution of one part ammonium sulfide (reagent strength) and four parts water. Purines and pyrimidines give black spots against a white to gray background. The minimum amount detectable is from 5 to 10 μg. The spots are permanent.

α-Naphthol-hypochlorite reagent: Chromatograms are first sprayed with a 0.1 per cent solution of α-naphthol in 1 *N* sodium hydroxide. The α-naphthol reagent may be used for as long as 1 to 2 months. After having been dried, the sheets are sprayed with a solution consisting of one volume of Clorox diluted with one volume of water or ethanol. Urea appears as a blue-green spot. Arginine appears as a red spot against a white background but fades rapidly. Arginine is detected only at levels above 10 μg.

Naphthoresorcinol reagent: To 90 ml of 2 per cent trichloroacetic acid is added 0.100 g naphthoresorcinol dissolved in 10 ml of 95 per cent ethanol. The reagent must be prepared immediately before use. The sheets, after having been sprayed, are heated 10 min at 85 to 90°C. Hexoses produce blue and brown colors.

Naphthylethylenediamine reagent: Chromatograms are sprayed with a mixture of equal volumes of 0.5 per cent sodium nitrite and 0.5 *N* sulfuric acid. After drying, the sheets are sprayed with a 0.1 per cent solution of *N*-1-naphthylethylenediamine hydrochloride. This reagent is useful in detecting diazotizable amines. No such compounds were observed in a large number of urine chromatograms.

Ninhydrin reagent: This reagent consists of a 0.2 per cent solution of ninhydrin (triketohydrindene hydrate) in water-saturated *n*-butanol. The reagent, if kept tightly stoppered in a brown bottle, may be used for as long as 1 month. After having been sprayed, the sheets are heated for 5 to 7 min at 90°C to promote color development. Most amino acids react to give purple spots, although there are notable exceptions. Phenylalanine, tyrosine, and aspartic acid give blue colors; tryptophan, olive-brown; asparagine, brown; proline, yellow. The reagent is not specific for amino acids; certain amines, ethanolamine, peptides, ephedrine, etc., give colors. As little as 0.2 μg of certain amino acids may be detected. The presence of high salt concentrations may cause rapid fading of the colors and may even prevent color development entirely. The presence of strong acids in the atmosphere or on the chromatograms (as with the butanol-ethanol-hydrochloric acid solvent) causes reddening of the usual purple color and promotes rapid fading.

Orcinol reagent: To prepare the reagent, 0.1 g orcinol in 10 ml of 95 per cent ethanol is added to 90 ml of 2 *N* hydrochloric acid containing 0.01 per cent ferric chloride. The reagent should be prepared immediately before use. The sheets are sprayed and heated 10 min at 85 to 95°C. Pentoses produce green spots. Heating must be carefully controlled to prevent destruction of the paper by the strong acid.

Phenol-hypochlorite reagent: Chromatograms are first sprayed with 5 per cent phenol in 95 per cent ethanol. After having been dried, the sheets are sprayed with 5.25 per cent sodium hypochlorite (Clorox). Colors develop immediately. The background darkens on standing. This reagent reveals a number of common urinary constituents. Urea, at concentrations above about 5.0 μg, appears as a yellow-green spot. Chloride, at concentrations as low as 1.0 μg, produces a blue spot. Basic cations produce yellow areas. Most amino acids at high concentration (25 μg) produce blue or green colors. Arginine, however, yields orange; cystine and cysteine, brown; and tryptophan, pink.

If urea alone is to be measured, preliminary spraying of the resolved chromatograms with 1 *N* sodium hydroxide solution prevents the color development of other urinary constituents. For chromatograms resolved in a phenol solvent, the preliminary spraying with phenol may be ignored.   In this case the amount of phenol remaining on the chromatogram must be controlled by rather careful partial drying for 8 min ($\pm$ 30 sec) at 90°C.   The sheets must be sprayed immediately after this drying.

Picric acid reagent: Chromatograms are sprayed with 0.5 N sulfuric acid and heated for 1 hr at 100°C.   They are then sprayed with a 1.3 per cent solution of picric acid in 95 per cent ethanol, which is combined immediately before use with one-fifth its volume of 10 per cent sodium hydroxide.   Creatine and creatinine appear as orange spots against a yellow background.   Allantoin gives a faint orange spot.   A number of other urinary constituents cause a slight fading of the yellow background color. The colors developed for creatinine and creatine are permanent.   As little as 0.2 μg is detectable.   If creatinine alone is to be determined, the preliminary hydrolytic treatment with sulfuric acid may be omitted.

Silver nitrate reagent (ammoniacal): Equal volumes of 0.1 N silver nitrate and 5 N ammonium hydroxide are mixed immediately before use.   Chromatograms may be sprayed with or dipped into the reagent.   It is advisable that the sprayer be washed immediately after use several times with 5 N ammonium hydroxide, followed by washing with water to prevent clogging by deposition of silver and insoluble silver salts.   Uric acid develops almost immediately as a black spot against a white background.   For further development the sheet should be heated for 10 min at 100°C, thus darkening the background to light brown.   Carbohydrates then appear as dark brown spots.   Chloride and phosphate produce bleached areas on the paper.   The weak-acid alkaline area produces a spot slightly darker brown than the background, but at high concentrations (50 to 100 μg sodium acetate) this may also appear as a bleached area.   Most of the amino acids cause a slow bleaching of the background color to white or yellow.   The bleaching effect of the amino acids appears to be different from the immediate bleaching of inorganic ions.   The latter seems to be due to simple interference with the contact of the reagent with the paper.   As little as 0.2 μg uric acid and 0.5 μg glucose can be detected using this reagent.   The amino acids can be seen only at concentrations of 30 to 50 μg; chloride and phosphate are detectable at 5 to 10 μg.   The chromatogram becomes very dark after standing for several days, and the originally darkened areas can no longer be detected.   This reagent cannot be used for the color development of chromatograms that have been developed in solvents containing phenol unless the phenol is previously removed by drying the sheet for at least 48 hr at room temperature.

Sulfanilic acid reagent (diazotized): Sulfanilic acid (4.5 g) is dissolved in 45 ml of 12 N hydrochloric acid with warming, and the solution is diluted to 500 ml with water. A 100-ml aliquot of this dilute solution is chilled in an ice bath, and 100 ml of a 4.5 per cent solution of sodium nitrite is added.   This mixture is allowed to stand for 15 min in the ice bath.   This reagent may be kept in the refrigerator without deterioration for 1 to 3 days.   Immediately before use an aliquot of this solution is mixed with an equal volume of a 10 per cent solution of sodium carbonate.   This reagent is particularly useful in the determination of histidine and a number of unidentified substances present in urine.   Pink, red, orange, and purple spots are developed against a light yellow background.   The colors are stable, but contact with vapors of phenol, collidine, or lutidine causes darkening of the background.   The minimum concentration of histidine detectable is about 0.2 μg.   This is a general reagent for phenols and may be used to detect thyroxine and its analogues.

Zinc uranyl acetate reagent: Uranyl acetate (5.0 g) is mixed with 3 ml of warm 30 per cent acetic acid, and the mixture diluted to 25 ml.   A second solution is prepared, consisting of 15 g zinc acetate mixed with 3 ml of 30 per cent acetic acid and diluted to 25 ml.   The two solutions are mixed and warmed gently.   Sodium chloride (0.1 g) is added to the warm solution, and the reagent allowed to stand for 24 hr. It is then filtered and is ready for use. This reagent is stable indefinitely. It is used exclusively for the determination of sodium.

Quantitative Aspects. Numerous methods have been suggested for the quantitative estimation of substances separated on the paper chromatogram. Again, where radioactive materials are involved, the estimation of amounts of substance present is greatly simplified. Advantage may be taken of isotope-dilution procedures (see Chap. 1) to avoid the time and trouble necessary for complete separations.

Color Comparison. Since the intensity of the color varies with the quantity of material present, it is possible to make estimations by visual comparison with known samples chromatographed in exactly the same way as the unknown. Difficulties arise on account of (*a*) lack of contrast between spot and background, (*b*) necessity of using an amount in the concentration range in which the visible gradation of color will be a function of concentration, and (*c*) interfering substances that may be present in the sample and not in the standard. The success of this method will be primarily dependent upon standardization of experimental conditions.

Various modifications have been employed using densitometers or colorimeters in an effort to determine the total color of the spot or the maximum color density and to relate these empirically to standard solutions (8). Commercial equipment is now available specifically designed for this purpose.

Determination of Spot Area. It has been shown that usually the logarithm of the area of a spot is a linear function of the concentration (8). The area can be experimentally determined by use of a planimeter or by cutting out the spot and weighing the paper. The area method is usually less sensitive than the color-comparison method but is less affected by experimental variables. It can be used only where the boundaries are distinct, and in any event standards are required.

Elution. Of most general application, perhaps, is the procedure of cutting out the spot of the chromatogram containing the separated material, and analyzing it by the appropriate method. The limiting factor will usually be the sensitivity of the analytical method.

Use of an Electrical Field. The differential migration of solutes due to application of an electrical current also provides a means for resolution of mixtures (10b). Haugaard and Kroner (28) combined the chromatographic and electrophoretic procedures to increase the degree of separation of basic and acidic amino acids. The chromatogram was developed with phenol in the usual way, the electrical potential being applied at right angles to the direction of solvent flow. This procedure allows separation of substances under conditions in which either the migrations due to electrical current or the R_f values are different. An excellent review of this method has been compiled by Strain and Sullivan (29). Sato et al. (30) have presented a detailed discussion of an apparatus used in the separation of calcium and phosphate ions, and also of the various factors that influence the separation. Of particular interest is the equipment now commercially available that operates on the continuous-flow principle. Some advantages are as follows: (a) relatively large amounts of materials can be separated, (b) difficulties due to absorption by the filter paper are minimized, (c) the choice of solvent or background electrolyte is not as critical as in conventional paper electrophoresis, and (d)

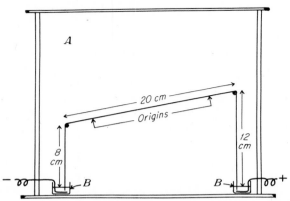

FIG. 8-6. Paper-electrophoresis apparatus. A is a covered glass cylinder, and B indicates containers for buffer solution into which carbon or nichrome electrodes are placed. The paper strip is supported on two glass rods. [From D. B. Zilversmit and S. L. Hood, The Use of Blood Serum as Buffer for Paper-electrophoretic Studies of Radioactive Yttrium, Proc. Soc. Exptl. Biol. Med., **84**: 573–576 (1953).]

no cutting up or elution of paper is required, since the fractions are collected off drip points.

Considerable application has been made of the technique in which paper electrophoresis is utilized without chromatographic separation. Equipment is now commercially available. Durrum (31) has described a method suitable for the separation of amino acids, peptides, or proteins and has discussed many of the factors involved. Jermyn and Thomas (32) have presented considerations in regard to the problem of liquid flow in paper electrophoresis. Gordon et al. (33) described a simplified paper electrophoresis apparatus that was used to identify the protein associated with thyroxine. Zilversmit and Hood (34) reported the use of this procedure to study the state of injected yttrium 91 in blood. The apparatus employed was similar to that of Gordon et al. and is illustrated in Fig. 8-6. Evaporation of water from the strips was minimized, although not prevented, by covering the walls of the outer container with moist filter paper. The filter-paper strips were moistened with the buffer to be used; then 5 to 10 μl of sample was applied in a spot at a marked position on the strip. A potential of 5 volts/cm was employed. Most workers have used barbiturate (veronal) buffer of pH about 8.5 for the separation of plasma proteins. However, Zilversmit and Hood (34) have pointed out that such buffers may cause artifacts and should be employed with caution. It was shown that blood plasma itself may be used as a buffer to avoid these possible alterations.

Paper electrophoresis has been utilized for studies of sugars (35), serum and body fluids (36 to 38), and lipids (39).

ORGANIC SEPARATIONS

Table 8-2 presents a summary of paper-chromatographic procedures that have been used for various groups of organic substances. This table has been compiled primarily from general references (8, 10a), which should be consulted for additional details. A similar compilation has been presented by Williams (9). The listing is primarily by major groups of compounds and is presented to indicate the scope of the method.

INORGANIC SEPARATIONS

Tables 8-3 and 8-4 present a summary of paper-chromatographic procedures that have been used for various inorganic ions, as compiled by Block (8). The text of Smith (6) should be consulted for details of inorganic separations. Frierson and Jones (13) have demonstrated the use of radioisotopes in partition-chromatographic separation of various inorganic ions. Separations were made of the following mixtures of radioisotopes: (a) iron-cobalt, (b) iron-cobalt-nickel-manganese-zinc, (c) lead-bismuth, (d) lead-bismuth-polonium, (e) sodium-potassium, and (f) titanium-scandium. Location of the elements on the paper strip was determined by visual appearance, autoradiograms, or automatic scanning with a Geiger tube. In general, the definition of spots by scanning was not so precise as by autoradiography. However, the scanning method was faster. It was possible to differentiate the resolved mixtures by differences in radiation energies (Ni^{63}-Co^{58}, Na^{24}-K^{42}), by growth of daughter activities (Pb^{210} in Ra DEF), and by differences in decay (Ni^{65}-Zn^{69}-Fe^{59}). Of practical import is the use of such procedures to check the purity of radioisotope preparations before their use in experimental work.

APPLICATIONS

The widespread application of paper chromatography has been indicated by the summaries in Tables 8-2 to 8-4, and the current literature

TABLE 8-2. SUMMARY OF CHROMATOGRAPHIC SEPARATION OF ORGANIC SUBSTANCES

Substance	Amount	Paper	Solvents	Detection
Adrenalin and related compounds	2 μg	Whatman 1, Schleicher and Schuell 597	Aqueous phenol, n-butanol-HCl	Potassium ferricyanide, ninhydrin
Aliphatic acids.......	0.5–3 μg	Whatman 1	n-Butanol–acetic acid, n-butanol–ammonia, ethanol–ammonia, CCl₄–acetic acid	Bromophenol blue, bromocresol green, bromothymol blue, bromocresol purple
Aliphatic acids (α-keto)	....	....	n-Butanol–water–propionic acid, α-n-dimethylaminoisobutyric nitrile–n-butanol–water	o-Phenylenediamine, semicarbazide
Alkaloids (atropine compounds)	....	Durieux 122	n-Butanol-HCl	Bismuth subnitrate–KI reagents
Alkaloids (nicotine, pyrrolidine, pyridine)	....	....	n-Butanol-HCl	As the chlorohydrates
Alkaloids (sparteine and genistein)	....	....	n-Butanol–acetic acid–water	
Amines.............	5–10 μg	Whatman	Same as for amino acids, m-cresol–acetic acid–water, n-butanol–glycol monochlorohydrin–NH₄OH	Ninhydrin, Erlich's reagent, quinone, iodine
Amino acids.........	0.5–5 μg	Whatman 1, Whatman 4, Schleicher and Schuell 507	Phenol, m-cresol, lutidine, collidine mixtures, butanol, acetone	Ninhydrin, iodine, permanganate, orcinol
Amino acids (dinitrophenyl derivatives)	2–5 μg	Whatman 4	Chloroform–isopropanol–0.05 M K benzoate, propanol–petroleum ether, n-butanol–ethanol–water	
Amino alcohols......	....	Whatman 1	n-Butanol–acetic acid–water, n-butanol-NH₄OH, phenol-NH₄OH	Ninhydrin
Anthraquinone pigments	....	....	Petroleum ether–methanol	Magnesium acetate
Ascorbic acid........	1–15 μg	Whatman 1, Whatman 4	Butanol–acetic acid, phenol–acetic acid	2,6-Dichlorophenol-indophenol
Chloromycetin.......	5–20 μg	Whatman 1, Whatman 2, Whatman 4, Eaton and Dikeman 613, Schleicher and Schuell 112	Butanol–acetic acid–water, butanol–phenol-pyridine	SnCl₂ reagent and P-dimethylaminobenzaldehyde
Choline, ethanolamine, serine	....	....	n-Butanol–glycol monochlorohydrin–NH₄OH, n-butanol–acetic acid–water	Ninhydrin, iodine
Flavonoid pigments..	....	....	Ethyl acetate, phenol	Fluorescence, alcohol AlCl₃, lead acetate, Na₂CO₃, FeCl₃
Hexachlorocyclohexane isomers	....	Paper treated with acetic anhydride	n-Hexane–acetic anhydride	FeSO₄
Indicator dyes.......	....	....	Isopropanol, butanol, amyl alcohol	Dilute NaOH
β-Indoleacetic acid and tryptophan	....	....	Methylethylketone-pyridine-water	Cinnamic aldehyde–HCl
Lignin oxidation products	....	Whatman 1	Petroleum ether–water, n-butyl ether–water	2,4-Dinitrophenylhydrazine
Nicotinic acid and related compounds	30 μg	....	n-Butanol-HCl-water	Ninhydrin, phosphomolybdic acid–stannous chloride
Penicillin...........	1–2 units	Whatman 1, Whatman 2, Whatman 4, Eaton and Dikeman 613, Schleicher and Schuell 112	Ether-water, anhydrous ether	Microbiological assay

TABLE 8-2. SUMMARY OF CHROMATOGRAPHIC SEPARATION OF ORGANIC SUBSTANCES
(*Continued*)

Substance	Amount	Paper	Solvents	Detection
Phenols and aromatic acids	1–20 μg	Whatman 4, Whatman 1	Butanol–pyridine–saturated aqueous NaCl, methylethyl-ketone-water, benzene–acetic acid–water, butanol–water, butanol–ammonium carbonate buffer	Diazotized sulfanilic acid, sucrose, diazotized *p*-nitraniline, $AgNO_3$-NH_4OH, NaOH, methyl red, $FeCl_3$
Porphyrins..........	2–3 μg	Whatman 1, Schleicher and Schuell 2043b	Lutidine-water	Fluorescence, ultraviolet absorption, natural red color
Proteins............	20 μg	Whatman 1, Whatman 3	Aqueous acetone and alcohol, phosphate buffers, molar sucrose	Bromothymol blue, bromophenol blue, solway purple
Pterins.............	....	....	Butanol–acetic acid–water	Fluorescence
Purines, pyrimidines, etc.	1–200 μg	Whatman 1, Schleicher and Schuell 597	*n*-Butanol–water–formic acid, *n*-butanol–boric acid, isopropanol-water–HCl, *tert*-butanol-water-HCl, ammonium sulfate–isopropanol	Molybdic acid reagent, cysteine-sulfuric acid reagent, mercuric nitrate
Riboflavin..........	1 μg	Whatman 1, Whatman 4	Butanol–acetic acid	Fluorescence, microbiological assay
Steroids............	3–30 μg	Whatman 4	Petroleum ether–methanol–water	NaOH-fluorescence
Streptomycin........	3–12 units	Whatman 1, Whatman 2, Whatman 4, Eaton and Dikeman 613, Schleicher and Schuell 112	Butanol–water–piperidine–*p*-toluenesulfonic acid, butanol–water–*p*-toluenesulfonic acid	Microbiological assay
Sugars (simple)......	30–40 μg	Whatman 1, Schleicher and Schuell 589	Phenol-water, collidine, *n*-butanol–acetic acid–water	$AgNO_3$-NH_4OH, aniline hydrogen phthalate, naphthoresorcinol, *m*-phenylenediamine, permanganate, benzidine
Sugar alcohols.......	1–10 μg	Whatman 1	*n*-Butanol, *n*-butanol-ethanol-water, *n*-butanol–acetic acid–water	$AgNO_3$-NH_4OH
Sugars (amino)......	....	....	Phenol-ammonia, collidine, *n*-butanol–acetic acid	Acetylacetone reagent, *p*-dimethylaminobenzaldehyde reagent
Sugars (lactone derivatives)............	....	....	Methyl-ethyl-ketone, methyl-ethyl-ketone–petroleum ether	Hydroxylamine
Sugars (methylated)	....	Whatman 1	*n*-Butanol-ethanol-water-ammonia, methyl-ethyl-ketone	$AgNO_3$-NH_4OH, *p*-anisidine-HCl, aniline phthalate
Sugars (phosphate esters)	....	....	*tert*-Butanol–picric acid, *n*-propanol-ammonia, methanol-ethanol, methanol–formic acid	Molybdic acid
Sulfonamides........	5–20 μg	Whatman 1, Whatman 2, Whatman 4, Eaton and Dikeman 613, Schleicher and Schuell 112	Butanol-ammonia-water	
Urea, creatine, creatinine	2–5 μg	....	Phenol, butanol–acetic acid, butanol-ethanol, isobutyric acid, lutidine	Phenol-hypochlorite, ninhydrin, diazotized sulfanilic acid, bromocresol green, ferric chloride

TABLE 8-2. SUMMARY OF CHROMATOGRAPHIC SEPARATION OF ORGANIC SUBSTANCES
(Continued)

Substance	Amount	Paper	Solvents	Detection
Vitamin A..........	1 μg	Whatman 1, Whatman 4	Petroleum ether	Carr-Price reagent
Vitamin B6.........	1 μg	Whatman 1, Whatman 4	Butanol-water	Microbiological assay
Vitamin B12........	1 μg	Whatman 1, Whatman 4	Butanol-water	Microbiological assay

contains ample testimony to its ever-increasing use. It is the intention here to illustrate how the combined techniques of paper chromatography and radiotracers are mutually advantageous.

The use of radioisotopes extends the sensitivity of an ordinary chromatographic procedure by facilitating the detection and estimation of the separated components. There are three general methods for association of the radioisotope with the resolved constituents of the chromatogram, as discussed by Winteringham et al. (25): *Labeling of initial mixture:* This is usually accomplished by incorporation of the radioisotope into the metabolizing system, e.g., growing of plants with C^{14} and S^{35} and later separating the amino acids; or by administering I^{131} to animals and later separating the thyroid hormones and/or protein complex. It is also possible to treat the mixture with a labeled reagent before the chromatographic separation. *Labeling of chromatogram:* It is possible that labeled reagents could be applied to the completed chromatogram so as to react selectively with the separated constituents. *Neutron activation of the chromatogram:* It is also possible that the completed chromatogram could be irradiated in the pile to produce measurable radioactivity in the separated constituents. The success of this method would be dependent upon producing a significantly higher radioactivity in the elements of the separated constituents than in the filter paper.

A classical illustration of the use of paper chromatography to resolve mixtures is the research of Calvin and coworkers (40, 41) in studies on photosynthesis (see Chap. 1). In a typical study, *Chlorella* were exposed to C^{14} for a 60-sec period of photosynthesis and then killed and extracted with alcohol. The extracts were concentrated to a small volume, and an aliquot placed in the corner of a square sheet of filter paper and dried with an air stream. A two-dimensional chromatogram was prepared using phenol-water as the first solvent and butanol–propionic acid–water as the second solvent. The chromatogram was exposed on X-ray film to produce the results shown in Fig. 8-7. In this chromatogram the origin was near the lower right corner, and the phenol-water was used to develop running from right to left, whereas the second solvent was employed running from bottom to top.

TABLE 8-3. SUMMARY OF CHROMATOGRAPHIC SEPARATION OF INORGANIC CATIONS

	R_f values*					Detection reagents†
	A	B	C	D	E	
Aluminum	0.03	0	0.03	0.07	....	a
Antimony	0	0.38	0.65	....	....	b, c
Arsenic	0.43	0.65	0.18	....	....	b, c
Barium	0.02	0.26	0.02	....	....	d
Beryllium	....	....	....	0.33	....	e
Bismuth	0.02	0	0.63	....	....	b, c
Cadmium	0.05	0.76	0.18	....	....	b, c
Calcium	0.05	0.52	0.10	....	....	a
Chromium (3+)	0.03	0	0.01	0.07	....	e, f
Cobalt	0.06	0.74	0.05	....	....	b, g
Copper	0.22	0.76	0.24	0.1	....	b, c, g, h
Gold	....	....	....	1.1	....	f, i
Indium	....	....	....	0.30		
Iridium	....	....	....	....	0.10	
Iron (3+)	0.95	0	0.10	....	....	a, b, h
Lead	0.03	0	0.15	....	....	b, c, d
Magnesium	0.06	0.65	0.04			
Manganese	0.07	0.71	0.09	....	....	f, g
Mercury (+)	0.24	0	0.43	....	....	b
Mercury (++)	0.31	0	0.42	....	....	b, c
Nickel	0.03	0.76	0.05	....	....	b, g
Palladium	....	....	....	0.6	....	i
Platinum	....	....	....	0.8	....	i
Potassium	0.05	0.32	0.03	....	....	j
Rare earths	....	....	....	0.03	....	a, e
Rhodium	....	....	....	....	0.10	i
Silver	0.10	0.78	0.08	....	....	b
Sodium	0.06	0.42	0.04	....	....	k
Strontium	0.04	0.40	0.04	....	....	d
Tellurium (+)	....	....	....	0	....	i
Tellurium (3+)	....	....	....	1.11	....	i
Tin (++)	0.58	0	0.77	....	....	c
Tin (4+)	0.55	0	0.58	....	....	c
Titanium	....	....	....	0.07		
Vanadium	....	....	....	0.17		
Zinc	0.05	0.75	0.08	0.77	....	h

* Solvent composition: A, butanol-benzoylacetone; B, collidine-water; C, dioxane-antipyrine; D, butanol-1 N HCl; E, methylethylketone–30 per cent HCl.

† Detection reagents: a, alizarin; b, ammoniacal aqueous H_2S; c, dithizone; d, sodium rhodizonate; e, ammoniacal quinalizarin; f, benzidine; g, rubeanic acid–benzidine; h, potassium ferrocyanide; i, stannous chloride; j, sodium lead cobaltous hexanitrite; k, zinc uranyl acetate.

(From Richard J. Block, Raymond Lestrange, and Gunter Zweig, "Paper Chromatography, A Laboratory Manual," Academic Press, Inc., New York, 1952.)

TABLE 8-4. SUMMARY OF CHROMATOGRAPHIC SEPARATION OF INORGANIC ANIONS

	R_f values*			Detection
	A	B	C	
Arsenate.............	....	0.05	0	
Arsenite.............	....	0.19	0.21	Ammoniacal $AgNO_3$
Bromate.............	....	0.25	0.13	KI, HCl
Bromide.............	0.47	0.36	0.16	$AgNO_3$, H_2S
Carbonate............	....	0.06		
Chlorate.............	....	0.42		
Chloride.............	0.23	0.24	0.10	$AgNO_3$, H_2S
Iodate...............	....	0.09	0.03	KI, HCl
Iodide...............	0.71	0.47	0.30	$Fe(NO_3)_3$, H_2O_2; $AgNO_3$, H_2S
Nitrate...............	....	0.40	0.24	Universal indicator
Nitrite...............	....	0.25	0.20	KI, HCl
Phosphate............	....	0.04	0	Ammoniacal $AgNO_3$
Sulfate...............	....	0.07	0	Universal indicator
Thiocyanate..........	....	0.56	0.45	$Fe(NO_3)_3$, H_2O_2; $AgNO_3$, H_2S

* Solvent composition: A, pyridine–10 per cent H_2O; B, butanol-pyridine–1.5 N NH_3; C, butanol–1.5 N NH_4OH.
(From Richard J. Block, Raymond Lestrange, and Gunter Zweig, "Paper Chromatography, A Laboratory Manual," Academic Press, Inc., New York, 1952.)

It was obvious that the C^{14} had been incorporated into several different compounds, but the identification of the compounds corresponding to the darkened areas or spots required further investigation. It was first necessary to prepare a "map" for the given solvent system using known compounds detected by chemical reagents or known isotope-labeled compounds. Comparison of the experimental chromatogram with the map gives a clue as to the nature of the compound. Further evidence was obtained by elution of the spot and chemical treatment to yield a substance that could be chromatographed again for comparison with a known sample of the expected resultant compound. For example, a characteristic spot was believed to be due to phosphoglyceric acid; hydrolysis gave a radioactive compound that was found to be identical with a sample of authentic glyceric acid. As added identification, the unknown radioactive material can be chromatographed together with an authentic sample of the suspected substance. If the two compounds are identical, there should be complete coincidence of the spots due to the two substances.

Another example in plant metabolism is presented by the papers of Steward and associates in connection with the estimation of the free amino acids of plant cells. Dent, Stepka, and Steward (42) were able to isolate from potato tuber 24 well-defined spots giving typical ninhydrin reactions.

A list of the amino acids that were positively identified is as follows: cystine, aspartic acid, glutamic acid, serine, glycine, asparagine, threonine, alanine, glutamine, α-amino-n-butyric acid, histidine, arginine, lysine, methionine sulfoxide, proline, valine, methionine, isoleucine, phenylalanine, tryptophan, and tyrosine. The potato tissue was extracted with cold 70 to 80 per cent alcohol to give a protein-free solution. The alcohol extracts were evaporated to dryness under reduced pressure and redissolved in water to give a solution containing about

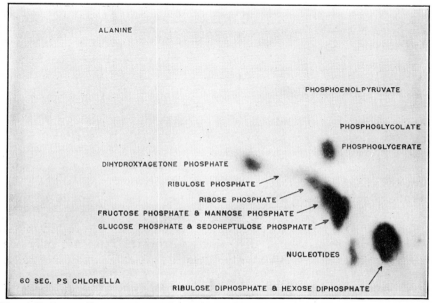

Fig. 8-7. Autoradiogram of two-dimensional chromatogram showing incorporation of radioactivity in various substances by *Chlorella* during 60 sec of photosynthesis while exposed to C[14]. (*From M. Calvin and J. A. Bassham, Studies in Photosynthesis with Isotopes, University of California Radiation Laboratory Report* UCRL-1861, 1952.)

10 mg/ml of nitrogen. Five microliters of the solution was applied to the filter paper and developed chromatographically for about 30 hr in phenol saturated with water. After drying, the paper was turned at right angles for another 30-hr development in a collidine-lutidine mixture. Dent (43) studied in detail the chromatographic behavior of some 60 amino acids and ninhydrin-reacting substances.

Steward et al. (44) were able to gain additional information on the occurrence of sulfur-containing amino acids by chromatography and autoradiography of extracts of alfalfa into which S[35] had been introduced via the roots. Thompson et al. (45) investigated the variables affecting the chromatographic separation of plant amino acids and the ninhydrin reaction. On the basis of these studies, a standardized quantitative procedure was developed.

Paper chromatography used in conjunction with I^{131} has been of particular value in the study of the various closely related iodine compounds involved in animal metabolism, as illustrated in a series of papers by Chaikoff and associates (46 to 49). The general procedure employed was as follows (46): Strips of Whatman No. 1 filter paper 10 by 36 cm were employed. The butanol extract, containing the substances to be separated, was added in a thin band, 5 cm long, at 2.5 cm from the edge of the paper. Up to 250 μl of extract was added in successive 25-μl applications, each being allowed to dry before the next was added. The paper strips were suspended in cylindrical pyrex jars (18 in. high and 8½ in. in diameter) containing 150 ml of solvent. The strips were hung from a rack attached to plate glass (which also served as a cover for the jar), with the bottom of the strip dipping into the solvent. The solvent was prepared by the addition of 44 ml water to 125 ml of redistilled collidine. A small beaker of concentrated NH_4OH was placed in the jar. The chromatogram was allowed to develop for 16 hr at 25 to 26°C. When I^{131} was used, the dried chromatogram was placed in contact with X-ray film to give an autoradiogram. When known stable compounds were used for reference purposes, the dried chromatogram was sprayed with 2.5 per cent Na_2CO_3 and then an aqueous solution of sulfanilic diazonium chloride to give the colored bands.

Figure 8-8 (49) illustrates some of the results obtained in regard to the enterohepatic circulation of thyroxine and demonstrates not only the resolution of a mixture but also the isolation of a pure substance to be used for further study. The autoradiogram on the left represents the bile from a rat that had been injected more than 3 hr previously with I^{131}-labeled thyroxine and shows that the principal excretion product was not thyroxine but an unidentified I^{131} component, which was called *compound U*. Purified samples of compound *U* were obtained by paper-chromatographic separation from other I^{131} components of bile. A rat was injected with I^{131}-labeled thyroxine, and the bile collected between the eighth and fourteenth hour postinjection. The bile was brought to pH 3.5 to 4.0 with dilute HCl and extracted with butanol, and a total of 200 μl of the extract delivered in 25-μl portions to each of 24 filter-paper strips. Compound *U* was separated by chromatography as previously described, and the sections of paper corresponding to compound *U* were cut out and eluted with dilute NaOH. Figure 8-8, *right*, demonstrates the purity of the compound *U* preparation thus obtained. The eluates from the 24 strips were combined for administration to other rats for study of the metabolism of this particular substance.

An illustration of quantitative determination of labeled bromine analogues of DDT in insect metabolism studies is given in the papers of Winteringham et al. (21, 50). Mixtures of the following compounds were resolved and analyzed: $(Br^*C_6H_4)_2CH \cdot CCl_3$, $(Br^*C_6H_4)_2C : CCl_2$, and $(Br^*C_6H_4)_2CH \cdot COOH$. For a reversed-phase chromatogram, strips of Whatman No. 1 filter paper, 100 by 2.5 cm, were drawn through a bath of ether containing 2.5 per cent vaseline, then drained and dried. Mix-

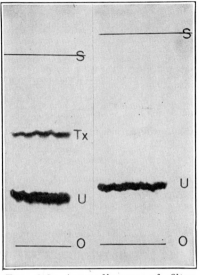

tures of these three components in benzene were applied at the top of the strip. The mobile phase consisted of 80 per cent ethanol, 15 per cent water, and 5 per cent ammonia, and the chromatogram was developed in the usual way. The amounts of each compound used were in the range of 0.2 to 50 μg, and the recoveries as dete: mined by Geiger counting were excellent. Winteringham et al. (25) also separated an unlabeled mixture of these compounds and determined the amounts present by exposure of the chromatogram to neutron bombardment and measurement of induced radioactivity. Recoveries ranged from 62 to 126 per cent.

Another quantitative application is given in the work of Ruliffson et al. (51), who separated the hydrazones of ketosteroids which had been formed with I^{131}-labeled acethydrazide-3-iodo-pyridinium bromide. After reaction between this compound and the ketosteroid, a 20- to 200-μl aliquot was placed on a spot 2 cm from the base of a 1-in. strip of Whatman No. 1 paper. Ascending chromatography was carried out with 84 per cent n-butanol–16 per cent water. The position of the steroid hydrazones and also of unre-

FIG. 8-8. Autoradiogram of filter-paper chromatogram. *O* indicates origin; *U*, compound *U*; *Tx*, thyroxine; *S*, solvent front. *Left*, from bile of rat injected with I^{131}-labeled thyroxine, shows formation and biliary excretion of unidentified product. *Right*, shows purity of unidentified product, compound *U*, isolated by paper chromatography for study of its metabolism when administered to rats. [*From F. N. Briggs, Alvin Taurog, and I. L. Chaikoff, The Enterohepatic Circulation of Thyroxine in the Rat, Endocrinology, **52**: 559–567 (1953).*]

acted labeled reagent was determined by radioactivity as well as the use of iodoplatinate reagent. R_f values were reported for 18 different ketosteroids. Quantitative recoveries were obtained by radioactivity measurements, provided an excess of the labeled reagent was used.

Williams and associates (9, 52) have pointed out that, although interpretations of paper chromatograms are fairly straightforward when pure solutions are dealt with, the direct use of biological fluids may introduce complications. Interfering substances may mask the spots, change their size, or alter the R_f value. In some cases, multiple spots have appeared for a single substance, thus indicating the possible existence of multiple ionic species. These difficulties can often be overcome by use of varying solvent mixtures or, if necessary, the prior removal of interfering substances. In any event, it is always wise to chromatograph known samples in the presence of the same biological substances as contained in the test samples in order to aid in the interpretation.

GENERAL REFERENCES

1. Weil, Herbert, and Trevor I. Williams: History of Chromatography, *Nature*, **166**: 1000–1001 (1950).
2. Zechmeister, L., and L. Cholnoky: "Principles and Practice of Chromatography," John Wiley & Sons, Inc., New York, 1941.
3. Strain, Harold H.: "Chromatographic Adsorption Analysis," Interscience Publishers, Inc., New York, 1945.
4. Cassidy, Harold Gomes: "Adsorption and Chromatography," Interscience Publishers, Inc., New York, 1951.
5. Strain, Harold H., and George W. Murphy: Chromatography, *Anal. Chem.*, **24**: 50–60 (1952).
6. Smith, O. C.: "Inorganic Chromatography," D. Van Nostrand Company, Inc., New York, 1953.
7. Wilson, J. Norton: A Theory of Chromatography, *J. Am. Chem. Soc.*, **62**: 1583–1591 (1940).
8. Block, Richard J., Raymond Lestrange, and Gunter Zweig: "Paper Chromatography, A Laboratory Manual," Academic Press, Inc., New York, 1952.
9. Williams, Roger J.: Biochemical Institute Studies. IV. Individual Metabolic Patterns and Human Disease: An Exploratory Study Utilizing Predominantly Paper Chromatographic Methods, *Univ. Texas Publ. No.* 5109, May 1, 1951.
10. Toennies, Gerrit, and Joseph J. Kolb: Techniques and Reagents for Paper Chromatography, *Anal. Chem.*, **23**: 823–826 (1951).
10a. Lederer, Edgar, and Michael Lederer: "Chromatography," Elsevier Press, Inc., New York, 1953.
10b. Block, Richard J., E. L. Durrum, and Gunter Zweig: "Paper Chromatography and Paper Electrophoresis, a Laboratory Manual," Academic Press, Inc., New York, 1955.

CITED REFERENCES

11. Martin, A. J. P., and R. L. M. Synge: A New Form of Chromatogram Employing Two Liquid Phases, *Biochem. J. London*, **35**: 1358–1368 (1941).
12. Consden, R., A. H. Gordon, and A. J. P. Martin: Qualitative Analysis of Proteins: A Partition Chromatographic Method Using Paper, *Biochem. J. London*, **38**: 224–232 (1944).
13. Frierson, W. Joe, and John W. Jones: Radioactive Tracers in Paper Partition Chromatography of Inorganic Ions, *Anal. Chem.*, **23**: 1447–1452 (1951).
14. Datta, S. P., C. E. Dent, and H. Harris: An Apparatus for the Simultaneous Production of Many Two-dimensional Paper Chromatograms, *Science*, **112**: 621–623 (1950).

15. Winteringham, F. P. W.: Two-dimensional Paper Chromatography of Radioactive Substances, *Nature*, **172**: 727–728 (1953).
16. Rockland, Louis B., and Max S. Dunn: A Capillary-ascent Test Tube Method for Separating Amino Acids by Filter Paper Chromatography, *Science*, **109**: 539–540 (1949).
17. Yanofsky, Charles, Elga Wasserman, and David M. Bonner: Large Scale Paper Chromatography, *Science*, **111**: 61–62 (1950).
18. Wolfson, W. Q., C. Cohn, and W. A. Devaney: An Improved Apparatus and Procedure for Ascending Paper Chromatography on Large Size Filter Paper Sheets, *Science*, **109**: 541–543 (1949).
19. Mitchell, Herschel K., and Francis A. Haskins: A Filter Paper "Chromatopile," *Science*, **110**: 278–279 (1949).
20. Heden, C. G.: A Method for Large-scale Separation of Amino-acids on Filter Paper, *Nature*, **166**: 999–1000 (1950).
21. Winteringham, F. P. W., A. Harrison, and R. G. Bridges: Analysis of DDT Derivatives by Reversed-phase Paper Partition Chromatography, *Nature*, **166**: 999 (1950).
22. Lederer, Michael: Gradient-Elution Analysis in Inorganic Paper Chromatography, *Nature*, **172**: 727 (1953).
23. Rockland, Louis B., Jeremiah L. Blatt, and Max S. Dunn: Small Scale Filter Paper Chromatography, *Anal. Chem.*, **23**: 1142–1146 (1951).
24. Kowkabany, George N., and Harold G. Cassidy: Investigation of Paper Strip Chromatography, *Anal. Chem.*, **22**: 817–819 (1950).
25. Winteringham, F. P. W., A. Harrison, and R. G. Bridges: Radioactive Tracer-paper Chromatography Techniques, *Analyst*, **77**: 19–28 (1952).
26. Soloway, Sidney, Frank J. Rennie, and Dewitt Stetten, Jr.: An Automatic Scanner for Paper Radiochromatograms, *Nucleonics*, **10**: 52–53 (1952).
27. Williams, Robert R., and Robert E. Smith: A Continuously Recording Scanning Device for Radiochromatographic Analysis of Labeled Antigen-Antibody Reactions, *Proc. Soc. Exptl. Biol. Med.*, **77**: 169–174 (1951).
28. Haugaard, Gotfred, and Thomas D. Kroner: Partition Chromatography of Amino Acids with Applied Voltage, *J. Am. Chem. Soc.*, **70**: 2135–2137 (1948).
29. Strain, Harold H., and James C. Sullivan: Analysis by Electromigration Plus Chromatography, *Anal. Chem.*, **23**: 816–823 (1951).
30. Sato, Takuya R., Walter E. Kisieleski, William P. Norris, and Harold H. Strain: Electrochromatographic Separations of Calcium and Phosphate Ions, *Anal. Chem.*, **25**: 438–446 (1953).
31. Durrum, E. L.: A Microelectrophoretic and Microionophoretic Technique, *J. Am. Chem. Soc.*, **72**: 2943–2948 (1950).
32. Jermyn, M. A., and R. Thomas: Reduction of Liquid Flow in Paper Electrophoresis, *Nature*, **172**: 728–729 (1953).
33. Gordon, A. H., J. Gross, D. O'Connor, and Rosalind Pitt-Rivers: Nature of the Circulating Thyroid Hormone-Plasma Protein Complex, *Nature*, **169**: 19–20 (1952).
34. Zilversmit, D. B., and S. L. Hood: The Use of Blood Serum as Buffer for Paper-electrophoretic Studies of Radioactive Yttrium, *Proc. Soc. Exptl. Biol. Med.*, **84**: 573–576 (1953).
35. Consden, R., and W. M. Stanier: Ionphoresis of Sugars on Papers and Some Applications to the Analysis of Protein Polysaccharide Complexes, *Nature*, **169**: 783–785 (1952).
36. Schultz, D. M., and C. J. Weger: Electrophoresis in Filter Paper Strips, *Lab. Invest.*, **1**: 186–196 (1952).

37. Levin, B., and V. G. Oberholzer: Paper Electrophoresis of Serum Proteins, *Nature*, **170**: 123 (1952).

38. Griffiths, Louis L.: The Electrophoresis of Serum and Other Body Fluids in Filter Paper, *J. Lab. Clin. Med.*, **41**: 188–198 (1953).

39. Durrum, E. L., Milton H. Paul, Elizabeth R. B. Smith: Lipid Detection in Paper Electrophoresis, *Science*, **116**: 428–430 (1952).

40. Calvin, M., and J. A. Bassham: Studies in Photosynthesis with Isotopes, University of California Radiation Laboratory Report UCRL-1861, 1952.

41. Buchanan, J. G., J. A. Bassham, A. A. Benson, D. F. Bradley, M. Calvin, L. I. Daus, M. Goodman, P. M. Hayes, V. H. Lynch, L. T. Norris, and A. T. Wilson: The Path of Carbon in Photosynthesis. XVII. Phosphorus Compounds as Intermediates in Photosynthesis, *Phosphorus Metabolism*, **2**: 440–466 (1952).

42. Dent, C. E., W. Stepka, and F. C. Steward: Detection of the Free Amino-acids of Plant Cells by Partition Chromatography, *Nature*, **160**: 682 (1947).

43. Dent, C. E.: A Study of the Behavior of Some 60 Amino Acids and Other Ninhydrin-reacting Substances on Phenol-"Collidine" Filter Paper Chromatograms, with Notes as to the Occurrence of Some of Them in Biological Fluids, *Biochem. J. London*, **43**: 169–180 (1948).

44. Steward, F. C., J. F. Thompson, F. K. Millar, M. D. Thomas, and R. H. Hendricks: The Amino Acids of Alfalfa as Revealed by Paper Chromatography with Special Reference to Compounds Labelled with S^{35}, *Plant Physiol.*, **26**: 123–135 (1951).

45. Thompson, John F., and F. C. Steward: Investigations of Nitrogen Compounds and Nitrogen Metabolism in Plants. II. Variables in Two-directional Paper Chromatography of Nitrogen Compounds: A Quantitative Procedure, *Plant Physiol.*, **26**: 421–440 (1951).

46. Taurog, Alvin, W. Tong, and I. L. Chaikoff: The Monoiodotyrosine Content of the Thyroid Gland, *J. Biol. Chem.*, **184**: 83–97 (1950).

47. Taurog, Alvin, F. N. Briggs, and I. L. Chaikoff: I^{131}-Labeled *l*-Thyroxine.   I. An Unidentified Excretion Product in Bile, *J. Biol. Chem.*, **191**: 29–34 (1951).

48. Taurog, Alvin, F. N. Briggs, and I. L. Chaikoff: I^{131}-Labeled *l*-Thyroxine.   II. Nature of the Excretion Product in Bile, *J. Biol. Chem.*, **194**: 655–668 (1952).

49. Briggs, F. N., Alvin Taurog, and I. L. Chaikoff: The Enterohepatic Circulation of Thyroxine in the Rat, *Endocrinology*, **52**: 559–567 (1953).

50. Winteringham, F. P. W., A. Harrison, C. R. Jones, J. L. McGirr, and W. H. Templeton: The Fate of Labelled Insecticide Residues in Food Products, *J. Sci. Food Agr.*, **1**: 214–219 (1950).

51. Ruliffson, Willard S., Helga M. Lang, and J. P. Hummel: Radiochemical Determination of Ketosteroids, *J. Biol. Chem.*, **201**: 839–846 (1953).

52. Berry, Helen Kirby, and Louise Cain: Biochemical Individuality. IV. A Paper Chromatographic Technique for Determining Excretion of Amino Acids in the Presence of Interfering Substances, *Arch. Biochem.*, **24**: 179–189 (1949).

CHAPTER 9

ION EXCHANGE

GENERAL METHODS—Cation Exchangers; Anion Exchangers. GENERAL TECHNIQUES—Apparatus; Procedures. PHYSICAL BASIS OF SEPARATION—Ions of Opposite Charge; Ions from Nonelectrolytes; Substances of Different Acidic or Basic Strength; Ions of Different Size; Conversion of Nonelectrolytes to Ions by Complex Formation. TYPES OF APPLICATIONS—Removal of Impurities or Interfering Substances: Concentration of Trace Constituents; Separation of Materials; Estimation of Total Salt Concentration; Properties of Complex Ions; Miscellaneous Applications.

As the name implies, this method is based on the exchange of ions in a solution for ions of the same charge from an ion exchanger. Ion exchangers are insoluble substances from which ions may be readily and reversibly replaced by others from solutions that are brought into contact with the exchanger. The occurrence of ion exchange between soil particles and soil solution has been recognized for more than a hundred years, and the agricultural application contributed the first systematic study of the phenomenon.

Exchange has been shown to occur with many types of substances, such as cellulose, lignin, wool, protein, bone, resins, and inorganic precipitates. The relatively recent development of synthetic exchange resins having optimum physical and chemical properties for specific applications has extended the use of exchange techniques for analytical and biological purposes, in addition to promoting increased industrial usage. The texts of Kunin and Myers (1), Samuelson (2), Lederer and Lederer (3), Cassidy (4), and Nachod (5) may be consulted for historical and operational details.

Ion exchange offers many of the advantages mentioned for paper chromatography, namely, simplicity of equipment, rapidity, and ease of manipulation. Also, less skill and judgment are required on the part of the analyst than for conventional analytical techniques. A primary consideration is that ion exchange permits separations or concentrations that would otherwise be impracticable or time-consuming. In comparison with paper chromatography, ion-exchange methods are not generally so applicable but do allow larger amounts of substances to be fractionated and collected. Thus ion-exchange methods offer many advantages in studies with radioisotopes along the lines of analytical separation, identification, and isolation of labeled compounds in pure form.

GENERAL METHODS

Ion-exchange separation methods usually fall into either of two general classifications: *ion exchange,* in which exchangeable ions are separated from nonexchangeable ions or from nonelectrolytes; and *ion-exchange chromatography,* in which exchangeable ions are separated from each other on the basis of differences in affinity for the exchanger.

The general principles and terminology may be illustrated by schematic diagrams showing the deionization of an aqueous mixture of potassium phosphate and ethyl alcohol [after (2)].   As indicated in Fig. 9-1, if the mixture is passed over a cation exchanger, the potassium ions will be removed by the exchanger to give a solution containing only the alcohol plus phosphate.   If the exchanger is then treated with acid, the cation solution that results contains the potassium ions from the original sample but none of the alcohol molecules or phosphate ions (Fig. 9-2).   Similarly, by the use of an anion exchanger, it is possible to produce a solution containing the alcohol and potassium with no phosphate (Fig. 9-3), and also, by elution, a solution containing the phosphate but with no alcohol or potassium (Fig. 9-4).   Finally, if the cation and anion exchanger are used in sequence, it is possible to obtain the deionized solution, that is, the alcohol free of both potassium and phosphate (Fig. 9-5).

Cation Exchangers.   Cation or base exchangers can be regarded as polyvalent anions with attached positively charged exchangeable ions. Many of the organic cation exchangers utilize sulfonic acid as the functional group.   These materials can be used over practically the entire pH range.   The weakly acid type of exchanger may contain carboxylic or phenolic groups that can be employed only above pH 4 and pH 8, respectively.   Table 9-1 presents a listing of some of the commonly used cation exchangers that are commercially available.

Anion Exchangers.   Naturally occurring anion exchangers are not generally available.   Anion exchangers are polyvalent cations with negatively charged exchangeable ions, or polymeric insoluble bases or salts thereof.   The active groups are usually amino or quaternary ammonium groups.   Table 9-2 presents a listing of commonly used anion exchangers that are commercially available.

GENERAL TECHNIQUES

For general discussions of technique, the reader is referred to the texts of Samuelson (2) and Kunin and Myers (1).   Detailed procedures for

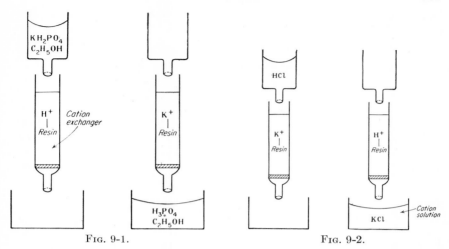

FIG. 9-1.   FIG. 9-2.

FIG. 9-1. Cation or base exchange: sorption step in which potassium is adsorbed.
FIG. 9-2. Cation or base exchange: regeneration or elution step in which previously retained potassium is removed from column.

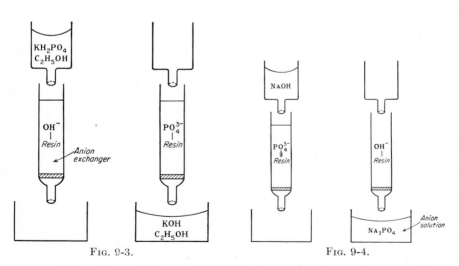

FIG. 9-3.   FIG. 9-4.

FIG. 9.3. Anion exchange: sorption step in which phosphate is adsorbed.
FIG. 9-4. Anion exchange: regeneration or elution step in which previously retained phosphate is removed from column.

TABLE 9-1. SOME COMMERCIALLY AVAILABLE CATION EXCHANGERS*

Type	Name	Manufacturer†
Sulfonated phenolic resin.............	Amberlite IR-100	a
	Amberlite IR-105	a
	Amberlite IR-112	a
	Dowex 30 (Nalcite MX)	b
	Duolite C-3	c
	Ionac C-200	d
	Wofatit P	e
	Wofatit K	e
	Wofatit KS	e
	Zeo Rex	d
Sulfonated hydrocarbon...............	Amberlite IR-120	a
	Dowex 50 (Nalcite HCR)	b
	Permutit Q	d
Carboxylic........................	Amberlite IRC-50	a
	Duolite CS-100	c
	Permutit 216	d
	Wofatit C	e
Aluminum silicate..................	Decalso	d
	Permutit	d
	Zeo Dur	d

* Total exchange capacity ranges from about 2 to 10 milliequivalents/g.
† a, The Rohm and Haas Co.; b, Dow Chemical Co.; c, Chemical Process Co.; d, The Permutit Co.; e, Farbenfabriken Bayer.

TABLE 9-2. SOME COMMERCIALLY AVAILABLE ANION EXCHANGERS*

Type	Name	Manufacturer†
Weak base...............	Amberlite IR-4B	a
	Amberlite IR-45	a
	De Acidite	b
	Dowex 3 (Nalcite WBR)	c
	Duolite A-2	d
	Duolite A-3	d
Medium base.............	Ionac A-300	b
	Lewatit MI	e
Strong base...............	Amberlite IRA-400	a
	Amberlite IRA-410	a
	Dowex 1	c
	Dowex 2 (Nalcite SAR)	c

* Total exchange capacity ranges from about 3 to 10 milliequivalents/g.
† a, The Rohm and Haas Co.; b, The Permutit Co.; c, Dow Chemical Co.; d, Chemical Process Co.; e, Farbenfabriken Bayer.

specific applications may best be found in the literature dealing with the particular method. It is the intention here to present an over-all commentary that may aid the inexperienced reader in the understanding and application of the published procedures.

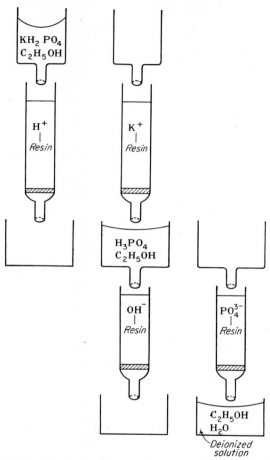

Fig. 9-5. Use of cation and anion exchange in sequence to remove both potassium and phosphate from solution.

Apparatus. The operation may be carried out either by use of a column or by a batchwise procedure. Column methods are by far the most widely used on account of their relatively high efficiency. However, in a few instances, batch operations may offer an advantage, for example, in a system where gas is produced in the resin bed which would interfere with solution flow, or where the objective is the adjustment of pH or ion concentration. As an example of concentration adjustment, a batch procedure has been recommended for the fractional precipitation of blood plasma proteins (2), in which case the salt content is reduced stepwise to precipitate the specific globulin fractions.

The column itself may be improvised from a burette or any kind of glass tube. For general analytical work, columns 8 to 15 mm in diameter are employed with a length/diameter ratio of about 10 to 20 (2). A typical and widely used arrangement is shown in Fig. 9-6. A plug of glass wool is placed at the bottom of the column to support the resin bed. The resin is slurried and then washed into the column, care being taken to keep the bed covered with water so as to prevent the entrance of air. The outlet tube should be much narrower than the column, and the outlet

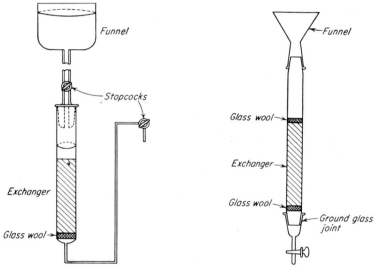

FIG. 9-6. Typical ion-exchange apparatus.   FIG. 9-7. Typical ion-exchange apparatus.

is located above the top of the resin bed so as to avoid a siphoning action in the event the upper funnel goes dry with inadvertent entry of air during the operation. The test solution is placed in the funnel, and the stopcock adjusted to give the proper flow rate. After the test solution has passed onto the resin bed, an appropriate amount of water is added to displace the test solution. The regeneration solution is then added to the funnel and allowed to pass down through the resin bed. Another modification for use with small columns is shown in Fig. 9-7. In this case the upper glass-wool plug should be well packed.

In some procedures it is desirable to use both downflow and upflow operations on account of the specific gravities of the solutions or to avoid moving the ions through the whole column in the elution or regeneration step. Figure 9-8 shows a convenient and easily assembled arrangement, as described by Applezweig (6), in which the sorption step can be accomplished by downflow operation, and the elution step by upflow operation. The solution is introduced through C and, after passing through the resin, can be withdrawn at A or passed through the second resin column via B-C'; the effluent can then be removed through A'. Backwashing is accomplished by attaching a tube from the raised water bottle to B', as indicated, or to B.

Procedures. Commercial exchangers are now generally satisfactory in regard to physical characteristics, adequate descriptions of which are obtainable from the manufacturer, and the choice for a particular application will be governed by experience under the conditions to be encountered. Most ion-exchange resins are delivered in moist condition, and

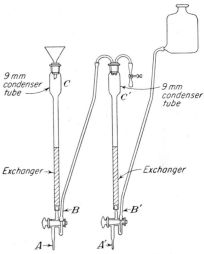

FIG. 9-8. Semimicrocolumn arrangement that permits reversal of direction of flow. [*From Norman Applezweig, Semimicro Ion-exchange Column, Ind. Eng. Chem. Anal. Ed.,* **18**: 82 (1946).]

although they may be air-dried if necessary, they should not be oven-dried. It will usually be necessary to grind and screen the commercial resin in order to obtain the desired particle size; this can be done in the moist or air-dry state. Coarse particles tend to decrease the capacity of a resin bed, whereas fine particles tend to decrease the flow rate. Cation exchangers of particle size 0.2 to 0.4 mm in diameter and anion exchangers of 0.12 to 0.30 mm are usually employed (2). Cation resins may be pretreated by soaking in 5 N HCl to remove impurities, and the carboxylic resins are usually conditioned by use of 2 N NaOH, followed by water, and then 2 N HCl, followed by distilled water. Most anion exchangers are pretreated by alternate additions of 1 N HCl and 0.5 N NaOH.

The flow rate may be regulated by the height of the top reservoir, by the particle size, or by adjusting the stopcock of the outlet tube. However, it must be remembered that, as the filtration rate is increased by any method, the exchange efficiency of a given resin bed will be decreased. When it is desired to decrease the flow rate, it is better to use a smaller particle size than mechanical regulation of the liquid flow.

For general analytical purposes a solution concentration range of 0.05 to 0.1 N has been employed. However, solutions as low as 10^{-6} M have been used satisfactorily. For very low concentrations, as with radio-isotopes, the procedures should be carefully examined to ensure that quantitative retention on the column does occur under the specific experimental conditions. The acidity of the test solution should be taken into account, particularly in regard to the amount of ion exchanger required for complete removal of the ions in question. For retention of monovalent or divalent cations, the acidity should not exceed 0.05 N; however, with trivalent cations, 0.1 N solutions may be employed without too much loss of capacity (2). When complexing agents such as citrate are used, the retention of certain cations may be increased by the addition of acid.

After the test solution has been placed on the column, the washing procedure is usually carried out with distilled water at about the same filtration rate as for sorption. This serves to displace the test solution left in the column, to remove adsorbed nonelectrolytes, and particularly to remove adsorbed acids from cation exchangers. Solutions other than water may be used for specific purposes, e.g., alcohol for the removal of organic compounds from cation resins, or CO_2-water for the removal of alkali from certain anion resins.

Regeneration or elution of cation exchangers is generally done with 3 to 4 N HCl, although complexing agents may sometimes be used (2). Anion resins are regenerated with NaOH, Na_2CO_3, NaCl, or HCl. Regeneration becomes more difficult as particle size is increased.

PHYSICAL BASIS OF SEPARATION

As a matter of emphasis, illustrative applications in this section are classified on the basis of physical principles utilized in the separation.

Ions of Opposite Charge. An application based on the separation of ions of opposite charge has been described by Samuelson (2). In the analysis of raw phosphate, the estimation of iron, aluminum, magnesium, and calcium is complicated by the presence of phosphate; conversely, the metals interfere with the estimation of phosphate. This is overcome by dissolving the sample in acid and passing through a cation exchanger (H^+ form), in which case the effluent contains the phosphoric acid, which can then be readily determined since there are no metal ions present. The exchanger is then eluted with HCl to displace the metal ions for estimation in a phosphate-free solution. Similarly, Helrich and Rieman (7) determined phosphorus in phosphate rock by dissolving the sample in HCl, evaporating to dryness, redissolving, and passing through a hydrogen-ion exchanger. The filtrate, containing only HCl and H_3PO_4, was adjusted to pH 4.63 and titrated with NaOH to a pH of 8.98 to give a measure of the phosphorus present.

In the gravimetric determination of sulfate as the barium salt, it has been found advantageous to eliminate, by exchange, such cations as sodium, aluminum, and iron which tend to coprecipitate (5). Conversion of a metal to an anion and subsequent separation are illustrated by studies with potassium and vanadium in which the latter was converted to vanadate. After passage through a cation exchanger saturated with ammonium ions, the potassium only was retained, thus effecting the separation (2).

Ions from Nonelectrolytes. An application of this principle has been the development of a convenient method for the estimation of ammonia in urine. The urine is treated with zeolite previously saturated with sodium ion, which then retains ammonium ion (5). After the exchanger is washed, it is treated with NaOH, which serves to liberate the ammonium ion and convert it to ammonia, which can then be estimated by the Nessler method. This principle has also been employed to retain the ammonia from urine so as to permit determination of urea in the filtrate by the standard method of hydrolysis with urease and subsequent estimation of the liberated ammonia (5).

An especially important application has been in the determination of thiamine (8). The standard fluorimetric method is based on the oxidation of thiamine to thiochrome and the measurement of its fluorescence in the absence of other fluorescing substances. The thiamine can be freed from interfering substances by treatment with an exchanger that retains thiamine but not the impurities. Elution generally provides an extract satisfactory for analysis. In a typical procedure the sample is heated with 0.1 N HCl to extract the vitamin, and the extract is treated with an acetate-buffered phosphatase (Takadiastase or Clorase) to hydrolyze the thiamine esters. The mixture is filtered, and the filtrate passed through a column of Decalso which has been previously saturated with potassium ion. After the column has been washed with water, the thiamine is displaced with an acid solution of KCl. An aliquot of the eluate is treated with sodium hydroxide, potassium ferricyanide, and isobutyl alcohol, and the fluorescence measured in comparison with standards.

Substances of Different Acidic or Basic Strength. An important application of separations based on differences in acidic or basic strength has been in studies with amino acids. For purposes of discussion, the amino acids resulting from the hydrolysis of most proteins may be classified as follows:

Basic amino acids: arginine, histidine, lysine, hydroxyglycine, ornithine.

Dicarboxylic amino acids: glutamic acid, aspartic acid.

Aromatic amino acids: tyrosine, phenylalanine, tryptophan.

Neutral amino acids: alanine, cysteine, cystine, glycine, hydroxyproline, isoleucine, leucine, methionine, proline, serine, threonine, valine.

A scheme for group separation is illustrated in Fig. 9-9 (2). This procedure is based on removal of the aromatic amino acids with charcoal, followed by isolation of the basic amino acids after adsorption on a carboxylic-type cation exchanger and finally by separation of the neutral

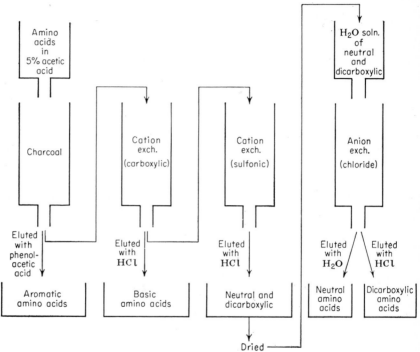

FIG. 9-9. Scheme for separation of amino acids. (*From Olof Samuelson, "Ion Exchangers in Analytical Chemistry," John Wiley & Sons, Inc., New York,* 1953.)

and dicarboxylic amino acids by use of an anion exchanger in the chloride form.

Another procedure, as illustrated in Fig. 9-10, has been proposed by Winters and Kunin (9) which not only separates the amino acids into the various groups but also resolves the basic amino acids arginine, lysine, and histidine. In principle, the dicarboxylic acids are separated after adsorption on the weakly basic anion exchanger (Amberlite IR-4B), with the neutral and remaining basic acids passing on through. These are put through a carboxylic cation exchanger (Amberlite IRC-50) at pH 7 which retains the arginine and lysine but allows the neutrals and histidine to pass. The neutrals and histidine are put through another column of IRC-50 at pH 4.7 which retains the histidine, thus effecting its separation from the neutral amino acids. The arginine and lysine are separated by

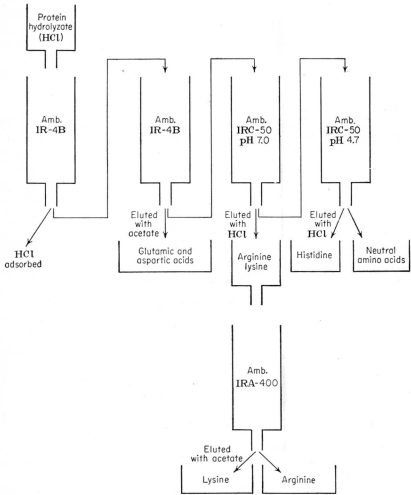

FIG. 9-10. Scheme for separation of amino acids. [*From James C. Winters and Robert Kunin, Ion Exchange in the Pharmaceutical Field, Ind. Eng. Chem.*, **41**: 460–463 (1949)].

use of a strongly basic anion exchanger (Amberlite IRA-400) which retains the lysine but permits the arginine to pass through.

Ion-exchange chromatography has been successfully employed to separate almost all the common amino acids. A satisfactory method has been based on the use of a sulfonated hydrocarbon cation exchanger

(Dowex 50) in the sodium form, with stepwise elution accomplished by sodium citrate buffers of increasing pH (10, 10a, 10b).

Ions of Different Size. Williams and Johnson (11) noted that inorganic salts interfered in an otherwise satisfactory method for the estimation of pectin by electrodeposition. Interfering electrolytes were readily removed by passing the solution through a sulfonic acid resin (H^+ form) and then through a weakly basic anion exchanger (free-base form). The large size of the anion prevented the pectic acid from being retained by the anion exchanger. This principle has also been used for the characterization of pectins, the determination of the degree of substitution of cellulose xanthate, and the purification of direct cotton dyes (2).

Conversion of Nonelectrolytes to Ions by Complex Formation. The isolation of radiochemically pure compounds has been a major difficulty in biosynthetic procedures. This is particularly true for the sugars. Advantage has been taken of the fact that sugars and certain other polyhydroxy compounds react with borate ions to form negatively charged complexes that can then be resolved by ion-exchange chromatography (12 to 16). This method has been most fruitful both for quantitative analysis of sugars found in biological materials and for isolation of labeled sugars prepared biosynthetically. Advantages in isolation are that carrier is not needed, thus allowing the sugars to be obtained with a high specific activity, and also that the method can handle large amounts of sugar.

The details of procedure can be noted from Table 9-3, which presents a summary of some of the separations that have been accomplished. The concentration of sugar in the eluate can be measured by the radioactivity present, usually C^{14}, when radioisotopes are used. The colorimetric anthrone method has been used for hexoses and polysaccharides, and the orcinol reaction has been used for the pentoses. These procedures are not specific for any one carbohydrate, but if a single sugar is present, as in the eluates from the resin column, then the method can be made quantitative for that sugar. The borate ions were not found to interfere with the colorimetric determinations.

With similar techniques, phosphoglyceric acid, fructose diphosphate, and the adenosine polyphosphates were separated from sugar monophosphates and from each other. A sequence of eluting solutions of varying borate concentration, chloride concentration, and pH was used (17).

TYPES OF APPLICATIONS

Illustrative applications described in this section have been grouped to point up the various experimental objectives that can be and have been achieved.

TABLE 9-3. SUMMARY OF SUGAR SEPARATIONS BY ION EXCHANGE OF BORATE COMPLEXES[a]

	Eluting agent	Liters through column to peak of elution
Hexose mixture		
Fructose...............	$0.018\ M$ $Na_2B_4O_7$	0.7
Galactose.............	$0.018\ M$ $Na_2B_4O_7$	1.4
Glucose...............	$0.03\ M$ $Na_2B_4O_7$	1.8
Hexose mixture		
Mannose..............	$0.05\ M$ boric acid $+\ 0.004\ M$ $K_2B_4O_7$	0.6
Fructose..............	$0.015\ M$ $K_2B_4O_7$	1.2
Pentose mixture		
Ribose.................	$0.015\ M$ $K_2B_4O_7$	0.2
Arabinose.............	$0.015\ M$ $K_2B_4O_7$	1.4
Xylose................	$0.015\ M$ $K_2B_4O_7$	2.2
Sucrose hydrolysis mixture		
Sucrose...............	$0.005\ M$ $K_2B_4O_7$	0.2
Fructose..............	$0.02\ M$ $K_2B_4O_7$	1.6
Glucose...............	$0.03\ M$ $K_2B_4O_7$	2.2
Sugar mixture		
Ribose.................	$0.015\ M$ $K_2B_4O_7$	0.3
Fructose..............	$0.015\ M$ $K_2B_4O_7$	1.2
Arabinose.............	$0.015\ M$ $K_2B_4O_7$	1.5
Galactose.............	$0.015\ M$ $K_2B_4O_7$	2.0
Xylose................	$0.015\ M$ $K_2B_4O_7$	2.4
Glucose...............	$0.03\ M$ $K_2B_4O_7$	3.0
Sugar alcohols		
Sorbitol...............	$0.015\ M$ $K_2B_4O_7$	2.2
Dulcitol...............	$0.015\ M$ $K_2B_4O_7$	3.0
Mannitol..............	$0.03\ M$ $K_2B_4O_7$	4.0
Analysis of sugar mixture		
Sucrose...............	$0.001\ M$ $K_2B_4O_7$	0.08
Raffinose.............	$0.001\ M$ $K_2B_4O_7$	0.17
Stachyose.............	$0.02\ M$ $K_2B_4O_7$	0.28
Fructose..............	$0.02\ M$ $K_2B_4O_7$	0.44

[a] Original solutions contained from 1 to 10 mg of each sugar in 0.001 to 0.01 M $K_2B_4O_7$; column dimensions, 0.85 cm² by 11 cm; strong-base anion resin, approximately 300 mesh, borate form; flow rate, approximately 1 ml/min.

[Compiled from G. R. Noggle, and L. P. Zill, Ion Exchange as a Tool for Studying Plant Carbohydrates, in "The Role of Atomic Energy in Agricultural Research," Proceedings of the Fourth Annual Oak Ridge Summer Symposium (Sponsored by the Oak Ridge National Laboratory and Oak Ridge Institute of Nuclear Studies, Aug. 25–30, 1952), TID-5115, pp. 378–403, January, 1953.]

Removal of Impurities or Interfering Substances. A simplified ion-exchange procedure has been described for the removal of metal contamination from adenosine triphosphate preparations (18). The purified barium salt was passed through Amberlite IR-100 resin, which removed all the barium as well as all traces of metal. Before use the resin was activated with 4 per cent Na_2CO_3, then washed free of excess alkali with distilled water. The barium salt was dissolved in a minimum amount of 0.1 N HCl and washed through the resin column in proportions of 2 to 3 g of dry resin per 100 mg of the monobarium salt of ATP. The resin was then washed with double-distilled water.

Wolfrom et al. (19) were able to isolate a galactogen from beef lung by a procedure that included passage through an acid-cation exchange column (Amberlite IR-100), followed by passage through an anion column (Amberlite IR-4). Platt and Glock (2) employed a mixed bed of cation and anion exchangers to remove creatine, creatinine, and other interfering substances from extracts of animal tissues prior to the determination of inositol.

The flame photometer is now being widely used in determination of the alkali metals. A major difficulty has been the mutual interference of sodium and potassium and the effect of sodium on the photometer readings for calcium. Sutton and Almy (20) have described exchange procedures for the complete separation of sodium, potassium, magnesium, and calcium in milk ash prior to the flame-photometric determination. The general procedure follows: A 100-g sample of milk was treated with a few drops of glacial acetic acid, evaporated to dryness, and muffled at 550°C, and the ash extracted in 0.7 N HCl. Colloidal Dowex 50, used in a 23-mm-diameter by 61-cm column, was converted to the hydrogen form, and the ash solution passed through and eluted with 0.7 N HCl. Preliminary trials based on a simple flame test served to approximate the limits of sodium and potassium elution. After complete elution of potassium, a 1.0 N HCl treatment was commenced in order to elute the magnesium and calcium. The eluate fractions were evaporated to dryness on a steam bath to remove all uncombined HCl, and each residue was extracted in 50 ml of distilled water for estimation of the metal cation.

Concentration of Trace Constituents. A major difficulty in the determination of copper in dairy products has resulted from the extremely small amounts naturally present. In the usual methods the practice has been to destroy the organic matter by ashing; this has limited the size of sample that can be used for routine determinations. Cranston and Thompson (21) have described an ion-exchange procedure that concentrates the copper from milk and serves to increase the over-all sensitivity of the determination while at the same time eliminating the tedious ashing step. This type of procedure should have wide application for the determination of traces of metals other than copper in any food or biological materials that can be converted to liquid form. It may be particularly helpful for the radioassay of soft-beta emitters when necessary to increase the radioactivity/mass ratio in the sample counted. In this method the milk copper was converted to the cupric form by adjustment of the pH to less than 3 with perchloric acid, which also precipitated the protein and carried the fat into the curd so that these substances could be eliminated by filtration. The filtrate was neutralized with ammonia to pH 5 and passed through a cation exchanger (Amberlite IR-100, H$^+$ form), which retained the copper and other cations. After washing with distilled water, the cations were eluted with 3 N HCl for conventional analysis. As in any low-level determination of copper, it is essential that the filter paper and reagents be essentially copper-free.

Another useful application is illustrated by the paper of Schubert et al. (22) on the isolation of radioelements from urine. It is of considerable importance to be able to detect low levels of various radioisotopes, particularly fission products, in urine; such data may be related to the exposure or body burden of an individual. The procedure for yttrium employed 70 g of Amberlite IR-1 resin and may be described by a listing of the solutions used in sequence:

1. 1000 ml of urine, 12.5 ml concentrated HCl, 500 ml H$_2$O; the acidification of the urine prevents the precipitation of calcium salts and keeps the yttrium in ionic form.

2. 1500 ml of 0.4 M HCl; this removes some adsorbed organic matter, monovalent cations, and divalent cations.

3. 1000 ml of 7 M HCl; this elutes the yttrium quantitatively in a small volume.

4. 500 ml H$_2$O.

5. 1500 ml of 95 per cent alcohol, then 100 ml H$_2$O; this removes the remaining organic matter so that the column can be used again.

If necessary to remove the last traces of salt, the yttrium eluate can be passed through another resin column with a similar sequence of solutions. Similar procedures have been described for the determination of radium (23) and barium, strontium, and rare earths in urine (24).

Exchange methods have been convenient for the concentration of trace substances from natural waters. Abrahamczik (25) has described a procedure in which a number of exchange tubes, as in Fig. 9-7, were taken into the field along with one funnel and one stopcock section. Two hundred and fifty liters of water was passed through each column, which was then taken back to the laboratory for elution. This procedure eliminated the need for carrying a large amount of water from the field to the laboratory. The separation and concentration of trace metals from natural waters have also been accomplished by an interesting method (26) which, however, is not based on ion exchange. A 1-cm-diameter by 25-cm column is packed with granular cellulose acetate carrying a carbon tetrachloride solution of dithizone. Metals that form dithizonates would be expected to be retained from the water as it passes through the column. Studies have shown that lead, zinc, manganese, cadmium, cobalt, and copper are retained under the conditions described. Removal from the column and partial separation of these elements were achieved by such solvents as hydrochloric acid and ammonia.

Separation of Materials. Early in the large-scale atomic-energy developments (Plutonium Project) there was an urgent need for methods of separation, concentration, and purification of the small but highly radioactive masses of fission products. These substances included the rare earths, notoriously difficult to separate. Ion-exchange methods made an outstanding contribution to this problem, and references (2, 3, 5) may be consulted for reviews of historical and procedural details. A major factor was the use of organic acid complexing agents in such a way as to enhance the differences in adsorbability normally existing among the inorganic cations to be separated. Some of the complexing agents employed were oxalic, citric, tartaric, and lactic acids.

In principle, the fission-product mixture is percolated through a sulfonic cation exchanger, and a water wash removes the anions. Treatment with 0.05 M oxalic acid forms complexes with and removes selectively the tetravalent ions, such as zirconium and niobium, which tend to form radiocolloids. Elution with citrate solution of pH 3 removes the trivalent species (the rare-earth group). Elution with citrate solution of pH 5 then removes the divalent and monovalent cations and the alkaline earths and metals. The individual ions of each group can be subsequently separated by passage through another column and elution chro-

TABLE 9-4. SUMMARY OF SEPARATIONS OF ALKALINE METALS, ALKALINE EARTHS, AND RARE EARTHS

Ions separated	Resin	Elutriant
Na, K, Rb, Cs	Dowex 50	0.15 N HCl; 0.3 N HCl
Ba, Sr	. . . .	Citrate, pH 5
Ra, Ba	Colloidal Dowex 50	0.5 M citrate, pH 7.5 to 8
Pb, Ba	Amberlite IR-1	
Nd, Pr, Ce	Dowex 50	5% citrate
Ce, La	Dowex 50	5% citrate, pH 2.9
Ac, La	. . . .	Citrate
Nd, Sm, Pr	. . . .	0.5% citrate, pH 3.9
Lu, Yb, Tm, Er, Ho, Y	Dowex 50	4.75% citrate, pH 3.2 to 3.4

(Compiled from Frederick C. Nachod, ed., "Ion Exchange," Academic Press, Inc., New York, 1949.)

matographically with citrate buffers.   Table 9-4 summarizes some of the separations that have been attained within these groups of elements. Samuelson (2) may be consulted for a discussion of other useful inorganic separations.

The application of ion-exchange methods to nucleic acid chemistry may serve to illustrate separations of particular biochemical importance. Nucleoproteins are apparently an essential constituent of all cells.   The composition and nomenclature for yeast nucleoprotein are illustrated below, although it must be pointed out that the more recent experimental observations cannot be explained on the basis of a simple tetranucleotide structure (27).   Thymus nucleic acid, which has also been well

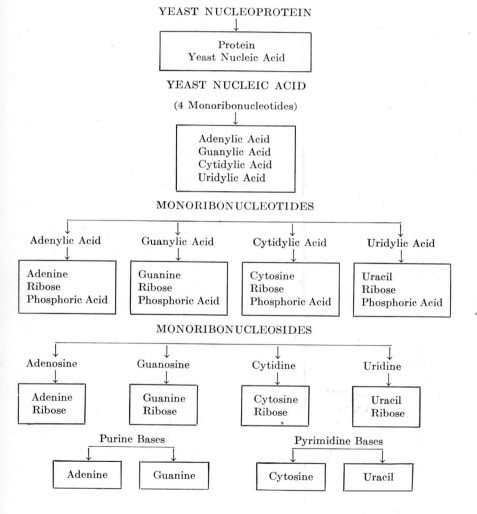

YEAST NUCLEOPROTEIN

Protein
Yeast Nucleic Acid

YEAST NUCLEIC ACID

(4 Monoribonucleotides)

Adenylic Acid
Guanylic Acid
Cytidylic Acid
Uridylic Acid

MONORIBONUCLEOTIDES

| Adenylic Acid | Guanylic Acid | Cytidylic Acid | Uridylic Acid |

| Adenine
Ribose
Phosphoric Acid | Guanine
Ribose
Phosphoric Acid | Cytosine
Ribose
Phosphoric Acid | Uracil
Ribose
Phosphoric Acid |

MONORIBONUCLEOSIDES

| Adenosine | Guanosine | Cytidine | Uridine |

| Adenine
Ribose | Guanine
Ribose | Cytosine
Ribose | Uracil
Ribose |

Purine Bases   Pyrimidine Bases

| Adenine | Guanine | Cytosine | Uracil |

characterized, is similar to yeast nucleic acid except that 2-desoxyribose and thymine are substituted for ribose and uracil, respectively. Ion-exchange chromatography of the nucleic acids has been reviewed by Cohn (28) and Samuelson (2).

The nucleotides may be retained by anion exchangers above pH 6 where the phosphate group is functional, or by cation exchangers in the low pH region where the amino group tends to adsorb. Anion exchange appears to be the more effective. Both cation and anion exchange can

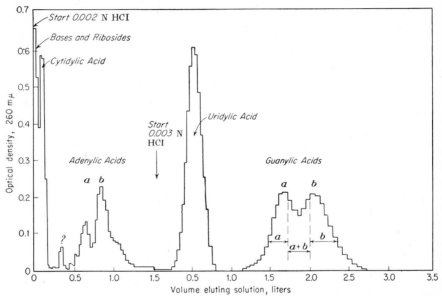

Fig. 9-11. Demonstration of isomers in the separation of mononucleotides of rat liver ribonucleic acid by anion exchange. Exchanger: Dowex 1, 12.5 cm by 0.74 cm². Test material: about 14 mg of mixed nucleotides from Ba(OH)₂ hydrolysis of rat liver nucleic acid, in 10 ml H₂O. [*From W. E. Cohn, The Anion-exchange Separation of Ribonucleotides, J. Am. Chem. Soc.,* **72**: 1471–1478 (1950).]

be used for separation of the nucleosides as well as of the purine and pyrimidine bases. The details of separations accomplished may be noted in Table 9-5, compiled from (28). In addition to the discovery of new nucleotides, an outstanding contribution has been the unequivocal demonstration of the existence of isomers. Figure 9-11 illustrates the appearance and resolution of isomers of adenylic acid and of guanylic acid from rat liver ribonucleic acid after passage through an anion exchanger (29). Other experiments have confirmed this interpretation. Methods have also been described for separation of the adenosine phosphates.

Estimation of Total Salt Concentration. After passage of a neutral solution containing several salts through a hydrogen-ion exchanger, the

TABLE 9-5. ILLUSTRATION OF SEPARATIONS OF NUCLEIC ACIDS AND DERIVATIVES

	Ion exchanger	Eluting agent	Liters through column to peak of elution
Yeast nucleic acid hydrolysate...	Dowex 5, 300 mesh, H^+ form, 24 cm by 0.74 cm²		
Uridylic acid..............	....	0.1 M acetic acid	0.010
Guanylic acid..............	.. ..	0.1 M acetic acid	0.030
Cytidylic acid..............	....	0.1 M acetic acid	0.20
Adenylic acid..............	....	0.1 M acetic acid	0.42
Mixed monoribonucleotides.....	Dowex 2, Cl^- form, 12.5 cm by 0.94 cm²		
Cytidylic...................	....	0.003 N HCl	0.20
Adenylic...................	....	0.003 N HCl	0.40
Uridylic...................	....	0.003 N HCl	1.8
Guanylic...................	....	0.003 N HCl	3.5
Purine and pyrimidine bases....	Dowex 1, 300 mesh, Cl^- form, 85 mm by 0.74 cm²		
Cytosine...................	....	0.2 M NH_4OH-NH_4Cl buffer, pH 10.6, 0.025 M Cl^-	0.02
Uracil.....................	....	0.2 M NH_4OH-NH_4Cl buffer, pH 10.6, 0.025 M Cl^-	0.16
Thymine...................	....	0.2 M NH_4OH-NH_4Cl buffer, pH 10.6, 0.025 M Cl^-	0.27
Guanine...................	....	0.2 M NH_4OH-NH_4Cl buffer, pH 10.6, 0.025 M Cl^-	0.45
Adenine...................	....	0.2 M NH_4OH-NH_4Cl buffer, adjusted to pH 10.0, 0.1 M Cl^-	0.65
Commercial adenylic acids......	Dowex 1, 250 to 500 mesh, 14 cm by 0.74 cm²		
Adenosine-5-phosphate.......	....	0.1 M formic acid, pH 2.4	0.21
Adenylic acid A.............	....	0.1 M formic acid, pH 2.4	0.37
Adenylic acid B.............	....	0.1 M formic acid, pH 2.4	0.56

[Compiled from Waldo E. Cohn, Some Results of the Applications of Ion-exchange Chromatography to Nucleic Acid Chemistry, *J. Cellular Comp. Physiol.*, **38** (Supplement 1): 21–40 (1951).]

filtrate contains an amount of acid equivalent to the salt content of the original solution.	Titration of the acid then gives a measure of the original salt content.	This type of application may be illustrated by the method of Polis and Reinhold (30) for the determination of the total base of serum.	Amberlite IR-100 resin was converted to the hydrogen form by treatment with dilute acid.	To a microcolumn of resin was added 0.2 ml of serum, followed by a distilled-water wash.	The effluent was aerated with CO_2-free air to remove CO_2 and was titrated with standard alkali until the indicator color matched that of a control sample that had been aerated but not passed through the ion exchanger.	Base bound as bicarbonate was determined separately by gasometric measurement of the serum CO_2-combining capacity.

Properties of Complex Ions.	Ion-exchange methods can be used for study of the composition and stability of complex ions.	Such studies have been simplified by the use of radioisotopes and, conversely, have contributed important information on the physical properties of radio-tracers in dilute solution.	The metabolic behavior of the radioisotopes of the alkaline-earth elements as affected by the presence of complexing agents has been of considerable interest.	An example of the determination of the dissociation of the radium citrate complex is described from the paper of Schubert et al. (31).

The dissociation reaction for the radium citrate complex is

$$RaCit^- \rightleftharpoons Ra^{++} + Cit^{3-} \tag{9-1}$$

and

$$K_c = \frac{[Ra^{++}][Cit^{3-}]}{[RaCit]^-} \tag{9-2}$$

where K_c = the dissociation constant.	The equilibrium distribution of a tracer ion between exchanger and solution may be readily determined experimentally and is defined as

$$K_d = \frac{\% \text{ in exchanger}}{\% \text{ in solution}} \times \frac{\text{volume of solution}}{\text{mass of exchanger}} \tag{9-3}$$

To permit calculation of K_c from estimations of K_d, Schubert et al. (31) have derived an expression that, for the radium citrate complex, may be expressed as

$$K_c = \frac{Cit^{3-}}{K_d^0/K_d - 1} \tag{9-4}$$

where K_d^0 = distribution coefficient in absence of complex

K_d = distribution coefficient in presence of complex

In practice, K_d is determined by shaking the radioisotope solution (in this case Ra*) with the ion exchanger until equilibrium is reached and then measuring the amount of radioactivity remaining in the solution.

This is done at various concentrations of the complexing agent (in this case citrate ion), and K_d is calculated for each concentration by use of Eq. (9-3). The value of K_d^0 can be determined by plotting $1/K_d$ vs. the concentration of complexing agent and extrapolating to zero concentration. The value of K_c can be calculated from Eq. (9-4) or estimated graphically from a log-log plot of $K_d^0/K_d - 1$ against Cit^{3-}. Table 9-6 presents an example of experimental details and data that can be used to work through the above procedures.

TABLE 9-6. DETERMINATION OF DISSOCIATION CONSTANT OF RADIUM AND CITRIC ACID[a]

Citric acid, moles/liter	Ra^{++} adsorbed, %	K_d	K_d^0 (extrapolated)	K_c
0.0050	68.3	4.31	7.05	0.0079
0.010	63.8	3.52	....	0.0100
0.020	56.4	2.58	....	0.0115
0.030	47.5	1.81	....	0.0104

[a] 100 ml of solution; pH 7.2 to 7.4; 0.005 μc Ra^{228}; total cation concentration, $Na^+ = 0.16$ M as NaCl; resin, 50 mg of Dowex 50, sodium form, 100 to 150 mesh.

[From Jack Schubert, Edwin R. Russell, and Lawrence S. Myers, Jr., Dissociation Constants of Radium-Organic Acid Complexes Measured by Ion Exchange, *J. Biol. Chem.*, **185**: 387–398 (1950).]

Similar studies have been reported with complex ions of calcium and strontium and numerous organic acids; these complex ions were of the 1:1 type (32). When the complex ions do not have a 1:1 ratio of anion and cation, the above equations are simply modified in accordance with the usual law of mass action. The composition of the complex can be determined from the log-log plot of $K_d^0/K_d - 1$ vs. the concentration of complexing ion, in which case the slope represents the ratio of anions to cations.

In addition to determination of the dissociation constants, it is possible to use similar principles to estimate the activity coefficients of electrolytes at nearly zero concentration levels, to detect and study radiocolloids, and to determine the probable valence and relative basicity of cations.

Miscellaneous Applications. Some rather unusual uses of ion exchangers in biological studies may be listed as follows: (a) determination of available phosphorus in soils (33); (b) removal of potassium from uremic dogs by continuous circulation of blood through a cation exchanger (34); and (c) feeding of ion-exchange resins to neutralize acidity, withhold sodium from the body in edema, and divert the sodium, potassium, calcium, and magnesium of the food (35 to 38).

A summary of biological applications to indicate scope is presented in Table 9-7, as compiled primarily from the general references.

TABLE 9-7. SURVEY OF BIOLOGICAL APPLICATIONS OF ION EXCHANGE

Substance	Objective	Type of exchanger	Elutriant
Acetal	Separation from aldehydes and ketones	Ethanol solution on anion type, bisulfite form	
Adrenalin	Isolation and purification	Carboxylic	
Alcohol	Determination in presence of aldehydes and ketones, removal of aldehyde impurities	Anion, strongly basic, bisulfite form	Water
Aldehydes and ketones	Separation of aldehydes from ketones	Anion, bisulfite form	Water
Alkaloids	Liberation of bases from alkaloidal salts	Anion, weakly basic	Alcohol
Alkaloids (morphine)	Removal of interfering substances from urine	Zeolite	Sodium carbonate
Alkaloids (nicotine)	Analytical separations	Carboxylic, hydrogen form	
Alkaloids (quinine)	Analytical separations	Cation, sodium form	
Amino acids	Preparation, purification, and analysis	See text	
Ammonia	Determination in urine	Sodium zeolite	Sodium hydroxide
Ascorbic acid	Isolation from urine	Anion, weakly basic, free-base form	Hydrochloric acid
Ascorbic acid oxidase	Separation of ionic copper	Sulfonic	
Aureomycin	Determination in blood and urine	Zeolite	Sodium carbonate
Blood	Removal of Ca to prevent coagulation	Cation	
Cellulose xanthate	Determination of degree of substitution	Anion, strongly basic, free-base form	
Coenzyme A	Removal from liver extracts	Anion, chloride form	
Cytochrome C	Purification	Carboxylic	Buffer, pH 10.8
Gastric acidity	In vivo determination by measurement of quinine appearing in urine	Carboxylic plus quinine base	
Glycerol	Removal of borate complex from aqueous solution	Anion, strongly basic	Water

TABLE 9-7. SURVEY OF BIOLOGICAL APPLICATIONS OF ION EXCHANGE (*Continued*)

Substance	Objective	Type of exchanger	Elutriant
Histamine..........	Removal from biological fluids	Carboxylic	Dilute acid
Inositol............	Determination in animal tissue extracts	Mixed cation and anion	
Lactic acid.........	Determination in biological fluids	Sulfonic, free-acid form	
Nucleosides........	Removal of anionic compounds	Anion-free-base form	
Nucleotides, nucleosides, purine and pyrimidine bases	Isolation, purification, and analysis	See text	
Organic acids........	Separation from fruit juices with elimination of alcohols, sugars, aldehydes, ketones, high-polymer acids, amino acids, cations	Anion	
Organic acids........	Separation from each other in studies of sugar-beet liquors	Anion, chloride form	Hydrochloric or sulfuric acid at pH 1.5
Organic acids (citric, malic, succinic, fumaric)	Separation from plant extracts with removal of cations, sugars, and pigments	Anion, strongly basic, bicarbonate form	Sodium carbonate
Organic acids (*l*-malic)	Determination in maple sirup and apple juice	Cation, anion	
Pectin materials.....	Analysis and characterization	Sulfonic, hydrogen form; anion, weakly basic, free-base form	
Pectin-methyl-esterase	Purification from commercial pectinase	Sulfonic, free-acid form	
Penicillin...........	Purification	Sulfonic at pH 6.7; anion, weakly basic	
Peptides............	Removal of acidic amino acids and peptides from wool hydrolysates	Anion	Hydrochloric acid
Phosphoglycerates...	Isolation and identification from plant extracts	Anion, strongly basic	

TABLE 9-7. SURVEY OF BIOLOGICAL APPLICATIONS OF ION EXCHANGE (*Continued*)

Substance	Objective	Type of exchanger	Elutriant
Proteins............	Removal of salt for fractional precipitation	Sulfonic, free-acid form; anion, strongly basic, free-base form	
Pyridoxine..........	Removal of substances interfering in determination	Anion	
Riboflavin..........	Determination after removal of thiamine	Zeolite to retain thiamine, sulfonic to retain riboflavin	
Ribonuclease........	Purification	Carboxylic	
Streptomycin........	Determination	Carboxylic	Hydrochloric acid
Sugars.............	Removal of non-sugar-reducing substances in analysis of food products	Mixed resins	
Sugars.............	Separation of gluconic acid and 2-ketogluconic acid from ribose	Anion, strongly basic, chloride form	
Sugars (glucose-1-phosphate)	Isolation and purification	Sulfonic, hydrogen form; anion, weakly basic	Alkali
Sugars (monosaccharides)	Separation by formation of borate complexes	Anion, free-base form	
Thiamine..........	Removal of substances interfering in determination	Zeolite	25 % KCl in 0.1 N HCl
Uridine............	Separation from cytidine and adenosine	Sulfonic, hydrogen form	
Viruses............	Isolation	Anion, strongly basic	Disodium phosphate
Water.............	Purification for trace-element work, removal of radioisotopes from waste	Sulfonic	

(Primarily compiled from the general references.)

GENERAL REFERENCES

1. Kunin, Robert, and Robert J. Myers: "Ion Exchange Resins," John Wiley & Sons, Inc., New York, 1950.
2. Samuelson, Olof: "Ion Exchangers in Analytical Chemistry," John Wiley & Sons, Inc., New York, 1953.

3. Lederer, Edgar, and Michael Lederer: "Chromatography," Elsevier Press, Inc., New York, 1953.
4. Cassidy, Harold Gomes: "Adsorption and Chromatography," Interscience Publishers, Inc. New York, 1951.
5. Nachod, Frederick C., ed.: "Ion Exchange," Academic Press, Inc., New York, 1949.

CITED REFERENCES

6. Applezweig, Norman: Semimicro Ion-exchange Column, *Ind. Eng. Chem. Anal. Ed.*, **18**: 82 (1946).
7. Helrich, Kenneth, and William Rieman III: Determination of Phosphorus in Phosphate Rock, *Anal. Chem.*, **19**: 651–652 (1947).
8. "Methods of Vitamin Assay," ed. by Association of Vitamin Chemists, Inc., Interscience Publishers, Inc., New York, 1947.
9. Winters, James C., and Robert Kunin: Ion Exchange in the Pharmaceutical Field, *Ind. Eng. Chem.*, **41**: 460–463 (1949).
10. Stein, William H., and Stanford Moore: Chromatographic Determination of the Amino Acid Composition of Proteins, *Cold Spring Harbor Symposia Quan. Biol.*, **14**: 179–190 (1950).
10a. Moore, Stanford, and William H. Stein: Chromatography of Amino Acids on Sulfonated Polystyrene Resins, *J. Biol. Chem.*, **192**: 663–681 (1951).
10b. Hirs, C. H. W., Stanford Moore, and William H. Stein: Isolation of Amino Acids by Chromatography on Ion Exchange Columns: Use of Volatile Buffers, *J. Biol. Chem.*, **195**: 669–683 (1952).
11. Williams, Kenneth T., and Clarence M. Johnson: Determination of Soluble Pectin and Pectic Acid by Electrodeposition, *Ind. Eng. Chem. Anal. Ed.*, **16**: 23–25 (1944).
12. Khym, J. X., and L. P. Zill: The Separation of Sugars by Ion Exchange, *J. Am. Chem. Soc.*, **74**: 2090–2094 (1952).
13. Noggle, G. R., and R. A. Bolomey: The Biosynthesis of Carbon-14-labeled Compounds. I. The Chromatographic Separation of Glucose and Fructose, *Plant Physiol.*, **26**: 174–181 (1951).
14. Noggle, G. R., and M. E. Schumacher: The Biosynthesis of Carbon-14-labeled Compounds. II. The Chromatographic Separation of the Monosaccharides, Disaccharides, and Trisaccharides from Plant Extracts, *Plant Physiol.*, **27**: 422–426 (1952).
15. Noggle, G. R., and L. P. Zill: Ion Exchange as a Tool for Studying Plant Carbohydrates, in "The Role of Atomic Energy in Agricultural Research," Proceedings of the Fourth Annual Oak Ridge Summer Symposium (Sponsored by the Oak Ridge National Laboratory and Oak Ridge Institute of Nuclear Studies, Aug. 25–30, 1952), TID-5115, pp. 378–403, January, 1953.
16. Noggle, G. R., and L. P. Zill: The Biosynthesis of Carbon-14-labeled Compounds. III. The Separation and Isolation of Sugars by Ion-exchange Chromatography, *Plant Physiol.*, **28**: 731–735 (1953).
17. Khym, Joseph X., and Waldo E. Cohn: The Separation of Sugar Phosphates by Ion Exchange with the Use of the Borate Complex, *J. Am. Chem. Soc.*, **75**: 1153–1156 (1953).
18. Polis, B. David, and Otto Meyerhof: Studies on Adenosinetriphosphatase in Muscle. I. Concentration of the Enzyme on Myosin, *J. Biol. Chem.*, **169**: 389–401 (1947).
19. Wolfrom, M. L., D. I. Weisblat, and J. V. Karabinos: A Galactogen from Beef Lung, *Arch. Biochem.*, **14**: 1–6 (1947).

20. Sutton, William J. L., and Emory F. Almy: Separation of Sodium, Potassium, Magnesium, and Calcium in Milk Ash by Ion-exchange Chromatography. *J. Dairy Sci.*, **36**: 1248–1254 (1953).

21. Cranston, H. A., and J. B. Thompson: Use of an Ion-exchange Resin in Determination of Traces of Copper, *Ind. Eng. Chem. Anal. Ed.*, **18**: 323–326 (1946).

22. Schubert, Jack, Edwin R. Russell, and Lawrence B. Farabee: The Use of Ion Exchange for the Determination of Radioelements in Large Volumes of Urine, *Science*, **109**: 316–317 (1949).

23. Russell, Edwin R., Roman C. Lesko, and Jack Schubert: A Direct Method for Determining Radium in Exposed Humans, *Nucleonics*, **7**: 60–64 (1950).

24. Tompkins, P. C., L. B. Farabee, and J. X. Khym: Procedure for the Radiochemical Analysis of Barium, Strontium, and the Rare Earths in Human Urine, AECD-2692, 1949.

25. Lafferty, R. H., Jr.: Use of Ion Exchangers in Analytical Chemistry, AECD-2414, Nov. 19, 1948.

26. Carritt, Dayton E.: Separation and Concentration of Trace Metals from Natural Waters, *Anal. Chem.*, **25**: 1927–1928 (1953).

27. Cohn, W. E., D. G. Doherty, and Elliott Volkin: The Products of Ribonucleic Acid Hydrolysis and Their Relationship to Its Structure, *Phosphorus Metabolism*, **2**: 339–354 (1952).

28. Cohn, Waldo E.: Some Results of the Applications of Ion-exchange Chromatography to Nucleic Acid Chemistry, *J. Cellular Comp. Physiol.*, **38** (Supplement 1): 21–40 (1951).

29. Cohn, W. E.: The Anion-exchange Separation of Ribonucleotides, *J. Am. Chem. Soc.*, **72**: 1471–1478 (1950).

30. Polis, B. D., and John G. Reinhold: The Determination of Total Base of Serum by Ion Exchange Reactions of Synthetic Resins, *J. Biol. Chem.*, **156**: 231–236 (1944).

31. Schubert, Jack, Edwin R. Russell, and Lawrence S. Myers, Jr.: Dissociation Constants of Radium-Organic Acid Complexes Measured by Ion Exchange, *J. Biol. Chem.*, **185**: 387–398 (1950).

32. Schubert, Jack: Ion Exchange Studies of Complex Ions as a Function of Temperature, Ionic Strength, and Presence of Formaldehyde, *J. Phys. Chem.*, **56**: 113–118 (1952).

33. Moller, Jorgen, and Thorkil Mogensen: Use of an Ion-exchanger for Determining Available Phosphorus in Soils, *Soil Sci.*, **76**: 297–306 (1953).

34. Kessler, Bruce J., John B. Liebler, Jesse I. Abrahams, and Martin Sass: Reduction of Hyperkalemia by Circulating Blood through a Cation Exchange Resin, *Proc. Soc. Exptl. Biol. Med.*, **84**: 508–510 (1953).

35. McChesney, Evan W.: Studies of Cation Exchange Resins; Their Optimal Potassium Content for Clinical Use, *J. Lab. Clin. Med.*, **38**: 199–209 (1951).

36. McChesney, Evan W.: In Vivo Uptake of Cations by Two Types of Exchange Resins, *Am. J. Physiol.*, **168**: 44–54 (1952).

37. McChesney, Evan W.: Neutrality Regulation Mechanisms in Rats Receiving Sulfonic Ion Exchange Resin, *Proc. Soc. Exptl. Biol. Med.*, **79**: 531–534 (1952).

38. Best, Maurice M., and Joan D. Wathen: Biochemical and Clinical Effects Resulting from the Administration of a Cation-Anion Exchange Resin in Decompensated Hepatic Cirrhosis, *J. Lab. Clin. Med.*, **42**: 518–529 (1953).

CHAPTER 10

RADIOACTIVATION ANALYSIS

PRINCIPLES. SENSITIVITY. SOURCES OF RADIATION. PROCEDURES. BIOLOGICAL APPLICATIONS—Arsenic; Sodium and Potassium; Gold; Cobalt; Strontium; Rare Earths. MISCELLANEOUS APPLICATIONS

The discovery of artificial radioactivity in 1934 and the availability of methods for the production of artificial radioisotopes have led to a truly novel method of analysis. In principle, the sample to be analyzed is placed in a flux of bombarding particles long enough for the production of a measurable amount of a radioisotope of the element to be determined. After elimination of radiocontaminants by one means or another, measurement of the induced radioactivity provides a determination of the amount of the particular element in the sample.

References to the early work in the field are documented in the general references (1 to 7), particularly in the review of Boyd (1). Hevesy and Levi, perhaps the first workers to use the method, in 1936–1938 estimated dysprosium in samples of yttrium, and europium in gadolinium, with the avoidance of the difficult rare-earth chemical separations. Seaborg and Livingood in 1938 demonstrated gallium contamination in iron after bombardment of the latter in the cyclotron. King and Henderson in 1939 detected traces of copper in silver, and Sagane et al. in 1942 estimated sodium in aluminum. Ardenne and Bernard in 1944 used an electrostatic accelerator to determine carbon in steel. Tobias (8) and Brues and Robertson (9) in 1947 employed the method for the determination of trace elements in biological tissue. Clark and Overman (10) in 1947 reported studies using the Oak Ridge chain-reacting pile and coined the term *radioactivation analysis*, which is sometimes abbreviated in usage to *activation analysis*.

A primary advantage of activation analysis is the extreme sensitivity for many elements which exceeds that of conventional chemical and physical methods. Besides the inherent sensitivity in the production and detection of radioactivity, the over-all sensitivity may be increased by the use of relatively large samples. Contamination problems are virtually nonexistent since, *after* the bombardment has been completed, the results are independent of any contamination by the inactive element under

413

investigation which might occur in processing the sample material; very little processing is needed *before* bombardment, so that the opportunity for contamination is minimal.   Thus the difficulties with large "blanks" which are usually an obstacle in the conventional estimation of trace amounts of elements are avoided.   There is usually little trouble from interfering substances except when samples contain large amounts of neutron-absorbing material or of an extraneous element that will produce gross amounts of radioactivity in the sample.   Activation analysis offers specificity in that the radioisotope to be assayed has a definite half-life and radiation characteristics that can be identified or measured.   Both of these properties are never exactly duplicated in any two radioisotopes. Difficult chemical separations are often avoided, and the procedure has particular advantage for those elements for which there are no adequate traditional methods of analysis.   In some cases the sample is unchanged after decay of the induced activity and can be used for other analyses. As always, there are limitations.   These result primarily from radiation characteristics and are discussed in some detail later on.

PRINCIPLES

When a sample is exposed to a flux of bombarding particles, the elements contained therein become activated to form radioactive species. There are then two opposing processes in operation: the growth of radioactivity, as governed by the flux of radiation and cross section of the element; and the decay, as governed by the half-life of the radioisotope formed.   The amount of radioactivity present at any given time during the exposure can be expressed by the following equation, derived from the usual growth and decay laws (1):

$$A = \frac{G(6.02 \times 10^{23})f\sigma(1 - e^{-\lambda t})(\Theta)}{M} \tag{10-1}$$

where A = disintegrations per second in radioisotope produced
G = grams of element of natural isotopic composition in sample
f = flux of bombarding particles in units of particles/cm^2/sec
σ = cross section of nuclear reaction in units of cm^2/target atom
λ = radioactive-decay constant
t = time of bombardment
Θ = fractional abundance of target isotope in naturally occurring element
M = atomic weight of element

It is theoretically possible to calculate G, the grams of unknown element, by substitution of measured and known values in Eq. (10-1). However, it is much more practical to *evaluate G by use of a comparison sample, comprised of a known amount of the element to be determined, which is simultaneously exposed to the same flux and treated in the identical way as the unknown.* The physical significance of the various terms in Eq. (10-1) will be further explained in the later discussion of sensitivity.

After the irradiation the sample may contain several radioactive species. There is then the problem of measuring the particular radio-isotope produced by the element for which the analysis is made. In simple cases the methods described in Chap. 5 for the radioassay of mixtures can be employed. For example, radioactivation analysis of manganese in aluminum was accomplished readily, since the aluminum radioisotope has a half-life of 2.3 min, whereas that of manganese has a half-life of 2.59 hr. After irradiation the sample was allowed to stand at least 23 min before counting, so that the aluminum radioactivity was reduced to an insignificant level and the counting measurements reflected only the level of manganese present (6). Biological material, however, is usually complex, and it becomes necessary to make chemical separations so as to isolate the element being determined from extraneous activities associated with other elements. This is usually done by the addition of a known amount of the stable element, as an isotopic carrier, to the test sample and to an aliquot of the comparison sample after irradiation. The test sample and comparator are then chemically processed to isolate the element being determined for radioassay. Since the separation yields are seldom quantitative, it is often necessary to make a correction for the actual yield obtained. This can be done by chemical determination of the recovery of the known amount of added carrier.

The general procedure may then be summarized as follows: (*a*) A known weight of the sample to be analyzed is irradiated, together with a comparative sample containing a known weight of the element to be determined. (*b*) After irradiation a known weight of the element to be determined is added as a carrier to the solutions of both the test and comparator samples. (*c*) Each solution is chemically processed to separate the desired element and its radioisotope(s) from extraneous radioactivities. (*d*) The chemical yield of the carrier is determined. (*e*) The radioactivities in the test and comparator samples are measured under similar conditions. The purity of the separated radioactivity can be checked by a measurement of decay and radiation-energy characteristics.

SENSITIVITY

Equation (10-1) is useful in explanation of the factors that govern the sensitivity of the determination. To give a maximum value of produced radioactivity (A), it is clear that

1. The neutron flux f should be large, since the sensitivity is directly proportional thereto.

2. The activation cross section σ should be high.   This is characteristic of the element and is a main determinant as to which elements can or cannot be adequately analyzed by the method.

3. The half-life, as expressed by the decay constant, should fall between a few minutes and several days.   It can be shown that an irradiation period equal to several half-lives is required to give the maximum activity available and that an irradiation period equal to one half-life gives about one-half the maximum value.   This means that prohibitively long irradiation periods are required for radioisotopes of long half-lives.   On the other hand, the radioisotope starts to suffer a net loss of activity after removal from the pile, and if the half-life is too short, it may be impossible to get the measurements made before the desired activity has been reduced below detectable amounts.   This decay factor has not been included in Eq. (10-1).

4. The lower the atomic weight M, the greater will be the sensitivity.

5. The higher the abundance of the target element Θ, the greater will be the sensitivity.

6. There is an important factor that is not contained in Eq. (10-1), namely, the efficiency with which the induced radioactivity can be measured.   An estimate of counting efficiency for a given radioisotope can be obtained from the data presented in Chap. 6.

A listing of sensitivities has been compiled by Leddicotte and Reynolds (5) for the conditions in the Oak Ridge National Laboratory graphite reactor.   Table 10-1 presents these values.   The listing is limited to elements producing a radioisotope with a half-life greater than about 10 min and does not include elements of atomic number greater than 83. The sensitivity values are based on a *flux of* 5×10^{11} *neutrons/cm²/sec* and represent the micrograms of the element required to give an amount of radioactivity measurable by usual counting methods after exposure to saturation or to a 1-month bombardment.   For example, sodium could be measured by bombardment to saturation in any sample containing at least 0.007 μg of this element.   These sensitivity values are valid only when the sample does not contain large amounts of other elements that become highly radioactive under irradiation, and when there are no substances present that interfere with the chemical separation procedures.

SOURCES OF RADIATION

The nuclear chain reactor will probably be most widely used because of technical reasons and the availability of radioactivation-analysis service to the public.   However, other sources of bombarding particles such as the cyclotron, betatron, and linear accelerator may also be employed. Table 10-2 presents a listing of such sources and estimates of the flux

TABLE 10-1. SENSITIVITIES OF RADIOACTIVATION ANALYSIS IN ORNL GRAPHITE REACTOR[a]

Element	Iso-tope pro-duced	Half-life		"Atomic" cross section, barns	% satura-tion, 1 month	Sensitivity, μg of element
Antimony	Sb^{122}	2.8	days	3.89	.....	0.004
Arsenic	As^{76}	26.8	hr	4.3	.....	0.002
Barium	Ba^{139}	85.0	min	0.36	.....	0.05
Bismuth	Bi^{210}	5.02	days	0.015	98.4	2
Bromine	Br^{80m}	4.58	hr	4.09	.....	0.003
Bromine	Br^{82}	35.87	hr	1.11	.....	0.01
Cadmium	Cd^{115}	53	hr	0.317	.....	0.05
Calcium	Ca^{45}	152	days	0.013	11.9	3.8
Cerium	Ce^{141}	33.1	days	0.35	52.3	0.1
Cerium	Ce^{143}	33	hr	0.122	.....	0.2
Cesium	Cs^{134m}	3.15	hr	0.016	.....	~1
Cesium	Cs^{134}	2.3	yr	26	2.4	0.03
Chlorine	Cl^{38}	37.29	min	0.14	.....	0.03
Chromium	Cr^{51}	27.8	days	0.732	54.3	0.2
Cobalt	Co^{60}	5.27	yr	34	1.08	0.02
Copper	Cu^{64}	12.8	hr	2.97	.....	0.007
Dysprosium	Dy^{165}	139.2	min	738	.....	0.00003
Erbium	Er^{171}	~7	hr	1.0	.....	0.02
Europium	Eu^{152}	9.2	hr	659	.....	0.00003
Gadolinium	Gd^{159}	18	hr	0.9	.....	0.02
Gallium	Ga^{72}	14.3	hr	1.35	.....	0.007
Germanium	Ge^{75}	82	min	0.22	.....	0.04
Gold	Au^{198}	2.69	days	96	.....	0.003
Hafnium	Hf^{181}	45	days	3.5	34.2	0.02
Holmium	Ho^{166}	27.3	hr	60	.....	0.0004
Indium	In^{116m}	54	min	139	.....	0.0001
Iodine	I^{128}	24.99	min	7.0	.....	0.002
Iridium	Ir^{192}	74.37	days	285	25	0.0004
Iridium	Ir^{194}	19	hr	80	.....	0.0003
Iron	Fe^{59}	45.1	days	0.0024	33.2	9
Lanthanum	La^{140}	40	hr	8	.....	0.002
Lutetium	Lu^{176m}	3.7	hr	19.5	.....	0.001
Lutetium	Lu^{177}	6.8	days	91	95.2	0.0003
Magnesium	Mg^{27}	10	min	0.0056	.....	0.6
Manganese	Mn^{56}	2.59	hr	13	.....	0.0006
Mercury	Hg^{203}	47.9	days	0.71	38	0.13
Molybdenum	Mo^{99}	2.85	days	0.099	.....	0.1
Neodymium	Nd^{147}	11.3	days	0.26	.....	0.1
Neodymium	Nd^{149}	2	hr	0.14	.....	0.1
Nickel	Ni^{65}	2.6	hr	0.03	.....	0.03
Niobium	Nb^{94m}	6.6	min	1.20	.....	~10
Osmium	Os^{191}	16.0	days	1.4	75	0.02

TABLE 10-1. SENSITIVITIES OF RADIOACTIVATION ANALYSIS IN ORNL GRAPHITE
REACTOR[a] (*Continued*)

Element	Isotope produced	Half-life		"Atomic" cross section, barns	% saturation, 1 month	Sensitivity, μg of element
Osmium	Os^{193}	30.6	hr	1.0	. . . .	0.03
Palladium	Pd^{109}	13.6	hr	3.1	. . . .	0.005
Phosphorus	P^{32}	14.3	days	0.029	76.7	0.02
Platinum	Pt^{197}	18	hr	0.28	. . . .	0.1
Potassium	K^{42}	12.44	hr	0.067	. . . .	0.08
Praseodymium	Pr^{142}	19.2	hr	10	. . . .	0.002
Rhenium	Re^{186}	3.87	days	37	99.5	0.0007
Rhenium	Re^{188}	16.9	hr	47.2	. . . .	0.0006
Rubidium	Rb^{86}	19.5	days	0.52	65.6	0.03
Ruthenium	Ru^{103}	39.8	days	0.38	39.0	0.1
Ruthenium	Ru^{105}	4.5	hr	0.12	. . . .	0.1
Samarium	Sm^{153}	47	hr	36	. . . .	0.0006
Scandium	Sc^{46}	85	days	14.4	21.5	0.002
Selenium	Se^{81}	17	min	0.23	. . . .	0.05
Silicon	Si^{31}	2.62	hr	0.0037	. . . .	1
Silver	Ag^{110m}	270	days	1.1	7.0	0.11
Sodium	Na^{24}	15.06	hr	0.4	. . . .	0.007
Strontium	Sr^{87m}	2.8	hr	0.13	. . . .	0.6
Sulfur	S^{35}	87.1	days	0.0052	21.2	4
Tantalum	Ta^{182}	115	days	21	16.2	0.007
Tellurium	Te^{127}	9.3	hr	0.15	. . . .	0.1
Terbium	Tb^{160}	73.5	days	22	26	0.004
Thallium	Tl^{204}	3.5	yr	2.25	2.0	0.6
Thulium	Tm^{170}	129	days	100	15.0	0.002
Tin	Sn^{121}	1.1	days	0.072	. . . .	0.2
Tungsten	W^{187}	24.1	hr	9.9	. . . .	0.003
Ytterbium	Yb^{175}	102	hr	15	99.3	0.002
Yttrium	Y^{90}	2.54	days	1.24	. . . .	0.01
Zinc	Zn^{69}	57	min	0.20	. . . .	0.04
Zirconium	Zr^{95}	65	days	0.06	27.3	0.7
Zirconium	Zr^{97}	17	hr	0.045	. . . .	0.3

[a] Based on 5×10^{11} neutrons/cm^2/sec.
(From G. W. Leddicotte, and S. A. Reynolds, Neutron Activation Analysis, A Useful Analytical Method for Determination of Trace Elements, ORNL-1443, Feb. 23, 1953.)

available from each.   It will be recalled from Eq. (10-1) that the sensitivity is directly proportional to the flux.   Thus, for example, if 0.007 μg sodium can be detected with a flux of 5×10^{11}, then 35 μg will be required for detection if the flux is 10^8.   Thus the sensitivities listed in Table 10-1 can readily be calculated on the basis of the fluxes listed in Table 10-2.

TABLE 10-2. NEUTRON SOURCES AND AVAILABLE FLUX

Source	Flux, neutrons/cm^2/sec	Ref. No.
Materials Testing Reactor	2×10^{14}	(11)
Chalk River Pile	5×10^{13}	(11)
Brookhaven National Laboratory Pile	4×10^{12}	(12)
Argonne National Laboratory Heavy Water Pile (CP-3')	4×10^{12}	(11)
Harwell Pile	1×10^{12}	(13)
Oak Ridge National Laboratory Graphite Pile	5×10^{11}	(5)
Van de Graaff generator	5×10^8	(14)
Cyclotron	10^8–10^9	(2)
Ra-Be (1 g)	10^4–10^5	(2)
Sb-Be (1 c, 60-day half-life)	10^3–10^4	(2)
Po-Be (1 c, 140-day half-life)	10^3–10^4	(2)
Ra-Be (25 mg)	10^2	(15)

It is clear that for high fluxes, and therefore high sensitivities, one must depend upon accessible nuclear reactors or accelerators, which, of course, are too expensive to be constructed and used primarily for analytical purposes. It would be convenient to have a neutron source for the use of the individual analytical laboratory, and the possibilities have been discussed by Meinke and Anderson (15). The 1-g radium-beryllium source costs about $25,000 and is too expensive for this purpose. The 25-mg radium-beryllium source costs about $600 and may be satisfactory for certain elements of high cross section where sensitivity is not an important consideration. This source was found useful for rapid assay of rhodium and silver ores (15). The antimony-beryllium source costs about $150. However, it has to be reactivated periodically on account of the relatively short half-life (16).

PROCEDURES

The Oak Ridge National Laboratory is presently offering to perform radioactivation analyses at a cost ranging from $30 to $50 per element per sample (17). The cost figure is given only to indicate an order of magnitude and will vary with many factors, such as the bombardment time required and the number of samples submitted. The individual desiring this service should make known to the Laboratory the nature and history of the sample, including data on boiling point, melting point, gross elements present, hygroscopic properties, explosive properties, etc., as well as the element or elements to be analyzed for. The Laboratory will indicate whether the analysis can be made and will provide appropriate forms to be filled out. Upon receipt of authorization the samples should be submitted ready for analysis.   Usually, solid samples of 0.5 g and liquid samples of about 25 ml are employed.   Solid samples should be shipped in small glass vials closed with a plastic cap or rubber stopper, whereas liquid samples should be sealed in glass ampoules or sample bottles.

An example of the procedures employed may be cited from the studies of Smales and Pate (13, 18, 19) on the determination of arsenic in submicrogram amounts in biological material.   Up to 11 ml of liquid samples such as urine was placed in containers consisting of silica tubes sealed at one end and joined at the other to a short length of capillary tubing; these containers were irradiated unsealed.   A solution containing 1 μg/ml of As was used as a standard and was irradiated in a similar tube at the same time as the sample.   Small volumes of liquid, up to 0.2 ml of blood or urine, for example, were irradiated in small silica pipettes which were sealed before irradiation.   Standard solutions containing 1 μg/ml of As were treated in the same way.   Solid samples such as tissue, hair, or nails were irradiated after being sealed in short lengths of polythene tubing or in bags made of polythene sheet.   The standard was a mixture of alumina containing 100 μg/g of As which was prepared by grinding the two oxides together.

After irradiation and a waiting period of 1 to 24 hr, the weighed sample or standard was transferred to a beaker, and 50 mg of carrier arsenic added.   Oxidation was carried out with hydrogen peroxide and nitric, sulfuric, and perchloric acids.   After oxidation, hydrochloric acid was added, and the arsenic precipitated with ammonium hypophosphite. The precipitate was collected, washed, and dissolved in hydrogen peroxide and hydrochloric acid solution.   The solution was distilled under oxidizing and reducing conditions, first from hydrochloric acid and hydrogen peroxide solution and then from hydrobromic acid solution.   The distillates were combined and treated with ammonium hypophosphite to precipitate the arsenic, which was collected, washed, dried, and weighed to establish the chemical yield.   The precipitate was counted with a Geiger tube.   The counts of all standards and samples were corrected to a common basis of chemical yield, decay, and radioassay conditions. The half-life and the beta energy were checked to ensure that only As[76] was being measured.   Calculations were made as follows:

$$\begin{pmatrix} \text{Grams of As} \\ \text{in sample} \end{pmatrix} = \begin{pmatrix} \text{grams of As} \\ \text{in standard} \end{pmatrix} \times \frac{\text{corrected sample count}}{\text{corrected standard count}}$$

BIOLOGICAL APPLICATIONS

Arsenic.   The studies of Smales and Pate on arsenic, procedures for which have been previously described, furnish an excellent example of useful biological application of radioactivation analysis. These analyses were performed using a neutron flux of 10^{12}. Table 10-3 summarizes typical results. Particularly noteworthy is the small sample that can be used and yet give reliable values. The recoveries and reproducibility were excellent in all cases.

TABLE 10-3. TYPICAL RADIOACTIVATION ANALYSES FOR ARSENIC

Sample	Sample weight, g	Arsenic, g	Arsenic, ppm
Sea water	11.12	3.9×10^{-8}	0.0035
Human urine	0.0885	0.2×10^{-8}	0.023
Human blood	0.0533	0.9×10^{-8}	0.17
Human hair	0.4237	0.344×10^{-8}	0.81
Fingernails	0.0474	7.7×10^{-8}	1.6
Toenails	0.0082	4.6×10^{-8}	5.6
Mouse brain	0.398	0.7×10^{-8}	0.02
Beans	1.0015	35×10^{-8}	0.35

[Compiled from A. A. Smales and B. D. Pate, The Determination of Sub-microgram Quantities of Arsenic by Radioactivation, II–III, *Analyst*, **77**: 188–195, 196–202 (1952).]

It is pointed out that this method is more than a hundred times as sensitive as the methods previously available. Although radioactivation analysis for arsenic will not replace routine chemical methods, there may be situations where the added sensitivity will be valuable. A limiting factor in the sensitivity of most conventional methods is the presence in reagents of trace amounts of the element to be determined. The procedure for arsenic illustrates how the arsenic content of the reagents cannot interfere with the analyses, since the reagents are not used until after the irradiation. Another important point is that quantitative separations are not required, since known amounts of carrier are added after irradiation and a correction can be applied for losses from the measured chemical yield.

Sodium and Potassium. Cephalopod nerve fibers have been analyzed for sodium, potassium, and chlorine employing radioactivation procedures by Keynes and Lewis (20). Giant axons were dissected and, after having been washed, weighed, and dried, were placed in transparent quartz tubes about 3 cm long with an internal diameter of 2 mm. The tubes were then sealed at both ends with an oxygen flame. These samples were irradiated in the Harwell pile for 1 week in batches of 20. Three tubes each containing about 20 mg K_2CO_3, 3 mg Na_2CO_3, and 1 mg KH_2PO_4 were placed with each batch of sample tubes.

After bombardment, each sample tube was broken open, and the nerve transferred to a nickel dish containing a drop of K_2CO_3 solution. The inside of the tube was rinsed with small amounts of distilled water which were added to the nickel dish. The sample was dried and then counted with an end-window Geiger tube using a thick absorber of 4.6 g/cm² and again with a thin absorber of 0.46 g/cm². From these differential absorption measurements it was possible to calculate the Na^{24} and K^{42} content of each sample. The tubes containing the standard or comparison samples were opened, the contents made to 25 ml, and aliquots taken for titration of carbonates and preparation of counting samples.

P³² was measured in all the samples after allowing them to stand for 2 weeks so as to let the Na^{24} and K^{42} decay and using a 25-mg/cm² absorber to eliminate the soft-beta radiation from S^{35}. The counts were standardized against the P^{32} in the comparison samples of KH_2PO_4.

Some samples were counted again about 3 months after irradiation to determine the amount of S^{35}, and hence of chloride, present. Comparison samples of NaCl were irradiated with the nerves for the chloride estimation.

Some typical counting rates are shown in Table 10-4 which illustrate the differential effects of the absorbers. Consideration of the chemical elements present in the tissue indicated that there was little error except that Br^{82} may have increased the apparent Na content by about 1 per cent. Quantities of the order of 0.3 μg Na and 3 μg K were easily determined with a standard error of about ±2 per cent.

TABLE 10-4. PRINCIPAL RADIOISOTOPES IN IRRADIATED SEPIA AXON[a]

	No absorber	Beta absorber, 0.46 g/cm²	Gamma absorber, 4.6 g/cm²
Na^{24}	15,000	450	400
K^{42}	12,000	3000	20
P^{32}	1,500	15	0
S^{35}	150	0	0

[a] Counts per minute for a 1-mg sample at 10 hr after removal from pile.

[From R. D. Keynes, and P. R. Lewis, The Sodium and Potassium Content of Cephalopod Nerve Fibers, *J. Physiol. London,* **114:** 151–182 (1951).]

Gold. In addition to radioactivation analysis for elements naturally occurring in tissue, it is possible to introduce a foreign element into the biological system and to follow its fate by this procedure. This is very similar to the conventional tracer methods. Advantages are offered in that elements may be used whose radioisotopes are too short-lived for conventional procedures. Also the study can be carried out without any possibility of radiation effects on the organism.

Gold has been used in this manner by Tobias and Dunn (21). A mouse was intravenously injected with 10 μg of stable Au as a soluble sodium gold thiosulfate. At sacrifice, tissue samples were wet-ashed and irradiated in the pile. At the same time, a standard solution containing 10 μg Au as the chloride was irradiated with the same flux as received by the ashed tissue samples. Carrier gold was added to each sample and was then separated along with the induced Au[198] by precipitating as the metal and then electroplating on platinum planchets for radioassay of Au[198]. Decay curves for each sample indicated that excellent separation of Au[198] had been obtained. Some typical values are presented in Table 10-5.

TABLE 10-5. DISTRIBUTION OF GOLD AS DETERMINED BY RADIOACTIVATION ANALYSIS IN MOUSE TISSUES AT 30 DAYS AFTER INTRAVENOUS ADMINISTRATION OF 10 μG OF STABLE GOLD

	Tissue mass, g	Gold, ppm wet tissue
Liver.................	1.458	0.44
Adrenals..............	0.012	0.31
Lymph nodes..........	0.031	0.22
Bone.................	2.600	0.11
Brain................	0.502	0.02
Muscle...............	11.2	0.065
Plasma...............	1.0	0.005

[From Cornelius Tobias and Rayburn W. Dunn, Analysis of Microcomposition of Biological Tissue by Means of Induced Radioactivity, *Science*, **109**: 109–113 (1949).]

Tobias and Dunn (21) also reported the levels of induced radioactivity in tissue ash after exposure to thermal neutrons. From radioactivation of 10 ml of blood from a leukemic patient, it was found that the total white cells, red cells, and plasma of the body contained 14.3, 10.5, and 18.5 μg, respectively, of naturally occurring Au[197].

Cobalt. About 1-g portions of crude biological material were placed in quartz ampoules for irradiation (7); milligram amounts of cobalt metal were used as standards. A weighed portion of the irradiated sample was wet-ashed with H_2SO_4 and HNO_3. A known amount of cobalt carrier and copper, iron, nickel, zinc, strontium, and sodium holdback carriers were added. Strontium was separated as the sulfate, copper as the sulfide, and iron as the hydroxide. The cobalt, nickel, and zinc were precipitated as the basic sulfides, and cobalt separated from nickel and zinc as a precipitate of potassium cobaltinitrite. The latter precipitate was washed, dried, weighed, mounted, and counted with a scintillation counter.

Strontium. For determination of strontium, about 0.2-g samples of animal tissue were placed in small quartz tubes for irradiation; milligram amounts of strontium carbonate were used as standards (7). The irradiated tissue sample was dissolved in concentrated nitric acid, and a standard amount of strontium carrier plus barium, iron, and copper holdback carriers was added. Strontium and barium nitrates were twice precipitated from strong acid solution, the precipitate dissolved in water, additional iron holdback carrier added, and the iron precipitated with ammonium hydroxide. The barium was separated from strontium as the chromate in buffered acetic acid solution. The filtrate was made slightly ammoniacal, and the strontium precipitated as the oxalate, which was dried, weighed, and counted with a scintillation counter. Table 10-6 shows the agreement obtained between replicates of the same sample.

TABLE 10-6. REPRODUCIBILITY OF STRONTIUM DETERMINATIONS IN ANIMAL TISSUES BY RADIOACTIVATION ANALYSIS

Sample No.	Strontium, ppm
1	5.6, 5.9, 6.1, 6.1
2	14.4, 13.6, 14.4, 13.0
3	33.2, 34.1, 31.0, 31.1
4	44.8, 45.6, 45.9, 45.4
5	56.1, 58.5, 55.8
6	42.2, 45.7, 44.3

(From W. A. Brooksbank, G. W. Leddicotte, and H. A. Mahlman, Analysis for Trace Impurities by Neutron Activation, ORNL-CF-53-10-52, Oct. 23, 1953.)

Rare Earths. Brooksbank and Leddicotte (22) have described the use of radioactivation and ion-exchange procedures to estimate rare-earth elements in bone. After irradiation, cerium and lanthanum carrier was added to a hydrochloric acid and nitric acid solution of the sample. The rare earths were precipitated with sodium hydroxide, dissolved, and reprecipitated in hydrofluoric acid. The fluoride precipitate was washed and dissolved, and the rare earths precipitated again as the hydroxides, which were dissolved and put on a small Dowex-50 column to separate the lanthanum. The rare earths in the remaining fraction were precipitated

TABLE 10.7. DETERMINATION OF RARE EARTHS IN BONE BY RADIOACTIVATION ANALYSIS AND ION-EXCHANGE SEPARATION

Element	Concentration, ppm	Element	Concentration, ppm
Lanthanum	0.27	Holmium	0.50
Samarium	0.009	Erbium	2.20
Europium	0.20	Thulium	1.30
Gadolinium		Ytterbium	1.30
Terbium	0.0004	Lutetium	0.08
Dysprosium	0.00	Yttrium	0.04

(From W. A. Brooksbank, G. W. Leddicotte, and H. A. Mahlman, Analysis for Trace Impurities by Neutron Activation, ORNL-CF-53-10-52, Oct. 23, 1953.)

twice, and aliquots of the solutions put on Dowex-50 columns, one operated at pH 3.26 and one at pH 3.43, for separation of the other rare earths. Identification was accomplished by use of known standards of high-purity rare earths. Table 10-7 shows typical analytical results on bone.

MISCELLANEOUS APPLICATIONS

Some illustrative results, primarily in the field of inorganic chemistry, are presented in Table 10-8.

A possibility that has not as yet been exploited in the biological field is the use of autoradiography following irradiation of the sample. This technique should provide the advantage of visualization of the localization of elements in heterogeneous samples. Yagoda (23) has summarized some of the work that has been done along these lines with metals and minerals.

TABLE 10-8. TYPICAL RESULTS OF RADIOACTIVATION ANALYSES

Element	Sample	Concentration, ppm	Ref. No.
Arsenic	Germanium dioxide	0.062–0.076	(13)
Cadmium	Vinylite resin	38–449	(7)
Cesium	Rubidium carbonate	200	(22)
Cobalt	Aluminum alloy	7000	(5)
Gallium	Aluminum	100–1400	(7)
Gallium	Iron meteorites	11.2–90.5	(24)
Manganese	Alloys	111–193	(7)
Manganese	Aluminum alloy	7000	(5)
Palladium	Iron meteorites	2.02–6.52	(24)
Potassium	Rubidium carbonate	600–800	(22)
Sodium	Lithium chloride	10	(22)
Sodium	Magnesium	8–15	(5)
Sodium	Potassium carbonate	50	(22)
Tantalum	Stainless steel	800–3100	(5)
Thallium	Potassium iodide	0.33	(25)
Vanadium	Motor oil	0.7–1.0	(7)

GENERAL REFERENCES

1. Boyd, G. E.: Method of Activation Analysis, *Anal. Chem.*, **21**: 335–347 (1949).
2. Taylor, T. I., and W. W. Havens, Jr.: Neutron Spectroscopy for Chemical Analysis, III, *Nucleonics*, **6**: 54–66 (1950).
3. Muehlhause, C. O., and G. E. Thomas: Use of the Pile for Chemical Analysis, *Nucleonics*, **7**: 9–17/59 (1950).
4. Leddicotte, G. W., and S. A. Reynolds: Activation Analysis with the Oak Ridge Reactor, *Nucleonics*, **8**: 62–65 (1951).

5. Leddicotte, G. W., and S. A. Reynolds: Neutron Activation Analysis: A Useful Analytical Method for Determination of Trace Elements, ORNL-1443, Feb. 23, 1953.
6. Leddicotte, G. W., and S. A. Reynolds: The Determination of Trace Elements by Neutron Radioactivation Analysis, *ASTM Bull. No.* 188, February, 1953.
7. Brooksbank, W. A., G. W. Leddicotte, and H. A. Mahlman: Analysis for Trace Impurities by Neutron Activation, ORNL-CF-53-10-52, Oct. 23, 1953.

CITED REFERENCES

8. Tobias, C. A.: Analysis of Trace Elements in Biological Tissue by Means of Induced Radioactivity, Monthly Progress Report, NDP 48A, Div. 2, June, 1947; also AECD-2099 B.
9. Brues, A. M., and O. H. Robertson: Quarterly Report from Argonne National Laboratories, ANL-4108, Nov. 1, 1947.
10. Clark, Herbert M., and Ralph T. Overman: Determination of Trace Amounts of Elements by Radioactivation Analysis, MDDC-1329, Sept. 24, 1947.
11. Huffman, John R.: The Materials Testing Reactor as an Irradiation Facility, AECD-3587, July 6, 1953.
12. Hudgens, J. E., and L. C. Nelson: Determination of Small Concentrations of Indium by Radioactivation, *Anal. Chem.,* **24:** 1472–1475 (1952).
13. Smales, A. A., and B. D. Pate: Determination of Submicrogram Quantities of Arsenic by Radioactivation, *Anal. Chem.,* **24:** 717–721 (1952).
14. Leddicotte, G. W., and G. E. Boyd: Personal communication.
15. Meinke, W. Wayne, and Richard E. Anderson: Activation Analysis Using Low Level Neutron Sources, *Anal. Chem.,* **25:** 778–783 (1953).
16. "Oak Ridge National Laboratory Catalog and Price List: Isotopes, Radioactive-Stable," Jan. 2, 1953.
17. Leddicotte, G. W.: Personal communication.
18. Smales, A. A., and B. D. Pate: The Determination of Sub-microgram Quantities of Arsenic by Radioactivation, II, *Analyst,* **77:** 188–195 (1952).
19. Smales, A. A., and B. D. Pate: The Determination of Sub-microgram Quantities of Arsenic by Radioactivation, III, *Analyst,* **77:** 196–202 (1952).
20. Keynes, R. D., and P. R. Lewis: The Sodium and Potassium Content of Cephalopod Nerve Fibres, *J. Physiol. London,* **114:** 151–182 (1951).
21. Tobias, Cornelius, and Rayburn W. Dunn: Analysis of Microcomposition of Biological Tissue by Means of Induced Radioactivity, *Science,* **109:** 109–113 (1949).
22. Brooksbank, W. A., and G. W. Leddicotte: Ion Exchange Separation of Trace Impurities, ORNL-CF-53-5-228, May 1, 1953.
23. Yagoda, Herman: "Radioactive Measurements with Nuclear Emulsions," John Wiley & Sons, Inc., New York, 1949.
24. Brown, Harrison, and Edward Goldberg: The Neutron Pile as a Tool in Quantitative Analysis; The Gallium and Palladium Content of Iron Meteorites, *Science,* **109:** 347–353 (1949).
25. Delbecq, C. J., L. E. Glendenin, and P. H. Yuster: Determination of Thallium by Radioactivation, *Anal. Chem.,* **25:** 350–351 (1953).

GLOSSARY OF SELECTED TERMS IN NUCLEAR SCIENCE[1]

absorber: A sheet or other body of material placed between a source of radiation and a detector for purposes such as (a) determining the nature or the energy of the radiation; (b) reducing the intensity of the radiation at the detector, as in shielding; or (c) giving the radiation some desired characteristic, as by preferential transmission of one component of the radiation. Such an absorber may function through a combination of processes of true absorption, scattering, and slowing down.

absorption: The reduction in intensity of a beam of radiation as it traverses matter. For particulate radiation, energy is lost by collisions with electrons or nuclei. For photons, the reduction is due to the transfer of the energy to electrons by scattering and photoelectric processes and, at voltages greater than a million, by pair production.

activation analysis: A method of chemical analysis, especially for small traces of material, based on the detection of characteristic radionuclides following a nuclear bombardment.

activity) **tivity):** The intensity or strength of a radioactive source. In absolute t number of atoms disintegrating per unit time and is often expressed in ter **tions** per second, curies, or rutherfords. In practice, activity is often **ervable** effects, such as counts per minute or roentgens per

a **denote** radiation exposure of short duration.

a of the molecules of a fluid or one of its constituents at a **ituents** need not be in true solution.

a **pressed** in roentgens delivered at a point in free air. In only of the radiation of the primary beam and tha **g air.**

a **ecting** and measuring air-borne radioactivity for wai

a **gamma rays):** Ionization chamber in which the mat **re** so selected as to produce ionization essentially equi **tion** chamber. This is possible only over limited rang **chamber** is more appropriately termed an *air-* *equi*

al **ting** alpha particles, including an alpha counter tube **nator,** scaler, and recorder, or the alpha counter tube **uits** for counting alpha particles. Often loosely appl **chamber** alone.

al **rged** particle emitted from a nucleus and composed **.** It is identical in all measured properties with

[1] **C** **erms** in Nuclear Science and Technology," Natior **e** on Nuclear Glossary, published by The Americ **ers**, New York, 1953.

the nucleus of a helium atom.   (b) By extension, the nucleus of a helium atom ($Z = 2$, $A = 4$), especially when it is in rapid motion, as when artificially accelerated.

alpha ray: A synonym for *alpha particle*.

anemia: A condition in which the blood is deficient either in quantity or in quality. The deficiency in quality may consist in diminution of the amount of hemoglobin or in diminution of the number of red blood corpuscles.

anticoincidence circuit: A circuit with two input terminals which delivers an output pulse if one input terminal receives a pulse, but delivers no output pulse if pulses are received by both input terminals simultaneously or within an assignable time interval.

artificial radioactivity: (a) A term used to denote the phenomenon of radioactivity produced by particle bombardment or electromagnetic irradiation.   (b) The radioactivity of synthetic nuclides.

atomic energy: In popular usage, nuclear energy released in sufficient quantity to be of engineering interest.

atomic mass: The mass of a neutral atom of a nuclide.   It is usually expressed in terms of the physical scale of atomic masses, that is, in atomic mass units.   The atomic mass unit, amu, is exactly one-sixteenth of the mass of a neutral atom of the most abundant isotope of oxygen, O^{16}; 1 amu $= 1.657 \times 10^{-24}$ g $= 931$ Mev $= 0.999728$ awu.

atomic number: An integer Z that expresses the positive charge of the nucleus in multiples of the electronic charge e.   In present theory, it is the number of protons in the nucleus and is also equal to the number of electrons outside the nucleus of the neutral atom.

atomic weight: The weighted mean of the masses of the neutral atoms of an element expressed in atomic weight units.   Unless otherwise specified, it refers to a naturally occurring form of the element.   The atomic weight unit, awu, is exactly one-sixteenth of the weighted mean of the masses of the neutral atoms of oxygen of isotopic composition found in fresh lake or rain water; 1 awu $= 1.660 \times 10^{-24}$ g $= 1.000272$ amu.

autoradiogram (radioautogram): Record of radiation from radioactive material in an object, made by placing its surface in close proximity to a photographic emulsion.

average life (mean life): The average of the individual lives of all the atoms of a particular radioactive substance.   It is 1.443 times the radioactive half-life.

background: Ever-present effects in physical apparatus above which a phenomenon must manifest itself in order to be measured.   Background can take various forms, depending on the nature of the measurement.   In electrical measurements of radioactivity and nuclear phenomena, the term usually refers to those undesired counts or currents which arise from cosmic rays, local contaminating radioactivity, insulator leakage, amplifier noise, power-line fluctuations, and so on.   In nuclear work and photographic emulsions, the term refers to developable grains unrelated to the tracks under investigation.

background counts: (a) Counts caused by any agency other than the one that it is desired to detect.   (b) Counts caused by radiation coming from sources external to the counter tube other than the source being measured, or by radioactive contamination of the counter tube itself.

backscatter: Scattering of radiation in a generally backward direction.   In radiation therapy, it is applied particularly to radiation scattered back to the skin from underlying tissues.   In the assay of radioactivity, it applies to the scattering of particles into the measuring device by the material on which the sample is mounted.

barn: A unit of area for nuclear cross section; 1 barn $= 10^{-24}$ cm^2.

beta decay, beta disintegration: Radioactive transformation of a nuclide in which the atomic number changes by ± 1 and the mass number remains unchanged.

Increase of atomic number occurs with negative beta-particle emission, decrease with positive beta-particle (positron) emission or upon electron capture.

beta particle : A negative electron or a positive electron (positron) emitted from a nucleus during beta decay.   The β, β^-, and β^+ are reserved for electrons of nuclear origin.

beta ray : A synonym for *beta particle*.

billion electron volts : A unit of energy, symbol Bev, equal to 10^9 ev.

binary scaler : A scaler whose scaling factor is 2.

biologic half-life (of a radioactive substance) : The time in which a living tissue, organ, or individual eliminates, through biologic processes, one-half of a given amount of a substance that has been introduced into it.

biophysics : The study of phenomena of living organisms by physical methods; the study of physical phenomena exhibited by living organisms or parts thereof.

bone marrow : Soft tissue that fills the cavity in most bones; one of the most important sites of formation of blood constituents.

bone seeker : Any compound or ion that migrates in vivo preferentially into bone.

bound water : In the drying of solids, water that is chemically combined.

break-through : That point in an adsorption cycle at which the effluent begins to show a marked increase in concentration of the substance being adsorbed.

bremsstrahlung : Secondary photon radiation produced by deceleration of charged particles passing through matter.

cancer : Any malignant neoplasm.

carrier : (*a*) A quantity of an element which may be mixed with radioactive isotopes of that element, giving a ponderable quantity to facilitate chemical operations.   (*b*) A substance in ponderable amount which, when associated with a trace of another substance, will carry the trace with it through a chemical or physical process, especially a precipitation process.   If the added substance is a different element from the trace, the carrier is called a *nonisotopic carrier*.

carrier-free : Designating a preparation of a radioactive isotope which for practical purposes is essentially free of stable isotopes of the element in question.

characteristic radiation : Radiation originating from an atom following the removal of an electron.   The wavelength of the emitted radiation depends only on the element concerned and the particular energy levels involved.

chemical exchange : A process in which isotopes of the same element in two different molecules exchange places.

chronic exposure : Term used to denote radiation exposure of long duration by fractionation or protraction.

cloud chamber, or expansion chamber : A device for observing the paths of ionizing particles, based on the principle that supersaturated vapor condenses more readily on ions than on neutral molecules.

coincidence : The occurrence of counts in two or more detectors simultaneously or within an assignable time interval, ideally as a result of the passage of a single particle or of several generically related particles.

coincidence circuit : An electronic circuit that produces a usable output pulse only when each of two or more input circuits receives pulses simultaneously or within an assignable time interval.

coincidence loss, coincidence correction : *See* dead-time correction.

condenser r-meter : An instrument consisting of an air-wall ionization chamber together with auxiliary equipment for charging and measuring its voltage, used as an integrating instrument for measuring the quantity of X or gamma radiation in roentgens.   *See* ionization chamber.

contamination, radioactive: (a) A condition in which an undesirable radioactive substance is mixed with a desired substance. (b) A condition in which radioactive material has spread to places where it may harm persons, spoil experiments, or make products or equipment unsuitable or unsafe for some specific use.

coprecipitation: (a) The carrying of trace amounts of (active) material on a ponderable precipitate of another composition. It may involve trace-ion replacement in the crystal lattice of the carrier when the two substances are truly isomorphous; it may involve the formation of anomalous mixed crystals; it may involve adsorption, at the time of formation or later, of the trace ion on the highly charged surface of the carrier precipitate; or it may involve the internal adsorption of the trace in aggregate spots within the carrier precipitate. (b) The precipitation of a substance from concentrations below its solubility when induced by the precipitation of another substance.

cosmic rays: Radiation that has its ultimate origin outside the earth's atmosphere, that is capable of producing ionizing events in passing through the air or other matter, and that includes constituents capable of penetrating many feet of material such as rock.

count (radiation measurements): The external indication of a device designed to enumerate ionizing events. It may refer to a single detected event or to the total registered in a given period of time. The term is loosely used to designate a disintegration, ionizing event, or voltage pulse.

counter: A device for counting ionizing events. The term may refer to a complete instrument or, loosely, to the detector.

counting loss: *See* dead-time correction.

counting rate: The average rate of occurrence of ionizing events as observed by means of a counting system.

counting-rate meter: A device that gives a continuous indication of the average rate of ionizing events.

cross section: A measure σ of the probability of occurrence of a given reaction. For a particular nuclear reaction, σ may be greater or smaller than the geometric cross section πR^2. If the reaction cannot take place, the cross section is zero. For any collision reaction between nuclear or atomic particles or systems, σ is an area such that the number of reactions taking place is equal to the product of the number of incident particles that would pass through this area at normal incidence and the number of target particles or systems.

curie: (a) A unit of radioactivity, symbol c, equal to 3.7×10^{10} dis/sec. It is approximately the activity of 1 g radium. (b) A quantity of a nuclide having an activity of 1 c.

cyclotron: A device for accelerating charged particles to high energies by means of an alternating electric field between electrodes placed in a constant magnetic field.

daughter: A synonym for *decay product*.

dead time (counters): The time interval, after a count, during which a radiation detector and/or its circuit are insensitive to ionizing events.

dead-time correction: Correction to the observed counting rate to allow for the probability of the occurrence of events within the dead time.

decade scaler: A scaler whose scaling factor is 10.

decay, radioactive: The decrease with time of the number of radioactive atoms in a sample, as a result of their spontaneous transformation.

decay constant: *See* disintegration constant.

decay curve: A curve showing the relative amount of radioactive substance remaining after any time interval.

decay product: A nuclide resulting from the radioactive disintegration of a radionuclide, being formed either directly or as the result of successive transformations in a radioactive series. A decay product may be either radioactive or stable.

decontamination: (a) The removal of unwanted radioactive substances from a desired material, e.g., removal of fission products from plutonium or uranium. (b) The removal of undesired dispersed radioactive material from personnel, instruments, rooms, equipment, etc.

densitometer: Instrument for measuring photographic density.

density (photographic): Logarithm of opacity of exposed and processed film. Opacity is the reciprocal of transmission; transmission is the ratio of transmitted to incident intensity. Density is used to denote the degree of darkening of photographic film.

desorption: The reverse process of adsorption whereby adsorbed matter is removed from the adsorbent. The term is also used for the reverse process of absorption.

detector (radiation): Any device for converting radiant energy to a form more suitable for observation.

differential absorption ratio: Ratio of the concentration of an isotope in a given organ or tissue to the concentration that would be obtained if the same administered quantity of this isotope were uniformly distributed throughout the body.

discriminator: *See* pulse-height discriminator.

disintegration (nuclear): A spontaneous nuclear transformation (radioactivity) characterized by the emission of energy from the nucleus. When numbers of nuclei are involved, the process is characterized by a definite half-life.

disintegration constant: The fraction of the number of atoms of a radioactive isotope which decay in unit time.

disintegration rate: Rate of decay of radioactive substance. It is usually expressed as disintegrations per unit time.

dose (dosage): According to current usage, the radiation delivered to a specified area or volume or to the whole body. Units for dose specification are roentgens for X or gamma rays, reps or equivalent roentgens for beta rays. The subject of dose units for particulate radiation and for very high-energy X rays has not been settled. In radiology the dose may be specified in air, on the skin, or at some depth beneath the surface; no statement of dose is complete without the specification of location. The entire question of radiation dosage units is under consideration by the International Congress of Radiology, and it is expected that new units based on the energy absorbed in tissue will be adopted (see text).

dose, threshold: *See* threshold dose.

dose, tissue: *See* tissue dose.

dose, tolerance: *See* tolerance dose.

dose-effect curve: A curve relating the dose of radiation to the effect produced.

dose fractionation: A method of administration of radiation in which relatively small doses are given daily or at longer intervals.

dose meter (dosimeter): Any instrument that measures radiation dose.

dose rate (dosage rate): Radiation dose delivered per unit time.

dose-rate meter: Any instrument that measures radiation dose rate.

effective half-life: Half-life of a radioactive isotope in a biological organism, resulting from the combination of radioactive decay and biological elimination.

$$\text{Effective half-life} = \frac{\text{biological half-life} \times \text{radioactive half-life}}{\text{biological half-life} + \text{radioactive half-life}}$$

efficiency (counters): A measure of the probability that a count will be recorded when radiation is incident on a detector.   Usage varies considerably, so that it is well to make sure which factors (window transmission, sensitive volume, energy dependence, etc.) are included in a given case.

electrometer: An instrument for measuring charge, usually by mechanical forces exerted on a charged electrode in an electric field.

electron: An elementary particle of rest mass m_e equal to 9.107×10^{-28} g and charge equal to 4.802×10^{-10} statcoul.   Its charge may be either positive or negative.   The positive electron is usually called a *positron;* the negative electron is sometimes called the *negatron.*   Most frequently the term *electron* means negatron.   The negative electron is a constituent of all atoms.   In a neutral atom the number of electrons is equal to the atomic number Z.

electron volt (ev): A unit of energy equal to the work done in transferring one electron against a potential difference of 1 volt.

electroscope: An instrument for detecting an electric charge by means of the mechanical forces exerted between electrically charged bodies.

electrostatic generator: A high-voltage generator in which the potential is produced by the work done in the mechanical transport of electrical charges.   *See* Van de Graaff generator.

element: (*a*) A substance all of whose atoms have the same atomic number.   (*b*) A naturally occurring mixture of isotopes.   (*c*) A class of atom having a particular atomic number as the distinguishing characteristic.

elementary particle: A term loosely applied today to the electron; proton; neutron; positron; positive and negative mu mesons; positive, negative, and neutral pi mesons; positive, negative, and neutral *V* particles; neutrino; and some similar entities, the existence of which is speculative or which have not yet been thoroughly characterized by experiment.

emulsion, nuclear: A photographic emulsion specially designed to permit observation of the individual tracks of ionizing particles.

endosteum: The tissue lining the internal cavity of the bone.

endothelium: The layer of simple squamous cells lining the inner surface of the circulatory organs and certain other closed body cavities.

enriched material: Material in which the amount of one or more isotopes of a constituent has been increased.

epilation (depilation): The temporary or permanent removal of hair.

epiphysis: A part or process of a bone which ossifies separately and subsequently becomes joined to the main part of the bone.   Growth persists until the epiphyses are closed.

epithelium: The purely cellular, nonvascular layer covering all the free surfaces of the body, cutaneous, mucous, and serous, including the glands and other structures derived therefrom.

erythema: An abnormal redness of the skin, due to distention of the capillaries with blood.   It can be caused by many different agents, e.g., heat, certain drugs, ultraviolet rays, and ionizing radiations.

erythrocyte: A red blood corpuscle.

exchange reaction: *See* isotopic exchange.

exit dose: Dose of radiation at surface of body opposite to that on which the beam is incident.

extrapolation ionization chamber: An ionization chamber with electrodes whose spacing can be adjusted and accurately determined to permit extrapolation of its readings to zero chamber volume.

film badge: An appropriately packaged photographic film for detecting radiation exposure of personnel; usually dental-size X-ray film, worn on the person and frequently combined with an identification badge.

fission products: The nuclides produced by the fission of a heavy-element nuclide such as U^{235} or Pu^{239}. Thirty-five fission-product elements from zinc through gadolinium have been identified from slow-neutron fission.

fluorescence: The emission of radiation of particular wavelengths by a substance as a result of absorption of radiation of shorter wavelength. This emission occurs essentially only during the irradiation.

flux: (a) For electromagnetic radiation, the power, or energy per unit time, passing through a surface. (b) For particles or photons, the number passing through a surface per unit time. (c) As commonly used in nuclear physics, the product nv, where n is the number of particles per unit volume and v is their mean velocity.

free-air ionization chamber: An ionization chamber in which a delimited beam of radiation passes between the electrodes without striking them or other internal parts of the equipment. The electric field is maintained perpendicular to the electrodes in the collecting region; as a result, the ionized volume can be accurately determined from the dimensions of the collecting electrode and the limiting diaphragm. This is the basic standard instrument for X-ray dosimetry, at least within the range from 5 to 400 kv.

free water: The amount of water removed in drying a solid to its equilibrium water content.

gamma ray (γ **ray**): A quantum of electromagnetic radiation emitted by a nucleus, each such photon being emitted as the result of a quantum transition between two energy levels of the nucleus. Gamma rays have energies usually between 10 kev and 10 Mev, with correspondingly short wavelengths and high frequencies. They are often associated with alpha and beta radioactivity, following transitions that leave the product nuclei in excited states; in general, they are more penetrating than alpha or beta particles. They also occur in isomeric transitions and in many induced nuclear reactions.

gas counter (radiation): A counter in which the sample is prepared in the form of a gas and introduced into the counter tube itself.

gas-flow counter (radiation): A counter in which an appropriate atmosphere is maintained in the counter tube by allowing a suitable gas to flow slowly through the volume.

Geiger counter: Historically, a "point counter." By popular usage, a Geiger-Müller counter tube, or such a tube together with its associated electronic equipment.

Geiger-Müller counter tube, Geiger-Müller tube. A gas-filled chamber usually consisting of a hollow cylindrical cathode and a fine wire anode along its axis. It is operated with a voltage high enough so that a discharge triggered by a primary ionizing event will spread over the entire anode until stopped by the reduction of the field by space charge.

genetic effect of radiation: Inheritable changes, chiefly mutations, produced by the absorption of ionizing radiations. On the basis of present knowledge these effects are purely additive, and there is no recovery.

geometry factor (radiation): The average solid angle at the source subtended by the aperture or sensitive volume of the detector, divided by the complete solid angle (4π). Frequently used loosely to denote counting yield or counting efficiency.

half-life (radioactive): *See* radioactive half-life.

half-thickness: The thickness of any given absorber which will reduce the intensity of a beam of radiation to one-half its initial value. It may be expressed in units of length or of mass per unit area.

half-time of exchange: The time required for half the net realizable exchange of atoms in a chemical exchange reaction to take place.

half-value layer: The thickness of any particular material necessary to reduce the dose rate of an X-ray beam to one-half its original value.

hardness (X rays): A term for qualitatively specifying the penetrating power of X rays. In general, the shorter the wavelength, the harder the radiation.

health physics: A term in common use for that branch of radiological physics which deals with the protection of personnel from the harmful effects of ionizing radiation. It includes the routine procedures of radiation-protection surveys, area and personnel monitoring, the recommendation of appropriate protective equipment and procedures, the determination of acceptable standards of operation, and the solution of problems incident to the effective and practical protection of all persons from the harmful effects of radiation. Out of this last phase has grown the study of environmental hazards, including the accumulation of radioactive material by plants and animals and possible injury to human beings ultimately utilizing these in food chains.

heavy water: Water in which the hydrogen of the water molecule consists entirely of the heavy-hydrogen isotope of mass 2. Written D_2O. Density, 1.1076 at 20°C. It is used as a moderator in certain types of nuclear reactors. The term is sometimes applied to water whose deuterium content is greater than that of natural water.

holdback agent: The inactive isotope or isotopes of a radioactive element(s) or an element of similar properties or some reagent which may be used to diminish (hold back) the amount of radionuclide coprecipitated or adsorbed on a particular carrier or adsorbent. The holdback agent, because of its relatively high concentration compared with that of the radionuclide, is presumed to play the major role in saturating the "active" spots on the carrier or adsorber, thus reducing the amount of radionuclide carried or adsorbed.

hot: A colloquial term meaning *highly radioactive.*

hot laboratory: A laboratory equipped for the safe manipulation and chemical processing of highly radioactive materials.

implant: In radiology, radioactive material in a suitable container, to be embedded in a tissue for therapeutic purposes. It may be permanent (seed) or temporary (needle).

indicator: A synonym for *tracer* which was introduced earlier than the latter term but now is less frequently used.

induced radioactivity: Radioactivity that is produced by nuclear reactions. *See* reaction, nuclear.

insensitive time (counters): *See* dead time.

integral dose (volume dose): A measure of the total energy absorbed by a patient or any object during exposure to radiation. According to British usage, the integral dose for X or gamma rays is expressed in gram-roentgens.

integrating dose meter: Ionization chamber and measuring system designed for determining the total radiation administered during an exposure. In medical radiology the chamber is usually designed to be placed on the patient's skin. A device may be included to terminate the exposure when it has reached a desired value.

intensitometer: A device for determining relative X-ray intensities during radiography in order to control exposure time.

intensity (of radiation): The amount of energy per unit time passing through a unit area perpendicular to the line of propagation at the point in question. Often this term is used incorrectly in the sense of *dose rate.*

interchange: The mixing of tracer and added isotopic carrier such that the two participate to the same degree in any chemical reaction, showing that mixing has occurred in whatever chemical forms the tracer may have been originally distributed.

ion: Any electrically charged particle of molecular, atomic, or nuclear size.

ion density: The number of ion pairs per unit volume.

ion exchange: A chemical process involving the reversible interchange of ions between a solution and a particular solid material such as an ion-exchange resin, consisting of a matrix of insoluble material interspersed with fixed ions of opposite charge.

ionization: The process whereby a neutral atom or molecule is split into positive and negative ions.

ionization chamber: An instrument designed to measure the quantity of ionizing radiation in terms of the charge of electricity associated with the ions produced within a defined volume. This is usually done by measuring the quantity of electricity in the form of ions carried to the chamber electrodes when a suitable potential difference is established between them.

ionization density: Number of ion pairs per unit volume.

ionization path (or track): The trail of ion pairs produced by an ionizing particle in its passage through matter.

ionizing radiation: Any electromagnetic or particulate radiation capable of producing ions, directly or indirectly, in its passage through matter.

irradiation: Exposure to radiation. One speaks of *radiation therapy*, but of *irradiation* of the patient.

isomer, nuclear: One of two or more nuclides having the same mass number A and atomic number Z, but existing for measurable times in different states. The state of lowest energy is the ground state. Those of higher energies are metastable states. To indicate the metastable isomer, the letter m is added to the mass number in the symbol for the nuclide; thus, Br^{80m}.

isomeric transition: The process by which a nuclide decays to an isomeric nuclide (i.e., one of the same mass number and atomic number) of lower quantum energy. Isomeric transitions, often abbreviated IT, proceed by gamma-ray and/or internal-conversion electron emission.

isotope: (a) One of several nuclides having the same number of protons in their nuclei and hence belonging to the same element, but differing in the number of neutrons and therefore in mass number A. (b) A synonym for isotopic tracer. (c) A radionuclide or a preparation of an element with special isotopic composition as an article of commerce, so called because of the principal use of such materials as isotopic tracers. (d) In common usage, a synonym for *nuclide*.

isotope-dilution analysis: A method of chemical analysis for a component of a mixture based on the addition to the mixture of a known amount of labeled component of known specific activity, followed by isolation of a quantity of the pure component and measurement of the specific activity of that sample.

isotope effect: The effect of the difference in mass between isotopes on the rate and/or equilibria of chemical transformations.

isotopic exchange: (a) A process whereby atoms of the same element in two different molecules or in different sites in the same molecule exchange places. (b) The transfer of isotopically tagged species, without net chemical reaction, from one chemical form or valence state of an element to another. This may come about by exchange of tagged atoms, by exchange of other atoms in the chemical complex, or by transfer of electrons.

K-electron capture: Electron capture from the K shell by the nucleus of the atom.

kilocurie: 1000 c; symbol kc.

kilo-electron-volt: 1000 ev; symbol kev.

labeled compound: A compound consisting, in part, of labeled molecules. By observations of radioactivity or isotopic composition, this compound or its fragments may be followed through physical, chemical, or biological processes.

labile: A synonym for *unstable.*

latent period (**radiology**): Interval between irradiation and appearance of the effect in question.

latent tissue injury (**radiology**): Injury which does not become manifest until some time after irradiation, and possibly until some other trauma has supervened. This second injury may be so slight that it would not, of itself, produce observable damage.

Lauritsen electroscope: A rugged yet sensitive electroscope employing a metalized quartz fiber as the sensitive element.

LD$_{50}$ dose: *See* median lethal dose.

LD$_{50}$ time: *See* median lethal time.

lead equivalent: The thickness of lead affording the same reduction in radiation dose rate under specified conditions as the material in question.

length of plateau: The voltage interval corresponding to the portion of the plateau characteristic in which a Geiger-Müller counter tube can be reliably operated. *See* plateau characteristic.

leukemia: A disease in which there is often great overproduction of white blood cells, or relative overproduction of immature white cells, and great enlargement of the spleen. The disease is variable, at times running a more chronic course in adults than in children. It is almost always fatal, although its progress can sometimes be delayed by radiation or by chemical agents. It can be produced in some animals by long-continued exposure to low intensities of ionizing radiation.

lifetime: A synonym for (*a*) *mean life,* (*b*) *half-life.*

Lindemann electrometer: A type of electrometer employing a metalized quartz fiber mounted on and perpendicular to a quartz torsion fiber in such a way that the former fiber is positioned in a system of electrodes.

linear absorption coefficient: A factor expressing the fraction of a beam of radiation absorbed in unit thickness of material.

linear accelerator: A device for accelerating particles employing alternate electrodes and gaps arranged in a straight line, so proportioned that, when their potentials are varied in the proper amplitude and frequency, particles passing through them receive successive increments of energy.

lymph: An almost colorless fluid circulating in the lymphatic vessels of vertebrates. It closely resembles blood plasma in composition and contains lymphocytes.

lymph node (**lymph gland,** *obs.*): An aggregation of connective tissue crowded with lymphocytes and surrounded with a fibrous capsule. It is provided with incoming and outgoing lymph vessels and a plexus of internal lymph spaces.

lymphocyte: A type of leukocyte characterized by a single sharply defined nucleus and scanty cytoplasm. Small lymphocytes constitute about 25 per cent of the white corpuscles of the circulating blood in adult men.

lymphopenia: Decrease in the proportion of lymphocytes in the blood.

mass absorption coefficient: The linear absorption coefficient per centimeter divided by the density of the absorber in grams per cubic centimeter.

mass spectrograph: A device for analyzing a substance in terms of the mass/charge ratios of its components. The term is usually restricted to devices that produce a focused mass spectrum of lines on a photographic plate.

mechanical register (**counting**): An electromechanical device for recording or registering counts.

median lethal dose (**MLD**): Dose of radiation required to kill, within a specified period, 50 per cent of the individuals in a large group of animals or organisms.

median lethal time (**MLT**): Time required, following administration of a specified dose of radiation, for the death of 50 per cent of the individuals in a large group of animals or organisms.

microcurie: One-millionth of a curie; symbol μc.

millicurie: One-thousandth of a curie; symbol mc.

million electron volts: A common unit of energy in nuclear science, equivalent to 10^6 ev; symbol Mev. *See* electron volt.

milliroentgen: One-thousandth of a roentgen.

mole fraction: As used in isotope separation, the number of atoms of a certain isotope of an element expressed as a fraction of the total number of atoms of that element present in the isotopic mixture.

monitoring: Periodic or continuous determination of the amount of ionizing radiation or radioactive contamination present in an occupied region, or in a person, as a safety measure for purposes of health protection.

monochromatic radiation: Electromagnetic radiation of a single wavelength, or radiation in which all the photons have the same energy.

monoenergetic radiation: Particulate radiation of a given type (alpha, beta, neutron, etc.) in which all the particles have the same energy.

mucosa: Mucous membrane lining the gastrointestinal tract and air passages.

natural radioactivity: Radioactivity exhibited by naturally occurring substances. Natural radionuclides may be classified as follows: (*a*) Primary, which have lifetimes exceeding several hundred million years and which presumably have persisted from the time of nucleogenesis to the present. They include the alpha emitters U^{238}, U^{235}, Th^{232}, and Sm^{147} and the beta-active nuclides K^{40}, Rb^{87}, La^{138}, In^{115}, Lu^{176}, and Re^{187}. (*b*) Secondary, which have geologically short lifetimes and are decay products of primary natural radionuclides. All presently known members of this class belong to the elements from thallium to uranium. Those derived from U^{238} are members of the uranium, or radium, series; those from U^{235}, of the actinium series; and those from Th^{232}, of the thorium series. (*c*) Induced, which have geologically short lifetimes and are products of nuclear reactions occurring currently or recently in nature. Examples are C^{14} (natural radiocarbon), produced by cosmic-ray neutrons in the atmosphere, and Pu^{239}, produced in uranium minerals by neutron capture. (*d*) Extinct, which have lifetimes that are too short for survival from the time of nucleogenesis to the present, but long enough for persistence into early geologic times with measurable effects. At present, I^{129} is the only suspected member of this class.

necrosis: Death of a circumscribed portion of tissue.

neoplasm: A new growth of cells which is more or less unrestrained and not governed by the usual limitations of normal growth. **Benign:** If there is some degree of growth restraint and no spread to distant parts. **Malignant:** If the growth invades the tissues of the host, spreads to distant parts, or both.

neutron: A neutral elementary particle of mass number 1. It is believed to be a constituent particle of all nuclei of mass number greater than 1. It is unstable with respect to beta decay, with a half-life of about 12 min. It produces no detectable primary ionization in its passage through matter but interacts with matter predominantly by collisions and, to a lesser extent, magnetically.

neutron flux: A term used to express the intensity of neutron radiation. The number of neutrons passing through a unit area in unit time.

neutron source: Any device or arrangement that utilizes a nuclear reaction for the purpose of generating neutrons.

nuclear species: (*a*) A kind of atom characterized by the charge, mass number, and quantum state of its nucleus. A nuclide. (*b*) A nucleus of given charge, mass number, and quantum state. Also a collection of such nuclei.

nucleic acid: A constituent of the cell nucleus, composed of a union between phosphoric acid, ribose or desoxyribose, and the four bases adenine, guanine, cystosine, and uracil (or thymine).

nucleonics: Nuclear technology; the applications of nuclear science in physics, astronomy, chemistry, biology, geology, industry, and armaments, and the techniques associated with these applications.

nucleus: The positively charged core of an atom, with which is associated practically the whole mass of the atom but only a minute part of its volume.

nucleus (of a cell): A definitely delineated body within a cell, containing the chromosomes.

nuclide: A species of atom characterized by the charge, mass number, and quantum state of its nucleus. In order to be regarded as a distinct nuclide, the species must be capable of existing for a measurable lifetime (generally greater than 10^{-10} sec). Thus, nuclear isomers are separate nuclides, but promptly decaying excited nuclear states and unstable intermediates in nuclear reactions are not so considered.

osseous: Bony.

osteogenic: Derived from or composed of tissue concerned in the growth or repair of bone.

parent, parent nuclide: A nuclide that undergoes decay into another nuclide, the daughter; a radioactive precursor.

percentage depth dose: Amount of radiation delivered at a specified depth in tissue, expressed as a percentage of the amount delivered at the skin.

periosteum: The tough fibrous membrane surrounding bone; a place of frequent radiation injury.

permissible dose: The amount of radiation that may be received by an individual within a specified period with the expectation of no harmful result to himself. For long-continued X- or gamma-ray exposure of the whole body, it is 0.3 r/week measured in air.

phantom (radiology): A volume of material behaving in essentially the same manner as tissue, with respect to the radiation in question, which is used to simulate a portion of the human body and into which ionization chambers can be placed. Measurements made in a phantom permit the determination of the radiation dose delivered to the skin and points within the body. Materials commonly used for X rays are water, Masonite Presdwood (unit density), and beeswax.

pile: A nuclear reactor. The term *pile* comes from the first nuclear reactor, which was made by piling up graphite blocks and pieces of uranium and uranium oxide. The term *reactor* is becoming more commonly used.

plateau characteristic, counting rate–voltage characteristic: The relation between counting rate and voltage applied to a counter tube for a given constant source of radiation.

platelet (thrombocyte): A small colorless corpuscle present in large numbers in the blood of all mammals, believed to play a role in the clotting of blood.

pocket chamber: A small pocket-sized ionization chamber used for monitoring the radiation exposure of personnel. Before use it is given a charge, and the amount of discharge is a measure of the quantity of radiation received.

pocket meter: A complete pocket-sized radiation instrument by means of which a quantity of radiation can be directly indicated.

polycythemia: A disease characterized by overproduction of erythrocytes.

positron: A positive electron. Positrons are formed in the process of pair production, in the beta decay of many radionuclides, and in some more specialized processes.

proportional counter: An instrument comprising a proportional counter tube with its associated circuits. Often loosely applied to the proportional counter tube itself.

proportional counter tube: A radiation counter tube or chamber operated in the proportional region.

proportional region : The range of operating voltage for a counter tube or ionization chamber in which the gas amplification is greater than 1 and is independent of the primary ionization. In this region the pulse size is proportional to the number of ions produced as a result of the initial ionizing event.

proton : A positively charged elementary particle of mass number 1 and charge equal in magnitude to the electronic charge e. It is one of the constituents of every nucleus. The number of protons in the nucleus of each atom of an element is given by the atomic number Z of the element.

pulse-height discriminator : A circuit designed to select and pass voltage pulses of a certain minimum amplitude.

quality : A term for the approximate characterization of radiation with regard to its penetrating power. It is usually expressed in terms of effective wavelength or half-value.

quenching : The process of inhibiting continuous or multiple discharges in a counter tube that uses gas amplification.

radiation : The emission and propagation of energy through space or through a material medium in the form of waves; for instance, the emission and propagation of electromagnetic waves or of sound and elastic waves.

radiation chemistry : The branch of chemistry that is concerned with the chemical effects (including decomposition) of high-energy radiation and particles on matter.

radiation counter tube : A radiation detector capable of providing discrete electrical pulses in response to the incidence of radiation.

radio- : A prefix denoting radioactivity or relationship to it.

radioactive : (*a*) Exhibiting radioactivity. (*b*) Pertaining to radioactivity.

radioactive equilibrium : A condition that may obtain in the course of the decay of a radioactive parent having shorter-lived descendants, in which the ratio of the activity of the parent to that of a descendant is independent of time. This condition can exist only when no activity longer-lived than that of the parent is interposed in the decay chain.

radioactive half-life : The time in which the amount of a particular radioactive isotope is reduced to half its initial value.

radioactive tracer : Small quantity of radioactive isotope, either with carrier or carrier-free, used to follow biological, chemical, or other processes. Since the stable and radioactive isotopes of an element have essentially the same chemical properties and the radioactive ones are readily detected, the movement and behavior of the stable atoms can be traced by following the radioactivity. In this case the compound under observation is said to be *labeled* with the radioactive isotope.

radioactivity : (*a*) The phenomenon of spontaneous transformation, with a measurable lifetime, of a nuclide. *See* decay, radioactive. (*b*) A term designating a particular spontaneously disintegrating nuclide. (*c*) A term for the intensity of emission from a sample undergoing spontaneous nuclear disintegration. (*d*) A term designating a particular component of radiation from a sample undergoing spontaneous nuclear disintegration.

radiobiology : That branch of biology which deals with the effects of radiation on biological systems.

radiocolloid : A clumping of radioactive atoms into colloidal aggregates.

radioelement : (*a*) An element with no stable isotopes. (*b*) An element tagged with a radioactive isotope.

radioisotope : (*a*) Any radioactive isotope of an element. (*b*) A word loosely used as a synonym for *radionuclide*.

radiology : The medical science of radioactive substances, X rays, and other ionizing radiations, and the application of the principles of this science to the diagnosis and treatment of disease.

radionuclide: Any nuclide that is radioactive.

radioresistance: Relative resistance of cells, tissues, organs, or organisms to the injurious action of radiation. The term may also be applied to chemical compounds or to any substances. *See also* radiosensitivity.

radiosensitivity: Relative susceptibility of cells, tissues, organs, organisms, or any substances to the injurious action of radiation. *Radioresistance* and *radiosusceptibility* are at present employed in a qualitative or comparative sense rather than in a quantitative or absolute one.

range: The thickness of matter, expressed in length or in mass per unit area, required to remove all detectable high-speed charged particles from a beam by slowing them down below the threshold for measurement. Alpha particles show well-defined ranges with some straggling; fission fragments show more straggling; and electrons show much less well-defined ranges. The ranges depend on the initial maximum energy of the particles in the beam.

reaction, nuclear: An induced nuclear disintegration; that is, a process occurring when a nucleus comes into contact with a photon, an elementary particle, or another nucleus. In many cases the reaction can be represented by the symbolic equation: $X + a \rightarrow Y + b$ or, in abbreviated form, $X(a,b)Y$, in which X is the target nucleus, a is the incident particle or photon, b is an emitted particle or photon, and Y is the product nucleus.

relative abundance of an isotope: The fraction or percentage of the atoms of an element which are a given isotope. It usually refers to the natural isotopic mixture of an element.

relative biological effectiveness of radiation (RBE): The inverse ratio of tissue doses of two different types of radiation which produce a particular biologic effect under otherwise identical conditions. In general, the RBE may vary with the kind and degree of biological effect considered, the duration of the exposure, and other factors.

relative plateau slope (counter tubes): The percentage of change in counting rate per 100 volts increase of applied potential along the plateau.

roentgen: The quantity of X or gamma radiation such that the associated corpuscular emission per 0.001293 g of air produces, in air, ions carrying one electrostatic unit of quantity of electricity of either sign.

roentgen rays: X rays.

sarcoma: Malignant neoplasm composed of cells imitating the appearance of the supportive and lymphatic tissues.

saturation: The condition that obtains when an induced nuclear reaction has continued sufficiently long to produce the asymptotic activity of a given radionuclide. In this condition the decay rate of the nuclide in question is equal to its rate of production.

scaler, scaling circuit: A device that produces an output pulse whenever a prescribed number of input pulses have been received.

scaling factor: The number of input pulses per output pulse of a scaling circuit.

scattered radiation (in radiology): Radiation that, during its passage through a substance, has been deviated in direction. It may also have been modified by an increase in wavelength.

scavenging: The use of an unspecific precipitate to remove from solution by adsorption or coprecipitation a large fraction of one or more undesirable radionuclides. Voluminous gelatinous precipitates are ordinarily used as scavengers, e.g., $Fe(OH)_3$.

scintillation: A flash of light produced in a phosphor by an ionizing event.

scintillation counter: The combination of phosphor, photomultiplier tube, and associated circuits for counting scintillations.

secondary radiation: Radiation originating as the result of absorption of other radiation in matter.   It may be either electromagnetic or particulate in nature.

selective localization (isotopes): In the use of radioisotopes, accumulation of a particular isotope to a significantly greater degree in certain cells or tissues.   *See* differential absorption ratio.

self-absorption: Absorption of radiation emitted by radioactive atoms by the matter in which the atoms are located; in particular, the absorption of radiation from a sample being assayed in the sample itself.

self-quenched counter tube: A Geiger-Müller counter tube that is quenched by means of a suitable component in the counting gas.

self-scattering: The scattering of radioactive radiations by the body of the substance emitting the radiation.   Self-scattering may outweigh self-absorption and may increase the measured activity over that expected for a weightless sample.

sensitive volume: That portion of a counter tube or ionization chamber which responds to a specific radiation.

sensitive volume (sensitive region) (in radiobiology): Part of a cell particularly sensitive to radiation.   *See* target theory.

shield: Any material used to reduce the amount of radiation reaching one region of space from another region of space.

specific activity, gram element: Total radioactivity of a given isotope per gram of element.

specific activity, isotope: Total radioactivity of a given isotope per gram of the radioactive isotope.

specific ionization: Number of ion pairs per unit length of path of the ionization particle in a medium, e.g., per centimeter of air or per micron of tissue.

spurious counts: Counts caused by imperfections of the counter.

stable: (*a*) Exhibiting no tendency to undergo any spontaneous nuclear reaction; not observably radioactive.   (*b*) Exhibiting no tendency to undergo a particular spontaneous nuclear reaction; thus, e.g., beta stable, stable with respect to beta decay.

starting voltage: For a counter tube, the minimum voltage that must be applied to obtain counts with the particular circuit with which it is associated.

statistical error (counting): Errors in counting due to the random time distributions of disintegrations.

stray radiation: Radiation not serving any useful purpose.   It includes direct radiation and secondary radiation from irradiated objects.

survey instrument: A portable instrument used for detecting and measuring radiation under various physical conditions.   The term covers a wide range of devices utilizing most of the detection methods defined elsewhere.

survival curve: (*a*) Curve obtained by plotting the number or percentage of organisms surviving at a given time against the dose of radiation.   (*b*) Curve showing the percentage of individuals surviving at different intervals after a particular dose of radiation.

syndrome: The complex of symptoms associated with any disease.

tagged atom: The atomic position in a molecule which is distinguished by isotopic tracer.

tagged atoms: Atoms of an isotopic tracer.

target: The material subjected to bombardment by accelerated particles to produce electromagnetic radiation or nuclear reactions within the material itself.

target theory (hit theory): Theory explaining some biologic effects of radiation on the basis of ionization occurring in a very small sensitive region within the cell.   One, two, or more "hits," i.e., ionizing events within the sensitive volume, may be necessary to bring about the effect.

thimble ionization chamber: A small cylindrical or spherical ionization chamber, usually with walls of organic material.

thin-window counter tube, thin-wall counter tube: Counter tubes in which a portion of the enclosure is of low absorption to permit the entry of short-range radiation.

threshold dose: The minimum dose that will produce a detectable degree of any given effect.

tissue dose: Dose received by a tissue in the region of interest. In the case of X rays and gamma rays, tissue doses are expressed in roentgens. At the present time there is no generally accepted unit of tissue dose for other ionizing radiations. In radiobiological studies it is customary to think of the tissue dose in terms of the energy absorbed per gram of tissue. Several units related to the roentgen have been suggested, such as the rep.

tissue-equivalent ionization chamber: Ionization chamber in which the material of the walls, electrode, and gas are so selected as to produce ionization essentially equivalent to that characteristic of the tissue under consideration. In some cases it is sufficient to have only tissue-equivalent walls, and the gas may be air, provided the air volume is negligibly small. The essential requisite in this case is that the contribution to the ionization in the air made by ionizing particles originating in the air is negligible compared with that produced by ionizing particles characteristic of the wall material.

tissue-equivalent material: Material made up of the same elements in the same proportions as they occur in some particular biological tissue. Such material is important in the construction of ionization chambers for neutron measurement. In some cases the equivalence may be brought about sufficiently closely without exact duplication of the elemental composition of the tissue.

tolerance dose: A term based on the assumption that an individual can receive such a dose of radiation without any harmful effects. It is now superseded by *permissible dose*.

trace: (*a*) A minute quantity. (*b*) A small quantity detectable only by special techniques. (*c*) An adjective pertaining to such minute quantities.

trace chemistry: The chemical behavior of a substance present in a system in imponderable amount or in very minute concentration. Trace chemical behavior is observable with radioactive nuclides free or nearly free of nonradioactive isotope and may be markedly different from the behavior of the same material in ordinary amounts and concentrations. Knowledge of trace chemical behavior may therefore be of great importance in the handling of radioactive materials. Characteristic features of trace chemical behavior include the prominence of surface effects (*see* adsorption), incorporation of the trace material in bulk precipitates (*see* carrier), and dissociation (e.g., the stability of bromine atoms in aqueous solutions of trace bromine).

tracer, isotopic: (*a*) The isotope or nonnatural mixture of isotopes of an element which may be incorporated into a sample to make possible the observation of the course of that element, alone or in combination, through a chemical, biological, or physical process. The observations may be made by measurement of radioactivity (in the case of radioactive tracer) or of isotopic abundance, e.g., by mass-spectrographic or density measurement. (*b*) Material in which isotopic tracer has been incorporated.

track: Visual manifestation of the path of an ionizing particle in a cloud chamber or nuclear emulsion.

transmutation: (*a*) Any process in which a nuclide is transformed into a different nuclide. (*b*) More specifically, the transformation of a nuclide into a nuclide of a different element by a nuclear reaction.

trauma: Injury.

tumor: A swelling. The term is usually synonymous with *neoplasm* but may be more vague.

unstable: Capable of undergoing spontaneous change. Of a nuclide, radioactive; of a state of a system, excited.

Van de Graaff generator: An electrostatic generator that employs a system of conveyer belt and spray points to charge an insulated electrode to a high potential.

vibrating condenser, vibrating-reed dynamic condenser: A condenser whose capacitance is varied in a cyclic fashion so that an alternating electromotive force is developed proportional to the charge on the insulated electrode. This device forms the basis for a type of electrometer.

vibrating-reed electrometer: An instrument using a vibrating condenser to measure a small charge. This term is often applied to denote the combination of an ionization chamber and a vibrating-reed electrometer.

volume dose: Integral dose.

volume ionization: Average ionization density in a given volume irrespective of the specific ionization of the ionizing particles.

water monitor: Any device for detecting and measuring water-borne radioactivity for warning and control purposes.

X rays: Penetrating electromagnetic radiations having wavelengths very much shorter than those of visible light. They are usually produced by bombarding a metallic target with fast electrons in a high vacuum. In nuclear reactions it is customary to refer to photons originating in the nucleus as *gamma rays* and to those originating in the extranuclear part of the atom as *X rays*. These rays were called *X rays* by their discoverer, Roentgen. Many medical radiologists prefer to call them by his name; nonmedical usage is generally *X rays*.

AVAILABILITY OF U.S. ATOMIC ENERGY
COMMISSION REPORTS

The code and identification of reports issued by the atomic-energy research organizations and other research organizations of the United States and foreign countries are given below.

The availability of the reports referred to in this compilation varies according to the type or origin of the reports.

A detailed discussion of AEC report availability is given in TID-4550 (Revision No. 1), Availability of USAEC Research and Development Reports, which is free upon request from

> Office of Technical Services
> Department of Commerce
> Washington 25, D.C.

Price lists of AEC reports on sale by the Office of Technical Services are also free upon request. All AEC reports on sale and many AEC reports not sold by the Office of Technical Services may be examined at or borrowed from the AEC depository libraries, and microfilm or photostat copies may be purchased from them. Copies of reports not contained in their files will be secured through the proper channels. A list of these libraries is contained in the afore-mentioned TID-4550.

The non-Project reports referred to herein are generally available from their issuing sources.

MDDC	A code assigned to declassified reports released by the Manhattan Engineer District and U.S. Atomic Energy Commission before Mar. 1, 1948
AECD	A code assigned to declassified reports released by the U.S. Atomic Energy Commission after Feb. 29, 1948
AECU	A code assigned to AEC unclassified reports
AD	Naval Radiological Defense Laboratory
AERE	Atomic Energy Research Establishment, Harwell, Berks, England
AMRL	Army Medical Research Laboratory, Fort Knox
ANL	Argonne National Laboratory
BNL	Brookhaven National Laboratory
CH	Metallurgical Laboratory, University of Chicago
HW	Hanford Engineer Works
LA	Los Alamos Scientific Laboratory
M	File designation for AEC Technical Information Service
NEPA	Nuclear Energy for Propulsion of Aircraft (Fairchild Engine and Airplane Corp.)
NM	Naval Medical Research Institute, Bethesda, Md.
NP	A file designation assigned by the Technical Information Service, U.S.

Atomic Energy Commission, to non-Project reports whose codes, if present, are not practical for TIS use

NYO	U.S. Atomic Energy Commission, New York Operations Office
ORNL	Oak Ridge National Laboratory
ORO	U.S. Atomic Energy Commission, Oak Ridge Operations Office
RAD	Rand Corporation
TID	Technical Information Service
UCLA	University of California, Los Angeles
UCRL	Radiation Laboratory, University of California, Berkeley
UR	Atomic Energy Project, University of Rochester
USAF	United States Air Force School of Aviation Medicine
UWFL	University of Washington Applied Fisheries Laboratory

SUMMARY OF AVAILABLE RADIOISOTOPE
PREPARATIONS

The following list was compiled from the 1955 Catalog and Price List of the Oak Ridge National Laboratory (operated for the United States Government by Carbide and Carbon Chemicals Company). The costs are unofficial and are included only to indicate the scale of experiments that are feasible, as explained in Chap. 6. Differences between this listing and that in Chap. 6 result from additional information made available since Chap. 6 was set in type.

Element	Cat. No.	Specific Activity, mc/g	Cost	Radiochemical Contaminants
Antimony	Sb-122-I	210	$15/210 mc	8 mc Sb^{124} (60 days)
	Sb-124-I	20	$45/20 mc	260 mc Sb^{122} (2.8 days)
	Sb-124-P	>500	$3/mc	
	Sb-125-I	CF	$45/0.18 mc	4100 mc Sn^{121} (27.5 hr)
				12 mc Sn^{121m} (>400 days)
				5.5 mc Sn^{123} (136 days)
				1.8 mc Sn^{113} (112 days)
				1.8 mc In^{113m} (104 min)
				0.59 mc Sn^{117m} (14 days)
				0.18 mc Sn^{125} (9.4 days)
				0.18 mc Te^{125m} daughter (58 days)
				0.16 mc Sn^{119m} (~250 days)
	Sb-125-P	CF	$100/mc	Te^{125m} daughter (58 days)
Argon	A-37-P	CF	$10/mc	
Arsenic	As-73-74-P	CF	$200/mc As^{73}	
	As-76-I	440	$15/33 mc	Trace Sb^{122} (2.8 days)
				Trace Sb^{124} (60 days)
	As-77-I	CF	$15/5.7 mc	89 mc Ge^{71} (11.4 days)
				5.7 mc Ge^{77} (12 hr)
Barium	Ba-131-I	0.015	$45/0.35 mc	67 mc Ba^{135m} (28.7 hr)
				8.3 mc Ba^{133m} (38.8 hr)
				8.3 mc Ba^{133} (~9.5 yr)
				0.35 mc Cs^{131} daughter (9.6 days)
				Trace Ba^{140} (12.8 days)

Element	Cat. No.	Specific Activity, mc/g	Cost	Radiochemical Contaminants
				Trace La^{140} (40 hr)
				Trace C^{14} (5568 yr)
	BaLa-140-P	CF	$2/mc Ba^{140}	La^{140} daughter (40 hr)
Beryllium	Be-7-P	CF	$40/mc	
Bismuth	Bi-210-I	0.41	$35/31 mc	31 mc Tl^{206} daughter (4.19 min)
				31 mc Po^{210} daughter (138.3 days)
				Trace Bi^{210} ($\sim 10^6$ yr)
Bromine	Br-82-I	180	$15/140 mc	5.3 mc K^{42} (12.44 hr)
Cadmium	Cd-115-I-1	20	$15/40 mc	40 mc In^{115m} daughter (4.5 hr)
				0.6 mc Cd^{115m} (43 days)
				0.001 mc Cd^{113m} (5.1 yr)
				Trace Cd^{109} (470 days)
				Trace Ag^{109m} (39.2 sec)
	Cd-115-I-2	1	$45/2 mc	45 mc Cd^{115} (53 hr)
				45 mc In^{115m} (4.5 hr)
				0.003 mc Cd^{113m} (5.1 yr)
				Trace Cd^{109} (470 days)
				Trace Ag^{109m} (39.2 sec)
	Cd-115-P	>5	$33/mc	
Calcium	Ca-45-I	0.28	$45/1.7 mc	2.5 mc A^{37} (35 days)
				Trace Ca^{41} (1.1×10^5 yr)
				Trace Ca^{47} (4.8 days)
				Trace Sc^{47} (3.43 days)
	Ca-45-P-1	>0.2	$2/mc	
	Ca-45-P-2	>5	$5/mc	
	Ca-45-P-3	>1,000	$45/mc	
	Ca-45-P-4	CF	$4000/mc	
Carbon	C-14-P	160–1,200	$36/mc	
Cerium	Ce-141-I	7.1	$45/5.8 mc	5.3 mc Ce^{143} (33 hr)
				5.3 mc Pr^{143} (13.7 days)
				2.3 mc Ce^{137} (36 hr)
				2.3 mc La^{137} (>400 yr)
				0.006 mc Ce^{139} (140 days)
	Ce-141-P	CF	$2/mc	<10% Ce^{144}-Pr^{144}
	CePr-144-P	CF	$1/mc Ce^{144}	Pr^{144} daughter (17.5 min)
				<10% Ce^{141} (33.1 days)
Cesium	Cs-134-I	37	$45/18 mc	
	Cs-134-P	>3,000	$1/mc	
	CsBa-137-P	CF	$.10/mc Cs^{137}	Ba^{137m} daughter (2.6 min)
Chlorine	Cl-36-I	8×10^{-5}	$45/0.01 mc	220 mc K^{42} (12.44 hr)
				85 mc S^{35} (87.1 days)

Element	Cat. No.	Specific Activity, mc/g	Cost	Radiochemical Contaminants
				32 mc P^{32} (14.3 days)
	Cl-36-P	>0.1	$1000/mc	
Chromium	Cr-51-I	39	$45/78 mc	
	Cr-51-P	>100	$1/mc	
Cobalt	Co-57-P	CF	$25/mc	
	Co-58-P	CF	$20/mc	
	Co-60-I	47	$45/100 mc	
	Co-60-P	>500	$2/mc	
Copper	Cu-64-I	340	$15/220 mc	Trace Ag^{110m} (270 days)
				Trace Ag^{110} (24.2 sec)
Europium	Eu-152-154-I	280 Eu^{152}	$75/62 mc	Trace Eu^{155} (1.7 yr)
		23 Eu^{154}	Eu^{152} plus 5.1 mc Eu^{154}	Trace Eu^{156} (15.4 days)
Fission products	FP-P-1		$1/mc	
Gallium	Ga-72-I	150	$25/46 mc	
Gold	Au-198-I	3,300	$15/1300 mc	Trace Au^{199} (3.15 days)
	Au-199-I	8.8	$20/13 mc	30 mc Pt^{193m} (4.33 days)
				3.8 mc Pt^{197} (18 hr)
				Trace Pt^{195m} (3.5 days)
Hafnium	Hf-181-I	55	$70/42 mc	23 mc Hf^{175} (70 days)
Hydrogen	H-3-P	CF	$.10/mc	
Indium	In-114-I	57	$45/17 mc	
	In-114-P	>15	$5/mc	
Iodine	I-129-P	~ 0.2	$100/mg	
	I-131-I	CF	$45/130 mc	130 mc Te^{125m} (58 days)
				15 mc Te^{121m} (154 days)
				15 mc Te^{121} (17 days)
				8.5 mc Te^{123m} (104 days)
				5.2 mc Te^{131m} (30 hr)
				5.2 mc Te^{131} (24.8 min)
				4 mc Te^{129m} (33.5 days)
				4 mc Te^{129} (72 min)
				3.9 mc Te^{127m} (115 days)
				3.9 mc Te^{127} (9.3 hr)
				1.3 mc Xe^{131m} daughter (12 days)
	I-131-P	CF	$.75/mc	Xe^{131m} daughter (12 days)
Iridium	Ir-192-P	$>1,000$	$1/mc	
	Ir-194-I	3,300	$15/140 mc	31 mc Ir^{192} (74.37 days)
Iron	Fe-55-59-I	0.4 (Fe^{55})	$45/13 mc Fe^{55} plus 5 mc Fe^{59}	
		0.15 (Fe^{59})		
	Fe-55-59-P	>1	$35/mc Fe^{59}	
	Fe-55-P	>500	$50/mc Fe^{55}	$<10\%$ Fe^{59} (45.1 days)
	Fe-59-P	>500	$50/mc Fe^{59}	$<10\%$ Fe^{55} (2.94 yr)

Element	Cat. No.	Specific Activity, mc/g	Cost	Radiochemical Contaminants
Krypton	Kr-85-P	$\sim$450 c	$50/c	
Lanthanum	La-140-I	460	$15/60 mc	Trace La^{141} (3.7 hr)
				Trace Ce^{141} (31.1 days)
Manganese	Mn-52-54-P	CF	$175/mc Mn^{54}	
Mercury	Hg-197-I	150	$15/2000 mc	61 mc Au^{197m} daughter (7.4 sec)
				40 mc Hg^{203} (47.9 days)
	Hg-203-I	13	$45/170 mc	2600 mc Hg^{197} (65 hr)
				78 mc Au^{197m} (7.4 sec)
				Isomeric Hg^{197m_2} (24 hr)
	Hg-203-P	>50	$1/mc	
Molybdenum	Mo-99-I	2.1	$15/21 mc	21 mc Tc^{99m} daughter (6.04 hr)
				0.006 mc Mo^{93} (>2 yr)
				Trace Tc^{99} (2.12 $\times$ 10^5 yr)
Neodymium	NdPm-147-P	CF	$50/mc Nd^{147}	Pm^{147} daughter(2.6 yr)
Nickel	Ni-63-I	0.044	$45/1.3 mc	0.009 mc Ni^{59} (8 $\times$ 10^4 yr)
	Ni-63-P	5–50	$45/mc	$\sim$0.01% Ni^{59} (8 $\times$ 10^4 yr)
Niobium	Nb-95-P	CF	$10/mc	
Osmium	Os-191-I	65	$55/130 mc	Isomeric Os^{191m} (14 hr)
				56 mc Os^{193} (30.6 hr)
				0.58 mc Os^{185} (97 days)
				Trace Os^{194} ($\sim$700 days)
				Trace Ir^{194} (19 hr)
Palladium	Pd-109-I	220	$22/1300 mc	1300 mc Ag^{109m} daughter (39.2 sec)
				11 mc Ag^{111} (7.6 days)
				Trace Pd^{103} (17 days)
				Trace Rh^{103m} (57 min)
Phosphorus	P-32-I	44	$45/310 mc	120 mc K^{42} (12.44 hr)
	P-32-P-1	$\sim$40,000	$1.10/mc	
	P-32-P-2	CF	$3/mc	
Potassium	K-42-I	14	$15/170 mc	
Praseodymium	Pr-142-I	630	$15/46 mc	
	Pr-143-P	CF	$50/mc	
Promethium	Pm-147-I	CF	$45/0.015 mc	0.7 mc Nd^{147} (11.3 days)
				0.05 mc Pm^{149} (54 hr)
				Trace Sm^{147} daughter (1.4 $\times$ 10^{11} yr)
	Pm-147-P	CF	$5/mc	Trace Am^{241}-Cm^{242}
Rhenium	Re-186-I	1,100	$15/110 mc	20 mc Re^{188} (16.9 hr)
				Trace Re^{189} (150 days)
Rubidium	Rb-86-I	31	$50/150 mc	$\sim$0.02 mc Cs^{134} (2.3 yr)

Element	Cat. No.	Specific Activity, mc/g	Cost	Radiochemical Contaminants
Ruthenium	Ru-97-I	0.035	$60/0.56 mc	160 mc Rh^{105} (36.5 hr)
				53 mc Ru^{103} (39.8 days)
				53 mc Rh^{103m} (57 min)
				0.04 mc Tc^{97m} daughter (90 days)
	Ru-103-P	>5,000	$10/mc	<10% Ru^{106}-Rh^{106} (1.0 yr, 30 sec)
	RuRh-106-P	>5,000	$10/mc Ru^{106}	<10% Ru^{103} (39.8 days)
				Rh^{106} daughter (30 sec)
Samarium	Sm-153-I	1,900	$15/50 mc	0.06 mc Eu^{155} (1.7 yr)
				0.004 mc Sm^{145} (~410 days)
				Trace Pm^{145} (~30 yr)
				Trace Sm^{151} (73 yr)
Scandium	Sc-46-I	450	$45/15 mc	Trace Ca^{45} (152 days)
	Sc-46-P	>5,000	$3/mc	
Selenium	Se-75-I	3.2	$45/130 mc	
	Se-75-P	>50	$1/mc	
Silver	Ag-110-I	7.1	$45/45 mc	45 mc Ag^{110} daughter (24.2 sec)
				Trace C^{14} (5568 yr)
	Ag-110-P	>100	$1/mc	
	Ag-111-I	CF	$19/5.7 mc	670 mc Pd^{109} (13.6 hr)
				670 mc Ag^{109m} (39.2 sec)
				Trace Pd^{103} (17 days)
				Trace Rh^{103m} (57 min)
Sodium	Na-22-P-1	>1,000	$200/mc	
	Na-22-P-2	>2	$50/mc	
	Na-24-I	210	$15/55 mc	Trace K^{42} (12.44 hr)
	Na-24-P	>1,000	$2/mc	
Strontium	Sr-89-I	0.12	$45/1.6 mc	Trace Sr^{85} (65 days)
				Trace C^{14} (5568 yr)
	Sr-89-P	CF	$2/mc	<10% Sr^{90}-Y^{90} (19.9 yr, 2.54 days)
	SrY-90-P	CF	$1/mc Sr^{90}	>10% Sr^{89} (53 days)
				Y^{90} daughter (2.54 days)
Sulfur	S-35-I	0.52	$45/13 mc	Trace P^{32} (14.3 days)
	S-35-P-1	CF	$2/mc	<0.1% P^{32} (14.3 days)
	S-35-P-2	>10,000	$4/mc	
	S-35-P-3	>1,000	$5/mc	
Tantalum	Ta-182-I	140	$45/57 mc	
	Ta-182-P	>500	$2/mc	
Technetium	Tc-99-I	CF	$45/0.0003 mc	10 mc Mo^{99} (2.85 days)
				0.009 mc Mo^{93} (2 yr)
	Tc-99-P	20	$20/mg	

Element	Cat. No.	Specific Activity, mc/g	Cost	Radiochemical Contaminants
Thallium	Tl-204-I	1.4	$50/33 mc	Trace C^{14} (5568 yr)
	Tl-204-P	>50	$5/mc	
Tin	Sn-113-I	0.14	$45/1.8 mc	4100 mc Sn^{121} (27.5 hr) 12 mc Sn^{121m} (>400 days) 5.5 mc Sn^{123} (136 days) 1.8 mc In^{113m} daughter (104 min) 0.59 mc Sn^{117m} (14 days) 0.18 mc Sn^{125} (9.4 days) 0.18 mc Sb^{125} (2.7 yr) 0.18 mc Te^{125m} (58 days) 0.16 mc Sn^{119m} (~250 days)
	Sn-113-P	>1	$35/mc	In^{113m} daughter (104 min)
Tungsten	W-185-I	6.6	$45/9.5 mc	600 mc W^{187} (24.1 hr) 0.12 mc W^{181} (140 days) Trace W^{188} (65 days) Trace Re^{188} (16.9 hr)
	W-185-P	>100	$4/mc	
	W-187-I	420	$15/40 mc	0.17 mc W^{185} (73.2 days) 0.002 mc W^{181} (140 days) Trace W^{188} (65 days) Trace Re^{188} (16.9 hr)
Yttrium	Y-90-I	93	$15/81 mc	Trace of rare earths
	Y-91-P	CF	$2/mc	
Zinc	Zn-65-I	2.2	$45/36 mc	36 mc Zn^{69m} (13.8 hr) 36 mc Zn^{69} (57 min)
	Zn-65-P-1	>75	$2/mc	
	Zn-65-P-2	~5,000	$100/mc	
Zirconium	Zr-95-I	0.66	$15/1.5 mc	1.5 mc Nb^{95} daughter (35 days) 0.32 mc Zr^{97} (17 hr) 0.32 mc Nb^{97m} (60 sec) 0.32 mc Nb^{97} (72.1 min) 0.01 mc Nb^{95m} daughter (90 hr)
	ZrNb-95-P	CF	$2/mc	Nb^{95} daughter (35 days)

NAME INDEX

453

SUBJECT INDEX

Page numbers in boldface type refer to Glossary items

478   RADIOISOTOPES IN BIOLOGY AND AGRICULTURE

Radioactive contamination (*see* Contamination)
Radioactive decay, 19–23
Radioactive equilibrium, **439**
Radioactive half-life (*see* Half-life)
Radioactive impurities, chemical state, 61–62
  cross section related to, 61
  detection, 64
  radiocolloids, 62
  in radioisotope preparations, 446–451
    (*See also* individual isotopes)
  removal or elimination, 65–66
    by chemical methods, 66
    by radioassay methods, 66
  in tracer studies, 61–66
Radioactive tracer, **439**
Radioactive waste disposal (*see* Waste disposal)
Radioactivity, artificial, **428**
  definition, 2, **439**
  induced, **434**
  natural, **437**
Radioactivity units, 86
Radioautography (*see* Autoradiography)
Radiobiology, **439**
Radiochemical analysis (*see* individual isotopes)
Radiochemical contamination of radioisotope preparations, 446–451
  (*See also* individual isotopes)
Radiochemical fume hoods, 121
Radiocolloids, **439**
  demonstration of, 341
  factors promoting, 62
  prevention of formation by citric acid, 304, 318, 322
  in tracer studies, 62, 318, 322–323
Radiocontamination, in isotope preparations, 61, 446–451
  (*See also* individual isotopes; Radioactive impurities)
  test for, in Zn^{65} preparation, 319
Radioelement, **439**
Radioisotopes, autoradiographic properties, 327
  availability, 446–451
  definition, 439
  dosage, continuous administration, 10, 75, 304
    general, 139–147
    inhalation and intratracheal, 147
    intravenous injection, 144–147
    oral administration, 141–144
    parenteral, 144–147
    to plants, 150–152
    tracer, physiological and massive, 60

Radioisotopes, incorporation into feed, 304
  laboratories (*see* Laboratory design)
  mixtures assay, by chemical separation, 192
    by differential absorption, 191
    by differential decay, 190
    by radiation differences, 191
    (*See also* Double labeling)
  naturally occurring, 2, 437
  in paper chromatography, 378–383
  in radioactivation analysis, 417–418
  storage in laboratory, 123–125
    (*See also* individual isotopes)
Radiology, **439–440**
Radionuclide, **440**
Radioresistance, **440**
Radiosensitivity, **440**
Radium, citrate-complex study, 406–407
  as insect label, 3
  radiation-effect levels, 67
Range, **440**
  relation to infinite thickness, 182
Rare earths, activation analysis in bone, 424
  separations, 402
Rats, administration of isotopes, 140–142, 144, 146–147
  blood collection, 147–148
  iron studies, 46
  management requirements, 129
  metabolism cages, 129–131
  radiation effects from isotopes, 67
Reactions, equations for first-order, 18–39
  exchange (*see* Exchange reactions)
  other than first-order, 38–40
  nuclear, **440**
Reactor (*see* Pile)
Reagents, for carbon combustion, 164
  for color development in chromatograms, 368–373
Red blood cells (*see* Erythrocytes)
Relative abundance of an isotope, **440**
Relative biological effectiveness (RBE), of different radiations, 88
  of radiation, **440**
Relative plateau slope (counter tubes), **440**
Removal from one phase, 18–20
Renewal rate (*see* Turnover rate)
Reports, identification of, 444–445
Resins for ion exchange, 390
Respiration apparatus for carbon-14 studies with cattle, 136
Respiration losses from samples, 160
Reversed phase, chromatography, 383